CALCULUS OF VECTOR FUNCTIONS

CALCULUS OF

Prentice-Hall, Inc.

Englewood Cliffs, New Jersey

Second Edition

VECTOR FUNCTIONS

RICHARD E. WILLIAMSON

Department of Mathematics
Dartmouth College

RICHARD H. CROWELL

Department of Mathematics
Dartmouth College

HALE F. TROTTER

Department of Mathematics
Princeton University

CALCULUS OF VECTOR FUNCTIONS, *2nd ed.*

Richard E. Williamson   Richard H. Crowell   Hale F. Trotter

© 1962, 1968 BY PRENTICE-HALL, INC.

Englewood Cliffs, N.J.

Current Printing (Last Digit):

10   9   8   7   6   5   4

Library of Congress Catalog Card Number 68–16739

Printed in the United States of America

PRENTICE-HALL INTERNATIONAL, INC. *London*
PRENTICE-HALL OF AUSTRALIA, PTY. LTD. *Sydney*
PRENTICE-HALL OF CANADA, LTD. *Toronto*
PRENTICE-HALL OF INDIA PRIVATE LTD. *New Delhi*
PRENTICE-HALL OF JAPAN, INC. *Tokyo*

PREFACE

This book presents the contents of a standard course on functions of several variables, following the unifying idea that calculus deals with linear approximations to functions. The only prerequisite is a course in calculus of functions of one variable; the necessary linear algebra is developed in Chapter 1.

This second edition is a substantial revision of the first. The chapter on linear algebra has been replaced by a new one designed to provide better for the needs of the rest of the book. New material on curves, line integrals, and the gradient has been added to Chapter 2. Some introductory material on Fourier series and related topics has been added to Chapter 3. Chapter 5, dealing with divergence, curl, and the various forms of Stokes's theorem (and an introduction to differential forms) is entirely new. Throughout the book explanations have been simplified, while examples and problems with an "applied" flavor have been added. In general there is more 2- and 3-dimensional material, and thus less emphasis on n-dimensional generality.

It is not necessary to complete the linear algebra in Chapter 1 before beginning work on the calculus. Sections 1 through 5 of Chapter 1 contain all that is needed for most of Chapter 2. Exceptions are that determinants are mentioned in Section 10 on the chain rule, that linear changes of coordinates are mentioned in Section 12 on curvilinear coordinates, and that subspaces are used in Section 14 on surfaces and tangents. The material on determinants in Chapter 1 has been split into two sections, the first of which, Section 6, will suffice for the computations in Chapter 2, 3, and 4. Section 7 on geometric properties of determinants should be taken up before the change-of-variables theorem in Chapter 4, and before Sections 3 through 8 in Chapter 5.

One-semester courses can be designed for students who have had no linear algebra by covering Sections 1 through 7 of Chapter 1, and then either Sections 1 through 12 of Chapter 2, or else Sections 1 through 9 of Chapter 2, followed by three or four sections from one of the later chapters. If the students have already had a course in linear algebra, then Chapter 1 can be used as a reference and the extra time can be spent on Chapters 3, 4, or 5.

Substantial suggestions from our colleagues, particularly Edward M. Brown and John Troutman, have contributed much to the second edition, and the first edition was influenced by many contributions from Hazleton Mirkil.

Ingrid Barr, Nancy French, Helen Hanchett, and Linda Wieselquist did the typing, and various editorial jobs were done by Stephen Campbell, Lawrence Carter, William Chang, David Salsbury, and James Williams.

CONTENTS

REAL-VALUED FUNCTIONS 3

MULTIPLE INTEGRALS 4

VECTOR FIELD THEORY 5

APPENDIX

CALCULUS OF VECTOR FUNCTIONS

LINEAR ALGEBRA   1

1. INTRODUCTION, VECTORS

A first course in calculus deals with real-valued functions of one variable, that is, functions defined on all or part of the real number line $\mathscr{R}$, and having values in $\mathscr{R}$. For example, a formula such as

$$y = x^2 + 3$$

yields a real number y for any real number x and so defines a function f from $\mathscr{R}$ to $\mathscr{R}$ with (for instance) $f(0) = 3$, $f(-2) = 7$, $f(\sqrt{3}) = 6$, etc. In this book we are concerned with functions of several variables whose values may be real numbers or, more generally, may be m-tuples of real numbers. For example, a pair of formulas

$$y_1 = \sqrt{x_1^2 + x_2^2 + x_3^2}$$
$$y_2 = x_1 x_2 + 5x_3$$

yields a pair of numbers (y_1, y_2) for any triple of numbers (x_1, x_2, x_3) and so defines a function g from "3-dimensional space" to "2-dimensional space." For example $g(0, 0, 0) = (0, 0)$, $g(1, 2, 3) = (\sqrt{14}, 17)$, $g(3, 2, 1) = (\sqrt{14}, 11)$,

1

etc. We shall use $\mathscr{R}^n$ to stand for the set of all n-tuples of real numbers. ($\mathscr{R}^1$ is thus the same as $\mathscr{R}$.) The **domain** of a function is the set on which it is defined and the **range** or **image** is the set of values assumed by the function. We write

$$\mathscr{R}^n \xrightarrow{\ f\ } \mathscr{R}^m$$

to indicate that f is a function whose domain is a subset of $\mathscr{R}^n$ and whose range is a subset of $\mathscr{R}^m$. $\mathscr{R}^n$ is then called the **domain space** of the function and $\mathscr{R}^m$ is called its **range space**.

While functions of one variable are basic and very useful, there are many situations whose mathematical formulation requires the more general functions we consider here. For example, just as certain curves in the plane can be represented as graphs of functions from $\mathscr{R}^1$ to $\mathscr{R}^1$, so certain surfaces in 3-space can be represented as graphs of functions from $\mathscr{R}^2$ to $\mathscr{R}^1$. Figure 1 illustrates the graph of the function $\mathscr{R}^2 \xrightarrow{\ f\ } \mathscr{R}^1$ defined by the formula

$$f(x, y) = x^2 + y^2.$$

Other examples showing how curves and surfaces can be described by functions are given at the beginning of Chapter 2.

Most of the problems and examples in this book involve functions from $\mathscr{R}^n$ to $\mathscr{R}^m$ with values of m and n not more than 2 or 3, since higher-dimensional problems are difficult to visualize and often require inordinate amounts of computation. In the theoretical development we nevertheless provide formulations valid for arbitrary dimensions. This is not an empty generality. An economist may wish to consider a mathematical model in which the prices of a number of commodities are determined by a number of other

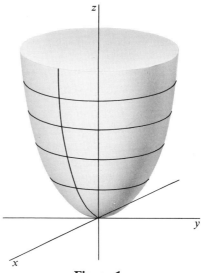

Figure 1

EXERCISES

1. Given $\mathbf{x} = (3, -1, 0)$, $\mathbf{y} = (0, 1, 5)$ and $\mathbf{z} = (2, 5, -1)$ compute $3\mathbf{x}$, $\mathbf{y} + \mathbf{z}$ and $4\mathbf{x} - 2\mathbf{y} + 3\mathbf{z}$. [*Ans.* $(18, 9, -13)$.]

2. Find numbers a and b such that $a\mathbf{x} + b\mathbf{y} = (9, -1, 10)$, where $\mathbf{x}$ and $\mathbf{y}$ are as in Problem 1. Is there more than one solution?

3. Show that no choice of numbers a and b can make $a\mathbf{x} + b\mathbf{y} = (3, 0, 0)$, where $\mathbf{x}$ and $\mathbf{y}$ are as in Problem 1. For what value(s) of c (if any) can the equation $a\mathbf{x} + b\mathbf{y} = (3, 0, c)$ be satisfied?

4. Write out proofs for laws 3 and 4 in Section 1, giving precise justification for each step.

5. Verify that the set $\mathscr{C}[a, b]$ of all continuous real-valued functions defined on the interval $a \le x \le b$ is a vector space, with addition and numerical multiplication defined by $(f + g)(x) = f(x) + g(x)$ and $(rf)(x) = rf(x)$.

6. Prove that the representation of a vector $\mathbf{x}$ in $\mathscr{R}^n$ in terms of the natural basis is unique. That is, show that if

$$x_1\mathbf{e}_1 + \ldots + x_n\mathbf{e}_n = y_1\mathbf{e}_1 + \ldots + y_n\mathbf{e}_n,$$

then $x_k = y_k$ for $k = 1, \ldots, n$.

7. Represent the first vector below as a linear combination of the remaining vectors, either by inspection or by solving an appropriate system of equations.

(a) $(2, 3, 4)$; $(1, 1, 1)$, $(1, 2, 1)$, $(-1, 1, 2)$.
(b) $(2, -7)$; $(1, 1)$, $(1, -1)$.

2. GEOMETRIC INTERPRETATIONS

Geometric representations of $\mathscr{R}^1$ as a line, of $\mathscr{R}^2$ as a plane, and of $\mathscr{R}^3$ as 3-dimensional space may be obtained by using coordinates.

To represent $\mathscr{R}^1$ as a line, one must first specify a point on the line to be called the **origin**, a unit of distance, and a direction on the line to be called positive. (The opposite direction is then called negative.) Then a positive number x corresponds to the point which is a distance x in the positive direction from the origin. A negative number x corresponds to the point which is a distance $|x|$ from the origin in the negative direction. The number zero of course corresponds to the origin. The number line is most often thought of as horizontal with the positive direction to the right. With this standard convention, we obtain the familiar Figure 2, in which the arrow indicates the positive direction.

In the plane, one takes an origin,

Figure 2

a unit of distance, a pair of perpendicular lines (called the **axes**) through the origin, and a positive direction on each axis. Given a vector in $\mathscr{R}^2$, that is, a pair of numbers (x_1, x_2), the procedure described in the preceding paragraph determines a point p_1 on the first axis corresponding to the number x_1 and a point p_2 on the second axis corresponding to the number x_2. Then the vector (x_1, x_2) corresponds to the point p in the plane whose projection on the first axis is p_1 and whose projection on the second axis is p_2. The (perpendicular) **projection** of a point p on a line L is defined as the foot of the perpendicular from p to L if p is not on L. If p is on L, then the projection of p on L is p itself.

The conventional choice is to take the first axis horizontal with the positive direction to the right, and the second axis vertical with the positive direction upwards. This leads to the usual picture shown in Figure 3.

Representing a vector by an arrow from the origin to the corresponding point, as we have done in Figure 3, often makes a better picture than simply marking the point.

An obvious extension of the procedure works in three dimensions. One takes an origin, three perpendicular axes through it, and a positive direction on each. A vector in $\mathscr{R}^3$ is a triple of numbers (x_1, x_2, x_3) and gives points p_1, p_2, and p_3 on the three axes. Then the point p, corresponding to (x_1, x_2, x_3), is the one whose projections on the three axes are p_1, p_2, and p_3.

There is no universally accepted convention for labeling the axes in 3-dimensional figures. Figure 4 illustrates the convention followed in this book, but several other schemes are also in common use.

We have described how to set up a correspondence between vectors (n-tuples of numbers) and points. We now consider the geometrical interpretation of the vector operations of addition and numerical multiplication. This time we represent a vector as an arrow from the origin to the point with given coordinates. Figures 5 and 6 show two vectors $\mathbf{u} = (u_1, u_2)$ and $\mathbf{v} = (v_1, v_2)$. By the definition of addition in $\mathscr{R}^2$, $\mathbf{u} + \mathbf{v} = (u_1 + v_1, u_2 + v_2)$, so the arrow representing $\mathbf{u} + \mathbf{v}$ must be drawn as shown.

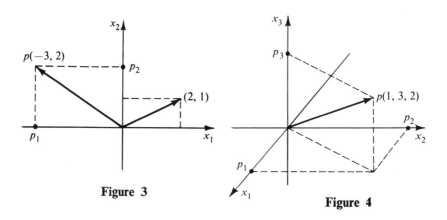

Figure 3   Figure 4

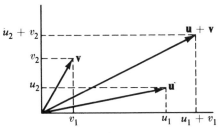

Figure 5

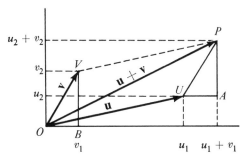

Figure 6

The lengths of OB and UA are both equal to v_1, and the lengths of BV and AP are both equal to v_2. (Why?) The angles OBV and UAP are both right angles, and therefore the triangles OBV and UAP are congruent. Hence OV and UP have the same length and the angles VOB and PUA are equal. The segment UA is by construction parallel to OB, so UP is parallel to OV, as well as having the same length. Consequently $OVPU$ is a parallelogram, and we have the result that the arrow representing the sum of two vectors in $\mathscr{R}^2$ goes from the origin to the opposite corner of the parallelogram whose sides are the arrows representing the two given vectors. Figure 6 illustrates only the case in which u_1, u_2, v_1, v_2 are all positive, but the same argument can be applied for any combination of signs. A more complicated argument using the same ideas shows that the same rule gives the geometric interpretation of addition in $\mathscr{R}^3$. This rule is sometimes referred to as the *parallelogram law of addition*. This formulation of the rule is actually defective in case the arrows representing **u** and **v** lie in the same straight line, since then (unless the definition of parallelogram is extended to include this case) they do not define a parallelogram. An alternative formulation without this defect is the following: Draw a line segment starting at the end of the arrow representing **u** and parallel to, and equal in length to, the arrow representing **v**. The end of this line segment is the end of the arrow representing **u** + **v**.

Figure 7 illustrates the effect of multiplying a vector by both positive and negative numbers. The triangles OPU and OQV have equal (right) angles

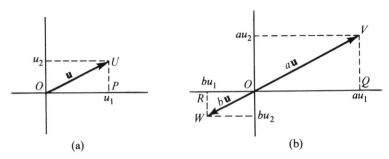

(a)   (b)

Figure 7

at P and Q. Also $VQ/UP = a = OQ/OP$ and it follows that the triangles UOP and VOQ are similar. Hence the angles UOP and VOQ are equal, and the ratio of lengths OV/OU is also equal to a. Thus if a is positive (which is implicitly assumed in the figure), the arrow representing $a\mathbf{u}$ has the same direction as the arrow representing $\mathbf{u}$ and is a times as long. Essentially the same argument shows that the triangles ORW and OPU are similar and we obtain the result that if b is negative, then the arrow representing $b\mathbf{u}$ is exactly opposite in direction to the arrow representing $\mathbf{u}$ and is $|b|$ times as long. The same result may be proved for the geometrical representation of vectors in $\mathscr{R}^3$.

So far we have used lines in $\mathscr{R}^2$ and $\mathscr{R}^3$ informally to get pictures of vector addition and numerical multiplication. Having done this, however, we can formally define what we shall mean by a line in $\mathscr{R}^n$. To begin, we fix a nonzero vector $\mathbf{x}_1$ and call the set of all numerical multiples $t\mathbf{x}_1$ a line $\mathscr{L}_0$ through the origin. Then we define a **line** $\mathscr{L}$ parallel to $\mathscr{L}_0$ to be the set of all points representable in the form $t\mathbf{x}_1 + \mathbf{x}_0$, where $\mathbf{x}_0$ is some fixed vector. The relationship between $\mathscr{L}_0$ and $\mathscr{L}$ is shown in Figure 8, for vectors $\mathbf{x}_1$ and $\mathbf{x}_0$ in $\mathscr{R}^3$.

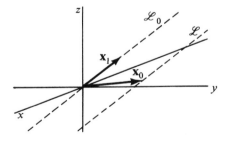

Figure 8

EXAMPLE 1. To find a representation for the line in $\mathscr{R}^3$ parallel to the vector $(1, 1, 1)$ and passing through the point $(-1, 3, 6)$ we form all multiples $t(1, 1, 1)$ to get a line through the origin. Then the set of all points

$t(1, 1, 1) + (-1, 3, 6)$ is a line containing the point $(-1, 3, 6)$, as we see by setting $t = 0$.

To determine a plane in $\mathscr{R}^3$ it is natural to start with two *noncollinear* vectors $\mathbf{x}_1$ and $\mathbf{x}_2$ (that is, such that neither is a multiple of the other) and consider all points $u\mathbf{x}_1 + v\mathbf{x}_2$, where u and v are numbers. The geometric interpretation of numerical multiplication and addition of vectors shows that the points $u\mathbf{x}_1 + v\mathbf{x}_2$ constitute what we would like to call a plane $\mathscr{P}_0$ through the origin. We then define a **plane** $\mathscr{P}$ parallel to $\mathscr{P}_0$ to be the set of all points $u\mathbf{x}_1 + v\mathbf{x}_2 + \mathbf{x}_0$, where $\mathbf{x}_0$ is some fixed vector. $\mathscr{P}_0$ and $\mathscr{P}$ are related as shown in Figure 9.

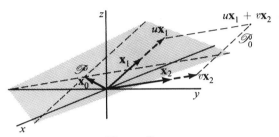

Figure 9

EXAMPLE 2. We represent a plane in $\mathscr{R}^3$ parallel to the two vectors $(1, 1, 1)$ and $(2, -1, 3)$, and passing through the point $(0, 1, -1)$. The set of all linear combinations $u(1, 1, 1) + v(2, -1, 3)$ is a plane $\mathscr{P}_0$ through the origin, and the set of all points $u(1, 1, 1) + v(2, -1, 3) + (0, 1, -1)$ is a parallel plane $\mathscr{P}$. That $\mathscr{P}$ contains the point $(0, 1, -1)$ becomes evident on setting $u = v = 0$.

EXERCISES

1. Show that if $\mathbf{u}$ and $\mathbf{v}$ are two distinct vectors, then the vectors $t\mathbf{u} + (1 - t)\mathbf{v}$ form a line through the points corresponding to $\mathbf{u}$ and $\mathbf{v}$.

2. Take $\mathbf{u}_1 = (0, 1)$, $\mathbf{v}_1 = (-1, 1)$, $\mathbf{u}_2 = (-3, 2)$, $\mathbf{v}_2 = (2, 1)$. Sketch the lines representing $\mathbf{u}_1 + a\mathbf{v}_1$, $\mathbf{u}_2 + b\mathbf{v}_2$. Find the vector $\mathbf{w}$ represented by the point of intersection of the lines by finding values of a and b for which $\mathbf{w} = \mathbf{u}_1 + a\mathbf{v}_1 = \mathbf{u}_2 + b\mathbf{v}_2$ holds. [*Ans.* $\mathbf{w} = (-\tfrac{5}{3}, \tfrac{8}{3})$.]

3. Show that for two vectors $\mathbf{u}$ and $\mathbf{v}$ in $\mathscr{R}^2$, the difference $\mathbf{v} - \mathbf{u}$ is represented by an arrow parallel and equal in length to the arrow from the point representing $\mathbf{u}$ to the point representing $\mathbf{v}$. What arrow represents $\mathbf{u} - \mathbf{v}$?

4. State explicitly the theorems about congruent and similar triangles that were used in the discussion of the geometric interpretation of addition and numerical multiplication in $\mathscr{R}^2$.

5. It is not essential to use perpendicular axes in setting up coordinates in

the plane. The same procedure can be used if the projection of a point on an axis is defined as the point of intersection of that axis and the line through the given point and parallel to the other axis. (If the axes are perpendicular, this is equivalent to our previous definition. Why?) It is also possible to choose different units of distance along the two axes. Show that the geometric interpretation of the vector operations in two dimensions remains the same in this more general setting. How would you extend the definition of projection to make the same generalization in three dimensions?

6. If x_1 and x_2 are two vectors in $\mathscr{R}^n$, then the set of all vectors $tx_1 + (1 - t)x_2$, where $0 \leq t \leq 1$, is the **line segment** joining x_1 and x_2. A set S in $\mathscr{R}^n$ is **convex** if, whenever S contains two points, it also contains the line segment joining them. Prove that the intersection of any collection of convex sets is convex.

7. Represent the following lines in the form $tx_1 + x_0$, where t runs over all real numbers. Sketch each line.

   (a) The line in $\mathscr{R}^3$ parallel to $(1, 2, 0)$ and passing through the point $(1, 1, 1)$.
   (b) The line in $\mathscr{R}^2$ joining the points $(1, 0)$ and $(0, 1)$.
   (c) The line in $\mathscr{R}^3$ joining the points $(1, 0, 0)$ and $(0, 0, 1)$.

8. Represent the following planes in $\mathscr{R}^3$ in the form $ux_1 + vx_2 + x_0$, where u and v run over all real numbers. Sketch each plane.

   (a) The plane parallel to the vectors $(1, 1, 0)$ and $(0, 1, 1)$ and passing through the origin.
   (b) The plane parallel to the vectors e_1 and e_2 and passing through the point $(0,0,1)$.
   (c) The plane passing through the three points $(1, 0, 0)$, $(0, 1, 0)$, and $(0, 0, 1)$.

3. MATRICES

A set of equations such as

$$y_1 = 2x_1 + 3x_2 - 4x_3$$
$$y_2 = x_1 - x_2 + 2x_3,$$

in which each y_i is given as a sum of constant multiples of the x_j defines a function (in this example from $\mathscr{R}^3$ to $\mathscr{R}^2$) of a particularly simple kind. It is an example of what we shall call a *linear* function. (The precise definition of "linear" appears in the next section.) An understanding of these functions is basic to the study of more general functions. Linear functions from $\mathscr{R}^1$ to $\mathscr{R}^1$ are so simple that they can be taken for granted in studying the calculus for functions of one variable. In higher dimensions, however, linear functions can be more complicated, and the main business of this first chapter is to develop their basic properties and to present notation and methods of calculation for dealing with them.

In the example above, the x's and y's are merely placeholders. The function is described completely by the array of coefficients

$$\begin{pmatrix} 2 & 3 & -4 \\ 1 & -1 & 2 \end{pmatrix}.$$

Any such rectangular array of numbers is called a **matrix**. Thus

$$\begin{pmatrix} 0 & 5 \\ -1 & \frac{1}{2} \\ 0 & 4 \end{pmatrix}, \quad \begin{pmatrix} 1 & .7 & 3 \\ .9 & 0 & 2.8 \end{pmatrix}, \quad \begin{pmatrix} 1 & 0 \\ 0 & -1 \end{pmatrix}, \quad (\tfrac{1}{2}, \ \tfrac{1}{3}, \ 0), \quad \begin{pmatrix} .325 \\ .007 \\ .579 \\ 3.142 \end{pmatrix}$$

are all examples of matrices. The horizontal lines of numbers in a matrix are called its **rows** and the vertical lines are called its **columns**. The number of rows and number of columns of a matrix determine its **shape**. Thus the five examples above have shapes 3-by-2, 2-by-3, 2-by-2, 1-by-3, and 4-by-1. Note that the number of rows always comes *before* the number of columns. The 1-by-n matrices are called **n-dimensional row vectors**, and n-by-1 matrices are called **n-dimensional column vectors**. A matrix is **square** if it has the same number of rows as it has columns.

The number in the ith row and jth column of a matrix is called the ijth **entry** of that matrix. Note that the row index is always put before the column index. Two matrices are equal if and only if they have the same shape and the entries in corresponding positions in the two matrices are equal.

We use capital letters to denote matrices, and often use the corresponding small letters with appropriate subscripts to denote their entries. Thus we write

$$A = \begin{pmatrix} a_{11} & a_{12} & a_{13} & a_{14} \\ a_{21} & a_{22} & a_{23} & a_{24} \\ a_{31} & a_{32} & a_{33} & a_{34} \end{pmatrix} \quad \text{or} \quad A = (a_{ij}), \quad \text{where} \quad i = 1, 2, 3, \quad j = 1, 2, 3, 4.$$

We usually write simply $x_1, x_2, \ldots, x_n$ for the entries of an n-dimensional column vector $\mathbf{x}$ rather than $x_{11}, x_{21}, \ldots, x_{n1}$.

The operations of addition and numerical multiplication which were defined in the last section for vectors in $\mathscr{R}^n$ can be extended to matrices. If A and B have the same shape, then their **sum** $A + B$ is defined as the matrix with the same shape, and ijth entry equal to $a_{ij} + b_{ij}$. For example

$$\begin{pmatrix} 2 & 3 \\ -2 & \frac{1}{2} \\ 0 & 4 \end{pmatrix} + \begin{pmatrix} 1 & -1 \\ 2 & \frac{2}{3} \\ 0 & 0 \end{pmatrix} = \begin{pmatrix} 3 & 2 \\ 0 & \frac{7}{6} \\ 0 & 4 \end{pmatrix}.$$

Addition is not defined between matrices of different shapes. Recall that we did not define addition between elements of $\mathscr{R}^n$ and $\mathscr{R}^m$ with $m \neq n$.

For any matrix A and number r, the **numerical multiple** rA is defined as the matrix with the same shape as A and ijth entry equal to ra_{ij}. For example,

$$2\begin{pmatrix} 3 & 4 \\ 5 & 6 \end{pmatrix} = \begin{pmatrix} 6 & 8 \\ 10 & 12 \end{pmatrix}.$$

$$5\begin{pmatrix} 1 & 0 \\ 3 & 2 \\ -1 & 0 \end{pmatrix} + 3\begin{pmatrix} -2 & 2 \\ -4 & 0 \\ 0 & 1 \end{pmatrix} = \begin{pmatrix} 5 & 0 \\ 15 & 10 \\ -5 & 0 \end{pmatrix} + \begin{pmatrix} -6 & 6 \\ -12 & 0 \\ 0 & 3 \end{pmatrix} = \begin{pmatrix} -1 & 6 \\ 3 & 10 \\ -5 & 3 \end{pmatrix}.$$

As with vectors in $\mathcal{R}^n$, we write $-A$ for $(-1)A$ and $A - B$ for $A + (-1)B$. For every shape there is a **zero matrix** which has all its entries equal to zero. We use 0 to denote any zero matrix; the shape intended will always be clear from the context.

It is easy to see that if the matrices X, Y, Z all have the same shape, and r and s are any numbers, then the formulas 1–7 in Section 1 all hold. (The proofs are just the same as when X, Y, and Z are all in $\mathcal{R}^n$.) In other words, according to the definition in Section 2, for any fixed m and n, the set of m-by-n matrices form a vector space with the operations of addition and numerical multiplication that we have just defined.

Another operation between matrices is suggested by the way they may be used to describe functions from $\mathcal{R}^m$ to $\mathcal{R}^n$. For example, suppose we have formulas

$$z_1 = 3y_1 - y_2$$
$$z_2 = 5y_1 + 2y_2,$$

and

$$y_1 = 2x_1 + 3x_2 + 4x_3$$
$$y_2 = x_1 - x_2 + 2x_3,$$

defining functions from $\mathcal{R}^2$ to $\mathcal{R}^2$ and from $\mathcal{R}^3$ to $\mathcal{R}^2$, respectively. These functions are described by the matrices A and B where

$$A = \begin{pmatrix} 3 & -1 \\ 5 & 2 \end{pmatrix} \quad \text{and} \quad B = \begin{pmatrix} 2 & 3 & 4 \\ 1 & -1 & 2 \end{pmatrix}.$$

If we express the z's directly in terms of the x's we obtain

$$z_1 = 3(2x_1 + 3x_2 + 4x_3) - (x_1 - x_2 + 2x_3)$$
$$z_2 = 5(2x_1 + 3x_2 + 4x_3) + 2(x_1 - x_2 + 2x_3).$$

Rearranging terms gives

$$z_1 = (3 \cdot 2 - 1 \cdot 1)x_1 + (3 \cdot 3 - 1 \cdot (-1))x_2 + (3 \cdot 4 - 1 \cdot 2)x_3$$
$$z_2 = (5 \cdot 2 + 2 \cdot 1)x_1 + (5 \cdot 3 + 2 \cdot (-1))x_2 + (5 \cdot 4 + 2 \cdot 2)x_3$$

and we see that the resulting function is described by a matrix C with

$$C = \begin{pmatrix} 3 \cdot 2 - 1 \cdot 1 & 3 \cdot 3 - 1 \cdot (-1) & 3 \cdot 4 - 1 \cdot 2 \\ 5 \cdot 2 + 2 \cdot 1 & 5 \cdot 3 + 2 \cdot (-1) & 5 \cdot 4 + 2 \cdot 2 \end{pmatrix} = \begin{pmatrix} 5 & 10 & 10 \\ 12 & 13 & 24 \end{pmatrix}.$$

We say that C is obtained from A and B by matrix multiplication and write $C = AB$.

To see how the general definition should be made, note that the ijth entry of C is the sum of products of entries in the ith row of A and the jth column of B. Thus $c_{21} = a_{21}b_{11} + a_{22}b_{21} = 5 \cdot 2 + 2 \cdot 1 = 12$.

We give the definition of matrix multiplication in two stages. First suppose $A = (a_1, \dots, a_k)$ is a row vector of dimension k and B is a column vector of the same dimension. Then the product AB is defined to be the number $a_1b_1 + a_2b_2 + \dots + a_kb_k$. Now let A be an m-by-k matrix and B be an k-by-n matrix. (It is important that the number of columns of A be equal to the number of rows of B.) Then each row of A is a k-dimensional row vector and each column of B is a k-dimensional column vector. We define the **matrix product** AB as the m-by-n matrix whose ijth entry is the product (in the sense just defined) of the ith row of A and the jth column of B. The product AB always has the same number of rows as A and the same number of columns as B. For instance, in our example

$$\begin{pmatrix} 3 & -1 \\ 5 & 2 \end{pmatrix}\begin{pmatrix} 2 & 3 & 4 \\ 1 & -1 & 2 \end{pmatrix} = \begin{pmatrix} 5 & 10 & 10 \\ 12 & 13 & 24 \end{pmatrix},$$

the entry in the second row and third column of the result is obtained by the calculation

$$(5 \quad 2)\begin{pmatrix} 4 \\ 2 \end{pmatrix} = 5 \cdot 4 + 2 \cdot 2 = 24.$$

You should check that the other entries in the product can be obtained by applying the rule stated above.

The following remark is an obvious consequence of the way matrix multiplication is defined. We state it formally for emphasis, and because we shall refer to it later.

3.1 Theorem. *The ith row of a matrix product AB is equal to the ith row of A times B. The jth column of AB is equal to A times the jth column of B.*

There are several important laws relating matrix multiplication and the operations of matrix addition and numerical multiplication. They hold for any number t and matrices A, B, C for which the indicated operations are defined. (Addition is only defined between matrices of the same shape. Multiplication is defined only if the left factor has exactly as many columns as the right factor has rows.)

1. $(A + B)C = AC + BC$.
2. $A(B + C) = AB + AC$.
3. $(tA)B = t(AB) = A(tB)$.
4. $A(BC) = (AB)C$.

According to the last law, it makes sense to talk of *the* product of three matrices and simply write ABC, since the result is independent of how the factors are grouped. In fact this 3-term associative law implies that the result of multiplying together any finite sequence of matrices is independent of how they are grouped. Not all the laws that hold for multiplication of numbers hold for multiplication of matrices. In particular, the value of a matrix product depends on the order of the factors, and AB is usually different from BA. It is also possible for the product of two matrices to be a zero matrix, without either of the factors being zero. Exercise 5 at the end of the section illustrates these points.

The laws stated above are easily proved by writing out what they mean, using the definitions of the operations, and then applying the associative, distributive, and commutative laws of arithmetic. Number 4 is the most complicated to prove, and we give its proof in full below. The other proofs are left as exercises.

To prove that $A(BC) = (AB)C$, let A, B, C have respective shapes p-by-q, q-by-r, and r-by-s. Let $U = BC$ and $V = AB$. (Then U has shape q-by-s, and V has shape p-by-r.) We have to show that $AU = VC$. The ijth element of AU is (by definition of matrix multiplication) equal to $\sum_{k=1}^{q} a_{ik}u_{kj}$. The kjth element of U is $\sum_{l=1}^{r} b_{kl}c_{lj}$. Thus the ijth element of AU equals $\sum_{k=1}^{q} a_{ik}\left(\sum_{l=1}^{r} b_{kl}c_{lj}\right)$. Similarly, the ijth element of VC is equal to $\sum_{l=1}^{r} v_{il}c_{lj}$ $= \sum_{l=1}^{r}\left(\sum_{k=1}^{q} a_{ik}b_{kl}\right)c_{lj}$. Both these expressions are equal to the sum

$$\sum_{\substack{1 \le l \le r \\ 1 \le k \le q}} a_{ik}b_{kl}c_{lj}$$

and hence are equal to each other. Thus corresponding entries of AU and VC are equal and the matrices are the same. This completes the proof.

A square matrix of the form

$$I = \begin{pmatrix} 1 & 0 & \cdots & 0 & 0 \\ 0 & 1 & \cdots & 0 & 0 \\ \cdot & \cdot & & \cdot & \cdot \\ \cdot & \cdot & & \cdot & \cdot \\ \cdot & \cdot & & \cdot & \cdot \\ 0 & 0 & \cdots & 0 & 1 \end{pmatrix}$$

that has 1's on its main diagonal and zeros elsewhere is called an **identity matrix**. It has the property that

$$IA = A, \quad BI = B$$

for any matrices A, B such that the products are defined. Thus it is an identity element for matrix multiplication just as the number 1 is an identity for multiplication of numbers. There is an $n \times n$ identity matrix for every value of n, but, as with the zero matrices, it is almost always clear from the context what the dimension of an identity matrix must be.

If A is a square matrix and there is a matrix B (of the same size) such that

$$AB = BA = I,$$

then we say that A is **invertible** and that B is the **inverse** of A. For any matrix A, there is at most one matrix B satisfying the condition above, for if $AB_1 = B_1A = I$ and $AB_2 = B_2A = I$, then the identity $(B_1A)B_2 = B_1(AB_2)$ gives $IB_2 = B_1I$, and so $B_1 = B_2$. This justifies speaking of *the* inverse of a matrix, and if A is an invertible matrix, we write A^{-1} for its inverse. For example, it is easy to check that

$$\begin{pmatrix} 1 & 2 \\ 3 & 7 \end{pmatrix}\begin{pmatrix} 7 & -2 \\ -3 & 1 \end{pmatrix} = \begin{pmatrix} 7 & -2 \\ -3 & 1 \end{pmatrix}\begin{pmatrix} 1 & 2 \\ 3 & 7 \end{pmatrix} = \begin{pmatrix} 1 & 0 \\ 0 & 1 \end{pmatrix},$$

and according to the definition this shows that

$$\begin{pmatrix} 1 & 2 \\ 3 & 7 \end{pmatrix} \text{ is invertible and that } \begin{pmatrix} 1 & 2 \\ 3 & 7 \end{pmatrix}^{-1} = \begin{pmatrix} 7 & -2 \\ -3 & 1 \end{pmatrix}.$$

Many matrices, on the other hand, are not invertible. No zero matrix can have an inverse, and several less obvious examples are given in the exercises.

In general it is difficult to tell whether a matrix is invertible, and it takes work to compute its inverse if it has one. Some easy special cases are included in the exercises of this section. General techniques for solving these problems are taken up in Section 6. One important property of invertible matrices is easily proved directly from the definition.

3.2 Theorem. If $A = A_1A_2 \ldots A_n$, and all of $A_1, \ldots, A_n$ are invertible, then A is invertible and $A^{-1} = A_n^{-1}A_{n-1}^{-1} \ldots A_2^{-1}A_1^{-1}$.

Proof. In the product $(A_n^{-1} \ldots A_2^{-1}A_1^{-1})(A_1A_2 \ldots A_n)$, the terms $A_1^{-1}A_1$ combine to give I, which may then be dropped. Then A_2^{-1} and A_2 cancel, and so on, until I is obtained as the final result. Similarly $(A_1 \ldots A_n)$ $(A_n^{-1} \ldots A_1^{-1})$ reduces to I, and this shows that the two products are inverses of each other.

There are some matrices, other than the identity, for which it is con-venient to have special names and notations. A matrix A is **diagonal** if its entries off the "main diagonal" are all zero, that is, if $a_{ij} = 0$ whenever $i \neq j$. The notation **diag** $(t_1, t_2, \ldots, t_n)$ is convenient for the $n \times n$ diagonal matrix which has entries $t_1, t_2, \ldots, t_n$ on the diagonal. For example **diag** $(2, 0, -1, 3)$ is a notation for

$$\begin{pmatrix} 2 & 0 & 0 & 0 \\ 0 & 0 & 0 & 0 \\ 0 & 0 & -1 & 0 \\ 0 & 0 & 0 & 3 \end{pmatrix}.$$

The m-by-n matrix which has 1 for its ijth entry and 0 for all other entries will be denoted by E_{ij}. Thus, for example, for the shape 3-by-2

$$E_{11} = \begin{pmatrix} 1 & 0 \\ 0 & 0 \\ 0 & 0 \end{pmatrix}, \quad E_{32} = \begin{pmatrix} 0 & 0 \\ 0 & 0 \\ 0 & 1 \end{pmatrix}, \quad E_{21} = \begin{pmatrix} 0 & 0 \\ 1 & 0 \\ 0 & 0 \end{pmatrix}.$$

For column and row vectors (i.e., n-by-1 and 1-by-n matrices) we use the notation introduced at the end of Section 1, and write $\mathbf{e}_i$ for a vector with 1 in the ith place and zeros elsewhere. Whether a row or a column vector is intended will always be clear from the context.

EXERCISES

1. Given the matrices

$$A = \begin{pmatrix} 1 & 3 \\ -4 & 2 \end{pmatrix}, \quad B = \begin{pmatrix} 0 & -2 & 1 \\ -1 & 3 & 0 \end{pmatrix}, \quad C = \begin{pmatrix} -2 & 0 & 1 \\ 0 & 3 & 0 \\ 2 & 3 & -1 \end{pmatrix},$$

$$D = \begin{pmatrix} 2 & -4 \\ 0 & 0 \\ 3 & 3 \end{pmatrix}, \quad G = \begin{pmatrix} 1 & -1 & 2 \\ 1 & 0 & 3 \end{pmatrix},$$

determine which of the following expressions are defined, and compute those that are.

(a) $2B - 3G$.
(b) AB.
(c) BA.
(d) BD.
(e) DB
(f) $CD + 3DB$.
(g) $2AB - 5G$.
(h) $2GC - 4AB$.
(i) CDC.
(j) DCD.

$$\left[Ans. \ (b) \ \begin{pmatrix} -3 & 7 & 1 \\ -2 & 14 & -4 \end{pmatrix}. \right]$$

2. Show that for any matrix A and zero matrices of appropriate shapes,

$$A0 = 0 \quad \text{and} \quad 0A = 0.$$

If A is m-by-n, for what possible shapes of zero matrices is $A0$ defined? For what shapes is $0A$ defined? What are the shapes of the products?

3. With A, B, C, D as in Exercise 1, determine what shapes X and Y would have to have for each of the following equations to be possible. (In some cases there may be no possible shape; in some cases there may be more than one.)

(a) $AX = B + Y$.
(b) $(D + 2X)YC = 0$.
(c) $AX = YD$.
(d) $CX + DY = 0$.
(e) $AX = YC$.
(f) $AX = CY$.

[(d) *Ans.* X is 3-by-n, Y is 2-by-n.]

4. Prove the distributive law

$$A(B + C) = AB + AC$$

for matrix multiplication.

5. Let $U = \begin{pmatrix} -1 & 2 \\ 2 & -4 \end{pmatrix}$, $V = \begin{pmatrix} 2 & 6 \\ 1 & 3 \end{pmatrix}$. Compute UV and VU. Are they the same? Is it possible for the product of two matrices to be zero without either factor being zero?

6. Let $X = \begin{pmatrix} 1 \\ 1 \\ 1 \end{pmatrix}$, $P = \begin{pmatrix} 0 & -1 \\ 4 & 3 \\ 2 & 0 \end{pmatrix}$, $Q = \begin{pmatrix} 1 & 2 & 0 \\ 3 & -4 & -1 \\ -1 & 2 & 0 \end{pmatrix}$.

Let $D = \mathbf{diag}\,(1, 2, 3) = \begin{pmatrix} 1 & 0 & 0 \\ 0 & 2 & 0 \\ 0 & 0 & 3 \end{pmatrix}$.

Compute DX, DP, and DQ.

7. Show that, as is illustrated by Exercise 6, the product DR, where D is a diagonal matrix $\mathbf{diag}\,(d_1, \ldots, d_n)$ and R is any n-rowed matrix, is obtained by multiplying the ith row of R by d_i, for all i. Suppose S has n columns. How may the product SD be defined? (Computing the product QD using the matrices of Exercise 6 should suggest the general rule.)

8. Using the matrices B, C, and G of Exercise 1, compute Be_1, Ce_1, Ge_1, Be_3, Ce_3, Ge_3. Prove the general rule that for any matrix M and column vector e_j with appropriate dimension, the product Me_j is the jth column of M.

9. (a) Show that $E_{ij}M$ contains zeros except in the ith row, which is a copy of the jth row of M.
   (b) Considering matrices of shape n-by-n, show that the product $E_{ij}E_{pq}$ is 0 unless $j = p$, while $E_{ij}E_{jq} = E_{iq}$.
   (c) Show that if i is different from j, then $I - E_{ij}$ is the inverse of $I + E_{ij}$. What if $i = j$?

10. What is the product $\mathbf{diag}\,(a_1, \ldots, a_n)\,\mathbf{diag}\,(b_1, \ldots, b_n)$? When is the result the identity matrix? Show that $\mathbf{diag}\,(a_1, \ldots, a_n)$ has an inverse provided none of the numbers a_i is zero.

11. Let $A = \begin{pmatrix} a & b \\ c & d \end{pmatrix}$ be an arbitrary 2-by-2 matrix, and let B be $\begin{pmatrix} d & -b \\ -c & a \end{pmatrix}$. Compute AB and BA and show that if $ad \neq bc$, then $(1/ad - bc)B$ is the inverse of A (so A is invertible).

12. Show that if there is any matrix $X \neq 0$ such that $AX = 0$, then A cannot be invertible. [*Hint.* Suppose $B = A^{-1}$, and consider $(BA)X = B(AX)$.] Use this result to show that $\mathbf{diag}\,(a_1, \ldots, a_n)$ is not invertible if any of the a_i is zero.

13. Show that if $ad = bc$, then $\begin{pmatrix} a & b \\ c & d \end{pmatrix}$ is not invertible.

14. If A is a square matrix, it can be multiplied by itself, and we can define $A^2 = AA$, $A^3 = AAA = A^2A$, $A^n = AA \ldots A$ (n factors). These powers of A all have the same shape as A. Find A^2 and A^3 if

(a) $A = \begin{pmatrix} 2 & 1 \\ 0 & 1 \end{pmatrix}$ (b) $A = \begin{pmatrix} 1 & 0 & -1 \\ -1 & 0 & 1 \\ 2 & 1 & -1 \end{pmatrix}$.

$$\left[Ans. \ (a) \ A^2 = \begin{pmatrix} 4 & 3 \\ 0 & 1 \end{pmatrix}. \right]$$

(Note that 0 is the only number whose cube is 0. Part (b) of this example thus illustrates another difference between the arithmetic of numbers and of matrices.)

15. The numerical equation $a^2 = 1$ has $a = 1$ and $a = -1$ as its only solutions.

(a) Show that if $A = I$ or $-I$, then $A^2 = I$, where I is an identity matrix of any dimension.

(b) Show that $\begin{pmatrix} a & b \\ c & -a \end{pmatrix}^2 = \begin{pmatrix} 1 & 0 \\ 0 & 1 \end{pmatrix}$ if $a^2 + bc = 1$, so the equation $A^2 = I$ has infinitely many different solutions in the set of 2-by-2 matrices.

(c) Show that every 2-by-2 matrix A for which $A^2 = I$ is either I, $-I$, or one of the matrices described in (b).

16. Let $A = \begin{pmatrix} 1 & 2 \\ 2 & 3 \end{pmatrix}$ and $B = \begin{pmatrix} 2 & 0 \\ 0 & 1 \end{pmatrix}$. Write down A^{-1} and B^{-1}, by using the result of Problem 11. Compute AB and $B^{-1}A^{-1}$ and check that they are inverses of each other, as predicted by Theorem 3.2.

4. LINEAR FUNCTIONS

The product of an m-by-n matrix and an n-dimensional column vector (n-by-1 matrix) is an m-dimensional column vector. An n-tuple in $\mathscr{R}^n$ obviously corresponds to a unique n-dimensional column vector, and vice versa. From here on we shall often simply consider elements of $\mathscr{R}^n$ to be column vectors. With this convention, multiplication by any given m-by-n matrix defines a function from $\mathscr{R}^n$ to $\mathscr{R}^m$. Indeed a matrix equation such as

$$\begin{pmatrix} y_1 \\ y_2 \end{pmatrix} = \begin{pmatrix} 2 & 3 & -4 \\ 1 & -1 & 2 \end{pmatrix} \begin{pmatrix} x_1 \\ x_2 \\ x_3 \end{pmatrix}$$

is equivalent to a set of numerical equations

$$y_1 = 2x_1 + 3x_2 - 4x_3$$
$$y_1 = x_1 - x_2 + 2x_3,$$

as may be seen by simply writing out the result of the matrix multiplication. Thus the vector function described by a matrix amounts to multiplication of a domain vector by the matrix.

Functions given by matrix multiplication can be characterized by some very simple properties. Note that the definition given below applies to functions between any two vector spaces although we are at present concerned only with the spaces $\mathscr{R}^n$.

A function f with domain a vector space $\mathscr{V}$ and range a subset of a vector space $\mathscr{W}$ is a **linear** function if the equations

$$f(\mathbf{x} + \mathbf{y}) = f(\mathbf{x}) + f(\mathbf{y})$$
$$f(r\mathbf{x}) = rf(\mathbf{x})$$

hold for all vectors $\mathbf{x}$, $\mathbf{y}$ in $\mathscr{V}$, and all numbers r.

4.1 Theorem. A function from $\mathscr{R}^n$ to $\mathscr{R}^m$ is linear if and only if it coincides with multiplication by some m-by-n matrix.

Proof. We show first that if f is defined by $f(\mathbf{x}) = A\mathbf{x}$ for a fixed matrix A, then f is linear. We must show that $f(\mathbf{x} + \mathbf{y}) = f(\mathbf{x}) + f(\mathbf{y})$ and $f(r\mathbf{x}) = rf(\mathbf{x})$ for any $\mathbf{x}$, $\mathbf{y}$, and r. But by the definition of f, these equations amount to $A(\mathbf{x} + \mathbf{y}) = A\mathbf{x} + A\mathbf{y}$ and $A(r\mathbf{x}) = r(A\mathbf{x})$, which hold by properties 2 and 3 for matrix multiplication.

The proof of the converse is a little more complicated. Suppose we are given a linear function g from $\mathscr{R}^n$ to $\mathscr{R}^m$. We have to find an m-by-n matrix A such that $g(\mathbf{x}) = A\mathbf{x}$ for every column vector $\mathbf{x}$ in $\mathscr{R}^n$. Let $\mathbf{e}_j$ be the column vector in $\mathscr{R}^n$ that has 1 for its jth entry and 0 for all other entries. Now let A be the matrix whose jth column is the m-dimensional vector $g(\mathbf{e}_j)$ for $j = 1, 2, \ldots, n$. (Thus A has m rows and n columns, as required.) Any column vector $\mathbf{x}$ with entries $x_1, x_2, \ldots, x_n$ can be written as $x_1\mathbf{e}_1 + \ldots + x_n\mathbf{e}_n$. Since g is linear

$$\begin{aligned} g(\mathbf{x}) &= g(x_1\mathbf{e}_1 + \ldots + x_n\mathbf{e}_n) \\ &= x_1 g(\mathbf{e}_1) + \ldots + x_n g(\mathbf{e}_n). \end{aligned}$$

By the definition of A we have

$$g(\mathbf{x}) = x_1 \begin{pmatrix} a_{11} \\ a_{21} \\ \cdot \\ \cdot \\ \cdot \\ a_{m1} \end{pmatrix} + \ldots + x_n \begin{pmatrix} a_{1n} \\ a_{2n} \\ \cdot \\ \cdot \\ \cdot \\ a_{mn} \end{pmatrix}$$

$$= \begin{pmatrix} a_{11}x_1 + \ldots + a_{1n}x_n \\ a_{21}x_1 + \ldots + a_{2n}x_n \\ \cdot \\ \cdot \\ \cdot \\ a_{m1}x_1 + \ldots + a_{mn}x_n \end{pmatrix}.$$

Finally, by the definition of matrix multiplication,

$$g(\mathbf{x}) = A\mathbf{x}.$$

The proof given above actually shows how to construct the matrix corresponding to a linear function. This construction is important and we summarize it as a theorem for emphasis.

4.2 Theorem. Let $\mathscr{R}^n \xrightarrow{f} \mathscr{R}^m$ be a linear function, and let A be the matrix whose jth column is $f(\mathbf{e}_j)$. Then $f(\mathbf{x}) = A\mathbf{x}$ for every $\mathbf{x}$ in $\mathscr{R}^n$.

EXAMPLE 1. Consider the function $\mathscr{R}^2 \xrightarrow{f} \mathscr{R}^2$ described in terms of the geometric representation of $\mathscr{R}^2$ as a counterclockwise rotation of 30°. Any rotation leaves the origin fixed, preserves distances, and carries figures such as parallelograms onto congruent figures. From these properties, and the way in which addition and numerical multiplication of vectors can be done by geometrical constructions (Section 2), it can be shown that a rotation is a linear function. Figure 10 shows the vectors $\mathbf{e}_1, \mathbf{e}_2, f(\mathbf{e}_1)$, and $f(\mathbf{e}_2)$. By trigonometry we see that $f(\mathbf{e}_1) = \begin{pmatrix} \dfrac{\sqrt{3}}{2} \\ \dfrac{1}{2} \end{pmatrix}$ and $f(\mathbf{e}_2) = \begin{pmatrix} -\dfrac{1}{2} \\ \dfrac{\sqrt{3}}{2} \end{pmatrix}$. By Theorem 4.2,

$$f\begin{pmatrix} x_1 \\ x_2 \end{pmatrix} = \begin{pmatrix} \dfrac{\sqrt{3}}{2} & -\dfrac{1}{2} \\ \dfrac{1}{2} & \dfrac{\sqrt{3}}{2} \end{pmatrix}\begin{pmatrix} x_1 \\ x_2 \end{pmatrix} = \begin{pmatrix} \dfrac{\sqrt{3}}{2}x_1 - \dfrac{1}{2}x_2 \\ \dfrac{1}{2}x_1 + \dfrac{\sqrt{3}}{2}x_2 \end{pmatrix}$$

for any vector $\begin{pmatrix} x_1 \\ x_2 \end{pmatrix}$ in $\mathscr{R}^2$.

A function f is said to be **one-to-one** if each point in the range of f corresponds to exactly one point in the domain of f. In other words, f is one-to-one if the equation $f(\mathbf{x}_1) = f(\mathbf{x}_2)$ always implies that $\mathbf{x}_1 = \mathbf{x}_2$. For example,

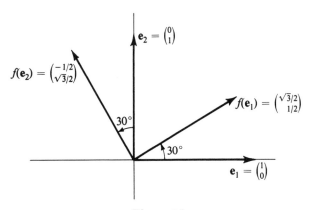

Figure 10

of the two real-valued function given by $f(x) = x$ and $g(x) = x^2$, it is obvious that f is one-to-one. But g is not one-to-one, because $g(x) = g(-x)$ for any number x. For *linear* functions, of which $f(x) = x$ is an example, we have the following criterion:

4.3 Theorem. A linear function is one-to-one if and only if $f(\mathbf{x}) = 0$ implies $\mathbf{x} = 0$.

Proof. First assume that $f(\mathbf{x}) = 0$ implies $\mathbf{x} = 0$. If $f(\mathbf{x}_1) = f(\mathbf{x}_2)$, we have, by the linearity of f, that $f(\mathbf{x}_1 - \mathbf{x}_2) = 0$. But then by assumption $\mathbf{x}_1 - \mathbf{x}_2 = 0$, so $\mathbf{x}_1 = \mathbf{x}_2$. Thus f must be one-to-one. Conversely, suppose $f(\mathbf{x}_1) = f(\mathbf{x}_2)$ always implies $\mathbf{x}_1 = \mathbf{x}_2$. Then because $f(0) = 0$ for a linear function, the equation $f(\mathbf{x}) = 0$ can be written $f(\mathbf{x}) = f(0)$. But then $\mathbf{x} = 0$ by assumption.

EXAMPLE 2. The function f of Example 1 is given by

$$f\begin{pmatrix} x_1 \\ x_2 \end{pmatrix} = \begin{pmatrix} \dfrac{\sqrt{3}}{2} x_1 - \dfrac{1}{2} x_2 \\ \dfrac{1}{2} x_1 + \dfrac{\sqrt{3}}{2} x_2 \end{pmatrix}.$$

Thus the relation $f\begin{pmatrix} x_1 \\ x_2 \end{pmatrix} = \begin{pmatrix} 0 \\ 0 \end{pmatrix}$ means that

$$\frac{\sqrt{3}}{2} x_1 - \frac{1}{2} x_2 = 0$$

$$\frac{1}{2} x_1 + \frac{\sqrt{3}}{2} x_2 = 0.$$

From these equations it follows that $x_1 = x_2 = 0$. Hence $f(\mathbf{x}) = 0$ implies $\mathbf{x} = 0$, so f is one-to-one. That f is one-to-one is also geometrically evident from the interpretation of f as a rotation of $30°$ about the origin in $\mathscr{R}^2$.

If f and g are any two functions (not necessarily linear) such that the range space of f is the same as the domain space of g we define the **composition** $g \circ f$ to be the function obtained by applying first f and then g. More explicitly, if $\mathbf{x}$ is in the domain of f and $f(\mathbf{x})$ is in the domain of g, then $g \circ f(\mathbf{x})$ is defined as $g(f(\mathbf{x}))$. If $f(\mathbf{x})$ or $g(f(\mathbf{x}))$ is not defined, then $g \circ f(\mathbf{x})$ is not defined.

Composition of linear functions lies behind matrix multiplication. In introducing the concept of matrix multiplication, we considered a function from $\mathscr{R}^2$ to $\mathscr{R}^2$ given by

$$z_1 = 3y_1 - y_2$$
$$z_2 = 5y_1 + 2y_2$$

and another from $\mathscr{R}^3$ to $\mathscr{R}^2$ given by

$$y_1 = 2x_1 + 3x_2 + 4x_3$$
$$y_2 = x_1 - x_2 + 2x_3,$$

and then computed that the composition of the two functions was given by the formulas

$$z_1 = 5x_1 + 10x_2 + 10x_3$$
$$z_2 = 12x_1 + 13x_2 + 24x_3.$$

The definition of matrix multiplication was set up to give the matrix $\begin{pmatrix} 5 & 10 & 10 \\ 12 & 13 & 24 \end{pmatrix}$ of the composite function as the product of the matrices

$$\begin{pmatrix} 3 & -1 \\ 5 & 2 \end{pmatrix} \begin{pmatrix} 2 & 3 & 4 \\ 1 & -1 & 2 \end{pmatrix}$$

for the original functions. The following theorem states the important fact that the composition of linear functions is always given by matrix multiplication:

4.4 Theorem. Let f and g be linear functions with $\mathscr{R}^n \xrightarrow{f} \mathscr{R}^m$, $\mathscr{R}^m \xrightarrow{g} \mathscr{R}^p$ given by matrices A, B. Thus $f(\mathbf{x}) = A\mathbf{x}$ and $g(\mathbf{y}) = B\mathbf{y}$ for all $\mathbf{x}$ in $\mathscr{R}^n$ and $\mathbf{y}$ in $\mathscr{R}^m$. Then the composition $g \circ f$ is given by the matrix BA, so that $g \circ f(\mathbf{x}) = BA\mathbf{x}$ for all $\mathbf{x}$ in $\mathscr{R}^n$.

Proof. Note that A is an m-by-n matrix and B a p-by-m matrix, so the matrix product BA is defined and has the appropriate shape, namely p-by-n. By the definition of $g \circ f$, $g \circ f(\mathbf{x}) = g(f(\mathbf{x})) = B(A\mathbf{x})$ for all $\mathbf{x}$ in $\mathscr{R}^n$. By the associative law of matrix multiplication this is equal to $(BA)\mathbf{x}$, as was to be proved.

EXAMPLE 3. Consider the function $\mathscr{R}^2 \xrightarrow{g} \mathscr{R}^2$ defined as $f \circ f \circ f$, where f is the function of Example 1. By Theorem 4.4, $g(\mathbf{x}) = B\mathbf{x}$, where

$$B = \begin{pmatrix} \dfrac{\sqrt{3}}{2} & -\dfrac{1}{2} \\ \dfrac{1}{2} & \dfrac{\sqrt{3}}{2} \end{pmatrix} \begin{pmatrix} \dfrac{\sqrt{3}}{2} & -\dfrac{1}{2} \\ \dfrac{1}{2} & \dfrac{\sqrt{3}}{2} \end{pmatrix} \begin{pmatrix} \dfrac{\sqrt{3}}{2} & -\dfrac{1}{2} \\ \dfrac{1}{2} & \dfrac{\sqrt{3}}{2} \end{pmatrix}$$

$$= \begin{pmatrix} \dfrac{1}{2} & -\dfrac{\sqrt{3}}{2} \\ \dfrac{\sqrt{3}}{2} & \dfrac{1}{2} \end{pmatrix} \begin{pmatrix} \dfrac{\sqrt{3}}{2} & -\dfrac{1}{2} \\ \dfrac{1}{2} & \dfrac{\sqrt{3}}{2} \end{pmatrix} = \begin{pmatrix} 0 & -1 \\ 1 & 0 \end{pmatrix}.$$

Thus $g(\mathbf{e}_1) = B\mathbf{e}_1 = \begin{pmatrix} 0 \\ 1 \end{pmatrix} = \mathbf{e}_2$ and $g(\mathbf{e}_2) = B\mathbf{e}_2 = \begin{pmatrix} -1 \\ 0 \end{pmatrix} = -\mathbf{e}_1$. As Figure 11 shows, g amounts geometrically to a counterclockwise rotation of $90°$, which of course is what the result of three successive $30°$ rotations ought to be.

In dealing with functions of one variable, it is customary to call any

function of the form $f(x) = ax + b$
a linear function. This terminology
is not consistent with our definition of
linearity. For example, if $f(x) = 2x + 1$,
then $f(x + y) = 2(x + y) + 1$, while
$f(x) + f(y) = 2x + 2y + 2$; so this
function fails to satisfy the condition
$f(x + y) = f(x) + f(y)$ that is required
for linearity. Since our definition of
linear functions between vector spaces

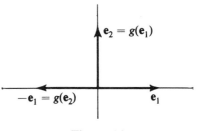

Figure 11

is the standard one, we shall not consider functions such as $2x + 1$ to be
linear. Functions of this more general type are important, however, and
there is a standard term for them. They are called affine functions, and are
characterized as having the form of a linear function (such as $2x$) plus a
constant (such as 1). The formal definitions follow.

If **b** is an element of a vector space $\mathcal{V}$, then the function t_b from $\mathcal{V}$
to itself defined by $t_b(\mathbf{x}) = \mathbf{x} + \mathbf{b}$ for all **x** in $\mathcal{V}$ is called the **translation** of
$\mathcal{V}$ induced by **b**.

EXAMPLE 4. Let **b** be the vector $(1, 0)$ in $\mathcal{R}^2$. Then t_b sends any vector
(x, y) into the vector $(x + 1, y)$. In geometrical language, every point of the
plane is moved one unit to the right.

A function from a vector space $\mathcal{V}$ to a vector space $\mathcal{W}$ is an **affine**
function if it is the composition of a linear function from $\mathcal{V}$ to $\mathcal{W}$ with a
translation of $\mathcal{W}$.

EXAMPLE 5. Let f from $\mathcal{R}^2$ to $\mathcal{R}^2$ have the matrix $\begin{pmatrix} 1 & 0 \\ 0 & -1 \end{pmatrix}$ and let **b**
be the vector $(0, 2)$. The affine function $t_b \circ f$ then sends any vector (x, y)
into $(x, -y + 2)$. Geometrically, this amounts to a reflection in the x-axis
followed by a motion of 2 units straight up. It is easy to see that all the points
of the line $y = 1$ remain fixed under this function, and that it may be
described as reflection in the line $y = 1$.

The following theorem is an immediate consequence of the definitions
and of Theorem 4.1.

4.5 Theorem. A function f from $\mathcal{R}^n$ to $\mathcal{R}^m$ is affine if and only if $f(\mathbf{x}) =
A\mathbf{x} + \mathbf{b}$ for some fixed m-by-n matrix A and m-dimensional column
vector **b**.

Finding the matrix A and vector **b** needed to describe an affine trans-
formation is easy. If $f(\mathbf{x}) = A\mathbf{x} + \mathbf{b}$, then $\mathbf{b} = f(0)$. Then the function
$g(\mathbf{x}) = f(\mathbf{x}) - f(0)$ is linear and the matrix A is found by using Theorem 4.2.

EXAMPLE 6. Let $\mathcal{R}^2 \xrightarrow{f} \mathcal{R}^2$ be defined in terms of the standard geometric representation as a counterclockwise rotation of $90°$ about the center $\begin{pmatrix} 1 \\ 0 \end{pmatrix} = e_1$. We see that $f(0) = \begin{pmatrix} 1 \\ -1 \end{pmatrix}$, $f(e_1) = \begin{pmatrix} 1 \\ 0 \end{pmatrix}$ (since the center of a rotation stays fixed) and $f\begin{pmatrix} 0 \\ 1 \end{pmatrix} = \begin{pmatrix} 0 \\ -1 \end{pmatrix}$. Introducing the linear function $g(x) = f(x) - f(0)$, we have $g(e_1) = \begin{pmatrix} 1 \\ 0 \end{pmatrix} - \begin{pmatrix} 1 \\ -1 \end{pmatrix} = \begin{pmatrix} 0 \\ 1 \end{pmatrix}$, and

$$g(e_2) = \begin{pmatrix} 0 \\ -1 \end{pmatrix} - \begin{pmatrix} 1 \\ -1 \end{pmatrix} = \begin{pmatrix} -1 \\ 0 \end{pmatrix}.$$

Therefore $g(x) = \begin{pmatrix} 0 & -1 \\ 1 & 0 \end{pmatrix} x$ for all x and

$$f(x) = \begin{pmatrix} 0 & -1 \\ 1 & 0 \end{pmatrix} x + \begin{pmatrix} 1 \\ -1 \end{pmatrix}.$$

As a check, let us compute

$$f\begin{pmatrix} 2 \\ 0 \end{pmatrix} = \begin{pmatrix} 0 & -1 \\ 1 & 0 \end{pmatrix}\begin{pmatrix} 2 \\ 0 \end{pmatrix} + \begin{pmatrix} 1 \\ -1 \end{pmatrix} = \begin{pmatrix} 0 \\ 2 \end{pmatrix} + \begin{pmatrix} 1 \\ -1 \end{pmatrix} = \begin{pmatrix} 1 \\ 1 \end{pmatrix},$$

which agrees with the geometric description of f. See Figure 12.

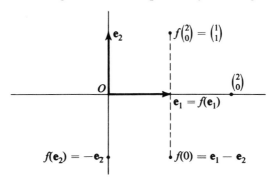

Figure 12

Linear and affine functions are often called linear and affine **transformations**, though we more often use the term function in this book.

EXERCISES

1. (a) Show that the two conditions on a linear function given in the text are equivalent to the single condition that

$$f(rx + sy) = rf(x) + sf(y)$$

hold for all x, y in the domain of f and all numbers r, s.

(b) Give a proof by induction on n that if f is linear, then $f(r_1 x_1 + \ldots + r_{n-1} x_{n-1} + r_n x_n) = r_1 f(x_1) + \ldots + r_{n-1} f(x_{n-1}) + r_n f(x_n)$ for any numbers $r_1, \ldots, r_n$ and vectors $x_1, \ldots, x_n$.

2. Show that $f(x) = ax + b$ is a linear function in the terminology of this book if and only if $b = 0$.

3. Let f and g be linear functions from $\mathcal{R}^2$ to $\mathcal{R}^2$ such that

(a) $f\begin{pmatrix} 1 \\ 0 \end{pmatrix} = \begin{pmatrix} 2 \\ 1 \end{pmatrix}$, $f\begin{pmatrix} 0 \\ 1 \end{pmatrix} = \begin{pmatrix} 1 \\ -1 \end{pmatrix}$

(b) $g\begin{pmatrix} 1 \\ 1 \end{pmatrix} = \begin{pmatrix} 2 \\ 1 \end{pmatrix}$, $g\begin{pmatrix} -1 \\ 1 \end{pmatrix} = \begin{pmatrix} 1 \\ -1 \end{pmatrix}$

In each case, find the matrix that represents the function.

4. Show that a counterclockwise rotation in $\mathcal{R}^2$ through an angle α is described by the matrix $R_\alpha = \begin{pmatrix} \cos \alpha & -\sin \alpha \\ \sin \alpha & \cos \alpha \end{pmatrix}$. Let β be another angle, and compute the product $R_\alpha R_\beta$. The composition of a rotation through angle α with one through angle β is a rotation through the angle $\alpha + \beta$. What is the relation between $R_\alpha R_\beta$ and $R_{\alpha+\beta}$? What is the inverse of R_α?

5. (a) Show that the matrix $\begin{pmatrix} 0 & 1 \\ 1 & 0 \end{pmatrix}$ gives a linear function from $\mathcal{R}^2$ to $\mathcal{R}^2$, which corresponds geometrically to reflection in the line through the origin 45° counterclockwise from the horizontal.

(b) What matrix corresponds to reflection in the line through the origin 135° counterclockwise from the horizontal?

(c) Compute the product of the matrices in (a) and (b) and interpret the result geometrically. $\left[Ans.\ (b) \begin{pmatrix} 0 & -1 \\ -1 & 0 \end{pmatrix}. \right]$

6. (a) Find the 2-by-2 matrix M_α corresponding to reflection in the line through the origin at an angle α from the horizontal. Check your result against Exercise 5 for $\alpha = 45°$, $\alpha = 135°$. What is M_α^2?

(b) Let β be another angle and compute the product $M_\alpha M_\beta$. Show that this represents a rotation, and identify the angle of rotation. When does $M_\alpha M_\beta = M_\beta M_\alpha$?

7. (a) Show that

$$U = \begin{pmatrix} 1 & 0 & 0 \\ 0 & 0 & -1 \\ 0 & 1 & 0 \end{pmatrix} \quad \text{and} \quad V = \begin{pmatrix} 0 & 0 & 1 \\ 0 & 1 & 0 \\ -1 & 0 & 0 \end{pmatrix}$$

represent 90°-rotations of $\mathcal{R}^3$ about the x_1-axis and x_2-axis, respectively. Find the matrix W which represents a 90°-rotation about the x_3-axis. Also find U^{-1} and V^{-1} (which represent rotations in the opposite direction).

(b) Compute UVU^{-1} and VUV^{-1} and interpret the results geometrically. (You may find it helpful to manipulate an actual 3-dimensional model.)

8. Show that a function f from one vector space to another is affine if and only if

$$f(r\mathbf{x} + (1 - r)\mathbf{y}) = rf(\mathbf{x}) + (1 - r)f(\mathbf{y})$$

for all numbers r and all $\mathbf{x}, \mathbf{y}$ in the domain of f. [*Hint.* Consider the function $g(\mathbf{x}) = f(\mathbf{x}) - f(0)$.]

9. Show that the composition of two affine functions from a space into itself is affine. Suppose $f(\mathbf{x}) = A\mathbf{x} + \mathbf{b}, g(\mathbf{x}) = C\mathbf{x} + \mathbf{d}$. Suppose $(f \circ g)(\mathbf{x}) = P\mathbf{x} + \mathbf{q}$. Express P and $\mathbf{q}$ in terms of A, $\mathbf{b}$, C, and $\mathbf{d}$. When is $f \circ g$ the same function as $g \circ f$?

10. Let $\mathbf{a} = \begin{pmatrix} 1 \\ 0 \end{pmatrix}, \mathbf{b} = -\mathbf{a} = \begin{pmatrix} -1 \\ 0 \end{pmatrix}$, and let $\mathscr{R}^2 \overset{g}{\longrightarrow} \mathscr{R}^2$ be a counterclockwise rotation of $90°$ with center at the origin. Find the matrix corresponding to the linear function g and compute the affine function $f = t_\mathbf{a} \circ g \circ t_\mathbf{b}$, where $t_\mathbf{a}$ and $t_\mathbf{b}$ are the translations induced by $\mathbf{a}$ and $\mathbf{b}$.

11. Compare the result of Exercise 10 with Example 4 in the text. Give a geometric interpretation of the composition $f = t_\mathbf{a} \circ g \circ t_\mathbf{b}$, where $\mathbf{a}$ is any vector in $\mathscr{R}^2$, $\mathbf{b} = -\mathbf{a}$, and g is any rotation about the origin. [*Hint.* What happens to the point corresponding to $\mathbf{a}$ under the function f?]

12. Show that an affine function A is one-to-one if and only if $A(\mathbf{x}) = A(0)$ always implies $\mathbf{x} = 0$.

13. Which of the following linear functions are one-to-one?

(a) $f(x_1, x_2) = (x_1 + 2x_2, 2x_1 + x_2)$.
(b) $g(x_1, x_2, x_3) = (x_2 - x_3, x_3 - x_1, x_1 - x_2)$.

5. EUCLIDEAN GEOMETRY

To allow the full application of vector ideas to euclidean geometry, we must have a means of introducing concepts such as length, angle, and perpendicularity. We will show in this section that all these concepts can be defined if we introduce a new operation on vectors. If $\mathbf{x} = (x_1, \ldots, x_n)$ and $\mathbf{y} = (y_1, \ldots, y_n)$ are vectors in $\mathscr{R}^n$, we define the **dot product** or **inner product** of X and Y to be the number

$$\mathbf{x} \cdot \mathbf{y} = x_1 y_1 + \ldots + x_n y_n.$$

It is easy to verify (see Exercise 7) that the dot product of vectors in $\mathscr{R}^n$ has the following properties.

5.1 **Positivity:** $\mathbf{x} \cdot \mathbf{x} > 0$ except that $0 \cdot 0 = 0$.
    Symmetry: $\mathbf{x} \cdot \mathbf{y} = \mathbf{y} \cdot \mathbf{x}$.
    Additivity: $(\mathbf{x} + \mathbf{y}) \cdot \mathbf{z} = \mathbf{x} \cdot \mathbf{z} + \mathbf{y} \cdot \mathbf{z}$.
    Homogeneity: $(r\mathbf{x}) \cdot \mathbf{y} = r(\mathbf{x} \cdot \mathbf{y})$.

Because of the symmetry of the dot product, it follows immediately that additivity and homogeneity hold for the second vector also, that is,

$$\mathbf{x} \cdot (\mathbf{y} + \mathbf{z}) = \mathbf{x} \cdot \mathbf{y} + \mathbf{x} \cdot \mathbf{z}$$

and

$$\mathbf{x} \cdot (r\mathbf{y}) = r(\mathbf{x} \cdot \mathbf{y}).$$

Let us first of all consider the length of a given vector $\mathbf{x}$ in $\mathscr{R}^3$. If $\mathbf{x} = (x_1, x_2, x_3)$, we think of the length of the vector as the distance from the origin to the point with coordinates (x_1, x_2, x_3). In $\mathscr{R}^3$ the Pythagorean theorem gives us a simple formula for the distance (see Figure 13). Letting $|\mathbf{x}|$ stand for the length of the vector $\mathbf{x}$, we have

$$|\mathbf{x}|^2 = x_1^2 + x_2^2 + x_3^2. \tag{1}$$

Thus we see that the **length** of the vector $\mathbf{x}$ can be expressed in terms of the dot product as $\sqrt{\mathbf{x} \cdot \mathbf{x}} = |\mathbf{x}|$. Note that we use the same symbol for the length of a vector as for the absolute value of a number. Indeed, if we think of a number as a one-component vector, its length is its absolute value. In $\mathscr{R}^n$ we define the **length** of a vector by the same formula that works in $\mathscr{R}^3$: $|\mathbf{x}| = \sqrt{\mathbf{x} \cdot \mathbf{x}}$.

Next we would like to express the angle between two nonzero vectors in $\mathscr{R}^n$. The usual convention is to take this angle θ to be in the interval $0 \leq \theta \leq \pi$ (see Exercise 1). The solution to this problem is provided by the following theorem.

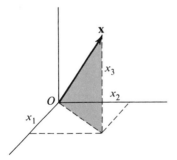

Figure 13

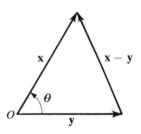

Figure 14

5.2 Theorem. If θ is the angle between $\mathbf{x}$ and $\mathbf{y}$, then

$$\cos \theta = \mathbf{x} \cdot \mathbf{y} / |\mathbf{x}||\mathbf{y}|.$$

Proof. Let us apply the law of cosines to the triangle shown in Figure 14. It states that

$$|\mathbf{x} - \mathbf{y}|^2 = |\mathbf{x}|^2 + |\mathbf{y}|^2 - 2|\mathbf{x}||\mathbf{y}| \cos \theta,$$

which we can rewrite, using $|\mathbf{x}|^2 = \mathbf{x} \cdot \mathbf{x}$, as

$$(\mathbf{x} - \mathbf{y}) \cdot (\mathbf{x} - \mathbf{y}) = \mathbf{x} \cdot \mathbf{x} + \mathbf{y} \cdot \mathbf{y} - 2|\mathbf{x}||\mathbf{y}| \cos \theta.$$

Expanding the left-hand member, we obtain

$$\mathbf{x} \cdot \mathbf{x} - \mathbf{x} \cdot \mathbf{y} - \mathbf{y} \cdot \mathbf{x} + \mathbf{y} \cdot \mathbf{y} = \mathbf{x} \cdot \mathbf{x} + \mathbf{y} \cdot \mathbf{y} - 2|\mathbf{x}||\mathbf{y}|\cos\theta.$$

Hence,

$$2\mathbf{x} \cdot \mathbf{y} = 2|\mathbf{x}||\mathbf{y}|\cos\theta,$$

and the theorem follows by dividing by $2|\mathbf{x}||\mathbf{y}|$.

We see from this theorem that $\mathbf{x} \cdot \mathbf{y}$ in absolute value is at most $|\mathbf{x}||\mathbf{y}|$, i.e., $|\mathbf{x} \cdot \mathbf{y}| \leq |\mathbf{x}||\mathbf{y}|$. This is known as the Cauchy-Schwarz inequality.

EXAMPLE 1. What is the angle θ between $\mathbf{x} = (1, 3)$ and $\mathbf{y} = (-1, 1)$? We easily compute that

$$\mathbf{x} \cdot \mathbf{x} = 1^2 + 3^2 = 10,$$

$$\mathbf{y} \cdot \mathbf{y} = (-1)^2 + 1^2 = 2,$$

and

$$\mathbf{x} \cdot \mathbf{y} = -1 + 3 = 2.$$

Hence

$$|\mathbf{x}| = \sqrt{10}, \quad |\mathbf{y}| = \sqrt{2}, \quad \text{and} \quad \cos\theta = \frac{1}{\sqrt{5}}.$$

By consulting a trigonometric table we find that $\theta = 1.1$ radians approximately (or about 63°).

The theorem also provides a simple test for perpendicularity of two vectors. They are perpendicular if and only if $\theta = \pi/2$, and hence $\cos\theta = 0$. Thus the condition for perpendicularity is simply

$$\mathbf{x} \cdot \mathbf{y} = 0. \tag{2}$$

EXAMPLE 2. Let us find a vector $\mathbf{x}$ of length 2 perpendicular to $(1, 2, 3)$ and to $(1, 0, -1)$. From geometric considerations we see that there will be two solutions, since if $\mathbf{x}$ is a solution, so is $-\mathbf{x}$. (See Figure 15.) We have to

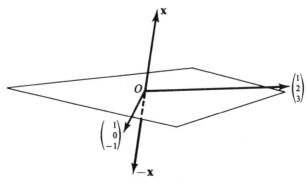

Figure 15

write down three conditions, two for the perpendicularity requirements, using (2), and a third condition to assure length 2:

$$x_1 + 2x_2 + 3x_3 = 0,$$

$$x_1 \qquad - x_3 = 0,$$

$$x_1^2 + x_2^2 + x_3^2 = 4.$$

These equations have the pair of solutions $\mathbf{x} = \pm(\sqrt{2/3}, -\sqrt{8/3}, \sqrt{2/3})$.

If $\mathbf{n}$ is a unit vector, that is, a vector of length 1, then the dot product $\mathbf{n} \cdot \mathbf{x}$ is called the **coordinate** of $\mathbf{x}$ in the direction of $\mathbf{n}$. The geometric interpretation of $\mathbf{n} \cdot \mathbf{x}$ is shown in Figure 16. For since $\cos\theta = (\mathbf{n} \cdot \mathbf{x})/|\mathbf{x}|$, it follows that $\mathbf{n} \cdot \mathbf{x}$ is either the length of the perpendicular projection on the line containing $\mathbf{n}$, or else its negative. The vector $(\mathbf{n} \cdot \mathbf{x})\mathbf{n}$ is called the **component** of $\mathbf{x}$ in the direction of $\mathbf{n}$ and is sometimes denoted $\mathbf{x_n}$.

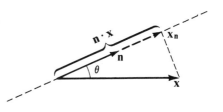

Figure 16

If $\mathbf{x}_1$ is a nonzero vector in $\mathscr{R}^2$ or $\mathscr{R}^3$, then the set of all numerical multiples $t\mathbf{x}_1$ is a line $\mathscr{L}_0$ passing through the origin. Furthermore, any line parallel to $\mathscr{L}_0$ consists of the set of all points $t\mathbf{x}_1 + \mathbf{x}_0$, where $\mathbf{x}_0$ is some fixed vector. We have defined a line in $\mathscr{R}^n$ to be any set of points representable in the form $t\mathbf{x}_1 + \mathbf{x}_0$, with $\mathbf{x}_1 \neq 0$. An alternative way to put the definition is to say that a **line** is the range of a function of the form $f(t) = t\mathbf{x}_1 + \mathbf{x}_0$, where $\mathbf{x}_1 \neq 0$.

EXAMPLE 3. The test for the perpendicularity of two vectors may be applied also to test the perpendicularity of two lines. Let $t\mathbf{x}_1 + \mathbf{x}_0$ and $t\mathbf{y}_1 + \mathbf{x}_0$ be two lines $\mathscr{L}$, $\mathscr{L}'$ through $\mathbf{x}_0$. We want to decide whether the lines are perpendicular. Clearly, this is equivalent to the question whether $\mathbf{x}_1$ and $\mathbf{y}_1$ are perpendicular. (See Figure 17.) Hence the condition is $\mathbf{x}_1 \cdot \mathbf{y}_1 = 0$.

For many purposes it is convenient to "normalize" the vector $\mathbf{x}_1$ in the parametric representation $t\mathbf{x}_1 + \mathbf{x}_2$ of a line. Since it may be replaced by any nonzero multiple, we may as well choose it to be of unit length (in which case $\mathbf{x}_1$ is determined up to a minus sign). This can be accomplished by dividing $\mathbf{x}_1$ by its length $|\mathbf{x}_1|$. If the vectors $\mathbf{x}_1$ and $\mathbf{y}_1$ are both chosen to be of unit length, then the cosine of the angle between the lines $\mathscr{L}$ and $\mathscr{L}'$ will simply be $\mathbf{x}_1 \cdot \mathbf{y}_1$. In particular let $\mathscr{L}$ be given by $t(3, 0, -4) + (1, 1, 1)$

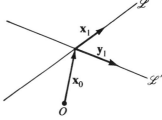

Figure 17

and $\mathscr{L}'$ by $t(12, -3, 4) + (1, 1, 1)$. In normalized form $\mathscr{L}$ is then given by $t(\frac{3}{5}, 0, -\frac{4}{5}) + (1, 1, 1)$ and $\mathscr{L}'$ by $t(\frac{12}{13}, -\frac{3}{13}, \frac{4}{13}) + (1, 1, 1)$. The lines intersect at the point corresponding to $t = 0$, namely at $(1, 1, 1)$. What is the angle between them? We have $\cos\theta = (\frac{3}{5}, 0, -\frac{4}{5}) \cdot (\frac{12}{13}, -\frac{3}{13}, \frac{4}{13}) = \frac{4}{13}$. Hence $\theta = 1.26$ radians (or about $72°$).

To determine a plane in $\mathscr{R}^3$, we take two *noncollinear* vectors $\mathbf{x}_1$ and $\mathbf{x}_2$ (that is, such that neither is a multiple of the other) and consider all points $u\mathbf{x}_1 + v\mathbf{x}_2$, where u and v are numbers. The geometric interpretations of addition and numerical multiplication show that the vectors $u\mathbf{x}_1 + v\mathbf{x}_2$ represent a plane $\mathscr{P}_0$ through the origin in $\mathscr{R}^3$. A parallel plane $\mathscr{P}$ will then consist of all points $u\mathbf{x}_1 + v\mathbf{x}_2 + \mathbf{x}_0$, where $\mathbf{x}_0$ is a fixed vector. We can restate the definition by saying that a **plane** in $\mathscr{R}^3$ is the range of a function $\mathscr{R}^2 \xrightarrow{g} \mathscr{R}^3$, where $g(u, v) = u\mathbf{x}_1 + v\mathbf{x}_2 + \mathbf{x}_0$, and the vectors $\mathbf{x}_1$ and $\mathbf{x}_2$ do not lie on a line.

Using the dot product gives an alternative way of describing a plane $\mathscr{P}$. For suppose $\mathbf{x}_0$ is an arbitrary point on $\mathscr{P}$, and that $\mathbf{p}$ is a nonzero vector perpendicular to $\mathscr{P}$. This means of course that $\mathbf{p}$ is perpendicular to $\mathbf{x} - \mathbf{x}_0$ for every point $\mathbf{x}$ on $\mathscr{P}$ or, in other words that $\mathbf{p} \cdot (\mathbf{x} - \mathbf{x}_0) = 0$ for every point $\mathbf{x}$ on $\mathscr{P}$. In fact every plane in $\mathscr{R}^3$ can be represented as the set of $\mathbf{x}$ satisfying an equation $\mathbf{p} \cdot (\mathbf{x} - \mathbf{x}_0) = 0$ for some $\mathbf{x}$ and some $\mathbf{p} \neq 0$. We state this formally:

5.3 Theorem. A plane $\mathscr{P}$ in $\mathscr{R}^3$ can be represented either as the set of all

$$\mathbf{x} = u\mathbf{x}_1 + v\mathbf{x}_2 + \mathbf{x}_0, \tag{1}$$

with $\mathbf{x}_1$ and $\mathbf{x}_2$ not collinear, or as the set of all $\mathbf{x}$ satisfying an equation

$$\mathbf{p} \cdot (\mathbf{x} - \mathbf{x}_0) = 0 \tag{2}$$

for some point $\mathbf{x}_0$ and vector $\mathbf{p} \neq 0$.

Proof. If $\mathscr{P}$ has the form (2) with $\mathbf{p} = (p_1, p_2, p_3)$, and we set $q = \mathbf{p} \cdot \mathbf{x}_0$, then Equation (2) becomes:

$$p_1 x + p_2 y + p_3 z = q. \tag{3}$$

Since $\mathbf{p} \neq 0$, at least one coordinate, say p_1, is not zero. We set $y = u$, $z = v$ and find from Equation (3) that $x = (q/p_1) - (p_2/p_1)u - (p_3/p_1)v$. Thus we can write

$$\begin{pmatrix} x \\ y \\ z \end{pmatrix} = u \begin{pmatrix} -\dfrac{p_2}{p_1} \\ 1 \\ 0 \end{pmatrix} + v \begin{pmatrix} -\dfrac{p_3}{p_1} \\ 0 \\ 1 \end{pmatrix} + \begin{pmatrix} \dfrac{q}{p_1} \\ 0 \\ 0 \end{pmatrix},$$

which has the form of Equation (1).

Conversely, if $\mathscr{P}$ consists of all points of the form (1) for noncollinear $\mathbf{x}_1 = (a_1, b_1, c_1)$ and $\mathbf{x}_2 = (a_2, b_2, c_2)$, then we can form the vector

$$\mathbf{p} = (b_1 c_2 - b_2 c_1, c_1 a_2 - c_2 a_1, a_1 b_2 - a_2 b_1).$$

Clearly $\mathbf{p}$ is not zero, for that would make $\mathbf{x}_1$ and $\mathbf{x}_2$ proportional. Also it is routine to check that $\mathbf{p} \cdot \mathbf{x}_1 = 0$ and $\mathbf{p} \cdot \mathbf{x}_2 = 0$. Hence, because $\mathbf{x} = u\mathbf{x}_1 + v\mathbf{x}_2 + \mathbf{x}_0$, we have

$$\mathbf{p} \cdot (\mathbf{x} - \mathbf{x}_0) = \mathbf{p} \cdot (u\mathbf{x}_1 + v\mathbf{x}_2)$$
$$= u\mathbf{p} \cdot \mathbf{x}_1 + v\mathbf{p} \cdot \mathbf{x}_2 = 0.$$

This shows that $\mathscr{P}$ can be represented in the form of Equation (2).

If $\mathbf{p}$ is a nonzero vector in $\mathscr{R}^n$ and $\mathbf{x}_0$ is a point in $\mathscr{R}^n$, we can define the $(n-1)$-dimensional plane perpendicular to $\mathbf{p}$ and containing $\mathbf{x}_0$ by the equation $\mathbf{p} \cdot (\mathbf{x} - \mathbf{x}_0) = 0$. In $\mathscr{R}^2$, if we set $\mathbf{p} = (p_1, p_2)$ and $\mathbf{x}_0 = (x_0, y_0)$, the equation becomes $(p_1, p_2) \cdot (x - x_0, y - y_0) = 0$, or $p_1(x - x_0) + p_2(y - y_0) = 0$, which is one of the familiar equations for a line in the plane.

The representation of a plane by an equation $\mathbf{p} \cdot (\mathbf{x} - \mathbf{x}_0) = 0$ is not unique because any nonzero multiple of $\mathbf{p}$ can replace it, leaving the set of vectors $\mathbf{x}$ satisfying the equation unchanged. However, it is sometimes useful to normalize the equation of a plane by requiring that $\mathbf{p}$ be a unit vector. The normalized equation then becomes $\mathbf{n} \cdot (\mathbf{x} - \mathbf{x}_0) = 0$, where $\mathbf{n} = \mathbf{p}/|\mathbf{p}|$. Alternatively we can write $\mathbf{n} \cdot \mathbf{x} = c$, where $c = \mathbf{n} \cdot \mathbf{x}_0$.

5.4 Theorem. If $\mathbf{n} \cdot \mathbf{x} = c$ is the normalized equation of a plane $\mathscr{P}$ and $\mathbf{y}$ is any point, then the distance from $\mathbf{y}$ to $\mathscr{P}$ is the absolute value of $c - \mathbf{n} \cdot \mathbf{y}$.

Proof. By definition the distance is to be measured along a line from $\mathbf{y}$ perpendicular to $\mathscr{P}$. This line can be represented by $t\mathbf{n} + \mathbf{y}$, and the intersection with $\mathscr{P}$ will occur for some $t = t_0$. The desired distance is then $|(t_0\mathbf{n} + \mathbf{y}) - \mathbf{y}| = |t_0\mathbf{n}|$, which is simply the absolute value of t_0, since $\mathbf{n}$ has length 1. Since $t_0\mathbf{n} + \mathbf{y}$ lies in $\mathscr{P}$, then $\mathbf{n} \cdot (t_0\mathbf{n} + \mathbf{y}) = c$. But $\mathbf{n} \cdot \mathbf{n} = 1$, so we obtain $t_0 + \mathbf{n} \cdot \mathbf{y} = c$, from which the theorem follows.

EXAMPLE 4. We shall find the distance from $(1, 1, 1)$ to the plane $(3, 0, -4) \cdot \mathbf{x} = -3$. The normalized equation of the plane is given by $(\frac{3}{5}, 0, -\frac{4}{5}) \cdot \mathbf{x} = -\frac{3}{5}$. Then

$$c - \mathbf{n} \cdot \mathbf{y} = -\tfrac{3}{5} - (\tfrac{3}{5}, 0, -\tfrac{4}{5}) \cdot (1, 1, 1)$$
$$= -\tfrac{2}{5}.$$

Hence the distance is $\frac{2}{5}$. Notice that the equation of the plane could also be written $3x - 4z = -3$, and in normalized form $(\frac{3}{5})x - (\frac{4}{5})z = -\frac{3}{5}$.

Any vector space on which there is defined a product with the properties 5.1 is called an **inner product space**. Thus $\mathscr{R}^n$ is an inner product space, and some other examples are given in Problems 15 and 16. Inner products in spaces other than $\mathcal{R}^n$ are used in this book only in Chapter 3, Section 7, and Chapter 5, Section 6.

In terms of the inner product we can always define the length or **norm** of a vector by

$$|\mathbf{x}| = \sqrt{\mathbf{x} \cdot \mathbf{x}}.$$

Then length has the following properties.

5.5 Positivity: $|\mathbf{x}| > 0$ except that $|\mathbf{0}| = 0$
Homogeneity: $|r\mathbf{x}| = |r||\mathbf{x}|$
Triangle inequality: $|\mathbf{x} + \mathbf{y}| \leq |\mathbf{x}| + |\mathbf{y}|$

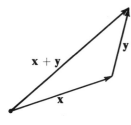

Figure 18

The proofs of the first two are easy and are left for the reader to check. The proof of the third is harder and will be taken up later, though we remark here on its geometric significance. This can be seen by looking at Figure 18.

The fact that length has been defined in terms of an inner product leads to some properties of length that are not derivable from those already listed in 5.5. First we prove the

5.6 Cauchy-Schwarz inequality

$$|\mathbf{x} \cdot \mathbf{y}| \leq |\mathbf{x}||\mathbf{y}|.$$

Proof. We assume first that $\mathbf{x}$ and $\mathbf{y}$ are unit vectors, that is, that $|\mathbf{x}| = |\mathbf{y}| = 1$. Then,

$$0 \leq |\mathbf{x} - \mathbf{y}|^2 = (\mathbf{x} - \mathbf{y}) \cdot (\mathbf{x} - \mathbf{y})$$
$$= |\mathbf{x}|^2 - 2\mathbf{x} \cdot \mathbf{y} + |\mathbf{y}|^2 = 2 - 2\mathbf{x} \cdot \mathbf{y},$$

or

$$\mathbf{x} \cdot \mathbf{y} \leq 1.$$

Assuming that neither $\mathbf{x}$ nor $\mathbf{y}$ is zero (for the inequality obviously holds if one of them *is* zero), we can replace $\mathbf{x}$ and $\mathbf{y}$ by the unit vectors $\mathbf{x}/|\mathbf{x}|$ and $\mathbf{y}/|\mathbf{y}|$, getting

$$\mathbf{x} \cdot \mathbf{y} \leq |\mathbf{x}||\mathbf{y}|.$$

Now replace $\mathbf{x}$ by $-\mathbf{x}$ to get

$$-\mathbf{x} \cdot \mathbf{y} \leq |\mathbf{x}||\mathbf{y}|.$$

The last two inequalities imply the Cauchy-Schwarz inequality.

Notice that if the Cauchy-Schwarz inequality is written as

$$\frac{|\mathbf{x} \cdot \mathbf{y}|}{|\mathbf{x}||\mathbf{y}|} \leq 1,$$

then there will always be an angle θ such that

$$\cos \theta = \frac{\mathbf{x} \cdot \mathbf{y}}{|\mathbf{x}||\mathbf{y}|}.$$

Defining the cosine of the angle θ between $\mathbf{x}$ and $\mathbf{y}$ is more satisfactory than defining θ itself, because then we do not have to worry about whether the angle is

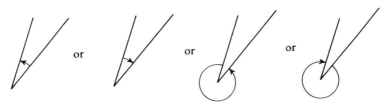

Using the Cauchy-Schwarz inequality, it is easy to give the deferred proof of the triangle inequality. For from

$$|\mathbf{x} \cdot \mathbf{y}| \leq |\mathbf{x}||\mathbf{y}|,$$

we get

$$|\mathbf{x} + \mathbf{y}|^2 = (\mathbf{x} + \mathbf{y}) \cdot (\mathbf{x} + \mathbf{y}) = |\mathbf{x}|^2 + 2\mathbf{x} \cdot \mathbf{y} + |\mathbf{y}|^2$$
$$\leq |\mathbf{x}|^2 + 2|\mathbf{x}||\mathbf{y}| + |\mathbf{y}|^2 = (|\mathbf{x}| + |\mathbf{y}|)^2,$$

from which follows

$$|\mathbf{x} + \mathbf{y}| \leq |\mathbf{x}| + |\mathbf{y}|.$$

Two vectors $\mathbf{x}$ and $\mathbf{y}$ that are perpendicular with respect to an inner product are sometimes called **orthogonal**. A set S of vectors that are mutually orthogonal and all of which have length 1 is called an **orthonormal** set. A matrix A whose columns form an orthonormal set in $\mathscr{R}^n$ is called an **orthogonal matrix**. It is very easy to compute the inverse of such a matrix. Suppose

$$A = \begin{pmatrix} a_{11} & a_{12} & \cdots \\ a_{21} & a_{22} & \cdots \\ \cdot & \cdot & \\ \cdot & \cdot & \\ \cdot & \cdot & \end{pmatrix}$$

is orthogonal. Then its inverse is simply

$$B = \begin{pmatrix} a_{11} & a_{21} & \cdots \\ a_{12} & a_{22} & \cdots \\ \cdot & \cdot & \\ \cdot & \cdot & \\ \cdot & \cdot & \end{pmatrix},$$

for when these two matrices are multiplied together in the order BA, the result is the identity matrix I. We shall see later (Problem 2, Section 7) that this implies $AB = I$, so A is invertible and $B = A^{-1}$. Then from $AA^{-1} = I$ it is clear that the rows as well as the columns of an orthogonal matrix form an orthonormal set.

The second of the above two matrices is obtained from the first by reflecting A across its main diagonal. When any two matrices are so related, we say that one is the **transpose** of the other. We denote the transpose of a matrix A by A^t. Thus, if

$$A = \begin{pmatrix} 1 & 2 & 3 \\ 4 & 5 & 6 \end{pmatrix}$$

then

$$A^t = \begin{pmatrix} 1 & 4 \\ 2 & 5 \\ 3 & 6 \end{pmatrix}.$$

Obviously,

$$(A^t)^t = A \qquad \text{for any matrix } A.$$

EXERCISES

1. Show that the natural basis vectors satisfy $\mathbf{e}_i \cdot \mathbf{e}_i = 1$, and $\mathbf{e}_i \cdot \mathbf{e}_j = 0$ if $i \neq j$.

2. Find an equation for the line in $\mathscr{R}^2$ perpendicular to the line $t\mathbf{x}_1 + \mathbf{x}_0$ that passes through the point $\mathbf{y}_2$.

3. Find the cosine of the angle between the planes $\mathbf{x}_1 \cdot \mathbf{x} = c_1$ and $\mathbf{y}_1 \cdot \mathbf{y} = c_2$.

4. Prove that if $\mathbf{x}_1 \cdot \mathbf{x} = c_1$ and $\mathbf{y}_1 \cdot \mathbf{y} = c_2$ are normalized equations of two planes, then the cosine of the angle between them is $\mathbf{x}_1 \cdot \mathbf{y}_1$.

5. (a) Find the angle between the vectors $(1, 1, 1)$ and $(1, 0, 1)$.
(b) Find a vector of length 1 perpendicular to both vectors in part (a).

6. Find the distance between $(1, 2)$ and $(0, 5)$.

7. Prove that the dot product has the properties listed in 5.1.

8. Prove the positivity and homogeneity properties of length listed in 5.5.

9. Find the *coordinate* of the vector $\mathbf{x} = (1, -1, 2)$:   (a) in the direction of $\mathbf{n} = (1/\sqrt{3}, 1/\sqrt{3}, 1/\sqrt{3})$; and (b) in the direction of the nonunit vector $(1, 1, 3)$. (c) What is the *component* of $\mathbf{x}$ in the direction of $\mathbf{n}$?

10. (a) Prove that if $\mathbf{x}$ is any vector in $\mathscr{R}^n$ and $\mathbf{n}$ is a unit vector, then $\mathbf{x}$ can be written as $\mathbf{x} = \mathbf{y} + \mathbf{z}$, where $\mathbf{y}$ is a multiple of $\mathbf{n}$ and $\mathbf{z}$ is perpendicular to $\mathbf{n}$. [*Hint.* Take $\mathbf{y}$ to be the component of $\mathbf{x}$ in the direction of $\mathbf{n}$].
(b) Show that the vectors $\mathbf{y}$ and $\mathbf{z}$ of part (a) are uniquely determined. The vector $\mathbf{z}$ so determined is called the component of $\mathbf{x}$ perpendicular to $\mathbf{n}$.

11. Sketch the lines determined in $\mathscr{R}^2$ or $\mathscr{R}^3$ by

(a) $t(1, 2) + (-1, -1)$.
(b) $t(1, 0, 1) + (1, 1, 0)$.
(c) $(1, 2) \cdot \mathbf{x} = 2$.

12. Sketch the plane determined in $\mathscr{R}^3$ by

(a) $u(1, 2, 0) + v(2, 0, 1) + (1, 0, 0)$.
(b) $(-1, -1, 1) \cdot \mathbf{x} = 1$.
(c) $2x + y + z = 0$.

13. For each of the points and planes or lines listed below, find the distance from the point to the plane or line.

(a) $(1, 0, -1)$; $(1, 1, 1) \cdot \mathbf{x} = 1$.
(b) $(1, 0, -1)$; $x + 2y + 3z = 1$.
(c) $(1, 2)$; $(3, 4) \cdot \mathbf{x} = 0$.

14. (a) If $\mathbf{x}_1 = (a_1, b_1, c_1)$ and $\mathbf{x}_2 = (a_2, b_2, c_2)$, then the vector $\mathbf{x}_1 \times \mathbf{x}_2$ with coordinates $(b_1 c_2 - b_2 c_1, c_1 a_2 - c_2 a_1, a_1 b_2 - a_2 b_1)$ is called the cross product of $\mathbf{x}_1$ and $\mathbf{x}_2$. Verify that $\mathbf{x}_1 \times \mathbf{x}_2$ is perpendicular to both $\mathbf{x}_1$ and $\mathbf{x}_2$.

(b) Find a representation for the line perpendicular to the plane consisting of all points $u(1, 2, 1) + v(-1, 0, 1) + (1, 1, 1)$ and passing through the origin.

15. (a) Consider the vector space $\mathscr{C}[0, 1]$ consisting of all continuous real-valued functions defined on the interval $0 \leq x \leq 1$. [The sum of f and g is defined by $(f + g)(x) = f(x) + g(x)$, and the numerical multiple rf by $(rf)(x) = rf(x)$.] Show that the product $\langle f, g \rangle$ defined by

$$\langle f, g \rangle = \int_0^1 f(x) g(x)\, dx$$

is an inner product on $\mathscr{C}[0, 1]$.

(b) Define the norm of f by $\|f\| = \langle f, f \rangle^{1/2}$. What is the norm of $f(x) = x$?

16. (a) Show that the product of $\mathbf{x} = (x_1, x_2)$ and $\mathbf{y} = (y_1, y_2)$ defined by

$$\mathbf{x} * \mathbf{y} = x_1 y_1 + 2 x_2 y_2$$

is an inner product.

(b) With length defined by $|\mathbf{x}|_* = (\mathbf{x} * \mathbf{x})^{1/2}$, sketch the set of points satisfying $|\mathbf{x}|_* = 1$.

17. Show that if $|\mathbf{x}| = |\mathbf{y}|$ in an inner product space, then $\mathbf{x} + \mathbf{y}$ is perpendicular to $\mathbf{x} - \mathbf{y}$.

18. Show that the matrix

$$\begin{pmatrix} \cos \theta & -\sin \theta \\ \sin \theta & \cos \theta \end{pmatrix}$$

is orthogonal, and find its inverse.

19. (a) Show that if A is a 2-by-2 orthogonal matrix, then $|A\mathbf{x}| = |\mathbf{x}|$ for all vectors $\mathbf{x}$ in $\mathcal{R}^2$.

(b) Prove the result of part (a) for $\mathcal{R}^n$.

(c) Prove that if $|A\mathbf{x}| = |\mathbf{x}|$ for all $\mathbf{x}$, then $(A\mathbf{x} \cdot A\mathbf{y}) = \mathbf{x} \cdot \mathbf{y}$ for all $\mathbf{x}$ and $\mathbf{y}$ in $\mathcal{R}^n$.

20. A real-valued linear function $\mathcal{R}^n \xrightarrow{f} \mathcal{R}$ is sometimes called a **linear functional**. Show that if f is a linear functional defined on $\mathcal{R}^n$, then there is a fixed vector $\mathbf{y}$ in $\mathcal{R}^n$ such that $f(\mathbf{x}) = \mathbf{y} \cdot \mathbf{x}$ for all $\mathbf{x}$ in $\mathcal{R}^n$. [*Hint.* What is the matrix of f?]

21. Let

$$A = \begin{pmatrix} 0 & 2 & -1 \\ 3 & -5 & 2 \end{pmatrix}, \qquad B = \begin{pmatrix} -3 & -1 \\ 1 & 0 \\ 2 & -2 \end{pmatrix}.$$

Compute AB, BA, $A^t B^t$, and $B^t A^t$.

22. (a) For any two matrices A and B, show that if AB is defined, so is $B^t A^t$, and that $B^t A^t = (AB)^t$.

(b) Show that if A is invertible, then so is A^t, and that $(A^t)^{-1} = (A^{-1})^t$.

6. DETERMINANTS

In this section we define and study a certain numerical-valued function defined on the set of all square matrices. The value of this function for a square matrix M is called the **determinant** of M, and written det M. Another common way to denote the determinant of a matrix in displayed form is to replace the parentheses enclosing the array of entries by vertical bars. Thus the notations

$$\begin{vmatrix} 1 & 4 & 5 \\ 6 & 7 & -3 \\ -2 & 1 & 0 \end{vmatrix}, \qquad \begin{vmatrix} a & b \\ c & d \end{vmatrix}$$

are completely synonymous with

$$\det \begin{pmatrix} 1 & 4 & 5 \\ 6 & 7 & -3 \\ -2 & 1 & 0 \end{pmatrix}, \qquad \det \begin{pmatrix} a & b \\ c & d \end{pmatrix}.$$

Our definition of determinant will be inductive, that is, we shall define det M first for 1-by-1 matrices, and then for each n define the determinant of an n-by-n matrix in terms of determinants of certain $(n-1)$-by-$(n-1)$ matrices. We first need a notation for certain submatrices of a given matrix.

For any matrix A, the matrix obtained by deleting the ith row and jth column of A is called the ijth **minor** of A, and denoted by A_{ij}. (Recall that we use the small letter a_{ij} to denote the ijth entry of a matrix A.)

EXAMPLE 1. Let

$$A = \begin{pmatrix} -5 & -6 & 7 \\ 8 & -9 & 0 \\ -3 & 4 & 2 \end{pmatrix}, \qquad B = \begin{pmatrix} 1 & 2 \\ 3 & 4 \end{pmatrix}.$$

Then

$$a_{11} = -5, \qquad A_{11} = \begin{pmatrix} -9 & 0 \\ 4 & 2 \end{pmatrix}$$

$$a_{23} = 0, \qquad A_{23} = \begin{pmatrix} -5 & -6 \\ -3 & 4 \end{pmatrix}$$

$$b_{11} = 1, \qquad B_{11} = (4), \quad b_{12} = 2, \quad B_{12} = (3).$$

We can now make the definition of **determinant**:

For a 1-by-1 matrix $A = (a)$, we define

$$\det A = a.$$

For an n-by-n matrix $A = (a_{ij})$, $i, j = 1, \ldots, n$, we define

6.1 $$\det A = \sum_{j=1}^{n} (-1)^{j+1} a_{1j} \det A_{1j}$$

$$= a_{11} \det A_{11} - a_{12} \det A_{12} + \ldots - (-1)^{n} a_{1n} \det A_{1n}.$$

EXAMPLE 2.

(a) $$\det \begin{pmatrix} 1 & 2 \\ 3 & 4 \end{pmatrix} = 1(4) - 2(3) = 4 - 6 = -2$$

(b) $$\det \begin{pmatrix} -5 & -6 & 7 \\ 8 & -9 & 0 \\ -3 & 4 & 2 \end{pmatrix} = -5 \det \begin{pmatrix} -9 & 0 \\ 4 & 2 \end{pmatrix}$$

$$- (-6) \det \begin{pmatrix} 8 & 0 \\ -3 & 2 \end{pmatrix} + 7 \det \begin{pmatrix} 8 & -9 \\ -3 & 4 \end{pmatrix}$$

$$= -5(-18 - 0) + 6(16 - 0) + 7(32 - 27)$$

$$= 90 + 96 + 35 = 221$$

(c) $$\det \begin{pmatrix} a & b \\ c & d \end{pmatrix} = ad - bc.$$

The result of the last example is worth remembering as a rule of calculation. *The determinant of a 2-by-2 matrix is the product of the entries on the main diagonal minus the product of the other two entries.* Thus 2-by-2 determinants can usually be computed mentally, and 3-by-3 determinants in one or two lines. In principle, any determinant can be calculated from the definition but this involves formidable amounts of arithmetic if the dimension is at all large. Some of the theorems we prove will justify other methods of calculation, which involve less arithmetic than that required in working directly from the definition for $n > 3$.

Determinants were originally invented (in the middle of the eighteenth century) as a means of expressing the solutions of systems of linear equations. To see how this works for two equations in two unknowns, consider the general system

$$a_{11}x_1 + a_{12}x_2 = r_1$$
$$a_{21}x_1 + a_{22}x_2 = r_2.$$

The variable x_2 can be eliminated by multiplying the first equation by a_{22} and the second by a_{12}, and then taking the difference. The result is the equation

$$(a_{22}a_{11} - a_{12}a_{21})x_1 = (a_{22}r_1 - a_{12}r_2).$$

This equation may be written as

$$x_1 \det A = \det B^{(1)}$$

where $A = \begin{pmatrix} a_{11} & a_{12} \\ a_{21} & a_{22} \end{pmatrix}$ is the matrix of coefficients and $B^{(1)} = \begin{pmatrix} r_1 & a_{12} \\ r_2 & a_{22} \end{pmatrix}$ is the result of replacing the first column of A by $\begin{pmatrix} r_1 \\ r_2 \end{pmatrix}$. The reader can easily derive the equation $x_2 \det A = \det B^{(2)}$, where $B^{(2)} = \begin{pmatrix} a_{11} & r_1 \\ a_{21} & r_2 \end{pmatrix}$ is the result of substituting $\begin{pmatrix} r_1 \\ r_2 \end{pmatrix}$ for the second column of A. As we shall see in Theorem 6.16, a similar result holds for systems of n linear equations in n unknowns, for all values of n.

Since our definition of determinants by 6.1 is inductive, most of the proofs have the same character. That is, to prove a theorem about determinants of all square matrices, we verify it for 1-by-1 (or in some cases, 2-by-2) matrices, and also show that if it is true for $(n - 1)$-by-$(n - 1)$ matrices, then it holds for n-by-n matrices. In the proofs we give only the argument for going from step $n - 1$ to step n. The reader should verify the propositions directly for 1-by-1 and 2-by-2 matrices; the verification is in all cases quite trivial. A, B, and C will always denote n-by-n matrices. We write $\mathbf{a}_j$ for the jth column of a matrix A. If A has n rows, then $\mathbf{a}_j$ is a vector in $\mathscr{R}^n$.

6.2 Theorem. If B is obtained from A by multiplying some column by a number r, then $\det B = r \det A$.

Proof. Suppose $\mathbf{b}_j = r\mathbf{a}_j$, while $\mathbf{b}_k = \mathbf{a}_k$ for $k \neq j$. Then in particular $b_{1j} = ra_{1j}$. For $k \neq j$, B_{1k} is obtained from A_{1k} by multiplying a column by r; since B_{1k} and A_{1k} are $(n - 1)$-by-$(n - 1)$, we have $\det B_{1k} =$

$r \det A_{1k}$. On the other hand, $B_{1j} = A_{1j}$, and $b_{1k} = a_{1k}$ for $k \neq j$. Thus whether $k = j$ or not, $b_{1k} \det B_{1k} = r a_{1k} \det A_{1k}$. Therefore

$$\det B = \sum_{k=1}^{n} (-1)^{k+1} b_{1k} \det B_{1k}$$

$$= \sum_{k=1}^{n} (-1)^{k+1} r a_{1k} \det A_{1k} = r \det A.$$

6.3 Corollary. If a matrix has a zero column, then its determinant is zero.

Proof. If $\mathbf{a}_j = 0$, then $\mathbf{a}_j = 0\mathbf{a}_j$. Then by Theorem 6.2, $\det A = 0 \cdot \det A = 0$.

EXAMPLE 3. Let

$$A = \begin{pmatrix} 1 & 2 & 3 \\ -1 & 2 & 4 \\ 0 & 1 & 2 \end{pmatrix}, \quad B = \begin{pmatrix} 1 & 6 & 3 \\ -1 & 6 & 4 \\ 0 & 3 & 2 \end{pmatrix}$$

B is obtained from A by multiplying the second column by 3.

$$\det A = (1)(4 - 4) - 2(-2 - 0) + 3(-1 + 0)$$
$$= 0 + 4 - 3 = 1$$
$$\det B = (1)(12 - 12) - 6(-2 - 0) + 3(-3 + 0)$$
$$= 0 + 12 - 9 = 3 = 3 \det A.$$

6.4 Theorem. Let A, B, and C be identical except in the jth column, and suppose that the jth column of C is the sum of the jth columns of A and B. Then $\det C = \det A + \det B$.

Proof. We have $c_{1j} = a_{1j} + b_{1j}$, and also $C_{1j} = A_{1j} = B_{1j}$. For $k \neq j$, $c_{1k} = a_{1k} = b_{1k}$, and C_{1k} is identical with A_{1k} and B_{1k} except for one column which is the sum of the corresponding columns of A_{1k} and B_{1k}. Thus for $k \neq j$, $\det C_{1k} = \det A_{1k} + \det B_{1k}$, by the inductive assumption. For $k \neq j$ we have

$$c_{1k} \det C_{1k} = c_{1k} \det A_{1k} + c_{1k} \det B_{1k}$$
$$= a_{1k} \det A_{1k} + b_{1k} \det B_{1k},$$

while

$$c_{1j} \det C_{1j} = a_{1j} \det C_{1j} + b_{1j} \det C_{1j}$$
$$= a_{1j} \det A_{1j} + b_{1j} \det B_{1j}.$$

Hence

$$\det C = \sum_{k=1}^{n} (-1)^{k+1} c_{1k} \det C_{1k}$$

$$= \sum_{k=1}^{n} (-1)^{k+1} a_{1k} \det A_{1k} + \sum_{k=1}^{n} (-1)^{k+1} b_{1k} \det B_{1k}$$

$$= \det A + \det B.$$

Theorems 6.2 and 6.4 have an important interpretation if the determinant of a matrix is viewed as a function of the columns of that matrix. Thus if $\mathbf{a}_1, \ldots, \mathbf{a}_n$ are the columns of an n-by-n matrix, we may write $\det A = \det(\mathbf{a}_1, \ldots, \mathbf{a}_n)$. Now suppose the $n - 1$ vectors $\mathbf{a}_2, \ldots, \mathbf{a}_n$ are held fixed and $f(\mathbf{x}) = \det(\mathbf{x}, \mathbf{a}_2, \ldots, \mathbf{a}_n)$ is considered as a function of $\mathbf{x}$. Then Theorems 6.2 and 6.4 assert that $f(r\mathbf{x}) = rf(\mathbf{x})$ and $f(\mathbf{x}_1 + \mathbf{x}_2) = f(\mathbf{x}_1) + f(\mathbf{x}_2)$. The same would hold if the "variable" vector were in the jth place instead of the first. In other words, we have

6.5 Theorem. If all but one of $\mathbf{a}_1, \ldots, \mathbf{a}_n$ are held fixed, then $\det(\mathbf{a}_1, \ldots, \mathbf{a}_n)$ is a linear function of the remaining vector.

To see how this works out for the first column of a 3-by-3 matrix, let

$$\mathbf{x} = \begin{pmatrix} x_1 \\ x_2 \\ x_3 \end{pmatrix}; \quad \mathbf{b} = \begin{pmatrix} b_1 \\ b_2 \\ b_3 \end{pmatrix}; \quad \mathbf{c} = \begin{pmatrix} c_1 \\ c_2 \\ c_3 \end{pmatrix}.$$

To exhibit $\det(\mathbf{x}, \mathbf{b}, \mathbf{c})$ as a linear function of $\mathbf{x}$ we need merely calculate

$$\det(\mathbf{x}, \mathbf{b}, \mathbf{c}) = \det \begin{pmatrix} x_1 & b_1 & c_1 \\ x_2 & b_2 & c_2 \\ x_3 & b_3 & c_3 \end{pmatrix}$$

$$= x_1 \det \begin{pmatrix} b_2 & c_2 \\ b_3 & c_3 \end{pmatrix} - b_1 \det \begin{pmatrix} x_2 & c_2 \\ x_3 & c_3 \end{pmatrix} + c_1 \det \begin{pmatrix} x_2 & b_2 \\ x_3 & b_3 \end{pmatrix}$$

$$= x_1(b_2c_3 - b_3c_2) - b_1(x_2c_3 - x_3c_2) + c_1(x_2b_3 - x_3b_2)$$

$$= x_1(b_2c_3 - b_3c_2) - x_2(b_1c_3 - b_3c_1) + x_3(b_1c_2 - c_1b_2),$$

which is a linear function of $\mathbf{x}$.

The coefficients of x_1, x_2, x_3 can be recognized as the determinants of 2-by-2 minors of the matrix. Indeed the calculation shows that for 3-by-3 matrices the formula

6.6 $$\det A = \sum_{i=1}^{n} (-1)^{i+1} a_{i1} \det A_{i1}$$

holds. The reader should make the easy check that it also holds for 2-by-2 matrices.

As we shall show, Formula 6.6 actually holds for matrices of all sizes. The following proposition is a preliminary step in the proof. Recall that $\mathbf{e}_i$ denotes the ith natural basis vector in $\mathscr{R}^n$ and is 0 except for a 1 in the ith entry.

6.7 Lemma. If the first column of the matrix A is $\mathbf{e}_i$, then

$$\det A = (-1)^{i+1} \det A_{i1}.$$

Proof. By the Definition 6.1, $\det A = \sum_{j=1}^{n} (-1)^{j+1} a_{1j} \det A_{1j}$.

If the first column of A is $\mathbf{e}_1$, then $a_{11} = 1$, while for $j > 1$ the first column of A_{1j} is 0 and so $\det A_{1j} = 0$ by Theorem 6.3. Thus the expression for $\det A$ reduces to one term, $\det A_{11}$, and Theorem 6.7 holds for the case $i = 1$. For $i > 1$ we need to use the inductive hypothesis that Lemma 6.7 holds for $(n-1)$-by-$(n-1)$ matrices. In this case $a_{11} = 0$ and $\det A = \sum_{j=2}^{n} (-1)^{j+1} a_{1j} \det A_{1j}$. Each minor A_{1j} has $\mathbf{e}_{i-1}$ for its first column. (Removing the top entry from the vector $\mathbf{e}_i$ in $\mathscr{R}^n$ gives $\mathbf{e}_{i-1}$ in $\mathscr{R}^{n-1}$.) By the inductive hypothesis,

$$\det A_{1j} = (-1)^i \det A_{1j,\,i1},$$

where we write $A_{1j,\,i1}$ for the matrix obtained from A by deleting the first row, the jth column, the ith row, and the first column. Let $B = A_{i1}$. Then (since the first column of B is formed from the second column of A, etc.), $A_{1j,\,i1} = B_{1,\,j-1}$, and $a_{1j} = b_{1,\,j-1}$. Combining the equations we have derived so far gives

$$\det A = \sum_{j=2}^{n} (-1)^{j+1} b_{1,\,j-1} (-1)^i \det B_{1,\,j-1}.$$

By Formula 6.1 the right side of this equation is $(-1)^{i+1} \det B$, which is $(-1)^{i+1} \det A_{i1}$, as was to be proved.

The proof of Theorem 6.6 is now easy. We can write the first column of A as $\mathbf{a}_1 = a_{11}\mathbf{e}_1 + a_{12}\mathbf{e}_2 + \ldots + a_{1n}\mathbf{e}_n$, so by Theorem 6.5,

$$\begin{aligned}
\det A &= \det (\mathbf{a}_1, \mathbf{a}_2, \ldots, \mathbf{a}_n) \\
&= a_{11} \det (\mathbf{e}_1, \mathbf{a}_2, \ldots, \mathbf{a}_n) + a_{12} \det (\mathbf{e}_2, \mathbf{a}_2, \ldots, \mathbf{a}_n) + \ldots \\
&\qquad\qquad\qquad\qquad\qquad + a_{1n} \det (\mathbf{e}_n, \mathbf{a}_2, \ldots, \mathbf{a}_n) \\
&= \sum_{i=1}^{n} (-1)^{i+1} a_{i1} \det A_{i1}.
\end{aligned}$$

Since 6.6 is exactly like 6.1 except that it refers to the first column instead of the first row of a matrix, it is clear that transposing a matrix (which just exchanges the roles of rows and columns) should not affect the value of the determinant. The formal statement and proof follow.

6.8 Theorem. For any square matrix A, $\det A^t = \det A$.

Proof. Let $B = A^t$. By definition of the transpose, $b_{ij} = a_{ji}$, and it is easy to see that $B_{ij} = A_{ji}^t$. Thus by 6.1,

$$\begin{aligned}
\det B &= b_{11} \det B_{11} - b_{12} \det B_{12} + \ldots + (-1)^{n+1} b_{1n} \det B_{1n} \\
&= a_{11} \det A_{11}^t - a_{21} \det A_{21}^t + \ldots + (-1)^{n+1} a_{n1} \det A_{n1}^t.
\end{aligned}$$

The A_{ij} are $(n-1)$-by-$(n-1)$ matrices, and by the inductive hypothesis, we may replace det A_{i1}^t by det A_{i1} in the formula above. The result is equal to det A by 6.6, and we have proved det $A^t =$ det $B =$ det A.

We may now take any theorem about determinants that involves columns of matrices and immediately derive a corresponding theorem involving rows instead, by applying the given theorem to the transposes of the matrices. We shall not always bother to write out these corresponding theorems, but shall refer to the "row" version of a numbered statement by using the same number with an R after it. For example, Theorem 6.2R would be the statement: If B is obtained from A by multiplying some row by the number r, then det $B = r$ det A.

Of equal importance with the linearity property of determinants expressed in Theorem 6.5 is the fact that if any two columns (or rows) of a matrix are interchanged, then its determinant changes sign. We first prove the result for *adjacent* columns.

6.9 Lemma. If B is obtained from A by exchanging two adjacent columns, then det $B = -$det A.

Proof. Suppose A and B are the same, except that $\mathbf{a}_j = \mathbf{b}_{j+1}$ and $\mathbf{a}_{j+1} = \mathbf{b}_j$. For $k \neq j$ or $j + 1$, we have $b_{1k} = a_{1k}$ and det $B_{1k} = -$det A_{1k} by the inductive hypothesis, so $(-1)^{k+1}b_{1k}$ det $B_{1k} = -(-1)^{k+1}a_{1k}$ det A_{1k}. On the other hand $b_{1j} = a_{1,j+1}$ and $B_{1j} = A_{1,j+1}$ so $(-1)^{j+1}b_{1j}$ det $B_{1j} = (-1)^{j+1}a_{1,j+1}$ det $A_{1,j+1} = -(-1)^{j+2}a_{1,j+1}$ det $A_{1,j+1}$. Similarly $(-1)^{j+2}b_{1,j+1}$ det $B_{1,j+1} = -(-1)^{j+1}a_{1j}$ det A_{1j}. Thus each term in the expansion of det B by 6.1 is matched by a term equal to its negative in the expansion of A, and it follows that det $B = -$det A.

EXAMPLE 5. Let

$$A = \begin{pmatrix} 1 & 3 & -2 \\ 2 & -4 & 1 \\ 3 & 5 & -2 \end{pmatrix}, \quad B = \begin{pmatrix} 1 & -2 & 3 \\ 2 & 1 & -4 \\ 3 & -2 & 5 \end{pmatrix}.$$

Then

$$\det A = (1)(8 - 5) - (3)(-4 - 3) + (-2)(10 - (-12))$$
$$= 3 + 21 - 44 = -20$$
$$\det B = (1)(5 - 8) - (-2)(10 - (-12)) + (3)(-4 - 3)$$
$$= -3 + 44 - 21 = 20$$
$$= -\det A$$

6.10 Theorem. If B is obtained from A by exchanging any two columns, then det $B = -$det A.

Proof. Suppose there are k columns between the two columns in question (so $k = 0$ if they are adjacent). The first column can be brought next to the second by k exchanges of adjacent columns; then the two columns can be exchanged, and with another k exchanges of adjacent columns, the second column can be put back in the original place of the first. There are $2k + 1$ steps in all, and by Theorem 6.9 each step changes the sign of the determinant. Since $2k + 1$ is an odd number, $\det B = -\det A$.

6.11 Theorem. If any two columns of A are identical, then $\det A = 0$.

Proof. Exchanging the two columns gives A again. Therefore $\det A = -\det A$, and so $\det A = 0$.

6.12 Theorem. If C is obtained from A by adding a numerical multiple of one column to another, then $\det C = \det A$.

Proof. Suppose C is the same as A except that $\mathbf{c}_j = \mathbf{a}_j + r\mathbf{a}_i$. Let B be the result of replacing $\mathbf{a}_j$ in A with $r\mathbf{a}_i$. By Theorem 6.4, $\det C = \det A + \det B$. By Theorem 6.2, $\det B$ is r times the determinant of a matrix with two identical columns. Therefore $\det B = 0$ and $\det C = \det A$.

EXAMPLE 6. (a) Let

$$A = \begin{pmatrix} 1 & 3 & -2 \\ 2 & -4 & 1 \\ 3 & 5 & -2 \end{pmatrix}, \quad C = \begin{pmatrix} 1 & 3 & 0 \\ 2 & -4 & 5 \\ 3 & 5 & 4 \end{pmatrix}.$$

The third column of C is equal to the third column of A plus 2 times the first column. As in Example 5, $\det A = -20$. Then $\det C = -20$. As a check,

$$\det C = (1)(-16 - 25) - (3)(8 - 15) + (0)(10 - (-12))$$
$$= -41 + 21 + 0 = -20.$$

(b) Let

$$A = \begin{pmatrix} 2 & 4 & -1 & 0 \\ 3 & 0 & 2 & 3 \\ -1 & 2 & 3 & 1 \\ 0 & 1 & -2 & -1 \end{pmatrix}.$$

By adding 2 times column 3 to column 1 and 4 times column 3 to column 2 we obtain

$$B = \begin{pmatrix} 0 & 0 & -1 & 0 \\ 7 & 8 & 2 & 3 \\ 5 & 14 & 3 & 1 \\ -4 & -7 & -2 & -1 \end{pmatrix},$$

and by Theorem 6.12, $\det A = \det B$. The expansion of B has only one nonzero term and we get

$$\det B = (-1) \det \begin{pmatrix} 7 & 8 & 3 \\ 5 & 14 & 1 \\ -4 & -7 & -1 \end{pmatrix}$$

$$= -\det \begin{pmatrix} 7 & 1 & 3 \\ 5 & 9 & 1 \\ -4 & -3 & -1 \end{pmatrix} \qquad \text{[subtract column 1 from column 2]}$$

$$= -\det \begin{pmatrix} 0 & 1 & 0 \\ -58 & 9 & -26 \\ 17 & -3 & 8 \end{pmatrix}. \qquad \begin{array}{l} \text{[subtract 7 times column 2} \\ \text{from column 1 and 3 times} \\ \text{column 2 from column 3]} \end{array}$$

Then $\det B = -(-1)[(-58)(8) - (17)(-26)] = -22$.

       This last example illustrates a way of computing determinants which is usually more efficient than direct calculation by Formula 6.1 or 6.6 for matrices of size larger than 3-by-3.

       Formulas 6.1 and 6.6 assert that a determinant is equal to a sum of terms involving the elements and minors of the first row or first column. Similar formulas can be given involving any row or column. They are

6.13. $$\det A = \sum_{i=1}^{n} (-1)^{i+j} a_{ij} \det A_{ij}$$

and

6.13R. $$\det A = \sum_{j=1}^{n} (-1)^{i+j} a_{ij} \det A_{ij}$$

Note that Formula 6.13R reduces to 6.1 for $i = 1$ and that 6.13 reduces to Formula 6.6 for $j = 1$. The right side of 6.13 is called the **expansion of** $\det A$ **by the** jth **column**, and the right side of 6.13R is called the **expansion of** $\det A$ **by the** ith **row**.

Proof of 6.13. Consider the matrix B obtained from A by moving the jth column into the first position. This move requires a series of $j - 1$ exchanges of adjacent columns, so by Theorem 6.9, $\det A = (-1)^{j-1} \det B$. For all i, we have $b_{i1} = a_{ij}$ and $B_{i1} = A_{ij}$. Thus we obtain

$$\det A = (-1)^{j-1} \det B$$

$$= (-1)^{j-1} \sum_{j=1}^{n} (-1)^{i+1} b_{i1} \det B_{i1} \qquad \text{(by 6.6)}$$

$$= \sum_{i=1}^{n} (-1)^{i+j} a_{ij} \det A_{ij},$$

as was to be proved. Formula 6.13R of course has a similar proof, using 6.9R and 6.1.

EXAMPLE 7. Let

$$A = \begin{pmatrix} 2 & 3 & 4 \\ 5 & 6 & 7 \\ 8 & 9 & 0 \end{pmatrix}.$$

The expansion of det A by the second row is

$$-5 \det \begin{pmatrix} 3 & 4 \\ 9 & 0 \end{pmatrix} + 6 \det \begin{pmatrix} 2 & 4 \\ 8 & 0 \end{pmatrix} - 7 \det \begin{pmatrix} 2 & 3 \\ 8 & 9 \end{pmatrix}$$
$$= (-5)(-36) + (6)(-32) - (7)(-6)$$
$$= 180 - 192 + 42 = 30$$

The expansion by the third column is

$$4 \det \begin{pmatrix} 5 & 6 \\ 8 & 9 \end{pmatrix} - 7 \det \begin{pmatrix} 2 & 3 \\ 8 & 9 \end{pmatrix} + 0 \det \begin{pmatrix} 2 & 3 \\ 5 & 6 \end{pmatrix}$$
$$= (4)(-3) - (7)(-6)$$
$$= -12 + 42 = 30$$

Let the matrix A be given and consider the expression

$$\sum_{i=1}^{n} (-1)^{i+j} x_i \det A_{ij},$$

where $x_1, \ldots, x_n$ may be any set of n numbers. From 6.13, we see that this is equal to a certain determinant; in fact it is the expansion by the jth column of the matrix obtained from A by replacing the jth column with $(x_1, \ldots, x_n)$. This obvious remark leads to an important result if we take $x_1, \ldots, x_n$ equal to the elements $a_{1k}, a_{2k}, \ldots, a_{nk}$ of the kth column of A. If $k = j$, of course we simply have the expansion of det A by the jth column. If $k \neq j$, we have the determinant of a matrix with two columns (the jth and kth) identical, and by Theorem 6.11 the result is 0. We have proved:

6.14 Theorem. For any n-by-n matrix A,

$$\sum_{i=1}^{n} (-1)^{i+j} a_{ik} \det A_{ij} = \begin{cases} \det A & \text{if } k = j \\ 0 & \text{if } k \neq j \end{cases}$$

The row form of this result is

6.14R. For any n-by-n matrix A,

$$\sum_{j=1}^{n} (-1)^{i+j} a_{kj} \det A_{ij} = \begin{cases} \det A & \text{if } k = i \\ 0 & \text{if } k \neq i \end{cases}$$

The number $(-1)^{i+j} \det A_{ij}$ is called the ijth **cofactor** of the matrix A. We shall abbreviate it as $\tilde{a}_{ij}$ and write $\tilde{A}$ for the matrix with entries $\tilde{a}_{ij}$. Theorem 6.14 can be formulated as a statement about the matrix product $\tilde{A}^t A$. The jth entry in the product is the product of the jth row of $\tilde{A}^t$ (i.e., the jth column of $\tilde{A}$) and the kth column of A. That is, it is the sum $\sum_{i=1}^{n} \tilde{a}_{ij} a_{ik}$. By Theorem 6.14 this is det A if $j = k$, and 0 otherwise. Hence $\tilde{A}^t A$ is equal to $(\det A)I$, a numerical multiple of the identity matrix. A similar calculation using 6.14R shows that $A\tilde{A}^t$ is also equal to $(\det A)I$. If $\det A \neq 0$, we may divide $\tilde{A}^t$ by it, and obtain a matrix B such that $AB = BA = I$. Thus we have proved:

6.15 Theorem. If $\det A \neq 0$, then A is invertible, and $A^{-1} = (\det A)^{-1}\tilde{A}^t$, where $\tilde{A}$ is the matrix of cofactors of A.

EXAMPLE 8. We shall compute the inverse of the matrix

$$A = \begin{pmatrix} 2 & 3 & 4 \\ 5 & 6 & 7 \\ 8 & 9 & 0 \end{pmatrix}$$

used in Example 7. Write b_{ij} as an abbreviation for $\det A_{ij}$; the matrix B is then easily calculated to be

$$\begin{pmatrix} -63 & -56 & -3 \\ -36 & -32 & -6 \\ -3 & -6 & -3 \end{pmatrix}.$$

To obtain the matrix of cofactors, insert the factors $(-1)^{i+j}$, which changes the sign of every second entry and gives

$$\begin{pmatrix} -63 & 56 & -3 \\ 36 & -32 & 6 \\ -3 & 6 & -3 \end{pmatrix}.$$

Finally, transpose and divide by $\det A$, which was found to equal 30 in Example 7. The result is

$$A^{-1} = \tfrac{1}{30} \begin{pmatrix} -63 & 36 & -3 \\ 56 & -32 & 6 \\ -3 & 6 & -3 \end{pmatrix},$$

as can be verified by computing AA^{-1} and $A^{-1}A$.

A system of n linear equations in n unknowns

$$
\begin{aligned}
a_{11}x_1 + a_{12}x_2 + \ldots + a_{1n}x_n &= b_1 \\
a_{21}x_1 + a_{22}x_2 + \ldots + a_{2n}x_n &= b_2 \\
\vdots \qquad\qquad\qquad \vdots \quad\; \\
a_{n1}x_1 + a_{n2}x_2 + \ldots + a_{nn}x_n &= b_n
\end{aligned}
\tag{1}
$$

may be written in matrix form as $A\mathbf{x} = \mathbf{b}$ where $\mathbf{a}$ is the n-by-n coefficient matrix with entries a_{ij} and $\mathbf{x}$ and $\mathbf{b}$ are vectors in $\mathscr{R}^n$. Doing the matrix multiplication in the equation

$$\begin{pmatrix} a_{11} & \cdots & a_{1n} \\ \cdot & & \cdot \\ \cdot & & \cdot \\ \cdot & & \cdot \\ a_{n1} & \cdots & a_{nn} \end{pmatrix} \begin{pmatrix} x_1 \\ \cdot \\ \cdot \\ \cdot \\ x_n \end{pmatrix} = \begin{pmatrix} b_1 \\ \cdot \\ \cdot \\ \cdot \\ b_n \end{pmatrix}$$

shows at once that it is equivalent to the system (1).

If A is invertible, then $Ax = b$ implies $A^{-1}Ax = A^{-1}b$ or $x = A^{-1}b$; on the other hand, $A(A^{-1}b) = (AA^{-1})b = b$. In other words, the equations have a unique solution, and it is $A^{-1}b$. The jth entry in the column vector $A^{-1}b$ is the matrix product of the jth row of A^{-1} and the vector b. If $\det A \neq 0$, we may express the elements of A^{-1} in terms of cofactors of A and obtain

$$(\det A)^{-1} \sum_{i=1}^{n} (-1)^{i+j} (\det A_{ij})b_i$$

for this product. From 6.13 this may be recognized as $(\det A)^{-1} \det B^{(j)}$ where $B^{(j)}$ is the result of replacing the jth column of A by b. We have proved:

6.16 Cramer's rule. If the determinant of the matrix of coefficients of a system of n linear equations in n unknowns $x_1, \ldots, x_n$ is different from zero, then

$$x_j = \frac{\det B^{(j)}}{\det A},$$

where A is the matrix of coefficients and $B^{(j)}$ is the result of replacing the jth column of A by the column of numbers that make up the right side of the equations.

EXAMPLE 9. Solve the system

$$\begin{aligned} x_1 & -2x_2 & +4x_3 &= 1 \\ -x_1 & +x_2 & -x_3 &= 2 \\ 2x_1 & +3x_2 & -x_3 &= 3. \end{aligned}$$

We have

$$A = \begin{pmatrix} 1 & -2 & 4 \\ -1 & 1 & -1 \\ 2 & 3 & -1 \end{pmatrix}, \qquad B^{(1)} = \begin{pmatrix} 1 & -2 & 4 \\ 2 & 1 & -1 \\ 3 & 3 & -1 \end{pmatrix},$$

$$B^{(2)} = \begin{pmatrix} 1 & 1 & 4 \\ -1 & 2 & -1 \\ 2 & 3 & -1 \end{pmatrix}, \qquad B^{(3)} = \begin{pmatrix} 1 & -2 & 1 \\ -1 & 1 & 2 \\ 2 & 3 & 3 \end{pmatrix}.$$

Expanding the determinants by their first rows gives

$\det A = (1)(2) - (-2)(3) + (4)(-5) = 2 + 6 - 20 = -12$

$\det B^{(1)} = (1)(2) - (-2)(1) + (4)(3) = 2 + 2 + 12 = 16$

$$\det B^{(2)} = (1)(1) - (1)(3) + (4)(-7) = 1 - 3 - 28 = -30$$
$$\det B^{(3)} = (1)(-3) - (-2)(-7) + (1)(-5) = -3 - 14 - 5 = -22.$$

Then $x_1 = -\frac{16}{12} = -\frac{4}{3}, x_2 = \frac{30}{12} = \frac{5}{2}, x_3 = \frac{22}{12} = \frac{11}{6}$.

We have not made any assertions in this section about what happens if the determinant of the coefficient matrix of a system of equations is zero. It is an easy consequence of Theorem 7.1 of the next section that a matrix with zero determinant cannot be invertible (see Problem 1 in Section 7), and it will be shown in Section 9, where we discuss the solution of linear systems in detail, that in this case the system of equations has either no solution or infinitely many. While Cramer's rule and the formula for A^{-1} in terms of cofactors are important as theoretical results, and are quite useful for solving systems of two or three linear equations, they are less efficient for larger systems than the methods of Section 9.

EXERCISES

1. Find AB, BA, and the determinants of A, B, AB, and BA when

(a) $A = \begin{pmatrix} 1 & -2 \\ 3 & 1 \end{pmatrix}$, $\quad B = \begin{pmatrix} 0 & 1 \\ 2 & -3 \end{pmatrix}$, $\qquad$ [*Ans.* det $AB = -14$].

(b) $A = \begin{pmatrix} 2 & 0 & 0 \\ 0 & 3 & 0 \\ 0 & 0 & 4 \end{pmatrix}$, $\quad B = \begin{pmatrix} -1 & 0 & 1 \\ 2 & -1 & -3 \\ 0 & 3 & 5 \end{pmatrix}$.

What relation do you observe between det A, det B, and det AB?

2. Show that if D is the diagonal matrix **diag** $(r_1, \ldots, r_n)$, then det $D = r_1 r_2 \ldots r_n$.

3. Show that if D is a diagonal matrix and A a square matrix of the same size, then det $(DA) = \det (AD) = (\det A)(\det D)$. (Note that Exercise 1(b) is a special case of this result.)

4. Find the coefficients needed to express each of the following as a linear function of the x's.

(a) $\begin{vmatrix} x_1 & -1 & 6 \\ x_2 & 4 & -3 \\ x_3 & 2 & 5 \end{vmatrix}$, $\quad$ (b) $\begin{vmatrix} 0 & 3 & 6 \\ -2 & -1 & 6 \\ x_1 & x_2 & x_3 \end{vmatrix}$,

(c) $\begin{vmatrix} 1 & x_1 & -3 & 2 \\ 0 & x_2 & 0 & 0 \\ 3 & x_3 & -1 & 5 \\ -2 & x_4 & 0 & 1 \end{vmatrix}$.

5. Give a proof of Theorem 6.3R by induction directly from Formula 6.1.

6. What is the relation between
   (a) det A and det $(-A)$?
   (b) det $(a_1, a_2, \ldots, a_{n-1}, a_n)$ and det $(a_n, a_{n-1}, \ldots, a_2, a_1)$?

7. Show that if Theorem 6.12 is assumed, then Theorem 6.10 can be derived from it. [*Hint.* What happens if you add column i to column j, then subtract column j from column i, then add column i to column j?]

8. Use the method of Example 6 (b) of the text to evaluate

   (a) det $\begin{pmatrix} -1 & 0 & 1 & 2 \\ 0 & 1 & 2 & -1 \\ 1 & 2 & -1 & 0 \\ 2 & -1 & 0 & 1 \end{pmatrix}$,   [*Ans.* (a) 32.]

   (b) det $\begin{pmatrix} 1 & 1 & 1 & 1 \\ 1 & 2 & 4 & 8 \\ 1 & 3 & 9 & 27 \\ 1 & 4 & 16 & 64 \end{pmatrix}$.

9. Prove that

$$\det \begin{pmatrix} 1 & x_1 & x_1^2 & \cdots & x_1^{n-1} \\ 1 & x_2 & x_2^2 & \cdots & x_2^{n-1} \\ \vdots & \vdots & \vdots & & \vdots \\ 1 & x_n & x_n^2 & \cdots & x_n^{n-1} \end{pmatrix} = \prod_{i>j} (x_i - x_j).$$

10. Find the inverses of

   (a) $\begin{pmatrix} 1 & 2 \\ 3 & 4 \end{pmatrix}$,   (b) $\begin{pmatrix} 0 & -1 & 3 \\ 2 & 5 & -4 \\ -3 & 7 & 1 \end{pmatrix}$,

   (c) $\begin{pmatrix} 1 & 0 & 1 & 0 \\ 0 & 2 & 3 & 0 \\ -1 & 0 & 0 & 2 \\ -3 & 1 & -2 & 0 \end{pmatrix}$. $\left[Ans. \text{ (b) } \frac{1}{77}\begin{pmatrix} 33 & 22 & -11 \\ 10 & 9 & 6 \\ 29 & 3 & 2 \end{pmatrix} \right]$.

   Check your answers by multiplication.

11. Solve the systems
   (a) $7x + 6y = 5$
       $6x + 5y = -3$.
   (b) $2x + y = 0$
       $3y + z = 1$
       $4z + x = 2$.   [*Ans.* $x = -\frac{2}{25}, y = \frac{4}{25}, z = \frac{13}{25}$.]
   (c) $x_1 + x_2 + x_3 + x_4 = -1$
       $x_1 - x_2 \qquad + 2x_4 = 0$
       $3x_2 - x_3 \qquad = 3$
       $x_2 \qquad - x_4 = 0$.

7. GEOMETRIC PROPERTIES OF DETERMINANTS

Although determinants were first investigated in connection with linear equations (before the idea of a matrix was clearly formulated), they turn out to have a number of interesting and useful properties not directly related to systems of equations. One of the most important is:

7.1 Product rule. If A and B are any two square matrices of the same size, then $\det(AB) = (\det A)(\det B)$.

Proof. Let $L(\mathbf{x}_1, \ldots, \mathbf{x}_n) = \det A \det(\mathbf{x}_1, \ldots, \mathbf{x}_n) - \det(A\mathbf{x}_1, \ldots, A\mathbf{x}_n)$, where $\mathbf{x}_1, \ldots, \mathbf{x}_n$ are vectors in $\mathscr{R}^n$. Clearly L is linear as a function of each vector $\mathbf{x}_j$. Furthermore, $L(\mathbf{e}_{i_1}, \ldots, \mathbf{e}_{i_n}) = 0$ for any set $\{\mathbf{e}_{i_1}, \ldots, \mathbf{e}_{i_n}\}$ of natural basis vectors. The reason is that if any of $\mathbf{e}_{i_1}, \ldots, \mathbf{e}_{i_n}$ are the same then both $\det(\mathbf{e}_{i_1}, \ldots, \mathbf{e}_{i_n})$ and $\det(A\mathbf{e}_{i_1}, \ldots, A\mathbf{e}_{i_n})$ are zero. Otherwise $\mathbf{e}_{i_1}, \ldots, \mathbf{e}_{i_n}$ are just $\mathbf{e}_1, \ldots, \mathbf{e}_n$ in some order, and

$$\det A \det(\mathbf{e}_{i_1}, \ldots, \mathbf{e}_{i_n}) = \pm\det A \det(\mathbf{e}_1, \ldots, \mathbf{e}_n) = \pm\det A \det I$$
$$= \pm\det A = \pm\det(A\mathbf{e}_1, \ldots, A\mathbf{e}_n)$$
$$= \det(A\mathbf{e}_{i_1}, \ldots, A\mathbf{e}_{i_n}).$$

But then $L(\mathbf{b}_1, \ldots, \mathbf{b}_n) = 0$, where

$$\mathbf{b}_j = \begin{pmatrix} b_{1j} \\ \cdot \\ \cdot \\ \cdot \\ b_{nj} \end{pmatrix}$$

is the jth column of B. For, using the linearity of L,

$$L(\mathbf{b}_1, \ldots, \mathbf{b}_n) = L\left(\sum_{i=1}^{n} b_{i1}\mathbf{e}_i, \ldots, \sum_{i=1}^{n} b_{in}\mathbf{e}_i\right)$$
$$= \sum_{i_1=1}^{n} \cdots \sum_{i_n=1}^{n} b_{i_11} \ldots b_{i_n n} L(\mathbf{e}_{i_1}, \ldots, \mathbf{e}_{i_n}) = 0.$$

Hence,

$$\det A \det B - \det AB = \det A \det(\mathbf{b}_1, \ldots, \mathbf{b}_n) - \det(A\mathbf{b}_1, \ldots, A\mathbf{b}_n)$$
$$= L(\mathbf{b}_1, \ldots, \mathbf{b}_n) = 0.$$

Multiplication by an n-by-n matrix gives a linear function from $\mathscr{R}^n$ to $\mathscr{R}^n$, and it is natural to ask if its determinant has a geometrical interpretation. It will be shown that, up to a sign, the determinant is the factor by which the function distorts volume. In $\mathscr{R}^2$, of course, "volume" is area.

EXAMPLE 1. Multiplication by $\begin{pmatrix} 3 & 0 \\ 0 & 2 \end{pmatrix}$ gives a function $R^2 \xrightarrow{f} R^2$ which multiplies lengths in the x-direction by 3 and in the y-direction by 2. All areas are magnified by a factor of 6, as illustrated in Figure 19, which shows the unit square S and its image $f(S)$. Observe that det $\begin{pmatrix} 3 & 0 \\ 0 & 2 \end{pmatrix} = 6$. For another example, consider the function g with matrix $\begin{pmatrix} 1 & 2 \\ 0 & 1 \end{pmatrix}$, which has determinant 1. Its effect is illustrated in Figure 20. The unit square is mapped into a parallelogram with the same base and altitude, so the area remains unchanged. These examples suggest that a linear function of $\mathcal{R}^2$ into itself multiplies areas by a factor equal to the determinant of the associated matrix. This is not quite right since, for example, a reflection in the y-axis is made by the transformation $r(x, y) = (-x, y)$, with matrix

$$\begin{pmatrix} -1 & 0 \\ 0 & 1 \end{pmatrix}.$$

The determinant of this matrix is -1, while the effect of the reflection is to leave areas unchanged. The solution to this difficulty is to take the absolute value of the determinant. The composition $g \circ f$ of f and g is also a linear function with matrix equal to the product

$$\begin{pmatrix} 1 & 2 \\ 0 & 1 \end{pmatrix} \begin{pmatrix} 3 & 0 \\ 0 & 2 \end{pmatrix}$$

of the matrices of g and f. From the product rule for determinants it follows that the matrix of $g \circ f$ has determinant $1 \cdot 6 = 6$. It will follow that $g \circ f$ has the effect of multiplying areas by 6.

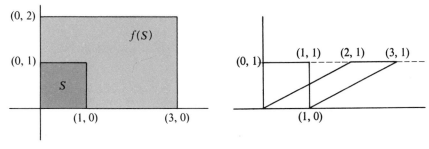

Figure 19   Figure 20

The previous examples suggest that the following theorem is true.

7.2 Theorem. A linear function from $\mathcal{R}^n$ to $\mathcal{R}^n$ with matrix A multiplies volumes by the factor $|\det A|$.

The theorem cannot be proved, except for special cases, without a rigorous definition of volume. This is given in Chapter 4, where the above theorem is stated as Theorem 3.2.

The natural unit of area in $\mathscr{R}^2$ is given by the unit square with edges $(1, 0)$ and $(0, 1)$, and the natural unit of volume in $\mathscr{R}^3$ is given by the unit cube with edges $(1, 0, 0)$, $(0, 1, 0)$, $(0, 0, 1)$. In general we take the unit of volume in $\mathscr{R}^n$ to be that of the cube whose edges are the natural basis vectors $\mathbf{e}_1, \ldots, \mathbf{e}_n$ that form the columns of the n-by-n identity matrix. Moreover, we can take any n vectors $\mathbf{x}_1, \ldots, \mathbf{x}_n$ in $\mathscr{R}^n$ and form all linear combinations $t_1\mathbf{x}_1 + \ldots + t_n\mathbf{x}_n$, where each of the real numbers $t_1, \ldots, t_n$ satisfies the condition $0 \leq t_i \leq 1$. The resulting set of points is called the **parallelepiped** determined by its **edges** $\mathbf{x}_1, \ldots, \mathbf{x}_n$. If we choose only two vectors $\mathbf{x}_1, \mathbf{x}_2$, then we speak of the *parallelogram* determined by $\mathbf{x}_1$ and $\mathbf{x}_2$. Figure 21 shows a parallelepiped.

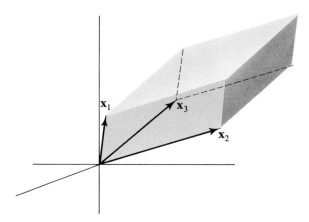

Figure 21

7.3 Theorem. Let $\mathbf{a}_1, \mathbf{a}_2, \ldots, \mathbf{a}_n$ be n vectors in $\mathscr{R}^n$. Then the volume of the parallelepiped with edges $\mathbf{a}_1, \ldots, \mathbf{a}_n$ is $|\det(\mathbf{a}_1, \ldots, \mathbf{a}_n)|$.

Proof. The linear function f whose matrix has columns $\mathbf{a}_1, \ldots, \mathbf{a}_n$ carries $\mathbf{e}_j$ into $\mathbf{a}_j$, by Theorem 4.2. Hence, f transforms the unit cube into the parallelepiped with edges $\mathbf{a}_j$. Since it multiplies volumes by the factor $|\det(\mathbf{a}_1, \ldots, \mathbf{a}_n)|$, and the cube has unit volume, the volume of the parallelepiped is $|\det(\mathbf{a}_1, \ldots, \mathbf{a}_n)|$.

EXAMPLE 2. Let $\mathbf{a}_1 = \begin{pmatrix} r_1 \cos \theta_1 \\ r_1 \sin \theta_1 \end{pmatrix}$, $\mathbf{a}_2 = \begin{pmatrix} r_2 \cos \theta_2 \\ r_2 \sin \theta_2 \end{pmatrix}$. The vectors have lengths r_1, r_2, and make angles θ_1 and θ_2 with the x-axis as shown in Figure 22.

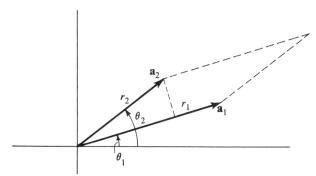

Figure 22

Then det $(\mathbf{a}_1, \mathbf{a}_2)$ is

$$\det \begin{pmatrix} r_1 \cos \theta_1 & r_2 \cos \theta_2 \\ r_1 \sin \theta_1 & r_2 \sin \theta_2 \end{pmatrix} = r_1 r_2 (\cos \theta_1 \sin \theta_2 - \sin \theta_1 \cos \theta_2)$$

$$= r_1 r_2 \sin (\theta_2 - \theta_1)$$

This number may be interpreted as the product of the base r_1 by the perpendicular height $r_2 \sin (\theta_2 - \theta_1)$.

We have seen that the absolute value of det $(\mathbf{a}_1, \ldots, \mathbf{a}_n)$ can be interpreted as a volume. The sign of this determinant also has a geometric interpretation. We say that an ordered set of vectors $(\mathbf{a}_1, \ldots, \mathbf{a}_n)$ in $\mathscr{R}^n$ has **positive orientation** (or is **positively oriented**) if det $(\mathbf{a}_1, \ldots, \mathbf{a}_n) > 0$, and has **negative orientation** if det $(\mathbf{a}_1, \ldots, \mathbf{a}_n) < 0$. If the determinant is equal to zero, the orientation is not defined.

Example 2 shows that in $\mathscr{R}^2$, the sign of det $(\mathbf{a}_1, \mathbf{a}_2)$ is the same as the sign of sin θ, where $\theta = \theta_2 - \theta_1$ is the angle from $\mathbf{a}_1$ to $\mathbf{a}_2$. Thus the orientation of $(\mathbf{a}_1, \mathbf{a}_2)$ is positive if some counterclockwise rotation of less than 180° will turn $\mathbf{a}_1$ to the direction of $\mathbf{a}_2$. The orientation is negative if a clockwise rotation is required, and is not defined if $\mathbf{a}_1$ and $\mathbf{a}_2$ lie in the same line. Thus in $\mathscr{R}^2$, orientation corresponds to a direction of rotation. (Note that the orientation of $(\mathbf{a}_1, \mathbf{a}_2)$ is opposite to that of $(\mathbf{a}_2, \mathbf{a}_1)$.) Property 6.10 of determinants, of course, implies that the orientation of a set of vectors is always reversed if two vectors of the set are exchanged.

The interpretation of orientation in $\mathscr{R}^3$ is less obvious. The sets of vectors $(\mathbf{x}, \mathbf{y}, \mathbf{z})$ and $(-\mathbf{x}, \mathbf{y}, \mathbf{z})$ shown in Figures 23(a) and 23(b) have opposite orientations, since by Theorem 6.2, det $(-\mathbf{x}, \mathbf{y}, \mathbf{z}) = -\det (\mathbf{x}, \mathbf{y}, \mathbf{z})$. The ordered set of vectors $(\mathbf{x}, \mathbf{y}, \mathbf{z})$ is said to form a right-handed system because, when the thumb and index finger of the right hand are made to point in the **x**- and **y**-directions, the middle finger will point in the **z**-direction. Similarly, $(-\mathbf{x}, \mathbf{y}, \mathbf{z})$ form a left-handed system. In this book we have chosen to draw

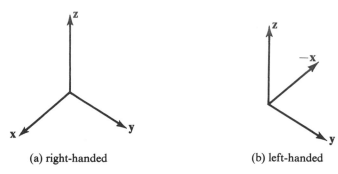

(a) right-handed   (b) left-handed

Figure 23

pictures in 3-space so that the vectors e_1, e_2, e_3 form a right-handed system. Since $\det (e_1, e_2, e_3) = \det I = 1$, this implies that our right-handed system has positive orientation, and a left-handed system would have negative orientation.

Let $u = (u_1, u_2, u_3)$ and $v = (v_1, v_2, v_3)$ be vectors in $\mathscr{R}^3$. The vector with coordinates

$$\begin{vmatrix} u_2 & v_2 \\ u_3 & v_3 \end{vmatrix}, \quad \begin{vmatrix} u_3 & v_3 \\ u_1 & v_1 \end{vmatrix}, \quad \begin{vmatrix} u_1 & v_1 \\ u_2 & v_2 \end{vmatrix}$$

is called the **cross product** of u and v, and is written $u \times v$. The significance of the cross product lies in the equation:

7.4 $$x \cdot (u \times v) = \det (x, u, v),$$

which holds for any x in $\mathscr{R}^3$. To prove it we let $x = (x_1, x_2, x_3)$. Then

$$\det (x, u, v) = \det \begin{pmatrix} x_1 & u_1 & v_1 \\ x_2 & u_2 & v_2 \\ x_3 & u_3 & v_3 \end{pmatrix}$$

$$= x_1 \begin{vmatrix} u_2 & v_2 \\ u_3 & v_3 \end{vmatrix} - x_2 \begin{vmatrix} u_1 & v_1 \\ u_3 & v_3 \end{vmatrix} + x_3 \begin{vmatrix} u_1 & v_1 \\ u_2 & v_2 \end{vmatrix}$$

$$= x \cdot (u \times v).$$

The preceding calculation shows that the coordinates in $\mathscr{R}^3$ of the cross product are just the cofactors of the first column in a matrix with u and v as second and third columns. Alternatively, we can write $u = u_1 e_1 + u_2 e_2 + u_3 e_3$ and $v = v_1 e_1 + v_2 e_2 + v_3 e_3$, where e_1, e_2, e_3 are the natural basis vectors in $\mathscr{R}^3$. Then the formal determinant expansion

$$\det \begin{pmatrix} e_1 & e_2 & e_3 \\ u_1 & u_2 & u_3 \\ v_1 & v_2 & v_3 \end{pmatrix} = \begin{vmatrix} u_2 & u_3 \\ v_2 & v_3 \end{vmatrix} e_1 + \begin{vmatrix} u_3 & u_1 \\ v_3 & v_1 \end{vmatrix} e_2 + \begin{vmatrix} u_1 & u_2 \\ v_1 & v_2 \end{vmatrix} e_3$$

gives the cross product in terms of the natural basis, and is a convenient way to remember the formula for the cross product.

If either **u** or **v** is zero, or if one is a numerical multiple of the other, **u** × **v** is obviously zero. Otherwise **u** and **v** determine a plane. Substituting **u** and **v** for **x** in 7.4 gives

$$\mathbf{u}\cdot(\mathbf{u}\times\mathbf{v}) = \det(\mathbf{u}, \mathbf{u}, \mathbf{v}) = 0, \qquad \mathbf{v}\cdot(\mathbf{u}\times\mathbf{v}) = \det(\mathbf{v}, \mathbf{u}, \mathbf{v}) = 0$$

by Theorem 6.11. Thus **u** × **v** is perpendicular to the plane of **u** and **v**. Let **x** be a vector of unit length in the direction of **u** × **v**. Then **x**·(**u** × **v**) = |**u** × **v**|. On the other hand **x**·(**u** × **v**) = det (**x**, **u**, **v**), and has absolute value equal to the volume of the parallelepiped with edges **x**, **u**, **v**. Since **x** has unit length and is perpendicular to the plane of **u** and **v**, this volume is equal to the area of the parallelogram with edges **u**, **v**. Thus the length of **u** × **v** is equal to the area of the parallelogram with edges **u**, **v**. Finally,

$$\det(\mathbf{u}\times\mathbf{v}, \mathbf{u}, \mathbf{v}) = (\mathbf{u}\times\mathbf{v})\cdot(\mathbf{u}\times\mathbf{v}) = |\mathbf{u}\times\mathbf{v}|^2 \geq 0.$$

Then, unless **u** × **v** = 0, the triple (**u** × **v**, **u**, **v**) has positive orientation and forms a right-handed system.

We can summarize what we have just proved as:

7.5 Theorem. If **u** and **v** are non-collinear vectors in $\mathscr{R}^3$, then the cross product **u** × **v** is a vector perpendicular to both **u** and **v**, with length equal to the area of the parallelogram with edges **u** and **v**. The ordered triple (**u** × **v**, **u**, **v**) is a right-handed system.

Figure 24 shows the relation between **u**, **v** and **u** × **v**.

EXAMPLE 2. Find the area of the parallelogram with edges **u** = (1, 2, 3), **v** = (3, 2, 1). We have

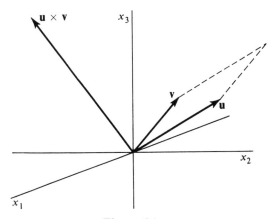

Figure 24

$$\mathbf{u} \times \mathbf{v} = ((2)(1) - (3)(2), \; -(1)(1) + (3)(3), \; (1)(2) - (2)(3))$$
$$= (-4, 8, -4).$$
$$\text{Area} = |\mathbf{u} \times \mathbf{v}| = (16 + 64 + 16)^{1/2}$$
$$= \sqrt{96} = 4\sqrt{6}.$$

It is sometimes appropriate to combine the ideas of volume and orientation in a single concept. We define the **oriented volume** determined by an n-tuple of vectors to be the ordinary volume if the orientation of the n-tuple is positive and to be the negative of the volume if the orientation is negative. Then the oriented volume of the ordered set $(\mathbf{a}_1, \ldots, \mathbf{a}_n)$ is equal to $\det (\mathbf{a}_1, \ldots, \mathbf{a}_n)$. The relation between oriented volume and ordinary volume is very much like the relation between directed distance on a line and ordinary distance. Indeed, oriented volume may be considered a generalization of directed distance, and we use the idea in Chapter 5, Section 7.

EXERCISES

1. Apply the product rule to show that if A is invertible, then $\det A \neq 0$ and $(\det A^{-1}) = (\det A)^{-1}$.

2. Prove that a product of square matrices $P_1 P_2 \ldots P_k$ is invertible if and only if each of the P_i is invertible. Hence show if A and B are square matrices and $AB = I$, then A and B are invertible and are inverses of each other.

3. Let A be an m-by-m matrix and B an n-by-n matrix. Consider the $(m + n)$-by-$(m + n)$ matrix $\begin{pmatrix} A & 0 \\ 0 & B \end{pmatrix}$ which has A in the upper left corner, B in the lower right corner, and zeros elsewhere. Show that its determinant is equal to $(\det A)(\det B)$. [*Suggestion.* First consider the case where one of A or B is an identity matrix, and derive the general result from the product rule.]

4. It is geometrically clear that a rotation in $\mathscr{R}^2$ preserves orientations, that a reflection reverses them, and that both leave areas unchanged. Verify this by finding the determinants of the associated matrices. (See Problems 4 and 5 in Section 4.)

5. Show that every orthogonal matrix has determinant ± 1, so that the linear transformation determined by such a matrix on $\mathscr{R}^n$ preserves volumes. [*Hint.* Recall that if A is orthogonal, then $AA^t = I$.]

6. By interpreting the determinant as a volume, show that $|\det (\mathbf{x}_1, \mathbf{x}_2, \mathbf{x}_3)|$ $\leq |\mathbf{x}_1| \cdot |\mathbf{x}_2| \cdot |\mathbf{x}_3|$ for any three vectors in $\mathscr{R}^3$, and that equality holds if and only if the vectors are mutually orthogonal.

7. Find the volume, and the area of each side, of the parallelepiped with edges $(1, 1, 0)$, $(0, 1, 2)$, $(-3, 5, -1)$.
[*Ans.* volume $= 17$, areas $= \sqrt{166}, \sqrt{66}, 3.$]

8. If $\mathbf{u} = (2, 1, 3)$, $\mathbf{v} = (0, 2, -1)$, and $\mathbf{w} = (1, 1, 1)$, compute $\mathbf{u} \times \mathbf{v}$, $\det(\mathbf{u}, \mathbf{v}, \mathbf{w})$, $(\mathbf{u} \times \mathbf{v}) \cdot \mathbf{w}$, $(\mathbf{u} \times \mathbf{v}) \times \mathbf{w}$, and $\mathbf{u} \times (\mathbf{v} \times \mathbf{w})$.

9. Prove that $\mathbf{u} \times \mathbf{v} = -\mathbf{v} \times \mathbf{u}$, that $\mathbf{u} \times (\mathbf{v} + \mathbf{w}) = (\mathbf{u} \times \mathbf{v}) + (\mathbf{u} \times \mathbf{w})$, and that $(a\mathbf{u}) \times \mathbf{v} = \mathbf{u} \times (a\mathbf{v}) = a(\mathbf{u} \times \mathbf{v})$, for a real.

10. Find a representation for a line perpendicular to $(2, 1, 3)$ and $(0, 2, -1)$, and passing through $(1, 1, 1)$.

11. Let $\mathscr{P}$ be a parallelogram determined by two vectors in $\mathscr{R}^3$. Let $\mathscr{P}_x$, $\mathscr{P}_y$, and $\mathscr{P}_z$ be the projections of $\mathscr{P}$ on the y, z-plane, the z, x-plane, and the x, y-plane, respectively. If $A(\mathscr{P})$ is the area of $\mathscr{P}$, show that $A^2(\mathscr{P}) = A^2(\mathscr{P}_x) + A^2(\mathscr{P}_y) + A^2(\mathscr{P}_z)$.

12. (a) Verify by direct coordinate computation that $|\mathbf{u} \times \mathbf{v}|^2 = |\mathbf{u}|^2|\mathbf{v}|^2 - (\mathbf{u} \cdot \mathbf{v})^2$.

(b) Use the result of part (a) to show that $|\mathbf{u} \times \mathbf{v}| = |\mathbf{u}||\mathbf{v}| \sin \theta$, where θ is the angle between $\mathbf{u}$ and $\mathbf{v}$ such that $0 \leq \theta \leq \pi$.

(c) Show that $|\mathbf{u}||\mathbf{v}| \sin \theta$ is the area of the parallelogram with edges $\mathbf{u}$ and $\mathbf{v}$.

13. The complex numbers can be extended to the quaternion algebra $\mathscr{H}$, which is a four-dimensional vector space with natural basis $\{1, i, j, k\}$. Thus a typical quaternion is written $q = a_1 + a_2 i + a_3 j + a_4 k$, where the a's are real numbers. A product is defined in $\mathscr{H}$ by requiring $i^2 = j^2 = k^2 = -1$ and $ij = -ji = k$, $jk = -kj = i$, $ki = -ik = j$. The product of two quaternions is got by multiplying out and using the above rules for products of basis vectors. $\mathscr{R}^3$ can be looked at as the vector subspace $\mathscr{G}$ of $\mathscr{H}$ consisting of quaternions with "real part" equal to zero and thus with natural basis $\{i, j, k\}$.

(a) Show that the quaternion product of two elements of $\mathscr{G}$ is not necessarily in $\mathscr{G}$.

(b) Define a product on $\mathscr{G}$ by first forming the quaternion product and then replacing its real part by zero. Show that the resulting product is the same as the cross product in $\mathscr{R}^3$.

14. Prove the identity $\mathbf{a} \times (\mathbf{b} \times \mathbf{c}) = (\mathbf{a} \cdot \mathbf{c})\mathbf{b} - (\mathbf{a} \cdot \mathbf{b})\mathbf{c}$ for vectors $\mathbf{a}$, $\mathbf{b}$, and $\mathbf{c}$ in $\mathscr{R}^3$. [*Hint.* Choose an orthonormal set of vectors $(\mathbf{u}_1, \mathbf{u}_2, \mathbf{u}_3)$ for $\mathscr{R}^3$ so that $(\mathbf{u}_1, \mathbf{u}_2, \mathbf{u}_3)$ is positively oriented and

$$\mathbf{a} = a_1\mathbf{u}_1 + a_2\mathbf{u}_2 + a_3\mathbf{u}_3$$
$$\mathbf{b} = b_1\mathbf{u}_1 + b_2\mathbf{u}_2$$
$$\mathbf{c} = c_1\mathbf{u}_1.]$$

8. SUBSPACES, ABSTRACT VECTOR SPACES, DIMENSION

Recall that a vector $\mathbf{x}$ is called a **linear combination** of the vectors $\mathbf{x}_1, \ldots, \mathbf{x}_n$ if there are numbers $r_1, \ldots, r_n$ such that

$$\mathbf{x} = r_1\mathbf{x}_1 + \ldots + r_n\mathbf{x}_n.$$

EXAMPLE 1. Let

$$\mathbf{x}_1 = (1, 0, 0), \qquad \mathbf{x}_2 = (0, 1, 0), \qquad \mathbf{x}_3 = (0, 0, 1), \qquad \mathbf{x}_4 = (1, 1, 1).$$

Then $\mathbf{y} = (2, 2, 0)$ is a linear combination of $\mathbf{x}_1$ and $\mathbf{x}_2$ because it is equal to $2\mathbf{x}_1 + 2\mathbf{x}_2$; it is a linear combination of $\mathbf{x}_3$ and $\mathbf{x}_4$ because it is equal to $2\mathbf{x}_4 - 2\mathbf{x}_3$. On the other hand, it is not a linear combination of $\mathbf{x}_2$ and $\mathbf{x}_3$, because $r\mathbf{x}_2 + s\mathbf{x}_3$ has a first entry of 0 whatever the values of r and s, so $\mathbf{y} = r\mathbf{x}_2 + s\mathbf{x}_3$ is impossible.

Since $0 = 0\mathbf{x}_1 + \ldots + 0\mathbf{x}_n$, the zero vector is a linear combination of any set of vectors. The linear combinations of a single vector $\mathbf{x}_1$ are just the numerical multiples $r\mathbf{x}_1$.

If a set of vectors lies in a plane through the origin in 3-space, then every linear combination of them lies in the same plane. For we recall that if $\mathbf{x}$ and $\mathbf{y}$ are in a plane through the origin, the parallelogram rule makes $\mathbf{x} + \mathbf{y}$ a vector in the same plane. Any numerical multiple of $\mathbf{x}$ lies in the same plane because it lies in the line containing $\mathbf{x}$. Any linear combination of $\mathbf{x}_1, \ldots, \mathbf{x}_n$ is built up by multiplications and additions, and if the vectors $\mathbf{x}_1, \ldots, \mathbf{x}_n$ lie in a plane, so do all linear combinations of them.

Similarly, if $\mathbf{x}_1, \ldots, \mathbf{x}_n$ all lie in one line through the origin (so they are all multiples of some one vector), any linear combination of them lies in the same line.

These remarks suggest the following generalization which includes lines and planes as special cases: A subset $\mathscr{S}$ of a vector space $\mathscr{V}$ is called a **linear subspace** (or, frequently, simply a **subspace**) if every linear combination of elements of $\mathscr{S}$ is also in $\mathscr{S}$.

EXAMPLE 2. We list some examples of subspaces.

(a) The set of all vectors in $\mathscr{R}^n$ with first entry equal to 0 is a subspace, since any linear combination of such vectors will also have a 0 for its first entry.

(b) For any vector space $\mathscr{V}$, $\mathscr{V}$ itself is a subspace. The term *proper* subspace is often used to refer to those subspaces that are not the whole space. In any vector space the zero vector forms a subspace all by itself. This subspace is called the *trivial* subspace (because it is).

(c) For any linear function $\mathscr{V} \xrightarrow{f} \mathscr{W}$, the set $\mathscr{N}$ of vectors $\mathbf{x}$ in $\mathscr{V}$ with $f(\mathbf{x}) = 0$ is a subspace of $\mathscr{V}$ called the **null space** of f. If $\mathbf{x}_1, \ldots, \mathbf{x}_k$ are in $\mathscr{N}$ and $\mathbf{x} = \sum_{i=1}^{k} r_i \mathbf{x}_i$, then $f(\mathbf{x}) = \sum_{i=1}^{k} r_i f(\mathbf{x}_i) = 0$, because f is linear and all the $f(\mathbf{x}_i)$ are 0. Hence $\mathbf{x}$ is also in $\mathscr{N}$, and so $\mathscr{N}$ is a subspace of $\mathscr{V}$. In particular, the set of vectors (x, y, z) in $\mathscr{R}^3$ such that

$$\begin{pmatrix} 1 & 2 & 3 \\ 4 & 5 & 6 \end{pmatrix} \begin{pmatrix} x \\ y \\ z \end{pmatrix} = \begin{pmatrix} 0 \\ 0 \end{pmatrix}$$

is a subspace because it is the null space of the linear function from $\mathscr{R}^3$ to $\mathscr{R}^2$ defined by the preceding 2-by-3 matrix.

(d) The range of a linear function f defined on a vector space is a subspace of the range space of f. The reason is that for $\mathbf{y}_1, \ldots, \mathbf{y}_k$ to be in the range of f means that there are vectors $\mathbf{x}_1, \ldots, \mathbf{x}_k$ in the domain of f such that $f(\mathbf{x}_i) = \mathbf{y}_i$ for $i = 1, \ldots, k$. But then, by the linearity of f, an arbitrary linear combination of the $\mathbf{y}_i$ has the form

$$r_1\mathbf{y}_1 + \ldots + r_k\mathbf{y}_k = r_1 f(\mathbf{x}_1) + \ldots + r_k f(\mathbf{x}_k)$$
$$= f(r_1\mathbf{x}_1 + \ldots + r_k\mathbf{x}_k).$$

Because the domain of f is a vector space, $r_1\mathbf{x}_1 + \ldots + r_k\mathbf{x}_k$ is in it, and so $r_1\mathbf{y}_1 + \ldots + r_k\mathbf{y}_k$ is in the range of f. In particular, the set of all vectors in $\mathscr{R}^3$ of the form

$$\begin{pmatrix} 1 & 4 \\ 2 & 5 \\ 3 & 6 \end{pmatrix}\begin{pmatrix} x \\ y \end{pmatrix} = x\begin{pmatrix} 1 \\ 2 \\ 3 \end{pmatrix} + y\begin{pmatrix} 4 \\ 5 \\ 6 \end{pmatrix}$$

is a subspace because it is the range of the linear function just defined by the above 3-by-2 matrix.

We define the **span** of a set S of vectors to be the set consisting of all linear combinations of elements of S. It is easy to show that the span of any set is a subspace. For suppose $\mathbf{x} = \sum\limits_{i=1}^{k} r_i\mathbf{x}_i$ is a linear combination of vectors $\mathbf{x}_1, \ldots, \mathbf{x}_k$, which are in the span of S. That is $\mathbf{x}_i = \sum\limits_{j=1}^{n} s_{ij}\mathbf{u}_j$ for some vectors $\mathbf{u}_j$ in S. Then $\mathbf{x} = \sum\limits_{i=1}^{k} r_i(\sum\limits_{j=1}^{n} s_{ij}\mathbf{u}_j) = \sum\limits_{j=1}^{n} t_j\mathbf{u}_j$, where $t_j = \sum\limits_{i=1}^{k} r_i s_{ij}$. This shows that $\mathbf{x}$ is itself in the span of S.

We recall from Section 1 the general definition of a vector space as a set $\mathscr{V}$ of elements with operations of addition and numerical multiplication such that for any elements $\mathbf{x}, \mathbf{y}, \mathbf{z}$ of $\mathscr{V}$ and real numbers r, s:

1. $r\mathbf{x} + s\mathbf{x} = (r + s)\mathbf{x}$.
2. $r\mathbf{x} + r\mathbf{y} = r(\mathbf{x} + \mathbf{y})$.
3. $r(s\mathbf{x}) = (rs)\mathbf{x}$.
4. $\mathbf{x} + \mathbf{y} = \mathbf{y} + \mathbf{x}$.
5. $(\mathbf{x} + \mathbf{y}) + \mathbf{z} = \mathbf{x} + (\mathbf{y} + \mathbf{z})$.
6. There exists an element 0 in $\mathscr{V}$ such that $\mathbf{x} + 0 = \mathbf{x}$.
7. For any $\mathbf{x}$ in $\mathscr{V}$, $\mathbf{x} + (-1)\mathbf{x} = 0$.

Now if $\mathscr{S}$ is any subspace of a vector space $\mathscr{V}$, then the operations of addition and numerical multiplication, as given for $\mathscr{V}$, always yield a result in $\mathscr{S}$ when they are applied to elements of $\mathscr{S}$, because $\mathbf{x} + \mathbf{y} = 1\mathbf{x} + 1\mathbf{y}$ and $r\mathbf{x} = r\mathbf{x} + 0\mathbf{y}$ are linear combinations of $\mathbf{x}$ and $\mathbf{y}$. The laws 1 through 5 certainly hold for $\mathbf{x}, \mathbf{y}, \mathbf{z}$ in $\mathscr{S}$, since they hold for all elements of $\mathscr{V}$. The zero vector belongs to $\mathscr{S}$, since $0 = 0 \cdot \mathbf{x}$ for any $\mathbf{x}$ in $\mathscr{S}$; also if $\mathbf{x}$ is in $\mathscr{S}$, then so is $(-1)\mathbf{x} = -\mathbf{x}$. Thus 6 and 7 hold as well. In other words, we have proved

8.1 Theorem. Any subspace of a vector space is a vector space, with the operations inherited from the original space.

Up to this point the only vector spaces we considered were $\mathcal{R}^n$ and the space of m-by-n matrices for arbitrary values of m and n. The subspaces of these spaces give many more examples, but there are vector spaces which are not subspaces of these familiar ones.

EXAMPLE 3.

(a) Let $\mathcal{V}$ consist of all continuous real-valued functions of a real variable. Define $f + g$ and rf in the obvious way as the functions whose values for any number x are $f(x) + g(x)$ and $rf(x)$, respectively. (Of course, we are using the theorems that $f + g$ and rf are continuous if f and g are.) It is easy to verify that the laws for a vector space are satisfied.

(b) Let $\mathcal{P}$ be the subspace of $\mathcal{V}$ consisting of all polynomials, i.e., all functions f that can be expressed by a formula $f(x) = a_0 + a_1x + \ldots + a_kx^k$ for some constants $a_0, \ldots, a_k$. (What needs to be checked to verify that this is a subspace?)

(c) Let $\mathcal{P}_n$ be the subspace of polynomials of degree less than or equal to n, i.e., those that require no power of x higher than the nth for their expression. For $k \leq n$, $\mathcal{P}_k$ is a subspace of $\mathcal{P}_n$, and all $\mathcal{P}_n$ are subspaces of $\mathcal{P}$.

The description of lines, planes, and ordinary space as 1, 2, and 3-dimensional is familiar. It is possible to define the dimension of any vector space. The examples of lines and planes suggest that the span of k vectors should have dimension k. This is not quite right, since, for example, the span of two vectors that happen to lie in the same line will be only a line instead of a plane. To handle the question properly requires the concept of linear independence, which we now define.

A set of vectors $\{\mathbf{x}_1, \ldots, \mathbf{x}_k\}$ is **(linearly) independent** if the only set of numbers $r_1, \ldots, r_k$ such that $r_1\mathbf{x}_1 + \ldots + r_k\mathbf{x}_k = 0$ is the set $r_1 = r_2 = \ldots = r_k = 0$. A set of vectors is **(linearly) dependent** if it is not independent. For $\{\mathbf{x}_1, \ldots, \mathbf{x}_k\}$ to be dependent therefore means that there are numbers $r_1, \ldots, r_k$ *not* all zero, such that $r_1\mathbf{x}_1 + \ldots + r_k\mathbf{x}_k = 0$.

EXAMPLE 4.

(a) The four vectors $\mathbf{x}_1 = (2, 0, 0)$, $\mathbf{x}_2 = (0, -2, 0)$, $\mathbf{x}_3 = (0, 0, 3)$, $\mathbf{x}_4 = (2, -2, 3)$ are linearly dependent since $\mathbf{x}_1 + \mathbf{x}_2 + \mathbf{x}_3 - \mathbf{x}_4 = 0$. The set of three vectors $\mathbf{x}_1, \mathbf{x}_2, \mathbf{x}_3$, is independent since $r\mathbf{x}_1 + s\mathbf{x}_2 + t\mathbf{x}_3 = 0$ only if $r = s = t = 0$.

(b) A set of two vectors $\mathbf{x}$, $\mathbf{y}$ is independent only if neither is a numerical multiple of the other. For example, if $\mathbf{y} = 3\mathbf{x}$, then $3\mathbf{x} - \mathbf{y} = 0$, and the vectors are dependent.

A set of vectors which is linearly independent and spans a space $\mathscr{V}$ is called a **basis** for $\mathscr{V}$.

EXAMPLE 5.

(a) The natural basis vectors $\mathbf{e}_1, \ldots, \mathbf{e}_n$, where $\mathbf{e}_i$ has 1 for its ith entry and 0 for all other entries form a basis for $\mathscr{R}^n$. Verification that the $\mathbf{e}_i$ are in fact linearly independent and span $\mathscr{R}^n$ is left to the reader.

(b) In the space $\mathscr{P}_n$ of Example 3(c), the polynomials $\mathbf{x}_0 = 1$, $\mathbf{x}_1 = x, \ldots,$ $\mathbf{x}_n = x^n$ form a basis. Obviously if $f(x) = a_0 + a_1x + \ldots + a_nx^n$ is a polynomial of degree less than or equal to n, it is the linear combination $a_0\mathbf{x}_0 + \ldots + a_n\mathbf{x}_n$ of the $\mathbf{x}$'s. If $a_0\mathbf{x}_0 + \ldots + a_n\mathbf{x}_n$ is the zero function, then (since a polynomial of degree less than or equal to n cannot have more than n roots unless its coefficients are all zero) $a_0 = a_1 = \ldots = a_n = 0$.

While it is true that every vector space has a basis, we shall usually consider only those which have a basis with a finite number of elements. The next theorem implies that if a space is spanned by a finite set (which is perhaps not linearly independent), then it has a finite basis.

8.2 Theorem. Let $\mathscr{V}$ be the span of the vectors $\mathbf{x}_1, \ldots, \mathbf{x}_n$. Either $\mathscr{V}$ consists of the zero vector alone, or some subset of the $\mathbf{x}$'s is a basis for $\mathscr{V}$.

Proof. If the set $\mathbf{x}_1, \ldots, \mathbf{x}_n$ is independent, then it is itself a basis for $\mathscr{V}$. Otherwise some relation $r_1\mathbf{x}_1 + \ldots + r_n\mathbf{x}_n = 0$ holds, with at least one r, say r_k, diferent from 0. Then we can divide by r_k and obtain $\mathbf{x}_k = -(r_1/r_k)\mathbf{x}_1 - \ldots - (r_n/r_k)\mathbf{x}_n$, where $\mathbf{x}_k$ does not appear on the right side. By substituting the right side for $\mathbf{x}_k$ in any linear combination of all the $\mathbf{x}$'s, a linear combination is obtained that does not involve $\mathbf{x}_k$. In other words, $\mathbf{x}_k$ can be dropped and the span of the remaining vectors will still be all of $\mathscr{V}$. If the resulting subset is not independent, the process can be repeated. It must end in a finite number of steps either because a basis has been obtained or because all the vectors have been discarded. The latter is possible only if the space contains only the zero vector.

The following theorem is the most important step in developing the theory of dimension.

8.3 Theorem. If a vector space is spanned by n vectors $\mathbf{x}_1, \ldots, \mathbf{x}_n$, and $\mathbf{y}_1, \ldots, \mathbf{y}_k$ is a linearly independent set of k vectors in the space, then $k \leq n$.

Proof. The statement is easy to prove if $n = 1$. In this case, the space spanned by $\mathbf{x}_1$ consists of all numerical multiples of $\mathbf{x}_1$. Then for any two vectors $\mathbf{y}_1$ and $\mathbf{y}_2$ in the space, one must be a multiple of the other, and so $\mathbf{y}_1$ and $\mathbf{y}_2$ cannot be independent. We proceed by induction, and assume that in any space spanned by $n - 1$ vectors, no independent subset can have more than $n - 1$ vectors in it. Suppose we now are given a space spanned by n vectors $\mathbf{x}_1, \ldots, \mathbf{x}_n$ and containing k vectors $\mathbf{y}_1, \ldots,$ $\mathbf{y}_k$ with $k > n$. If we can show that the $\mathbf{y}$'s are dependent, then we will have shown that the statement of the theorem holds for a spanning set of n elements, and the inductive proof will be complete. Each of the vectors $\mathbf{y}_1, \ldots, \mathbf{y}_{n+1}$ can be written as a linear combination of $\mathbf{x}_1, \ldots, \mathbf{x}_n$, which means that there are numbers a_{ij} such that $\mathbf{y}_i = \sum\limits_{j=1}^{n} a_{ij}\mathbf{x}_j$, for $i = 1, \ldots, n + 1$. If the $n + 1$ numbers a_{i1} are all zero, then the $\mathbf{y}$'s all lie in the space spanned by the $n - 1$ vectors $\mathbf{x}_2, \ldots, \mathbf{x}_n$, and so by the inductive assumption the $\mathbf{y}$'s would then be dependent, as we want to show. Otherwise (by renumbering, if necessary) we may suppose that a_{11} is not zero. Then define n vectors $\mathbf{z}_2, \ldots, \mathbf{z}_{n+1}$ by setting $\mathbf{z}_i = \mathbf{y}_i$ $- a_{11}^{-1}a_{i1}\mathbf{y}_1$. By using the equations giving $\mathbf{y}_i$ in terms of the $\mathbf{x}$'s, it is easy to see that

$$\mathbf{z}_i = \sum_{j=2}^{n} (a_{ij} - a_{11}^{-1}a_{i1}a_{1j})\mathbf{x}_j,$$

so that the $\mathbf{z}$'s are linear combinations of the $n - 1$ vectors $\mathbf{x}_2, \ldots, \mathbf{x}_n$. By the inductive assumption, there are numbers $r_2, \ldots, r_{n+1}$, not all zero, such that $r_2\mathbf{z}_2 + \ldots + r_{n+1}\mathbf{z}_{n+1} = 0$. Using the definition of the $\mathbf{z}$'s in terms of the $\mathbf{y}$'s, this last relation becomes

$$-a_{11}^{-1}(r_2a_{21} + \ldots + r_{n+1}a_{n+1\,1})\mathbf{y}_1 + r_2\mathbf{y}_2 + \ldots + r_{n+1}\mathbf{y}_{n+1} = 0.$$

But since not all the r's are zero, this implies that $\mathbf{y}_1, \ldots, \mathbf{y}_{n+1}$ are dependent, as we wanted to show.

8.4 Theorem. Let $\mathscr{V}$ be a vector space with a basis of n elements. Then every basis for $\mathscr{V}$ has n elements.

Proof. Let $\{\mathbf{x}_1, \ldots, \mathbf{x}_n\}$ and $\{\mathbf{y}_1, \ldots, \mathbf{y}_k\}$ be two bases for $\mathscr{V}$. Since both sets are independent, and both are spanning sets, Theorem 8.3 implies that $k \leq n$ and $n \leq k$.

The **dimension** of a vector space that has a finite spanning set is the number of elements in any basis for the space. (The dimension of the space consisting of the zero vector alone is defined to be 0.) We write $\dim(\mathscr{V})$ for the dimension of the vector space $\mathscr{V}$. Note that Theorem 8.2 guarantees the existence of a basis, and that Theorem 8.4 guarantees that the dimension does not depend on which basis is taken.

Example 6.

(a) By Example 5(a), $\dim(\mathscr{R}^n) = n$.
(b) By Example 5(b), $\dim(\mathscr{P}_n) = n + 1$.

(c) The space $\mathscr{P}$ of all polynomials (Example 4(b)) does not have any finite spanning set. If it did have one with k elements, then the fact that $1, x, x^2, \ldots, x^k$ are $k + 1$ linearly independent elements of $\mathscr{P}$ would contradict Theorem 8.3.

A vector space with a finite basis is said to be **finite-dimensional**. As we have just seen in Example 6(c), there are spaces which are not finite-dimensional.

Theorem 8.2 asserts that we can get a basis from a finite spanning set by deleting some of its members. The next theorem shows that, in a finite-dimensional space, we can get a basis from a linearly independent set by adding vectors to it.

8.5 Theorem. Let $S = \{\mathbf{x}_1, \ldots, \mathbf{x}_k\}$ be a linearly independent set in a vector space $\mathscr{V}$. If S is not already a basis, either it can be extended to a finite basis for $\mathscr{V}$, or else it can be extended to an infinite sequence of independent vectors, and $\mathscr{V}$ is not finite-dimensional.

Proof. Suppose $\mathbf{x}_1, \ldots, \mathbf{x}_k$ are linearly independent but do not span all of $\mathscr{V}$. Then there is some vector $\mathbf{y}$ that is not a linear combination of $\mathbf{x}_1, \ldots, \mathbf{x}_k$. Take $\mathbf{x}_{k+1} = \mathbf{y}$. We claim that the set $\mathbf{x}_1, \ldots, \mathbf{x}_k, \mathbf{x}_{k+1}$ is linearly independent. Suppose $r_1\mathbf{x}_1 + \ldots + r_{k+1}\mathbf{x}_{k+1} = 0$. We must show that all the r's are 0. If r_{k+1} were not 0, we could write $\mathbf{x}_{k+1} = -(r_1/r_{k+1})\mathbf{x}_1 - \ldots -(r_k/r_{k+1})\mathbf{x}_k$, which is impossible because $\mathbf{x}_{k+1}$ is not a linear combination of the other $\mathbf{x}$'s. Therefore we have $r_{k+1} = 0$ and $r_1\mathbf{x}_1 + \ldots + r_k\mathbf{x}_k = 0$. Since $\mathbf{x}_1, \ldots, \mathbf{x}_k$ are independent, the last equation implies $r_1 = \ldots = r_k = 0$. In other words, if a linearly independent set does not span a space, then a vector can be added to it so that the resulting set is also independent.

This process of adding vectors can be repeated unless a spanning set is reached. If a spanning set is reached, then it is a basis and $\mathscr{V}$ is finite-dimensional. Otherwise an arbitrarily large independent set can be found, and $\mathscr{V}$ cannot be finite-dimensional. This completes the proof of the theorem.

8.6 Theorem. If $\mathscr{S}$ is a subspace of a finite-dimensional space $\mathscr{V}$ with $\dim(\mathscr{V}) = n$, then $\mathscr{S}$ is finite-dimensional and $\dim(\mathscr{S}) \leq n$. Any basis for $\mathscr{S}$ can be extended to a basis for $\mathscr{V}$, and if $\dim(\mathscr{S}) = n$, then $\mathscr{S} = \mathscr{V}$.

Proof. If $\mathscr{S}$ consists of 0 alone it has dimension 0. Otherwise start with a nonzero vector $\mathbf{x}_1$ in $\mathscr{S}$ and apply Theorem 8.5. Since no independent subset of $\mathscr{V}$ can contain more than n elements, the construction must end with a finite basis for $\mathscr{S}$. This basis for $\mathscr{S}$ is a linearly independent subset of $\mathscr{V}$ and can if necessary be extended (Theorem 8.5 again) to a basis for $\mathscr{V}$. Thus we have a basis for $\mathscr{S}$ that is a subset of a basis for $\mathscr{V}$. If dim $(\mathscr{S}) = n$, the subset must be the whole set, so the same set is a basis for both $\mathscr{S}$ and $\mathscr{V}$, and $\mathscr{S} = \mathscr{V}$.

The following theorem states an important property of linear functions:

8.7 Theorem. Let f be a linear function defined on a finite dimensional vector space. Then

$$\text{dim (null space of } f) + \text{dim (range of } f) = \text{dim (domain of } f).$$

Proof. As with any theorem about dimension, the trick to proving this is to find suitable bases for the spaces involved. Let us write $\mathscr{V}$ for the domain of f, $\mathscr{N}$ for its null space, and $\mathscr{W}$ for its range. Let $\mathbf{v}_1, \ldots, \mathbf{v}_k$ be a basis for $\mathscr{N}$, and extend it to a basis $\mathbf{v}_1, \ldots, \mathbf{v}_k, \mathbf{u}_1, \ldots, \mathbf{u}_r$ for $\mathscr{V}$. (Theorem 8.6 guarantees the possibility of this construction.) Then dim $(\mathscr{N}) = k$ and dim $(\mathscr{V}) = k + r$. Let $\mathbf{w}_1 = f(\mathbf{u}_1), \ldots, \mathbf{w}_r = f(\mathbf{u}_r)$. We claim that $\mathbf{w}_1, \ldots, \mathbf{w}_r$ is a basis for $\mathscr{W}$, which implies that dim $(\mathscr{W}) = r$ and proves the theorem. It is obvious that the vectors $\mathbf{w}_1, \ldots, \mathbf{w}_r$ span $\mathscr{W}$, for if $\mathbf{y} = f(\mathbf{x})$ is any vector in the range of f, we may write

$$\mathbf{x} = \sum_{i=1}^{k} a_i \mathbf{v}_i + \sum_{i=1}^{r} b_i \mathbf{u}_i,$$

and then

$$\mathbf{y} = \sum_{i=1}^{k} a_i f(\mathbf{v}_i) + \sum_{i=1}^{r} b_i f(\mathbf{u}_i) = 0 + \sum_{i=1}^{r} b_i \mathbf{w}_i,$$

which shows that $\mathbf{y}$ is a linear combination of the $\mathbf{w}$'s. It remains to be shown that $\mathbf{w}_1, \ldots, \mathbf{w}_r$ are linearly independent. Suppose $\sum_{i=1}^{r} b_i \mathbf{w}_i = 0$. This means that the vector $\sum_{i=1}^{r} b_i \mathbf{u}_i$ is in the null space of f and is therefore equal to some linear combination $\sum_{i=1}^{k} a_i \mathbf{v}_i$, so $a_1 \mathbf{v}_1 + \ldots + a_k \mathbf{v}_k - b_1 \mathbf{u}_1 - \ldots - b_r \mathbf{u}_r = 0$. Since $\mathbf{v}_1, \ldots, \mathbf{v}_k, \mathbf{u}_1, \ldots, \mathbf{u}_r$ are linearly independent, this is possible only if all the b's (and all the a's) are zero, which shows that the $\mathbf{w}$'s are linearly independent.

EXAMPLE 8. Suppose $m \leq n$, and define f from $\mathscr{R}^n$ to $\mathscr{R}^m$ by letting $f(\mathbf{x})$ be the m-dimensional column vector consisting of the first m entries of $\mathbf{x}$. The range of f is all of $\mathscr{R}^m$, and the null space, of dimension $n - m$, consists of the vectors in $\mathscr{R}^n$ whose first m components are all 0.

EXERCISES

1. Which of the following subsets of $\mathscr{R}^3$ are subspaces? In each case either show that the subset is a subspace or find some linear combination of elements of the subset that is not in the subset.

(a) All vectors (x_1, x_2, x_3) with $x_1 + x_2 = 0$.

(b) All vectors with $x_3 = 0$.

(c) All vectors satisfying (a) *and* (b).

(d) All vectors satisfying (a) *or* (b).

(e) All vectors with $x_1 = (x_2)^3$.

(f) All vectors satisfying (a) *and* (e).

2. Let $x_1 = (1, 2, 3)$, $x_2 = (-1, 2, 1)$, $x_3 = (1, 1, 1)$, $x_4 = (1, 1, 0)$.

(a) Show that x_1, x_2, x_3, x_4 is a linearly dependent set by solving an appropriate system of equations.

(b) Express x_1 as a linear combination of x_2, x_3, x_4 by a method similar to that used in part (a).   [*Ans.* $x_1 = \frac{1}{3}x_2 + \frac{8}{3}x_3 - \frac{4}{3}x_4$.]

3. Let $\mathscr{C}[a, b]$ be the vector space of continuous real-valued functions defined on the interval $[a, b]$. Let $\mathscr{C}_0[a, b]$ be the set of functions f in $\mathscr{C}[a, b]$ such that $f(a) = f(b) = 0$.

(a) Show that $\mathscr{C}_0[a, b]$ is a proper subspace of $\mathscr{C}[a, b]$.

(b) What if the condition $f(a) = f(b) = 0$ is replaced by $f(a) = 1$, $f(b) = 0$?

4. Show that the intersection of two subspaces is always a subspace.

5. Part (d) of Exercise 1 shows that the union of two subspaces is not always a subspace. Show that the union of two subspaces is a subspace if and only if one of them is contained in the other.

6. Show that the range of a linear function may be a proper subspace of its range space.

7. Let $\mathscr{R}^n \xrightarrow{f} \mathscr{R}^m$ be the linear function defined by multiplication by the m-by-n matrix A. Show that its range is the span of the columns of A (considered as elements of $\mathscr{R}^m$).

8. For any two subsets $\mathscr{A}$ and $\mathscr{B}$ of a vector space, let $\mathscr{A} + \mathscr{B}$ be the set of all vectors that can be expressed as a sum $A + B$ with A in $\mathscr{A}$ and B in $\mathscr{B}$. Show that if $\mathscr{A}$ and $\mathscr{B}$ are subspaces then so is $\mathscr{A} + \mathscr{B}$.

9. Show that if 0 is the only element in the intersection of two subspaces $\mathscr{S}, \mathscr{T}$, then
$$\dim (\mathscr{S} + \mathscr{T}) = \dim (\mathscr{S}) + \dim (\mathscr{T})$$

[*Hint.* Show that a basis for $\mathscr{S}$ together with a basis for $\mathscr{T}$ gives a basis for $\mathscr{S} + \mathscr{T}$.]

10. Show that for any two subspaces $\mathscr{S}, \mathscr{T}$,
$$\dim (\mathscr{S} + \mathscr{T}) = \dim (\mathscr{S}) + \dim (\mathscr{T}) - \dim (\mathscr{S} \cap \mathscr{T}).$$

[*Hint.* Start with a basis for $\mathscr{S} \cap \mathscr{T}$ and extend it (Theorem 8.6) to a basis for $\mathscr{S}$ and a basis for $\mathscr{T}$.]

11. Let $\mathscr{R}^3 \xrightarrow{f} \mathscr{R}^2$ be defined by the matrix
$$\begin{pmatrix} 1 & -3 & 2 \\ -2 & 6 & -4 \end{pmatrix}.$$

Find a basis for the null space of f, and one for the range of f. Verify that Theorem 8.7 holds.

9. SYSTEMS OF LINEAR EQUATIONS, MATRIX EQUATIONS

A **system of linear equations** is a finite set of equations

$$
\begin{array}{c}
a_{11}x_1 + \ldots + a_{1n}x_n = b_1 \\
\vdots \qquad\qquad \vdots \\
a_{m1}x_1 + \ldots + a_{mn}x_n = b_m
\end{array}
$$

9.1

where the a's and b's are given and the x's are to be determined. The whole system can be written in matrix form as $A\mathbf{x} = \mathbf{b}$, where A is the m-by-n **coefficient matrix** with entries a_{ij}, $\mathbf{b}$ is a column vector in $\mathcal{R}^m$, and $\mathbf{x}$ is a column vector in $\mathcal{R}^n$. Doing the matrix multiplication in the equation

$$
\begin{pmatrix} a_{11} & \cdots & a_{1n} \\ \vdots & & \vdots \\ a_{m1} & \cdots & a_{mn} \end{pmatrix}
\begin{pmatrix} x_1 \\ \vdots \\ x_n \end{pmatrix} =
\begin{pmatrix} b_1 \\ \vdots \\ b_m \end{pmatrix}
$$

shows at once that it is equivalent to the System 9.1.

It frequently happens in applications that there are as many equations as there are unknowns, so that $m = n$. Then, if the determinant of the coefficient matrix is not zero, the solution can be obtained by Cramer's rule of Sec. 6. The methods of the present section do not use determinants, and we make no assumption about m and n.

Any vector $\mathbf{c}$ in $\mathcal{R}^n$ such that $A\mathbf{c} = \mathbf{b}$ is *a* solution of the system. As we shall show, some systems have no solution, some have exactly one, and some have infinitely many solutions.

We say that two systems are **equivalent** if they have exactly the same set of solutions. Our procedure will be to take a given system and alter it in a sequence of steps to obtain an equivalent system for which the solutions are obvious. We illustrate the process with an example before giving a general description.

EXAMPLE 1.

$$
\begin{array}{rcr}
3x + 12y + 9z &=& 3 \\
2x + 5y + 4z &=& 4 \\
-x + 3y + 2z &=& -5.
\end{array}
$$

Multiply the first equation by $\frac{1}{3}$, which makes the coefficient of x equal to 1 and gives

$$
\begin{array}{rcr}
x + 4y + 3z &=& 1 \\
2x + 5y + 4z &=& 4 \\
-x + 3y + 2z &=& -5.
\end{array}
$$

Add (-2) times the first equation to the second, and replace the second equation by the result. This makes the coefficient of x in the second equation equal to 0 and gives

$$x + 4y + 3z = 1$$
$$-3y - 2z = 2$$
$$-x + 3y + 2z = -5.$$

Add the first equation to the third, and replace the third equation by the result, to get

$$x + 4y + 3z = 1$$
$$-3y - 2z = 2$$
$$7y + 5z = -4.$$

Multiply the second equation by $-\frac{1}{3}$, to get

$$x + 4y + 3z = 1$$
$$y + \frac{2}{3}z = -\frac{2}{3}$$
$$7y + 5z = -4.$$

Add (-4) times the second equation to the first, and (-7) times the second equation to the third, to get

$$x + \frac{1}{3}z = \frac{11}{3}$$
$$y + \frac{2}{3}z = -\frac{2}{3}$$
$$\frac{1}{3}z = \frac{2}{3}.$$

Multiply the third equation by 3 to get

$$x + \frac{1}{3}z = \frac{11}{3}$$
$$y + \frac{2}{3}z = -\frac{2}{3}$$
$$z = 2.$$

Add $(-\frac{1}{3})$ times the third equation to the first, and $(-\frac{2}{3})$ times the third equation to the second to get

$$x = 3$$
$$y = -2$$
$$z = 2.$$

Clearly this system has just one solution, namely the column vector

$$\begin{pmatrix} 3 \\ -2 \\ 2 \end{pmatrix}.$$

It is easy to verify by substitution in the original equations that we have found a solution for them. This verification of course does not rule out the theoretical possibility that the original equations might have other solutions as well. In fact the final system is equivalent to the original system and has the same set of solutions. The same is true for any pair of systems where one is obtained from the other by steps such as were used in this example. Before we can prove this we must first state exactly what operations are allowed, and then investigate their properties.

The operations used were "multiplying an equation by a number", and "adding a multiple of one equation to another". We prefer to give the formal definitions in terms of matrices and accordingly consider the general matrix equation $A\mathbf{x} = \mathbf{b}$.

We define three types of **elementary operations** which can be applied to any matrix M:

An **elementary multiplication** replaces a row of M by a numerical multiple of the row, where the multiplier is different from 0.

An **elementary modification** replaces a row of M by the sum of that row and a numerical multiple of some other row.

An **elementary transposition** interchanges two rows of M. We did not use any transpositions in Example 1, but they are sometimes useful.

We claim that the effect of applying an elementary operation to an m-by-n matrix M can be obtained by multiplying it on the left by a suitable m-by-m matrix. A different type of matrix is needed for each type of elementary operation, and we introduce a notation for each one.

Define $D_i(r)$ to be the same as the identity matrix I except for having r in place of 1 in the ith place on the diagonal. $D_i(r)$ is a diagonal matrix and multiplying the ith row of M by r gives $D_i(r)M$ by the result of Problem 7 of Section 3.

Recall the definition of E_{ij} as the matrix (m-by-m in the present case) which is 0 except for a 1 in the ith row, jth column. Then $E_{ij}M$ is zero except in the ith row, which is a copy of the jth row of M. $(I + rE_{ij})M$ is the same as M except in the ith row, which is the sum of the ith row and r times the jth row. In other words, adding r times the jth row of M to the ith row gives $(I + rE_{ij})M$.

Define T_{ij} to be the matrix obtained from I by exchanging the ith and jth rows. We leave it to the reader to verify that exchanging the ith and jth rows of M gives $T_{ij}M$.

Now define an **elementary matrix** as any matrix having one of the following three forms: $D_i(r)$ with $r \neq 0$, or $I + rE_{ij}$ with $i \neq j$, or T_{ij}. Then the preceding remarks demonstrate:

9.2 **Theorem.** The result of applying an elementary operation to a matrix M is equal to PM for some elementary matrix P.

For illustration we repeat the calculation of Example 1 in terms of matrices, and describe the elementary operations in terms of elementary matrices. It should be pointed out that elementary matrices have been introduced to give a compact notation for elementary operations, and to make it easier to discuss their theoretical properties. The practical way to multiply a matrix by an elementary matrix is to carry out the related elementary operation. This involves less work and less chance of error than writing out the elementary matrix and actually doing the multiplication.

EXAMPLE 1 (Matrix Version). We start with the matrix equation

$$\begin{pmatrix} 3 & 12 & 9 \\ 2 & 5 & 4 \\ -1 & 3 & 2 \end{pmatrix} \mathbf{x} = \begin{pmatrix} 3 \\ 4 \\ -5 \end{pmatrix}.$$

Multiply each side on the left by $D_1(\frac{1}{3})$ to obtain

$$\begin{pmatrix} 1 & 4 & 3 \\ 2 & 5 & 4 \\ -1 & 3 & 2 \end{pmatrix} \mathbf{x} = \begin{pmatrix} 1 \\ 4 \\ -5 \end{pmatrix}.$$

Multiply by $I - 2E_{21}$ and then by $I + E_{31}$ to get

$$\begin{pmatrix} 1 & 4 & 3 \\ 0 & -3 & -2 \\ 0 & 7 & 5 \end{pmatrix} \mathbf{x} = \begin{pmatrix} 1 \\ 2 \\ -4 \end{pmatrix}.$$

Multiply by $D_2(-\frac{1}{3})$ to get

$$\begin{pmatrix} 1 & 4 & 3 \\ 0 & 1 & \frac{2}{3} \\ 0 & 7 & 5 \end{pmatrix} \mathbf{x} = \begin{pmatrix} 1 \\ -\frac{2}{3} \\ -4 \end{pmatrix}.$$

Multiply by $I - 4E_{12}$ and then by $I - 7E_{32}$ to get

$$\begin{pmatrix} 1 & 0 & \frac{1}{3} \\ 0 & 1 & \frac{2}{3} \\ 0 & 0 & \frac{1}{3} \end{pmatrix} \mathbf{x} = \begin{pmatrix} \frac{11}{3} \\ -\frac{2}{3} \\ \frac{2}{3} \end{pmatrix}.$$

Multiply by $D_3(3)$ to get

$$\begin{pmatrix} 1 & 0 & \frac{1}{3} \\ 0 & 1 & \frac{2}{3} \\ 0 & 0 & 1 \end{pmatrix} \mathbf{x} = \begin{pmatrix} \frac{11}{3} \\ -\frac{2}{3} \\ 2 \end{pmatrix}.$$

Finally, multiply by $I - \frac{1}{3}E_{13}$ and $I - \frac{2}{3}E_{23}$ to get

$$\begin{pmatrix} 1 & 0 & 0 \\ 0 & 1 & 0 \\ 0 & 0 & 1 \end{pmatrix} \mathbf{x} = I\mathbf{x} = \mathbf{x} = \begin{pmatrix} 3 \\ -2 \\ 2 \end{pmatrix}.$$

The next two theorems lead to the justification for our earlier assertion that elementary operations do not change the set of solutions of a matrix equation.

9.3 Theorem. Let Q be an invertible matrix. Then the matrix equations $Ax = b$ and $(QA)x = Qb$ have the same solutions.

Proof. If c is a solution of the first equation, then $Ac = b$. Therefore $QAc = Qb$, and so c is also a solution of the second equation. (Note that the invertibility of Q is not needed for this half of the argument.) If c is a solution of the second equation, then $QAc = Qb$. Since Q is invertible, this implies $Q^{-1}QAc = Q^{-1}Qb$, or $Ac = b$, so c is also a solution of the first equation.

9.4 Theorem. All elementary matrices are invertible.

Proof. We leave it to the reader to verify that for $r \neq 0$, $D_i(r^{-1})$ is the inverse of $D_i(r)$; that for $i \neq j$, $I - rE_{ij}$ is the inverse of $I + rE_{ij}$; and that T_{ij} is its own inverse.

From Theorem 9.2, the effect of applying a sequence of elementary operations to a matrix is to multiply it by a matrix Q, which is a product of elementary matrices. By Theorems 9.4 and 3.2, Q is invertible, so by Theorem 9.3, applying a sequence of elementary operations to both sides of an equation does not change its set of solutions.

EXAMPLE 2. We now exhibit a system of equations with infinitely many solutions. Consider the matrix equation

$$\begin{pmatrix} 1 & -2 & -3 \\ \frac{1}{2} & -2 & -\frac{13}{2} \\ -3 & 5 & 4 \end{pmatrix} x = \begin{pmatrix} 2 \\ 7 \\ 0 \end{pmatrix}.$$

Multiply by $I - \frac{1}{2}E_{21}$, and then by $I + 3E_{31}$ to produce zeros in the second and third entries of the first column, and obtain

$$\begin{pmatrix} 1 & -2 & -3 \\ 0 & -1 & -5 \\ 0 & -1 & -5 \end{pmatrix} x = \begin{pmatrix} 2 \\ 6 \\ 6 \end{pmatrix}.$$

Multiply by $D_2(-1)$ to obtain

$$\begin{pmatrix} 1 & -2 & -3 \\ 0 & 1 & 5 \\ 0 & -1 & -5 \end{pmatrix} x = \begin{pmatrix} 2 \\ -6 \\ 6 \end{pmatrix}.$$

Multiply by $I + 2E_{12}$ and then by $I + E_{32}$ to obtain

$$\begin{pmatrix} 1 & 0 & 7 \\ 0 & 1 & 5 \\ 0 & 0 & 0 \end{pmatrix} \mathbf{x} = \begin{pmatrix} -10 \\ -6 \\ 0 \end{pmatrix}.$$

At the corresponding stage in Example 1 we performed an elementary multiplication to make the third entry in the third row equal to 1, and were then able to obtain the identity matrix by further elementary operations. Obviously the row of zeros prevents us from following this procedure. Let us put

$\mathbf{x} = \begin{pmatrix} x \\ y \\ z \end{pmatrix}$, and translate the matrix equation back into a system of linear equations. The result is

$$\begin{aligned} x \quad\quad + 7z &= -10 \\ y + 5z &= -6 \\ 0x + 0y + 0z &= 0. \end{aligned}$$

The third equation is satisfied for any values of x, y, z. The first two equations may be rewritten as $x = -10 - 7z$ and $y = -6 - 5z$. Thus for any value of z,

$$\begin{pmatrix} -7z - 10 \\ -5z - 6 \\ z \end{pmatrix} = z \begin{pmatrix} -7 \\ -5 \\ 1 \end{pmatrix} + \begin{pmatrix} -10 \\ -6 \\ 0 \end{pmatrix}$$

is a solution, and every solution has this form for some value of z. We have now described the set of solutions of

$$\begin{pmatrix} 1 & 0 & 7 \\ 0 & 1 & 5 \\ 0 & 0 & 0 \end{pmatrix} \mathbf{x} = \begin{pmatrix} -10 \\ -6 \\ 0 \end{pmatrix},$$

and by Theorem 9.3 we know that this is the same as the set of solutions of the matrix equation we started with.

EXAMPLE 3. Consider the matrix equation

$$\begin{pmatrix} 1 & -2 & -3 \\ \frac{1}{2} & -2 & -\frac{13}{2} \\ -3 & 5 & 4 \end{pmatrix} \mathbf{x} = \begin{pmatrix} 2 \\ 7 \\ 2 \end{pmatrix}.$$

The matrix on the left is the same as the one in Example 2. Carrying out the same sequence of elementary operations yields

$$\begin{pmatrix} 1 & 0 & 7 \\ 0 & 1 & 5 \\ 0 & 0 & 0 \end{pmatrix} \mathbf{x} = \begin{pmatrix} -10 \\ -6 \\ 2 \end{pmatrix}.$$

Whatever $\mathbf{x}$ is, the third row in the product $\begin{pmatrix} 1 & 0 & 7 \\ 0 & 1 & 5 \\ 0 & 0 & 0 \end{pmatrix} \mathbf{x}$ will be zero because the third row of the left factor is zero. Thus no value of $\mathbf{x}$ can give a column vector with 2 in the third row, and we conclude that the equation has *no* solution.

(If we put $\mathbf{x} = \begin{pmatrix} x \\ y \\ z \end{pmatrix}$ and write the matrix equation out as a system of equations, we obtain

$$
\begin{aligned}
x \quad\quad\, + 7z &= -10 \\
y + 5z &= -\ 6 \\
0x + 0y + 0z &= \quad 2.
\end{aligned}
$$

The last equation obviously cannot be satisfied for any values of x, y, z.)

In these examples we used elementary operations to transform the original systems of equations into equivalent systems for which the solutions were easy to find. The property of the final set of equations that made the solutions obvious was that each equation involved a variable that did not appear in any of the other equations. Thus in Example 2 we found $x = -10 - 7z$, $y = -6 - 5z$, and because the first equation involved x but not y, and the second involved y but not x, we could find the values of (x, y, z) satisfying both equations by considering the equations separately. The following definitions express this "noninterference" property in terms of the coefficient matrix.

An entry in a matrix is called a **leading entry** if it is the first nonzero entry in its row. Thus in

$$
\begin{pmatrix} 3 & 0 & 2 & 4 \\ 0 & 0 & 4 & -10 \\ 0 & 0 & 0 & 0 \\ 2 & -2 & 3 & 1 \end{pmatrix},
$$

the leading entries are the first entry in the first row, the third entry in the second row and the first entry in the fourth row. There is no leading entry in the third row since it consists entirely of zeros. We say that a matrix is **reduced** if:

9.5 (a) Every column containing a leading entry is zero except for the leading entry.
　　(b) Every leading entry is 1.

In discussing reduced matrices it is frequently necessary to distinguish the columns that contain leading entries from those that do not. (Of course a row contains a leading entry if and only if it is nonzero.) We shall say that the columns that do contain leading entries are **pivotal**. Each leading entry belongs to one nonzero row and one pivotal column; we shall say that the row and column are **associated**. This gives a one-to-one correspondence between nonzero rows and pivotal columns, and establishes the following fact which will be referred to later.

9.6 In a reduced matrix, the number of pivotal columns equals the number of nonzero rows.

EXAMPLE 4. Consider the matrices

$$A = \begin{pmatrix} 1 & 2 & 0 & 5 \\ 0 & 0 & 1 & -3 \\ 0 & 0 & 0 & 0 \end{pmatrix}, \qquad B = \begin{pmatrix} 0 & 0 & 1 & 0 \\ 1 & 2 & 0 & 0 \\ 0 & 0 & 0 & 1 \end{pmatrix},$$

$$C = \begin{pmatrix} 2 & 4 & 0 & 0 \\ 0 & 0 & 1 & 0 \\ 0 & 0 & 0 & 1 \end{pmatrix}, \qquad D = \begin{pmatrix} 1 & 0 & 3 & 5 \\ 0 & 1 & 0 & -2 \\ 0 & 0 & 0 & 1 \end{pmatrix}.$$

A is reduced; its pivotal columns are the first (associated with the first row) and the third (associated with the second row). B is also reduced; its pivotal columns are the first, third, and fourth, associated with the second, first, and third rows, respectively. The matrix C fails to satisfy condition (b), but multiplying the first row by $\frac{1}{2}$ gives a reduced matrix. D does not satisfy condition (a), but subtracting 5 times the third row from the first, and adding 2 times the third row to the second, gives a reduced matrix.

We now present some theorems on the solutions of systems of equations for which the coefficient matrix is reduced. You will find it helpful to refer back to Examples 2 and 3 when studying the proofs. The first theorem shows how to tell whether an equation has any solutions at all.

9.7 **Theorem.** Suppose A is a reduced matrix. If A has a row of zeros for which the corresponding entry in $\mathbf{b}$ is not zero, then the equation $A\mathbf{x} = \mathbf{b}$ has no solution. Otherwise it has at least one solution.

Proof. If any row of A is zero, then the corresponding entry in $A\mathbf{x}$ will be zero, whatever $\mathbf{x}$ may be. Thus if the corresponding entry in $\mathbf{b}$ is not zero, there can be no solution.

To prove the other half of the theorem, we assume that every zero row of A (if there is any) is matched by a zero entry in $\mathbf{b}$, and show how to write down a vector $\mathbf{x}$ that is a solution. The vector $\mathbf{x}$ must of course have entries $x_1, \ldots, x_n$ corresponding to the n columns of A, while $\mathbf{b}$ has entries $b_1, \ldots, b_m$ corresponding to the m rows of A. If the jth column of A is nonpivotal, set $x_j = 0$. If the jth column of A is pivotal, let i be the number of the associated row, and set $x_j = b_i$. We claim that the vector $\mathbf{x}$ constructed in this way satisfies $A\mathbf{x} = \mathbf{b}$. The ith entry in the product is $\sum_{k=1}^{n} a_{ik} x_k$. We must show that it equals b_i. It is zero if the ith row of A is zero, and by assumption b_i is then also zero. If the ith row is not zero, then $a_{ij} = 1$, where j is the associated pivotal column. By construction, $x_j = b_i$, so $a_{ij} x_j = b_i$. The terms $a_{ik} x_k$ with $k \neq j$ are all zero because $a_{ik} = 0$ if the kth column is pivotal (because A is reduced) and $x_k = 0$ if the kth column is not pivotal (by construction).

EXAMPLE 5. Consider

$$
A = \begin{pmatrix} 0 & 0 & 1 & 5 & 0 \\ 1 & 2 & 0 & 3 & 0 \\ 0 & 0 & 0 & 0 & 0 \\ 0 & 0 & 0 & 0 & 1 \end{pmatrix}, \qquad
\mathbf{b}_1 = \begin{pmatrix} 1 \\ 4 \\ 2 \\ 3 \end{pmatrix}, \qquad
\mathbf{b}_2 = \begin{pmatrix} 1 \\ 4 \\ 0 \\ 3 \end{pmatrix}.
$$

The third row of A is zero, and the third entry of $\mathbf{b}_1$ is not, so according to Theorem 9.7, the equation $A\mathbf{x} = \mathbf{b}_1$ has no solution. On the other hand, the third entry of $\mathbf{b}_2$ is zero. The pivotal columns of A are the first, third, and fifth, with associated rows the second, first, and fourth. The proof of the theorem shows that if we construct

$$
\mathbf{x} = \begin{pmatrix} 4 \\ 0 \\ 1 \\ 0 \\ 3 \end{pmatrix}
$$

by making the first, third, and fifth entries equal to the second, first, and fourth entries of $\mathbf{b}_2$, and making the other rows zero, then $A\mathbf{x}$ will be equal to $\mathbf{b}_2$. This is easily verified by doing the matrix multiplication.

The next problem is how to tell whether an equation that has a solution has more than one. Theorem 9.8 and its corollary show that the question can be reduced to a special case, and Theorem 9.9 deals with this special case.

9.8 Theorem. Suppose $\mathbf{x}_0$ is a solution of $A\mathbf{x} = \mathbf{b}$. Then $\mathbf{x}_1$ is also a solution if and only if $\mathbf{x}_1 - \mathbf{x}_0$ is a solution of $A\mathbf{x} = 0$.

Proof. We have $A(\mathbf{x}_1 - \mathbf{x}_0) = A\mathbf{x}_1 - A\mathbf{x}_0 = \mathbf{b} - \mathbf{b} = 0$. Conversely if $A(\mathbf{x}_1 - \mathbf{x}_0) = 0$ then $A\mathbf{x}_1 = A\mathbf{x}_0 = \mathbf{b}$.

The equation $A\mathbf{x} = 0$ is often called the **homogeneous** equation associated with $A\mathbf{x} = \mathbf{b}$. Observe that the homogeneous equation always has at least one solution, namely $\mathbf{x} = 0$. From 9.8 we immediately obtain the

Corollary. Suppose $A\mathbf{x} = \mathbf{b}$ has at *least* one solution. Then it has *exactly* one solution if and only if $\mathbf{x} = 0$ is the only solution of the associated homogeneous equation.

9.9 Theorem. Suppose A is reduced. If every column of A is pivotal, then $\mathbf{x} = 0$ is the only solution of the homogeneous equation $A\mathbf{x} = 0$. Otherwise the equation has solutions with $\mathbf{x} \neq 0$.

Proof. Suppose every column of A is pivotal. Let i be the number of the row associated with column j. Then $a_{ij} = 1$ and $a_{ik} = 0$ for $k \neq j$ (because A is reduced and all columns are pivotal). Thus the ith entry in $A\mathbf{x}$ is $\sum_{k=1}^{n} a_{ik}x_k = x_j$, so if $A\mathbf{x} = 0$, $x_j = 0$ for all j.

Conversely, if r is the number of a nonpivotal column, we can construct a nonzero solution of $A\mathbf{x} = 0$ as follows. Take $x_r = 1$, (which guarantees $\mathbf{x} \neq 0$) and take $x_j = 0$ if j is the number of any other nonpivotal column of A. If the jth column is pivotal, take $x_j = -a_{ir}$, where i is the number of the row associated with column j. As in the proof of Theorem 9.8, we look at the product $A\mathbf{x}$ a row at a time. Zero rows of A, of course, give zero entries in the product. If the ith row of A is nonzero we get the sum $\sum_{k=1}^{n} a_{ik}x_k$. If k is the number of any pivotal column except the jth (where column j is associated with row i), we have $a_{ik} = 0$. If it is the number of any nonpivotal column except the rth, we have $x_k = 0$. Thus the sum reduces to $a_{ij}x_j + a_{ir}x_r = 1 \cdot (-a_{ir}) + a_{ir} \cdot 1 = 0$, as required.

EXAMPLE 6. Consider the homogeneous equation $A\mathbf{x} = 0$, where A is the matrix of Example 5. The second and fourth columns of A are nonpivotal. The construction given in the proof of Theorem 9.9 can thus be applied to give a solution with $x_2 = 1$, $x_4 = 0$, and one with $x_4 = 1$, $x_2 = 0$. The vectors obtained are

$$\mathbf{y} = \begin{pmatrix} -2 \\ 1 \\ 0 \\ 0 \\ 0 \end{pmatrix} \quad \text{and} \quad \mathbf{z} = \begin{pmatrix} -3 \\ 0 \\ -5 \\ 1 \\ 0 \end{pmatrix}.$$

Any combination $r\mathbf{y} + s\mathbf{z}$ is also a solution. (Why?) Using Theorem 9.8

to combine this information with the result of Example 5, we see that all vectors of the form

$$\begin{pmatrix} 4 \\ 0 \\ 1 \\ 0 \\ 3 \end{pmatrix} + r \begin{pmatrix} -2 \\ 1 \\ 0 \\ 0 \\ 0 \end{pmatrix} + s \begin{pmatrix} -3 \\ 0 \\ -5 \\ 1 \\ 0 \end{pmatrix}$$

are solutions of

$$\begin{pmatrix} 0 & 0 & 1 & 5 & 0 \\ 1 & 2 & 0 & 3 & 0 \\ 0 & 0 & 0 & 0 & 0 \\ 0 & 0 & 0 & 0 & 1 \end{pmatrix} \mathbf{x} = \begin{pmatrix} 1 \\ 4 \\ 0 \\ 3 \end{pmatrix}.$$

That we have in fact found all the solutions will follow from Theorems 9.8 and 9.14. This can also be verified directly by the sort of argument used in Example 2.

We have answered most of the questions about solutions of linear systems that have a reduced coefficient matrix. If we can convert any given system into a reduced one by elementary operations, then we have a general method of finding solutions of linear systems. The first three examples of this section illustrate a reduction process that can in fact be applied successfully to any matrix.

Suppose a matrix is not reduced. Then there must be some column containing a leading entry such that either 9.5(a) or 9.5(b) (or both) is violated. If the column contains the leading entry r for the ith row, multiplying the ith row by r^{-1} will make the leading entry 1. (Since r was a leading entry, it could not be zero. Of course it might be 1 to begin with, and the multiplication would be unnecessary.) If any other entries in the column are nonzero, they can be made zero by adding suitable multiples of the ith row to the rows they are in. Any column that was "correct" before these operations must have a zero for its ith entry, and therefore is unaltered by them. We have just described a process that can be applied to any unreduced matrix and that increases the number of columns that satisfy the Conditions 9.5. If the resulting matrix is not reduced, the process can be repeated. A reduced matrix will be obtained within at most n steps, where n is the number of columns in the matrix. We have proved

9.10 **Theorem.** Given any matrix A, a sequence of elementary operations can be found which convert A to a reduced matrix.

EXAMPLE 7. We shall apply the method given in the proof of Theorem 9.10 to reduce the matrix

$$A = \begin{pmatrix} 1 & 3 & -2 & 0 \\ 2 & 6 & 0 & -1 \\ -1 & -3 & 4 & 1 \end{pmatrix}.$$

Column 1 does not satisfy 9.5(a), but has a leading entry of 1 in the first row, so no elementary multiplication is necessary. Multiplying by $I - 2E_{21}$ and $I + E_{31}$ (i.e., subtracting 2 times row 1 from row 2, and adding row 1 to row 3), clears the other two entries to zero and gives

$$A_2 = \begin{pmatrix} 1 & 3 & -2 & 0 \\ 0 & 0 & 4 & -1 \\ 0 & 0 & 2 & 1 \end{pmatrix}.$$

Column 2 does not contain a leading entry. The 4 in column 3 can be converted to a 1 by multiplying by $D_2(\frac{1}{4})$, which gives

$$A_3 = \begin{pmatrix} 1 & 3 & -2 & 0 \\ 0 & 0 & 1 & -\frac{1}{4} \\ 0 & 0 & 2 & 1 \end{pmatrix}.$$

Multiplying by $I + 2E_{12}$ and $I - 2E_{32}$ clears out the other entries in column 3 and gives

$$A_4 = \begin{pmatrix} 1 & 3 & 0 & -\frac{1}{2} \\ 0 & 0 & 1 & -\frac{1}{4} \\ 0 & 0 & 0 & \frac{3}{2} \end{pmatrix}.$$

Multiplying by $D_3(\frac{2}{3})$ changes the last entry to 1 and then applying $I + 1/2E_{13}$ and $I + 1/4E_{23}$ gives the reduced matrix

$$\begin{pmatrix} 1 & 3 & 0 & 0 \\ 0 & 0 & 1 & 0 \\ 0 & 0 & 0 & 1 \end{pmatrix}$$

as the final result.

In working this example we stuck to the standard procedure given in the proof of 9.10. This of course is not the only sequence of steps that will give a reduced matrix, and a different sequence may require less arithmetic. For instance, multiplying A_2 by $I + E_{13}$ and $I - 2E_{23}$ gives

$$\begin{pmatrix} 1 & 3 & 0 & 1 \\ 0 & 0 & 0 & -3 \\ 0 & 0 & 2 & 1 \end{pmatrix},$$

and then multiplying by $I + 1/3E_{12}$ and $I + 1/3E_{32}$ gives

$$\begin{pmatrix} 1 & 3 & 0 & 0 \\ 0 & 0 & 0 & -3 \\ 0 & 0 & 2 & 0 \end{pmatrix}.$$

Finally, multiplication by $D_2(-\frac{1}{3})$ and $D_3(\frac{1}{2})$ gives the reduced matrix

$$\begin{pmatrix} 1 & 3 & 0 & 0 \\ 0 & 0 & 0 & 1 \\ 0 & 0 & 1 & 0 \end{pmatrix}.$$

We now turn to the special case of systems of n equations in n unknowns, that is, systems with square coefficient matrices. The following theorem is the one most important in applications:

9.11 **Theorem.** If A is a square matrix and the only solution of the homogeneous equation $Ax = 0$ is $x = 0$, then the equation $Ax = b$ has exactly one solution for every vector b.

Proof. Consider the linear function f from $\mathscr{R}^n$ to $\mathscr{R}^n$ given by multiplication by A. Since $Ax = 0$ only if $x = 0$, the null space of f has dimension 0. By Theorem 8.7, the range of f has dimension n and is therefore (by Theorem 8.6) all of $\mathscr{R}^n$. Therefore, $Ax = b$ has a solution, which is unique by the corollary of Theorem 9.8.

We can now give a criterion for whether or not a square matrix is invertible. If there is an $x \neq 0$ with $Ax = 0$, A cannot have an inverse, since then $Ax = 0$ would imply $A^{-1}Ax = A^{-1}0$, i.e., $x = 0$, which would be a contradiction. Otherwise A can be converted to a reduced matrix C, all of whose columns are pivotal. Every column of C then contains one 1 and has all other entries 0, and the 1's in different columns belong to different rows. Appropriately changing the order of the rows (which can be done by elementary transpositions) will give the identity matrix. Thus A can be converted to I by elementary operations. By Theorem 9.2, $I = QA$, where Q is a product of elementary matrices and therefore invertible. Multiplying by Q^{-1} gives $Q^{-1} = Q^{-1}I = Q^{-1}QA = A$, so $A = Q^{-1}$ and $AQ = QA = I$. Therefore $Q = A^{-1}$ and A is invertible. Note that $Q^{-1} = A$ is also a product of elementary matrices. Thus we have proved:

9.12. **Theorem.** Any invertible matrix is equal to a product of elementary matrices.

The sequence of elementary operations that converts A to QA above will convert I to Q. We thus arrive at the following method for computing inverses:

9.13 **Theorem.** Let A be a square matrix. Apply a sequence of elementary operations simultaneously to A and I, so as to put A in reduced form. If the reduced matrix has a zero row, A is not invertible. Otherwise reorder rows (if necessary) to produce the identity matrix. The matrix obtained by performing the operations on I will be A^{-1}.

EXAMPLE 8. We shall find the inverse of

$$A = \begin{pmatrix} 2 & 4 & 8 \\ 1 & 0 & 0 \\ 1 & -3 & -7 \end{pmatrix}.$$

We start with

$$\begin{pmatrix} 2 & 4 & 8 \\ 1 & 0 & 0 \\ 1 & -3 & -7 \end{pmatrix}; \qquad \begin{pmatrix} 1 & 0 & 0 \\ 0 & 1 & 0 \\ 0 & 0 & 1 \end{pmatrix}.$$

Apply $I - 2E_{12}$ and $I - E_{32}$ to get

$$\begin{pmatrix} 0 & 4 & 8 \\ 1 & 0 & 0 \\ 0 & -3 & -7 \end{pmatrix}; \qquad \begin{pmatrix} 1 & -2 & 0 \\ 0 & 1 & 0 \\ 0 & -1 & 1 \end{pmatrix}.$$

Apply $D_1(\frac{1}{4})$ and then $I + 3E_{31}$ to get

$$\begin{pmatrix} 0 & 1 & 2 \\ 1 & 0 & 0 \\ 0 & 0 & -1 \end{pmatrix}; \qquad \begin{pmatrix} \frac{1}{4} & -\frac{1}{2} & 0 \\ 0 & 1 & 0 \\ \frac{3}{4} & -\frac{5}{2} & 1 \end{pmatrix}.$$

Apply $D_3(-1)$ and then $I - 2E_{13}$ to get

$$\begin{pmatrix} 0 & 1 & 0 \\ 1 & 0 & 0 \\ 0 & 0 & 1 \end{pmatrix}; \qquad \begin{pmatrix} \frac{7}{4} & -\frac{11}{2} & 2 \\ 0 & 1 & 0 \\ -\frac{3}{4} & \frac{5}{2} & -1 \end{pmatrix}.$$

Apply T_{12} to get

$$\begin{pmatrix} 1 & 0 & 0 \\ 0 & 1 & 0 \\ 0 & 0 & 1 \end{pmatrix}; \qquad \begin{pmatrix} 0 & 1 & 0 \\ \frac{7}{4} & -\frac{11}{2} & 2 \\ -\frac{3}{4} & \frac{5}{2} & -1 \end{pmatrix}.$$

The last matrix on the right is A^{-1}, as may be verified by multiplying by A.

Linear subspaces all contain the zero vector, i.e., they correspond to lines, planes, etc., that pass through the origin. A line or plane that does not pass through the origin can be obtained from one that does by a translation (recall the definition from Section 4). We define a subset $\mathscr{S}$ of a vector space $\mathscr{V}$ to be an **affine subspace** if $\mathscr{S} = t_{\mathbf{b}}(\mathscr{U})$, where $\mathscr{U}$ is a linear subspace and $t_{\mathbf{b}}$ is the translation corresponding to some vector $\mathbf{b}$. The dimension of an affine subspace is defined as the dimension of the associated linear subspace.

EXAMPLE 9. In $\mathscr{R}^2$ the graph $\mathscr{W}$ of the equation $2x + y = 3$ is an affine subspace. The homogeneous equation $2x + y = 0$ has as its graph the sub-

space $\mathscr{U}$ spanned by $\begin{pmatrix} -1 \\ 2 \end{pmatrix}$. Since $\begin{pmatrix} 1 \\ 1 \end{pmatrix}$ is in $\mathscr{W}$, $\mathscr{W} = t_\mathbf{b}(\mathscr{U})$, where $\mathbf{b} = \begin{pmatrix} 1 \\ 1 \end{pmatrix}$.
Note that $\mathbf{b}$ could equally well be taken as any other element of $\mathscr{W}$, such as $\begin{pmatrix} 0 \\ 3 \end{pmatrix}$. The difference between any two $\mathbf{b}$'s would have to lie in $\mathscr{U}$.

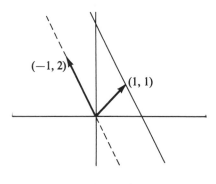

Figure 25

We left the discussion of the set of *all* solutions of a general linear system unfinished. The results can be expressed concisely in terms of subspaces. We consider homogenous equations first, and suppose that the coefficient matrix has already been put in reduced form.

9.14 **Theorem.** Suppose A is a reduced m-by-n matrix, and has p nonpivotal columns. Let $\mathbf{x}_1, \ldots, \mathbf{x}_p$ be the solutions of $A\mathbf{x} = 0$ constructed as in the proof of Theorem 9.9 so that $\mathbf{x}_j$ has 1 in the position corresponding to the jth nonpivotal column and 0 in the positions corresponding to the other nonpivotal columns. The vectors $\mathbf{x}_1, \ldots, \mathbf{x}_p$ form a basis for the solution set, which is a subspace of $\mathscr{R}^n$ of dimension p.

Proof. The proof of Theorem 9.9 showed that the vectors $\mathbf{x}_j$ are in the solution set, and any linear combination of the $\mathbf{x}_j$ is also a solution. It remains to be shown that every solution is a linear combination of the $\mathbf{x}_j$ and that the $\mathbf{x}_j$ are linearly independent.

Suppose $\mathbf{z}$ is a solution, so $A\mathbf{z} = 0$, and that it has entries $r_1, \ldots, r_p$ in the positions corresponding to the nonpivotal columns of A. Let $\mathbf{y} = r_1\mathbf{x}_1 + \ldots + r_p\mathbf{x}_p$, and consider the difference $\mathbf{w} = \mathbf{z} - \mathbf{y}$. It has 0 in all positions corresponding to nonpivotal columns of A, and also satisfies $A\mathbf{w} = 0$. We shall show that $\mathbf{w}$ must be 0, which implies that $\mathbf{z} = \mathbf{y}$ and therefore is a linear combination of the $\mathbf{x}$'s.

If $\mathbf{w}$ is not 0, it must have a nonzero entry in a position corresponding to some pivotal column of A. Let the column be the jth, and let i be the number of the associated row. The ith entry in $A\mathbf{w}$ (which we know is 0) is equal to $\sum_{k=1}^{n} a_{ik}w_k$. If column k is pivotal, $a_{ik} = 0$, unless $k = j$, while if column k is nonpivotal, $w_k = 0$ by construction. Thus the sum reduces to $a_{ij}w_j = w_j$, and we arrive at the contradiction $w_j = 0$. Hence $\mathbf{w}$ is 0 as was to be proved.

Any linear combination $r_1\mathbf{x}_1 + \ldots + r_p\mathbf{x}_p$ will have r_j in the position corresponding to the jth nonpivotal column of A. Hence if

$r_1 x_1 + \ldots + r_p x_p$ is 0, all the r_j must be 0, that is, the x's are linearly independent.

The solution sets of inhomogeneous equations are of course handled using Theorem 9.8. If x_0 is any solution of $Ax = b$, and $\mathcal{U}$ is the subspace of solutions of $Ax = 0$, then the solutions of $Ax = b$ are just those vectors $x_0 + u$ for u in $\mathcal{U}$, so the solution set is the affine subspace $t_{x_0}(\mathcal{U})$.

We can construct geometric interpretations for systems of equations in two and three variables. The reader is probably familiar with the 2-dimensional picture, and we leave its description in terms of linear and affine subspaces as an exercise.

With 3 unknowns the situation can be more complicated. A single equation has the form $A_1 x = b_1$, where A_1 is a row vector and b_1 a number. The row A_1 is reduced if its leading entry is a 1, which can always be arranged (except for the irrelevant case that $A_1 = 0$). Then A_1 has two nonpivotal columns, and Theorem 9.14 implies that the solution set is 2-dimensional, as we should expect. If we have a system of three equations, its solution set is the intersection of the solution sets of the three individual equations. The usual situation is that the three planes intersect in one point. Changing the right side of the equations shifts the planes parallel to themselves, and in this case they will always intersect in just one point. Another possibility is for all three planes to be parallel. The associated homogeneous system will have a two-dimensional solution set; the inhomogeneous system will have also, if the three planes happen to coincide. Otherwise there will be no solution. Another possibility (which has no analogue in two dimensions) is that no two of the planes are parallel, but that the planes representing the solutions of the *homogeneous* equations all pass through one line. Then (unless they all pass through one line) each pair of the planes representing the solution of the *in*homogeneous equations will intersect in a line parallel to the third plane, and there will be no common solution for all three equations.

EXERCISES

1. Determine which of the following matrices are reduced. For those that are not, state exactly how they violate the conditions. For those that are reduced, list the pivotal columns and their associated rows.

$$A = \begin{pmatrix} 1 & -1 & 0 & 1 \\ 0 & 0 & 1 & 2 \\ 0 & 0 & 0 & 0 \end{pmatrix} \qquad B = \begin{pmatrix} 1 & 0 & 1 \\ 0 & 1 & 0 \\ 1 & 0 & 0 \end{pmatrix}$$

$$C = \begin{pmatrix} 1 & 3 & 0 & 5 \\ 0 & 0 & 2 & 4 \\ 0 & 0 & 0 & 0 \end{pmatrix} \qquad D = \begin{pmatrix} 1 & 2 & 0 \\ 0 & 0 & 0 \\ 0 & 0 & 1 \end{pmatrix}.$$

2. For each matrix of Problem 1 which is not already reduced, find an elementary operation which changes it to a reduced matrix.

3. Let

$$\mathbf{r} = \begin{pmatrix} 0 \\ 1 \\ 2 \end{pmatrix}, \qquad \mathbf{s} = \begin{pmatrix} 2 \\ 0 \\ 1 \end{pmatrix}, \qquad \mathbf{t} = \begin{pmatrix} 1 \\ 2 \\ 0 \end{pmatrix}.$$

For each of the equations $A\mathbf{x} = \mathbf{r}$, $A\mathbf{x} = \mathbf{s}$, $A\mathbf{x} = \mathbf{t}$, where A is the matrix of Problem 1, determine whether the equation has no solutions, exactly one solution, or more than one solution. If there is one solution, give it; if there is more than one, give two different solutions.

4. Repeat Problem 3, using the matrices B, C, and D instead of A from Problem 1. (Remember to get the coefficient matrix in reduced form.)

5. Show that if a square n-by-n matrix is reduced and has no all-zero row, then every row and column contains $n - 1$ zeros and one 1. Hence show that it can be converted to an identity matrix by elementary transpositions.

6. Determine the solution sets of the following systems of equations.

(a) $\begin{pmatrix} 1 & 2 & 3 \\ 4 & 5 & 6 \\ 7 & 8 & 9 \end{pmatrix} \mathbf{x} = \begin{pmatrix} 10 \\ 11 \\ 12 \end{pmatrix}$

$\qquad\qquad\qquad$ [*Ans.* $r(1, -2, 1) + (0, -9, \frac{28}{3})$].

(b) $\quad x_1 + x_2 = 1$

$\qquad x_2 + x_3 = 2$

$\qquad x_3 + x_4 = 3$

$\qquad x_4 + x_1 = 4$

(c) $\begin{pmatrix} 1 & 1 & 1 \\ -1 & 2 & -4 \\ 1 & 3 & 9 \end{pmatrix} \mathbf{x} = \begin{pmatrix} 0 & 2 \\ 6 & 2 \\ 0 & 0 \end{pmatrix}$

(d) $\quad x_1 + 2x_2 + \ x_3 - \ x_4 = 1$

$\qquad\qquad x_2 - \ x_3 + \ x_4 = 0$

$\quad x_1 \qquad\quad + 3x_3 - 3x_4 = 3$

(e) $\quad x_1 + 2x_2 + \ x_3 - \ x_4 = 1$

$\qquad\qquad x_2 - \ x_3 + \ x_4 = 0$

$\quad x_1 \qquad\quad + 3x_3 - 3x_4 = 1$

7. For each of the following matrices A, find A^{-1} if A is invertible, and find a nonzero solution of $A\mathbf{x} = 0$ if A is not invertible.

(a) $\begin{pmatrix} 1 & 0 & 0 \\ 3 & 1 & 5 \\ -2 & 0 & 1 \end{pmatrix}$
$\qquad\qquad$ $\left[Ans. \begin{pmatrix} 1 & 0 & 0 \\ -13 & 1 & -5 \\ 2 & 0 & 1 \end{pmatrix}. \right]$

(b) $\begin{pmatrix} 1 & 2 & 3 \\ -1 & 1 & 0 \\ 0 & 3 & 3 \end{pmatrix}$

(c) $\begin{pmatrix} 4 & -1 & 0 & 0 \\ 0 & 5 & -2 & 0 \\ 0 & 0 & 6 & -3 \\ 0 & 0 & 0 & 7 \end{pmatrix}$

(d) $\begin{pmatrix} 1 & 1 & 2 & 3 \\ 0 & 5 & 4 & 2 \\ -1 & -3 & 1 & 0 \\ 0 & 3 & 7 & 5 \end{pmatrix}$

8. Prove that if there are more unknowns than there are equations in a linear system, then the system has either no solutions or infinitely many.

9. Suppose A is a square matrix. Prove that A is invertible if and only if every matrix equation $A\mathbf{x} = \mathbf{b}$ has *at least* one solution.

10. Let $p(x) = a_0 + a_1 x + \ldots + a_n x^n$ be a polynomial of degree $\leq n$. It is a well-known theorem of algebra that if there are more than n values of x which make $p(x) = 0$, then all of its coefficients are zero. Use this theorem to show that if $x_0, \ldots, x_n$ are any $n + 1$ different numbers, and $b_0, \ldots, b_n$ are any $n + 1$ numbers, then there is exactly one polynomial of degree $\leq n$ such that $p(x_0) = b_0, \ldots, p(x_n) = b_n$. [*Hint.* Show that the problem leads to a system of linear equations with $a_0, \ldots, a_n$ as unknowns.]

11. A reduced matrix in which the first pivotal column (starting from the left) is associated with the first row, the second pivotal column is associated with the second row, etc., is said to be in **echelon form**. Show that

    (a) Any reduced matrix can be put in echelon form by a sequence of elementary transpositions.

    (b) If a matrix is in echelon form, then the zero rows (if there are any) come last.

    (c) A square matrix in echelon form is either an identity matrix or has at least one zero row.

12. If A is in echelon form, P is an elementary matrix, and PA is also in echelon form, then show that $A = PA$.

13. Describe the solution sets for the equations of Problems 6(a) and 6(e) as affine subspaces, that is, as translates by a specified vector of linear subspaces with specified bases.

14. For each of the following sets of three equations in three unknowns, determine which of the geometric possibilities discussed at the end of this section hold.

(a) $x + 2y - 3z = 2$
       $3x + 6y - 9z = 0$
       $-2x - 4y + 6z = 3$

(b) $x + y - z = 1$
       $-x + y + z = 3$
       $x - y + z = 5$

(c) $x - y + z = 0$
       $-x + 2y - 3z = 2$
       $2x - y \qquad = 6$

15. Show that if $\mathscr{V} \xrightarrow{f} \mathscr{W}$ is an affine function and $\mathscr{U}$ an affine subspace of $\mathscr{V}$, then the image $f(\mathscr{U})$ is an affine subspace of $\mathscr{W}$.

10. COORDINATES

In this section we show how any problem about finite-dimensional vector spaces and linear functions on them can be reduced to an equivalent problem about $\mathscr{R}^n$ and matrices. This is done by introducing coordinates in the vector spaces. The familiar coordinates of 2-and-3 dimensional geometry may be considered a special case of what we are about to describe. The following theorem is fundamental.

10.1 Theorem. Let $V = (\mathbf{v}_1, \ldots, \mathbf{v}_n)$ be a basis for a vector space $\mathscr{V}$, so $\dim(\mathscr{V}) = n$. For any vector $\mathbf{x}$ in $\mathscr{V}$ there is one and only one n-tuple of numbers $r_1, \ldots, r_n$ such that $\mathbf{x} = r_1 \mathbf{v}_1 + \ldots + r_n \mathbf{v}_n$.

Proof. Since the v's span $\mathscr{V}$, $\mathbf{x}$ is a linear combination of them, so there is at least one n-tuple $(r_1, \ldots, r_n)$ satisfying the condition. If $(s_1, \ldots, s_n)$ is any other n-tuple such that $s_1 \mathbf{v}_1 + \ldots + s_n \mathbf{v}_n = \mathbf{x} = r_1 \mathbf{v}_1 + \ldots + r_n \mathbf{v}_n$, then $(r_1 - s_1) \mathbf{v}_1 + \ldots + (r_n - s_n) \mathbf{v}_n = 0$. Since the v's are independent, the numbers $r_i - s_i$ must all be zero, and so $(s_1, \ldots, s_n)$ is the same as $(r_1, \ldots, r_n)$.

Let $V = (\mathbf{v}_1, \ldots, \mathbf{v}_n)$ be a basis for a vector space $\mathscr{V}$, and let $\mathbf{x}$ be a vector in $\mathscr{V}$. The unique n-tuple $(r_1, \ldots, r_n)$ such that $\mathbf{x} = r_1 \mathbf{v}_1 + \ldots + r_n \mathbf{v}_n$ is the n-tuple of **coordinates of x with respect to the basis** V. The vector in $\mathscr{R}^n$ with entries $r_1, \ldots, r_n$ is the **coordinate vector** of $\mathbf{x}$ with respect to the basis.

EXAMPLE 1.

(a) The vectors $\mathbf{v}_1 = (-1, 1, 0)$, $\mathbf{v}_2 = (0, -1, 1)$ form a basis for the subspace $\mathscr{V}$ of $\mathscr{R}^3$ consisting of all vectors the sum of whose entries is 0. The vector $\mathbf{x} = (1, -3, 2)$ is in $\mathscr{V}$. An easy calculation shows that $\mathbf{x} = -\mathbf{v}_1 + 2\mathbf{v}_2$, so the coordinates of $\mathbf{x}$ with respect to the basis $\mathbf{v}_1, \mathbf{v}_2$ are $(-1, 2)$.

(b) In the plane, let $\mathbf{v}_1$ be the vector of unit length along the horizontal axis, and $\mathbf{v}_2$ the vector of unit length at an angle $60°$ counterclockwise from $\mathbf{v}_1$. Let $\mathbf{x}$ be the vector of unit length 60° beyond $\mathbf{v}_2$.

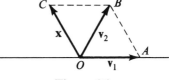

By geometry, CB is parallel to OA and OC is parallel to AB(Why?), so $OABC$ is a parallelogram and $\mathbf{v}_2 = \mathbf{x} + \mathbf{v}_1$. Hence $\mathbf{x} = -\mathbf{v}_1 + \mathbf{v}_2$ and the coordinates of $\mathbf{x}$ with respect to this basis are $(-1, 1)$.

Figure 26

Coordinates provide a way of representing vectors in a concrete form suitable for calculations. They also provide a concrete way of representing linear functions. The key point is that if the value of a linear function is known for each vector of a basis, then the function is known completely. This follows from the fact that any vector $\mathbf{x}$ can be expressed as a linear combination $r_1\mathbf{v}_1 + \ldots + r_n\mathbf{v}_n$ of the vectors in a basis. Then $f(\mathbf{x})$ is the combination $r_1 f(\mathbf{v}_1) + \ldots + r_n f(\mathbf{v}_n)$ of the vectors $f(\mathbf{v}_i)$ with the same coefficients, because f is linear. Suppose $\mathscr{V} \xrightarrow{f} \mathscr{W}$ is a given linear function, and that $V = (\mathbf{v}_1, \ldots, \mathbf{v}_n)$, $W = (\mathbf{w}_1, \ldots, \mathbf{w}_m)$ are bases in $\mathscr{V}$ and $\mathscr{W}$ respectively. The possibility that $\mathscr{V}$ and $\mathscr{W}$ are the same space is not ruled out. The **matrix of f with respect to the bases V and W** is defined to be the m-by-n matrix whose jth column is the coordinate vector of $f(\mathbf{v}_j)$ with respect to the basis W. The matrix of a linear function contains all the information needed to evaluate $f(\mathbf{x})$ for any $\mathbf{x}$. We remark that when $\mathscr{V}$ and $\mathscr{W}$ are the same space it is usually appropriate, though not logically necessary, to take V and W to be the same bases. We do this in all the examples for which $\mathscr{V}$ is the same as $\mathscr{W}$.

EXAMPLE 2.

(a) If f is the linear function from $\mathscr{R}^n$ to $\mathscr{R}^m$ given by multiplication by a matrix A, then the matrix of f with respect to the natural bases in $\mathscr{R}^n$ and $\mathscr{R}^m$ is A itself. This is just a rephrasing of Theorem 4.2.
(b) The function f from $\mathscr{R}^3$ to $\mathscr{R}^3$ defined by

$$f\begin{pmatrix} x_1 \\ x_2 \\ x_3 \end{pmatrix} = \begin{pmatrix} x_2 \\ x_3 \\ x_1 \end{pmatrix}$$

takes the subspace $\mathscr{V}$ spanned by $\mathbf{v}_1 = \begin{pmatrix} -1 \\ 1 \\ 0 \end{pmatrix}$, $\mathbf{v}_2 = \begin{pmatrix} 0 \\ -1 \\ 1 \end{pmatrix}$ into itself, and may

be considered as a linear function from $\mathscr{V}$ to $\mathscr{V}$. We have

$$f(\mathbf{v}_1) = \begin{pmatrix} 1 \\ 0 \\ -1 \end{pmatrix} = -1\mathbf{v}_1 - 1\mathbf{v}_2$$

and $f(v_2) = 1v_1 + 0v_2$, so the matrix of f with respect to the basis V is

$$\begin{pmatrix} -1 & 1 \\ -1 & 0 \end{pmatrix}.$$

(c) Let v_1, v_2 be the basis in $\mathscr{R}^2$ taken in Example 1(b), and let f be a rotation of 60° counterclockwise. Then $f(v_1) = v_2$ and $f(v_2)$, the vector x in Figure 1, is equal to $-v_1 + v_2$. The matrix of f with respect to the basis v is therefore

$$\begin{pmatrix} 0 & -1 \\ 1 & 1 \end{pmatrix}.$$

(d) Let $\mathscr{P}_2$ be the vector space of quadratic polynomials, and let $\mathscr{W}$ be $\mathscr{R}^4$. Define $f(p)$, for p a polynomial in $\mathscr{P}_2$, to be the vector in $\mathscr{R}^4$ with entries $p(1), p(-1), p(2), p(3)$. Take the polynomials $1, x, x^2$ as a basis for $\mathscr{P}_2$ and the natural basis as basis for $\mathscr{R}^4$. Then f takes the polynomial 1 into the 4-tuple $(1, 1, 1, 1)$; it takes the polynomial x into the 4-tuple $(1, -1, 2, 3)$; and it takes x^2 into $(1, 1, 4, 9)$. Its matrix with respect to the given bases is therefore

$$\begin{pmatrix} 1 & 1 & 1 \\ 1 & -1 & 1 \\ 1 & 2 & 4 \\ 1 & 3 & 9 \end{pmatrix}.$$

Given a basis $V = (v_1, \ldots, v_n)$ for $\mathscr{V}$ we may define a function c_V from $\mathscr{V}$ to $\mathscr{R}^n$ by setting $c_V(x)$ equal to the coordinate vector of x with respect to V for every x in $\mathscr{V}$. The function c_V is called the **coordinate map for the basis** V. The range of c_V is obviously all of $\mathscr{R}^n$, because for any n-tuple $r_1, \ldots, r_n$, we can take $x = r_1v_1 + \ldots + r_nv_n$; then $c_V(x)$ is the given n-tuple. By Theorem 10.1, c_V is one-to-one. Therefore there is an inverse function c_V^{-1} from $\mathscr{R}^n$ to $\mathscr{V}$. It is easily seen to be given by the formula $c_V^{-1}(r_1, \ldots, r_n) = r_1v_1 + \ldots + r_nv_n$. An obvious but important fact is:

10.2 Theorem. Coordinate maps and their inverses are linear functions.

Proof. To show that c_V is linear we must verify that $c_V(rx + sy) = rc_V(x) + sc_V(y)$. This follows at once from the fact that if $x = \sum_{i=1}^{n} a_iv_i$, and $y = \sum_{i=1}^{n} b_iv_i$, then $rx + sy = \sum_{i=1}^{n} (ra_i + sb_i)v_i$. The linearity of c_V^{-1} is an immediate consequence of the same equation.

Note that if $\mathscr{V} = \mathscr{R}^n$, the coordinate map c for the natural basis is the identity function $c(x) = x$.

A linear function $\mathscr{V} \xrightarrow{f} \mathscr{W}$, which is one-to-one and whose range is all of $\mathscr{W}$, is called an **isomorphism**, and two spaces such that there exists an isomorphism between them are said to be **isomorphic**. We have shown that coordinate maps are isomorphisms, which proves:

10.3 Theorem. Every n-dimensional vector space is isomorphic to $\mathscr{R}^n$.

The significance of these concepts lies in the fact that isomorphic spaces are alike in all respects, when considered as abstract vector spaces. Any statement true for one space (provided it can be formulated entirely in terms of addition and numerical multiplication) can be carried over by an isomorphism to give a true corresponding statement for an isomorphic space. For example, if $\mathscr{V} \xrightarrow{f} \mathscr{W}$ is an isomorphism, then an equation $\mathbf{y} = \sum_{i=1}^{n} a_i \mathbf{x}_i$ is true in $\mathscr{V}$ if and only if $f(\mathbf{y}) = \sum_{i=1}^{n} a_i f(\mathbf{x}_i)$ is true in $\mathscr{W}$.

By using coordinate maps we can give an alternative description of the matrix of a linear function. Given $\mathscr{V} \xrightarrow{f} \mathscr{W}$, and bases $V = (\mathbf{v}_1, \ldots, \mathbf{v}_n)$ in $\mathscr{V}$ and $W = (\mathbf{w}_1, \ldots, \mathbf{w}_m)$ in $\mathscr{W}$, the composition $c_W \circ f \circ c_V^{-1}$ is a function from $\mathscr{R}^n$ to $\mathscr{R}^m$. It is therefore given by multiplication by some m-by-n matrix A; we claim that A is precisely the same as the matrix of f with respect to the bases V and W. To prove the assertion, note that the jth column of A is $(c_W \circ f \circ c_V^{-1})(\mathbf{e}_j) = c_W(f(\mathbf{v}_j))$, since $c_V^{-1}(\mathbf{e}_j) = \mathbf{v}_j$. Now $c_W(f(\mathbf{v}_j))$ is (by definition of c_W) the coordinate vector of $f(\mathbf{v}_j)$ with respect to the basis W, and this is just how the matrix of f with respect to bases V and W was defined. This description of the matrix of a function makes the proof of the following generalization of Theorem 4.4 very easy. It simply says that in general, matrix multiplication corresponds to composition of functions, provided one uses bases consistently.

10.4 Theorem. Let f and g be linear functions with $\mathscr{U} \xrightarrow{f} \mathscr{V}$ and $\mathscr{V} \xrightarrow{g} \mathscr{W}$. Suppose bases U, V, and W are given in $\mathscr{U}$, $\mathscr{V}$, and $\mathscr{W}$, that A is the matrix of f with respect to the bases U and V, and that B is the matrix of g with respect to the bases V and W. Then BA is the matrix of $g \circ f$ with respect to the bases U and W.

Proof. By Theorem 4.3 and the characterization of matrices of functions by coordinate maps, this is simply the statement that

$$(c_W \circ g \circ c_V^{-1}) \circ (c_V \circ f \circ c_U^{-1}) = c_W \circ (g \circ f) \circ c_U^{-1},$$

which is clear because composition of functions is associative.

The special case in which $\mathscr{U}$, $\mathscr{V}$, and $\mathscr{W}$ are all the same space with the same basis is particularly important. If $\mathscr{V} \xrightarrow{f} \mathscr{V}$ has matrix A, then $f \circ f$ has matrix A^2, $f \circ f \circ f$ has matrix A^3, etc.

EXAMPLE 3.

(a) For the function f of Example 2(b), it is clear that $f \circ f \circ f$ is the identity, and it is easy to verify that

$$\begin{pmatrix} -1 & 1 \\ -1 & 0 \end{pmatrix}^3 = I.$$

(b) Differentiation is a linear function from the space of polynomials to itself. If we define $D(p)$ to be p' for elements of the space of quadratic polynomials and use the basis $(1, x, x^2)$ as in Example 2(d), then the matrix of D is

$$A = \begin{pmatrix} 0 & 1 & 0 \\ 0 & 0 & 2 \\ 0 & 0 & 0 \end{pmatrix}.$$

It is easy to compute that

$$A^2 = \begin{pmatrix} 0 & 0 & 2 \\ 0 & 0 & 0 \\ 0 & 0 & 0 \end{pmatrix},$$

and $A^3 = 0$, which corresponds to the fact that the third derivative of any quadratic polynomial is 0.

The matrix of a linear function with respect to a pair of bases, of course, depends on the bases. Since the matrix with respect to any pair completely determines the function, it should be possible to compute the matrix of a function with respect to one pair of bases from its matrix with respect to any other.

Let us look at an example. Suppose f has the matrix

$$\begin{pmatrix} 1 & 2 & 0 \\ -1 & 1 & 3 \end{pmatrix}$$

with respect to the natural bases in $\mathscr{R}^3$ and $\mathscr{R}^2$. Consider the bases

$$\mathbf{v}_1 = \begin{pmatrix} 1 \\ 2 \\ 3 \end{pmatrix}, \qquad \mathbf{v}_2 = \begin{pmatrix} 0 \\ 1 \\ 2 \end{pmatrix}, \qquad \mathbf{v}_3 = \begin{pmatrix} 2 \\ 0 \\ 1 \end{pmatrix}$$

in $\mathscr{R}^3$ and

$$\mathbf{w}_1 = \begin{pmatrix} 1 \\ 2 \end{pmatrix}, \qquad \mathbf{w}_2 = \begin{pmatrix} 2 \\ 3 \end{pmatrix}$$

in $\mathscr{R}^2$. To find the matrix of f with respect to $(\mathbf{v}_1, \mathbf{v}_2, \mathbf{v}_3)$ and $(\mathbf{w}_1, \mathbf{w}_2)$ we compute

$$f(\mathbf{v}_1) = \begin{pmatrix} 5 \\ 10 \end{pmatrix} = 5\mathbf{w}_1,$$

$$f(\mathbf{v}_2) = \begin{pmatrix} 2 \\ 7 \end{pmatrix} = 8\mathbf{w}_1 - 3\mathbf{w}_2, \quad f(\mathbf{v}_3) = \begin{pmatrix} 2 \\ 1 \end{pmatrix} = -4\mathbf{w}_1 + 3\mathbf{w}_2.$$

Hence the required matrix for f is

$$\begin{pmatrix} 5 & 8 & -4 \\ 0 & -3 & 3 \end{pmatrix}.$$

A basis $V = (\mathbf{v}_1, \ldots, \mathbf{v}_n)$ can be described in terms of another basis $X = (\mathbf{x}_1, \ldots, \mathbf{x}_n)$ by giving the matrix whose jth column is the coordinate vector of $\mathbf{v}_j$ with respect to X. This matrix gives a function from $\mathscr{R}^n$ to $\mathscr{R}^n$, which can be recognized as $c_X \circ c_V^{-1}$ by observing its effect on the natural basis vectors $\mathbf{e}_j$. Multiplication by this matrix converts the V-coordinates of any vector $\mathbf{w}$ into the X-coodinates of $\mathbf{w}$, since $c_X(\mathbf{w}) = (c_X \circ c_V^{-1}) \circ c_V(\mathbf{w})$. The inverse matrix gives the $\mathbf{x}$'s in terms of the $\mathbf{v}$'s and corresponds to $c_V \circ c_X^{-1}$. In the example in the preceding paragraph, the matrices giving V and W in terms of the natural bases in $\mathscr{R}^2$ and $\mathscr{R}^3$ are

$$\begin{pmatrix} 1 & 0 & 2 \\ 2 & 1 & 0 \\ 3 & 2 & 1 \end{pmatrix} \quad \text{and} \quad \begin{pmatrix} 1 & 2 \\ 2 & 3 \end{pmatrix}.$$

Since $\mathbf{e}_1 = -3\mathbf{w}_1 + 2\mathbf{w}_2$ and $\mathbf{e}_2 = 2\mathbf{w}_1 - \mathbf{w}_3$ the matrix giving the $\mathbf{e}$'s in terms of the $\mathbf{w}$'s is

$$\begin{pmatrix} -3 & 2 \\ 2 & -1 \end{pmatrix},$$

which is easily checked to be

$$\begin{pmatrix} 1 & 2 \\ 2 & 3 \end{pmatrix}^{-1}.$$

In the general situation we have a space $\mathscr{V}$ with bases $X = (\mathbf{x}_1, \ldots, \mathbf{x}_n)$ and $V = (\mathbf{v}_1, \ldots, \mathbf{v}_n)$, and a space $\mathscr{W}$ with bases $Y = (\mathbf{y}_1, \ldots, \mathbf{y}_m)$ and $W = (\mathbf{w}_1, \ldots, \mathbf{w}_m)$. Let P and Q be the matrices giving V in terms of X, and W in terms of Y, and let f be a linear function from $\mathscr{V}$ to $\mathscr{W}$ whose matrix with respect to X and Y is A. Then the matrix of f with respect to V and W is $Q^{-1}AP$. This is most easily seen by working with the coordinate maps. The matrix for f with respect to V and W corresponds to

$$c_W \circ f \circ c_V^{-1} = (c_W \circ c_Y^{-1}) \circ (c_Y \circ f \circ c_X^{-1}) \circ (c_X \circ c_V^{-1})$$

and the three factors on the right correspond to Q^{-1}, A, and P respectively.

For the previous example,

$$Q^{-1}AP = \begin{pmatrix} -3 & 2 \\ 2 & -1 \end{pmatrix} \begin{pmatrix} 1 & 2 & 0 \\ -1 & 1 & 3 \end{pmatrix} \begin{pmatrix} 1 & 0 & 2 \\ 2 & 1 & 0 \\ 3 & 2 & 1 \end{pmatrix}$$

$$= \begin{pmatrix} 5 & 8 & -4 \\ 0 & -3 & 3 \end{pmatrix},$$

which of course is the same result as before.

If $\mathscr{V}$ and $\mathscr{W}$ are the same space, and X is the same basis as Y, and V is the same basis as W, then P and Q are the same, and the new matrix for f is $P^{-1}AP$. Two matrices A, B are said to be **similar** if there exists an invertible matrix P such that $B = PAP^{-1}$. A few properties of similarity are presented in the exercises.

EXAMPLE 4. The derivative function D has the matrix

$$\begin{pmatrix} 0 & 1 & 0 \\ 0 & 0 & 2 \\ 0 & 0 & 0 \end{pmatrix}$$

with respect to the basis $(1, x, x^2)$ for the space of quadratic polynomials (see Example 3(b)). The polynomials $1 + x$, $x + x^2$ and $1 + x^2$ are also a basis, given in terms of $1, x, x^2$ by the matrix

$$\begin{pmatrix} 1 & 0 & 1 \\ 1 & 1 & 0 \\ 0 & 1 & 1 \end{pmatrix}.$$

The inverse matrix is

$$\frac{1}{2}\begin{pmatrix} 1 & 1 & -1 \\ -1 & 1 & 1 \\ 1 & -1 & 1 \end{pmatrix}.$$

With respect to the new basis, D has the matrix

$$\frac{1}{2}\begin{pmatrix} 1 & 1 & -1 \\ -1 & 1 & 1 \\ 1 & -1 & 1 \end{pmatrix}\begin{pmatrix} 0 & 1 & 0 \\ 0 & 0 & 2 \\ 0 & 0 & 0 \end{pmatrix}\begin{pmatrix} 1 & 0 & 1 \\ 1 & 1 & 0 \\ 0 & 1 & 1 \end{pmatrix}$$

$$= \frac{1}{2}\begin{pmatrix} 1 & 1 & -1 \\ -1 & 1 & 1 \\ 1 & -1 & 1 \end{pmatrix}\begin{pmatrix} 1 & 1 & 0 \\ 0 & 2 & 2 \\ 0 & 0 & 0 \end{pmatrix}$$

$$= \frac{1}{2}\begin{pmatrix} 1 & 3 & 2 \\ -1 & 1 & 2 \\ 1 & -1 & -2 \end{pmatrix}.$$

EXERCISES

1. Let $\mathbf{v}_1 = \begin{pmatrix} 2 \\ 0 \\ 0 \end{pmatrix}$, $\mathbf{v}_2 = \begin{pmatrix} 1 \\ -1 \\ 2 \end{pmatrix}$, $\mathbf{v}_3 = \begin{pmatrix} 0 \\ -2 \\ 3 \end{pmatrix}$. Verify that $V = (\mathbf{v}_1, \mathbf{v}_2, \mathbf{v}_3)$ is a

basis for $\mathcal{R}^3$ and find the coordinate vectors of $\mathbf{x}_1 = \begin{pmatrix} 0 \\ 0 \\ 1 \end{pmatrix}$, $\mathbf{x}_2 = \begin{pmatrix} 1 \\ 0 \\ 2 \end{pmatrix}$,

$\mathbf{x}_3 = \begin{pmatrix} 3 \\ 0 \\ 1 \end{pmatrix}$ with respect to V.

2. Find the matrix of a rotation of $45°$ in $\mathcal{R}^2$ with respect to

(a) The basis $\mathbf{x}_1 = \begin{pmatrix} 1 \\ 1 \end{pmatrix}$, $\mathbf{x}_2 = \begin{pmatrix} 0 \\ -2 \end{pmatrix}$. $\left[Ans. \begin{pmatrix} 0 & \sqrt{2} \\ -1/\sqrt{2} & \sqrt{2} \end{pmatrix}. \right]$

(b) The basis of unit vectors in the directions of $\mathbf{x}_1$ and $\mathbf{x}_2$.

3. Show that the matrices E_{ij} of shape m-by-n form a basis for the vector space of m-by-n matrices. What is the dimension of the space?

4. Let $A = \begin{pmatrix} 1 & 2 \\ 0 & 1 \end{pmatrix}$. Show that each of the following functions from the space of 2-by-2 matrices to itself is linear, and find the matrix of each with respect to the basis of Exercise 3.

   (a) $f(X) = AX$,   (b) $g(X) = AXA^{-1}$.

5. Find bases for the null spaces of the linear functions defined on the space of 2-by-2 matrices by

   (a) $f(X) = AX - XA$,   (b) $g(X) = AX - X^t A^t$,
   where A is the same as in Exercise 4.

6. Let $\mathscr{V} \xrightarrow{f} \mathscr{W}$ be an isomorphism. Show that $\mathbf{v}_1, \ldots, \mathbf{v}_n$ form a basis for $\mathscr{V}$ if and only if $f(\mathbf{v}_1), \ldots, f(\mathbf{v}_n)$ form a basis for $\mathscr{W}$. This proves that isomorphic spaces have the same dimension.

7. For any two vector spaces $\mathscr{V}$, $\mathscr{W}$, let $\mathscr{L}(\mathscr{V}, \mathscr{W})$ consist of all linear functions from $\mathscr{V}$ to $\mathscr{W}$. For f and g in $\mathscr{L}(\mathscr{V}, \mathscr{W})$ and r a number, define functions

$$f + g \quad \text{by} \quad (f + g)(\mathbf{v}) = f(\mathbf{v}) + g(\mathbf{v})$$

and

$$r \cdot f \quad \text{by} \quad (r \cdot f)(\mathbf{v}) = r \cdot f(\mathbf{v}).$$

   Show that $f + g$ and $r \cdot f$ are linear and so are in $\mathscr{L}(\mathscr{V}, \mathscr{W})$, and show that with these operations, $\mathscr{L}(\mathscr{V}, \mathscr{W})$ is a vector space.

8. (a) Show that $\mathscr{L}(\mathscr{R}^n, \mathscr{R}^m)$ is isomorphic to the space of all m-by-n matrices.

   (b) Show that if dim $(\mathscr{V}) = n$ and dim $(\mathscr{W}) = m$, and bases are chosen in $\mathscr{V}$ and $\mathscr{W}$, then assigning to each f in $\mathscr{L}(\mathscr{V}, \mathscr{W})$ its matrix with respect to the given bases gives an isomorphism between $\mathscr{L}(\mathscr{V}, \mathscr{W})$ and the space of m-by-n matrices.

9. Let $\mathscr{P}_n$ be the space of polynomials of degree less than or equal to n. Show that the function t defined by $t(p(x)) = p(x + 1)$ (so that, for example, $t(2x + 1) = 2x + 3$) is a linear function from $\mathscr{P}_n$ to itself.

   (a) Write the matrix of t with respect to the basis $1, x, x^2$ for the space $\mathscr{P}_2$.

   (b) Verify by matrix calculation that on $\mathscr{P}_2$

$$t = 1 + D + \frac{D^2}{2},$$

   where D is the derivative function of Example 3(b). (Here "1" is to be interpreted as the identity function, and D^2 as $D \circ D$.)

   (c) Show that on $\mathscr{P}_n$

$$t = 1 + D + \frac{D^2}{2} + \frac{D^3}{6} + \ldots + \frac{D^n}{n!}$$

[*Hint.* Use the definitions of the functions directly, without bringing in coordinates.]

10. Show that if A and B are similar, then

(a) det A = det B.

(b) A^{-1} is similar to B^{-1} (if the inverses exist).

(c) A^n is similar to B^n for any positive integer n.

11. The **trace** of a square matrix A is defined to be the sum of its diagonal elements, and is written tr (A). For example tr$\begin{pmatrix} 1 & 2 \\ 3 & 4 \end{pmatrix} = 1 + 4 = 5$, and if I is the n-by-n identity matrix, tr $(I) = n$.

(a) Show that if A and B are square and have the same size, then tr (AB) = tr (BA).

(b) Show that if A and B are similar, then tr (A) = tr (B). [*Hint.* This can be proved in one line by applying part (a) to the right pair of matrices.]

12. Suppose $\mathcal{R}^3 \xrightarrow{f} \mathcal{R}^3$ is a rotation and $\mathbf{v}_1$ is a unit vector in the direction of the axis of the rotation. If $\mathbf{v}_2$ and $\mathbf{v}_3$ are chosen to make $(\mathbf{v}_1, \mathbf{v}_2, \mathbf{v}_3)$ an orthonormal basis, then $f(\mathbf{v}_1) = \mathbf{v}_1$ and $f(\mathbf{v}_2)$, $f(\mathbf{v}_3)$ will be perpendicular to $\mathbf{v}_1$.

(a) Show that the matrix of f with respect to $(\mathbf{v}_1, \mathbf{v}_2, \mathbf{v}_3)$ is

$$\begin{pmatrix} 1 & 0 & 0 \\ 0 & \cos \alpha & -\sin \alpha \\ 0 & \sin \alpha & \cos \alpha \end{pmatrix},$$

where α is the angle of the rotation. (Compare Exercise 4 of Section 4.)

(b) Use the result of Exercise 11 to show that if A is the matrix of a rotation of angle α with respect to *any* basis, then $\cos \alpha = \frac{1}{2}$ (tr $(A) - 1$).

13. The linear function on $\mathcal{R}^3$ defined by

$$f(\mathbf{e}_1) = \mathbf{e}_2, \quad f(\mathbf{e}_2) = \mathbf{e}_3, \quad f(\mathbf{e}_3) = \mathbf{e}_1$$

is clearly a rotation about the line $x_1 = x_2 = x_3$. Find its angle by geometrical reasoning (what is $f \circ f \circ f$?) and check the result of Exercise 12.   [*Ans.* 120°]

14. Show that the matrix

$$A = \begin{pmatrix} \frac{2}{7} & \frac{6}{7} & \frac{3}{7} \\ \frac{3}{7} & \frac{2}{7} & -\frac{6}{7} \\ -\frac{6}{7} & \frac{3}{7} & -\frac{2}{7} \end{pmatrix}$$

represents a rotation of $\mathcal{R}^3$ and find its axis and angle. (If $\mathbf{x}$ is a unit vector in the direction of the axis, then $A\mathbf{x} = \mathbf{x}$ or $(A - I)\mathbf{x} = 0$. To show that A represents a rotation, find its matrix with respect to an orthonormal basis that includes $\mathbf{x}$.)   [*Ans.* Axis is $(3, 3, -1)$.]

VECTOR CALCULUS   2

1. VECTOR FUNCTIONS

The functions considered in Chapter 1 are all linear. From here on we shall study nonlinear functions as well. One important difference between linear and nonlinear functions is that the domain of a linear function is always a subspace of a vector space, while this is not necessarily true for a nonlinear function. Likewise the image under a linear function of the domain of the function is also a vector space, and this may not hold for a nonlinear function.

EXAMPLE 1. The function $\mathscr{R}^3 \xrightarrow{f} \mathscr{R}^2$ defined by

$$f(x, y, z) = \begin{pmatrix} x^2 + y^2 + z^2 \\ x + y + z \end{pmatrix}$$

has as its domain all of $\mathscr{R}^3$, but its image contains only of those vectors in $\mathscr{R}^2$ for which the first coordinate is nonnegative. Another function $\mathscr{R}^3 \xrightarrow{g} \mathscr{R}^2$ is defined by

$$g(x, y, z) = \begin{pmatrix} 3x + 4y \\ 3y + 5z \end{pmatrix} = \begin{pmatrix} 3 & 4 & 0 \\ 0 & 3 & 5 \end{pmatrix} \begin{pmatrix} x \\ y \\ z \end{pmatrix},$$

and g is linear because it is given by matrix multiplication acting on the vectors of $\mathscr{R}^3$. The function $\mathscr{R}^2 \xrightarrow{h} \mathscr{R}^2$ defined by

$$h(x, y) = \begin{pmatrix} \sqrt{1 - x^2 - y^2} \\ x + y \end{pmatrix},$$

for vectors (x, y) such that $x^2 + y^2 \leq 1$, has as its domain a subset of $\mathscr{R}^2$ that is not a subspace of $\mathscr{R}^2$. We shall occasionally use the term *transformation* to refer to a function whose domain space is the same as its range space.

The set $\mathscr{R}$ of all real numbers is a vector space of dimension 1, and, as a result, all of the ordinary functions of one-variable calculus are vector functions.

EXAMPLE 2. The following functions have domain space and range space equal to the set $\mathscr{R}$ of real numbers.

$$f(x) = 3x^3 + 5x^2 + 2,$$

$$g(x) = x^2 - 1,$$

$$h(x) = \sin^{-1} x, \qquad -1 \leq x \leq 1.$$

It is not necessary that the domain of a vector function equal its domain space; it can be a proper subset. The same is true of the range. In particular, the domain of f = the range of f = the domain of $g = \mathscr{R}$. On the other hand, the range of g consists of all real numbers $y \geq -1$, the domain of h is the interval $-1 \leq x \leq 1$, and the range of h is the interval $-\pi/2 \leq y \leq \pi/2$. The last three sets are all proper subsets of $\mathscr{R}$.

A vector $\mathbf{x}$ in $\mathscr{R}^n$ whose coordinates are the real numbers $x_1, \ldots, x_n$ will be written either as a horizontal n-tuple or as a column matrix. Thus, we shall write both

$$\begin{pmatrix} x_1 \\ \cdot \\ \cdot \\ \cdot \\ x_n \end{pmatrix} \quad \text{and} \quad (x_1, \ldots, x_n)$$

for the vector $\mathbf{x}$. The practice of writing columns instead of horizontal tuples arises, of course, from the definition of matrix multiplication. If a function is determined by a matrix

$$\begin{pmatrix} a & b \\ c & d \end{pmatrix},$$

we usually write

$$\begin{pmatrix} a & b \\ c & d \end{pmatrix}\begin{pmatrix} x \\ y \end{pmatrix}$$

for the value of the function at

$$\begin{pmatrix} x \\ y \end{pmatrix} \quad \text{or} \quad (x, y).$$

A function whose range is a subset of the space $\mathscr{R}$ of all real numbers is called **real-valued**. Every function $\mathscr{R}^n \xrightarrow{f} \mathscr{R}^m$ defines a set of real-valued functions $f_1, \ldots, f_m$, called the **coordinate functions** of f. The definition is as follows: For every $\mathbf{x}$ in the domain of f and each $i = 1, \ldots, m$, we set $f_i(\mathbf{x})$ equal to the ith coordinate of $f(\mathbf{x})$. Thus,

$$f(\mathbf{x}) = (f_1(\mathbf{x}), \ldots, f_m(\mathbf{x})),$$

for every $\mathbf{x}$ in the domain of f.

EXAMPLE 3. Consider the vector function

$$f\begin{pmatrix} x \\ y \\ z \end{pmatrix} = \begin{pmatrix} x + y + z \\ xy + yz + zx \\ xyz \end{pmatrix}.$$

The coordinate functions of f are the three real-valued functions

$$f_1(x, y, z) = x + y + z,$$
$$f_2(x, y, z) = xy + yz + zx,$$
$$f_3(x, y, z) = xyz.$$

The **graph** of a function f is defined to be the set of all ordered pairs $(\mathbf{x}, f(\mathbf{x}))$ where $\mathbf{x}$ is in the domain of f. In studying real-valued functions of one real variable, graphs are a considerable aid to understanding. For example, the graph of the function defined by $f(x) = x^2 - 2$ is the set of all ordered pairs (x, y) with $y = x^2 - 2$, that is, it is the subset of the xy-plane consisting of the parabola shown in Figure 1. More generally, the graph of a function $\mathscr{R}^n \xrightarrow{f} \mathscr{R}^m$ is the subset of $\mathscr{R}^{n+m}$ consisting of all points $(x_1, \ldots, x_n, y_1, \ldots, y_m)$ such that

$$y_1 = f_1(x_1, \ldots, x_n)$$
$$\vdots$$
$$y_m = f_m(x_1, \ldots, x_n),$$

where $f_1, \ldots, f_m$ are the coordinate functions of f. As a practical means of increasing understanding by visualization, the usefulness of the graph is limited to functions $\mathscr{R}^n \xrightarrow{f} \mathscr{R}^m$ for which $m + n \leq 3$.

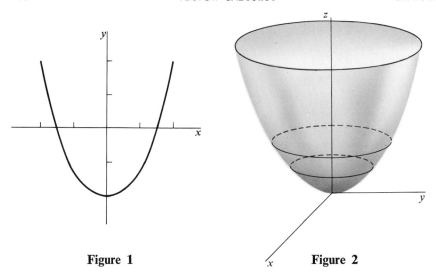

Figure 1   **Figure 2**

EXAMPLE 4. The length $|\mathbf{x}|$ of a vector $\mathbf{x}$ in $\mathscr{R}^2$ is defined by

$$|\mathbf{x}| = |(x, y)| = \sqrt{x^2 + y^2}.$$

The graph of the function f defined by $f(\mathbf{x}) = |\mathbf{x}|^2$ is the subset of $\mathscr{R}^3$ pictured in Figure 2. Notice that we have drawn the z-axis perpendicular to the xy-plane. This choice enables us to draw a recognizable graph, but is not logically necessary.

EXAMPLE 5. Consider the function $\mathscr{R} \xrightarrow{f} \mathscr{R}^2$ defined by

$$f(t) = \begin{pmatrix} \cos t \\ \sin t \end{pmatrix}, \qquad \text{for every } t \text{ in } \mathscr{R}.$$

Since the length $|\mathbf{x}|$ of a vector $\mathbf{x} = (x, y)$ is given by $|\mathbf{x}| = \sqrt{x^2 + y^2}$, we have $|f(t)| = \sqrt{\cos^2 t + \sin^2 t} = 1$. Thus the range of f is a subset of the unit circle $|\mathbf{x}| = 1$ in $\mathscr{R}^2$. The number t is interpreted geometrically as the angle in radians between the vector $f(t)$ and the positive x-axis. As t runs through $\mathscr{R}$, the unit circle is covered infinitely often. It follows that the range of f is the whole unit circle. The circle is not, however, the graph of f. The latter is a subset of $\mathscr{R}^3$ and is a spiral, the axis of which is the t-axis. See Figure 3.

EXAMPLE 6. Let the vector function f be defined by

$$f(t) = \begin{pmatrix} x \\ y \\ z \end{pmatrix} = \begin{pmatrix} t \\ t^2 \\ t^3 \end{pmatrix}, \qquad -\infty < t < \infty.$$

The graph of f is a subset of $\mathscr{R}^4$, so we shall not attempt to draw it. Instead we shall sketch the range. By setting $z = 0$, we obtain the equations $x = t$,

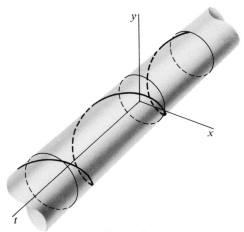

Figure 3

$y = t^2$, which are equivalent to $y = x^2$. Thus the projected image, on the xy-plane, of the range of f is the graph of $y = x^2$. Similarly, in the yz-plane we obtain $y = z^{2/3}$, and in the xz-plane we get $z = x^3$. From this information, we have drawn in Figure 4 that part of the range of f that lies above the first quadrant of the xy-plane.

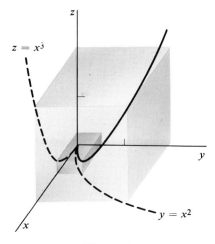

Figure 4

In drawing Figure 4 we have labeled the axes in the manner usually associated with a right-hand orientation. Of course, if we were to interchange x and y in this labelling, the picture would look different. A similar change in Figure 5(b) would result in a ramp that spirals down, turning always to the left instead of to the right. In order to make it easy to see the relationship between the pictures, we have always chosen the right-hand orientation for the axes in the 3-dimensional ones. For a discussion of orientation see Section 7 of Chapter 1.

EXAMPLE 7. Consider the function

$$f \begin{pmatrix} u \\ v \end{pmatrix} = \begin{pmatrix} x \\ y \\ z \end{pmatrix} = \begin{pmatrix} u \cos v \\ u \sin v \\ v \end{pmatrix} \qquad \begin{array}{l} 0 \leq u \leq 4. \\ 0 \leq v \leq 2\pi. \end{array}$$

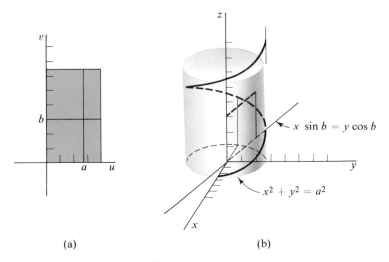

(a)   (b)

Figure 5

The domain of f is the shaded rectangle in Figure 5(a). In order to sketch the range, we proceed as follows: Choose a number a in the interval $0 \leq u \leq 4$, and set $u = a$. Then,

$$x = a \cos v,$$
$$y = a \sin v, \qquad 0 \leq v \leq 2\pi,$$
$$z = v,$$

and $x^2 + y^2 = a^2$. We interpret v both as distance along the z-axis and as the angle between $(x, y, 0)$ and the x-axis. It follows that the image under f of the line segment $u = a$, for $0 \leq v \leq 2\pi$ (see Figure 5(a)) is the spiral whose projection on the xy-plane is the circle of radius a and whose axis is the z-axis (see Figure 5(b)). Next, choose a number b in the interval $0 \leq v \leq 2\pi$, and set $v = b$. Then,

$$x = u \cos b,$$
$$y = u \sin b, \qquad 0 \leq u \leq 4,$$
$$z = b,$$

and $x^2 + y^2 = u^2$. The image under f of the line segment $v = b$, $0 \leq u \leq 4$ (see Figure 5(a)) is the line segment $x \sin b = y \cos b$, $z = b$ of length 4 where x runs from 0 to $4 \cos b$ (see Figure 5(b)). Letting a and b vary, we obtain the range of f as the spiral surface shown in Figure 6.

Notice that the range of f in Examples 5 and 6 is a curve, whereas in Example 7 it is a surface. Similarly, the graph of f in Example 4 is a surface, but in Example 5 it is a curve. The evidence suggests that when the dimen-

sion of the domain space is 1, one gets a
curve, and when it is 2, one gets a surface.
Exceptions to this are discussed in Section 14.

The curves and surfaces pictured in
Figures 2, 3, 4, and 6 are related to the vector
functions that define them in two essentially
different ways. The bowl-shaped surface in
Figure 2 is just the graph of the function which
defines it, and the same is true for the spiral
curve in Figure 3. We shall say that both
curve and surface are defined **explicitly**. On
the other hand, the curve in Figure 4 and
the surface in Figure 6 are the ranges of
their defining functions. They are said to be
defined **parametrically**. This terminology is
standard in discussing real-valued functions
of one real variable. For example, the function

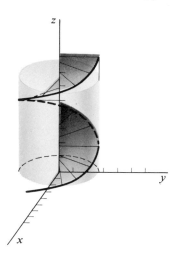

Figure 6

$$f(x) = \sqrt{16 - x^2}$$

explicitly defines the upper half of the circle of radius 4, and the same curve
is defined parametrically by the pair of functions

$$\begin{cases} x(t) = 4 \cos t, \\ y(t) = 4 \sin t, \end{cases} \quad 0 \le t \le \pi.$$

Parametric representations of lines in 3-dimensional space have been
studied in Chapter 1. Let x_1 and x_2 be any two vectors in $\mathscr{R}^3$. If $x_1 \ne 0$, the
range of the function $\mathscr{R} \xrightarrow{f} \mathscr{R}^3$ defined by

$$f(t) = t x_1 + x_2, \quad -\infty < t < \infty,$$

is a parametrically defined line.

Curves and surfaces can also be defined **implicitly**. In particular, implicitly defined planes were discussed in Chapter 1. Let (a, b, c) be a nonzero
vector, and let $\mathscr{R}^3 \xrightarrow{F} \mathscr{R}$ be the linear function defined for any $x = (x, y, z)$
by $F(x) = (a, b, c) \cdot (x, y, z)$. For any real number d, the set of all x such
that

$$F(x) = ax + by + cz = d$$

is an implicitly defined plane.

EXAMPLE 8. Consider the function f defined by $f(x, y, z) = xy + yz$
$+ zx$. The subset S of $\mathscr{R}^3$ consisting of all points (x, y, z) that satisfy

$$f(x, y, z) = xy + yz + zx = 1 \tag{1}$$

is said to be defined implicitly by Equation (1). Setting $z = 0$ in (1) we
obtain the equation $xy = 1$, which implicitly defines a hyperbola in the

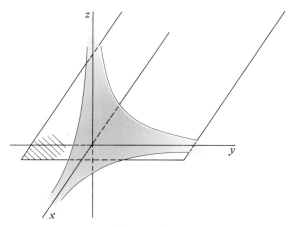

Figure 7

xy-plane. This hyperbola is the intersection of S and the xy-plane. Since $f(x, y, z)$ is symmetric in x, y, z, the other coordinate planes also intersect S in hyperbolas, as shown in Figure 7. More generally, the intersection of S with the plane $z = a$ is given by $xy + ya + ax = 1$. This equation is equivalent to

$$(x + a)(y + a) = xy + ya + ax + a^2 = a^2 + 1.$$

By substituting $u = x + a$ and $v = y + a$, we obtain the equation $uv = a^2 + 1$ of the hyperbola shown in Figure 8. It follows by symmetry that the intersection of S with any plane parallel to a coordinate plane is a hyperbola. We conclude that S looks like a surface, and the part of it that lies in the octant $x \geq 0$, $y \geq 0$, $z \geq 0$ is drawn in Figure 7.

EXAMPLE 9. Let $\mathscr{R}^3 \xrightarrow{f} \mathscr{R}^2$ be the function defined by

$$f(x, y, z) = \begin{pmatrix} xy + yz + zx \\ x + y - z \end{pmatrix}.$$

Consider the subset γ of $\mathscr{R}^3$ implicitly defined by the equation

$$f(\mathbf{x}) = \begin{pmatrix} 1 \\ 1 \end{pmatrix}.$$

That is, γ consists of all $\mathbf{x} = (x, y, z)$ such that

$$xy + yz + zx = 1,$$
$$x + y - z = 1.$$

We have seen in Example 8 that $xy + yz + zx = 1$ implicitly defines the surface pictured in Figure 7. The equation $x + y - z = 1$ implicitly defines the plane in Figure 9. The set γ of points that satisfy both equations is the curve in which the surface and the plane intersect.

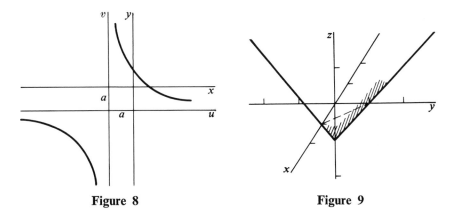

Figure 8   **Figure 9**

The distinctions among explicit, parametric, and implicit representations are not limited to dimensions 2 and 3. A set S is defined:

1. **explicitly** if S is the **graph** in $\mathscr{R}^{n+m}$ of a function
$$\mathscr{R}^n \xrightarrow{\;f\;} \mathscr{R}^m,$$

2. **parametrically** if S is the **range** in $\mathscr{R}^m$ of a function
$$\mathscr{R}^n \xrightarrow{\;f\;} \mathscr{R}^m,$$

3. **implicitly** if, for some function
$$\mathscr{R}^{n+m} \xrightarrow{\;f\;} \mathscr{R}^m,$$

S is a **level set** of f, that is, for some point $\mathbf{z}_0$ in $\mathscr{R}^m$, S is the set of all $\mathbf{x}$ in the *domain* of f such that $f(\mathbf{x}) = \mathbf{z}_0$.

A set S defined in some one of the above three ways will be called a curve or a surface provided that f satisfies certain smoothness conditions to be described in Sections 3 and 14. In the meantime we shall use the terms curve or surface informally.

When the domain and range spaces of a vector function are the same, it is often helpful to picture the domain vectors $\mathbf{x}$ as points, and the image vectors $f(\mathbf{x})$ as arrows. We picture $f(\mathbf{x})$ as an arrow with its tail at $\mathbf{x}$. One

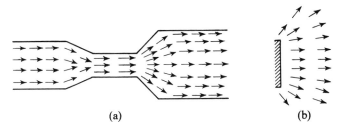

(a)   (b)

Figure 10

would do this, for example, in representing a 2-dimensional fluid flow in which the image vector at each point is the velocity and direction of the flow. See Figure 10(a). Another example is an electric field, where the value of the function at a point is the vector giving the force exerted by the field on a unit charge. See Figure 10(b). Vector functions looked at in this way are sometimes called **vector fields**.

EXERCISES

1. Suppose that the temperature at a point (x, y, z) in space is given by $T(x, y, z) = x^2 + y^2 + z^2$. A particle moves so that at time t its location is given by $(x, y, z) = (t, t^2, t^3)$. Find the temperature at the point occupied by the particle at $t = \frac{1}{2}$. What is the rate of change of the temperature at the particle when $t = \frac{1}{2}$?

2. Let the density per unit of volume in a cubical box of side length 2 vary directly as the distance from the center and inversely as $1 + t^2$ where t is time. If the density at a corner of the box is 1 when $t = 0$, find a formula for the density at any point and at any time. What is the rate of change of the density at a point $\frac{1}{2}$ unit from the center of the box at time $t = 1$?

3. Consider the function $f(x, y) = \sqrt{4 - x^2 - y^2}$.

(a) Sketch the domain of f (take it as large as possible).
(b) Sketch the graph of f.
(c) Sketch the range of f.

4. The function $\mathscr{R} \xrightarrow{g} \mathscr{R}^2$ is defined by

$$g(t) = \begin{pmatrix} 2\cos t \\ 3\sin t \end{pmatrix}, \qquad 0 \le t \le 2\pi.$$

(a) Draw the range of g.
(b) Draw the graph of g.

5. A transformation from the xy-plane to the uv-plane is defined by

$$f\begin{pmatrix} x \\ y \end{pmatrix} = \begin{pmatrix} u \\ v \end{pmatrix} = \begin{pmatrix} x \\ y(1 + x^2) \end{pmatrix}.$$

What are the images of horizontal lines in the xy-plane? What are the coordinate functions of f?

6. For each of the following linear functions: (i) What is the domain? (ii) Describe and sketch the range. (iii) Describe and sketch the set implicitly defined by the equation $L(\mathbf{x}) = 0$. What is this set usually called?

(a) $L\begin{pmatrix} x \\ y \end{pmatrix} = \begin{pmatrix} 2 & 1 \\ 4 & 3 \end{pmatrix}\begin{pmatrix} x \\ y \end{pmatrix}.$

(b) $L\begin{pmatrix} x \\ y \end{pmatrix} = \begin{pmatrix} 2 & 1 \\ 4 & 2 \end{pmatrix}\begin{pmatrix} x \\ y \end{pmatrix}.$

(c) $L\begin{pmatrix} x \\ y \\ z \end{pmatrix} = \begin{pmatrix} 1 & 0 & 2 \\ 3 & 2 & 1 \end{pmatrix}\begin{pmatrix} x \\ y \\ z \end{pmatrix}.$

(d) $L\begin{pmatrix} x \\ y \\ z \end{pmatrix} = \begin{pmatrix} 1 & 2 & 3 \\ -1 & 4 & 2 \\ 5 & -8 & 0 \end{pmatrix}\begin{pmatrix} x \\ y \\ z \end{pmatrix}.$

7. Sketch the surfaces defined explicitly by the following functions:

(a) $f\begin{pmatrix} x \\ y \end{pmatrix} = 2 - x^2 - y^2.$ (b) $h\begin{pmatrix} x \\ y \end{pmatrix} = \dfrac{1}{x^2 + y^2}.$

(c) $g(x, y) = \sin x.$ (d) $f(x, y) = 0.$

(e) $f(x, y) = e^{x+y}.$ (f) $g(x, y) = \begin{cases} 1 & \text{if } |x| < |y|, \\ 0 & \text{if } |x| \ge |y|. \end{cases}$

8. Sketch the curves defined parametrically by the following functions:

(a) $f(t) = \begin{pmatrix} 1 \\ 2 \\ 0 \end{pmatrix} t + \begin{pmatrix} 1 \\ 1 \\ 1 \end{pmatrix}, \qquad -\infty < t < \infty.$

(b) $f(t) = \begin{pmatrix} t \\ t^2 \\ t^3 \end{pmatrix}, \qquad 0 \le t \le 1.$

(c) $f(t) = (2t, t), \qquad -1 \le t \le 1.$
(d) $h(t) = (t, t, t^2), \qquad -1 \le t \le 2.$

(e) $f(t) = \begin{pmatrix} 2t \\ |t| \end{pmatrix}, \qquad -1 \le t \le 2.$

9. Draw the surfaces defined parametrically by the following functions:

(a) $f\begin{pmatrix} u \\ v \end{pmatrix} = \begin{pmatrix} x \\ y \\ z \end{pmatrix} = \begin{pmatrix} 1 & 0 \\ 0 & 1 \\ 1 & 0 \end{pmatrix}\begin{pmatrix} u \\ v \end{pmatrix} + \begin{pmatrix} 1 \\ 1 \\ 1 \end{pmatrix}, \qquad \begin{cases} -\infty < u < \infty, \\ -\infty < v < \infty. \end{cases}$

(b) $g\begin{pmatrix} u \\ v \end{pmatrix} = \begin{pmatrix} x \\ y \\ z \end{pmatrix} = \begin{pmatrix} \cos u \sin v \\ \sin u \sin v \\ \cos v \end{pmatrix}, \qquad \begin{cases} 0 \le u \le 2\pi. \\ 0 \le v \le \pi/2. \end{cases}$

(c) $\begin{pmatrix} x \\ y \\ z \end{pmatrix} = \begin{pmatrix} \cos u \cosh v \\ \sin u \cosh v \\ \sinh v \end{pmatrix}, \qquad \begin{cases} 0 \le u \le 2\pi, \\ -\infty < v < \infty. \end{cases}$

(d) $\begin{pmatrix} x \\ y \\ z \end{pmatrix} = \begin{pmatrix} 2 \cos u + v \sin (u/2) \cos u \\ 2 \sin u + v \sin (u/2) \sin u \\ v \cos u/2 \end{pmatrix}, \qquad \begin{cases} 0 \le u \le 2\pi, \\ -1 \le v \le 1. \end{cases}$

(Möbius strip)

10. Draw the following implicitly defined curves and surfaces.

(a) $f(x, y) = x + y = 1.$

(b) $g(x, y) = \dfrac{x^2}{a^2} + \dfrac{y^2}{b^2} = 1.$

(c) $f(x, y) = (x^2 + y^2 + 1)^2 - 4x^2 = 0$.

(d) $f(x, y, z) = xyz = 1$.

(e) $xyz = 0$.

(f) $g(x, y, z) = x^2 - y^2 = 2$.

(g) $\begin{pmatrix} x - y \\ y + z \end{pmatrix} = \begin{pmatrix} 0 \\ 0 \end{pmatrix}$.

(h) $\begin{cases} 2x + y + z = 2, \\ x \qquad - z = 3. \end{cases}$

(i) $\begin{pmatrix} xyz \\ x + y \end{pmatrix} = \begin{pmatrix} 1 \\ 0 \end{pmatrix}$.

11. Suppose that the density per unit of area of a thin film, referred to plane rectangular coordinates, is given by the formula $d(x, y) = x^2 + 2y^2 - x + 1$, for $-1 \le x \le 1$ and $-1 \le y \le 1$. Sketch the set of points at which the film has density $\frac{7}{4}$.

12. Sketch the indicated vector fields.

(a) $f\begin{pmatrix} x \\ y \end{pmatrix} = \begin{pmatrix} 1 \\ x \end{pmatrix}$ for $-1 \le x \le 2, y = 0, y = 1$.

(b) $f\begin{pmatrix} x \\ y \end{pmatrix} = \begin{pmatrix} -x \\ y \end{pmatrix}$ for $x^2 + y^2 \le 4$.

(c) $f\begin{pmatrix} x \\ y \end{pmatrix} = \begin{pmatrix} y \\ x \end{pmatrix}$ for $x^2 + y^2 \le 4$.

(d) $f\begin{pmatrix} x \\ y \end{pmatrix} = \frac{1}{x^2 + y^2} \begin{pmatrix} 1 \\ 1 \end{pmatrix}$ for $x^2 + y^2 \le 4$.

13. Let a transformation from the euclidean xy-plane to itself be given by

$$f\begin{pmatrix} x \\ y \end{pmatrix} = \begin{pmatrix} x + y \\ -x + y \end{pmatrix}.$$

Show that f accomplishes an expansion out from the origin by a factor $\sqrt{2}$ and a rotation through an angle $\pi/4$.

14. The vector function f is defined by

$$f\begin{pmatrix} x \\ y \end{pmatrix} = \begin{pmatrix} x^2 - y^2 \\ 2xy \end{pmatrix}.$$

What are the coordinate functions of f? Consider the domain space to be the xy-plane and the range space to be the uv-plane.

(a) Find the image of the segment of the line $y = x$ between

$$\begin{pmatrix} 0 \\ 0 \end{pmatrix} \quad \text{and} \quad \begin{pmatrix} 1 \\ 1 \end{pmatrix}.$$

(b) Find the image of the region defined by $0 < x$, $0 < y$, and $x^2 + y^2 < 1$.

(c) Find the angle between the images of the lines $y = 0$ and $y = (1/\sqrt{3})x$.   [Ans. $\pi/3$.]

15. A vector function f from the xy-plane to the uv-plane is defined by

$$f\begin{pmatrix} x \\ y \end{pmatrix} = \begin{pmatrix} u \\ v \end{pmatrix} = \begin{pmatrix} \dfrac{x}{(x+y)^2} \\ 4x \end{pmatrix}, \qquad x \neq 0.$$

What are the coordinate functions of f ? Find the image of the region bounded by the lines $x = y$, $y = x - 8$, $x = -y$, $y = 8 - x$.

2. LIMITS AND CONTINUITY

Any definition of limit is based on a notion of proximity. To assert, for example, that

$$\lim_{x \to 0} \frac{\sin x}{x} = 1$$

is to say that $(\sin x)/x$ is arbitrarily close to 1 provided x is sufficiently close to 0. Proximity on the real-number line can be expressed by inequalities. For example, $|x - 3| < 0.4$ says that the distance between the number x and the number 3 is less than 0.4, or, equivalently, that x lies in the interior of the interval with center 3 and half-length 0.4. See Figure 11. The statement "$(\sin x)/x$ is arbitrarily close to 1 provided x is sufficiently close to 0" is translated in terms of inequalities as: For any positive number ϵ, there exists a positive number δ such that if

$$0 < |x - 0| = |x| < \delta,$$

then

$$\left| \frac{\sin x}{x} - 1 \right| < \epsilon.$$

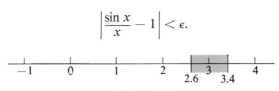

Figure 11

In $\mathscr{R}^n$ a definition of limit also requires the means of asserting that one point is close to another. Distance will be defined with respect to euclidean length. For any $\epsilon > 0$ and point $\mathbf{x}_0$ in $\mathscr{R}^n$, the set of all vectors $\mathbf{x}$ in $\mathscr{R}^n$ that satisfy the inequality

$$|\mathbf{x} - \mathbf{x}_0| < \epsilon$$

is a spherical ball with radius ϵ and center $\mathbf{x}_0$. For example, if $\mathbf{x}_0 = (1, 2, 1)$, the set of all $\mathbf{x}$ in $\mathscr{R}^3$ such that

$$|\mathbf{x} - \mathbf{x}_0| = \sqrt{(x-1)^2 + (y-2)^2 + (z-1)^2} < 0.5$$

is the ball shown in Figure 12.

Let S be a subset of $\mathscr{R}^n$ and $\mathbf{x}$ a point in $\mathscr{R}^n$. Then $\mathbf{x}$ is a **limit point** of S

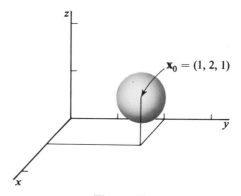

Figure 12

if, for any $\epsilon > 0$, there exists a point $\mathbf{y}$ in S such that $0 < |\mathbf{x} - \mathbf{y}| < \epsilon$. Translated into English, the definition says that $\mathbf{x}$ is a limit point of S if there are points in S other than $\mathbf{x}$ that are contained in a ball of arbitrarily small radius with center at $\mathbf{x}$. If, for example, S is the disc defined by

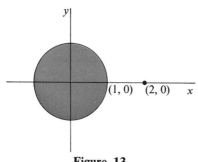

Figure 13

$x^2 + y^2 < 1$, together with the single point $(2, 0)$, then the set of limit points of S consists of S together with the circle $x^2 + y^2 = 1$. See Figure 13. However, the point $(2, 0)$ is not a limit point of S even though it is a point of S.

We come now to the definition of limit for a function $\mathscr{R}^n \xrightarrow{f} \mathscr{R}^m$. Let $\mathbf{y}_0$ be a point in $\mathscr{R}^m$ and $\mathbf{x}_0$ a limit point of the domain of f. Then $\mathbf{y}_0$ **is the limit of f at $\mathbf{x}_0$**, abbreviated

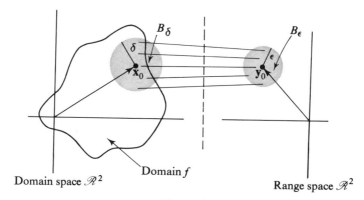

Domain space $\mathscr{R}^2$ Domain f Range space $\mathscr{R}^2$

Figure 14

$$\lim_{\mathbf{x} \to \mathbf{x}_0} f(\mathbf{x}) = \mathbf{y}_0,$$

if, for any $\epsilon > 0$, there exists $\delta > 0$ such that if $\mathbf{x}$ is in the domain of f and $0 < |\mathbf{x} - \mathbf{x}_0| < \delta$, then $|f(\mathbf{x}) - \mathbf{y}_0| < \epsilon$. The definition means that if the limit exists, then $f(\mathbf{x})$ is arbitrarily close to $\mathbf{y}_0$ provided $\mathbf{x}$ is sufficiently close to $\mathbf{x}_0$ and $\mathbf{x} \neq \mathbf{x}_0$. Geometrically the idea is this: Given any ϵ-ball B_ϵ centered at $\mathbf{y}_0$, there exists a δ-ball B_δ centered at $\mathbf{x}_0$ whose intersection with the domain of f, except possibly for $\mathbf{x}_0$ itself, is sent by f into B_ϵ. A 2-dimensional example is pictured in Figure 14. The statement

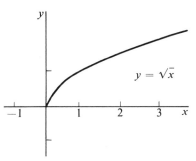

Figure 15

$$\lim_{\mathbf{x} \to \mathbf{x}_0} f(\mathbf{x}) = \mathbf{y}_0$$

is also commonly read "The limit of $f(\mathbf{x})$, as $\mathbf{x}$ approaches $\mathbf{x}_0$, is $\mathbf{y}_0$." To see why we have required that $\mathbf{x}_0$ be a limit point of the domain of f, consider a 1-dimensional example. The function $f(x) = \sqrt{x}$, the graph of which is drawn in Figure 15, has as its domain the interval $0 \leq x$. Clearly we want

$$\lim_{x \to 1/2} f(x) = 2^{-1/2}$$

and

$$\lim_{x \to 0^+} f(x) = 0.$$

But it makes no sense to ask for

$$\lim_{x \to -1} f(x).$$

EXAMPLE 1. Consider the function defined by

$$f(t) = (\cos t, \sin t).$$

The domain of f is all of $\mathscr{R}$, and at an arbitrary point t_0 of $\mathscr{R}$, f has limit $f(t_0)$. To see this we use known facts about $\cos t$ and $\sin t$ and consider

$$|f(t) - f(t_0)| = \sqrt{(\cos t - \cos t_0)^2 + (\sin t - \sin t_0)^2}$$
$$\leq |\cos t - \cos t_0| + |\sin t - \sin t_0|. \tag{1}$$

This holds because $\sqrt{a^2 + b^2} \leq |a| + |b|$. (See Problem 15.) Since, using the fact that $\sin t$ and $\cos t$ are continuous,

$$\lim_{t \to t_0} \cos t = \cos t_0, \quad \text{and} \quad \lim_{t \to t_0} \sin t = \sin t_0,$$

we can choose a $\delta > 0$ such that for any preassigned $\epsilon > 0$

$$|\cos t - \cos t_0| < \frac{\epsilon}{2} \quad \text{and} \quad |\sin t - \sin t_0| < \frac{\epsilon}{2},$$

whenever $|t - t_0| < \delta$. Hence, Equation (1) shows that $|f(t) - f(t_0)| < \epsilon$ whenever $|t - t_0| < \delta$.

EXAMPLE 2. Consider the real-valued function defined in all of $\mathscr{R}^2$ except $(x, y) = (0, 0)$ by

$$f(x, y) = \frac{e^{x+y}}{x^2 + y^2}.$$

There is no limit as $(x, y) \to (0, 0)$, for example, along the line $y = x$. We can write

$$\lim_{\mathbf{x} \to 0} f(\mathbf{x}) = \infty$$

to describe what happens.

EXAMPLE 3. The range space and the domain are the same as in the preceding example and

$$f(x, y) = \frac{x^2 - y^2}{x^2 + y^2}.$$

There is no limit as $(x, y) \to (0, 0)$. If (x, y) approaches $(0, 0)$ along the line $y = \alpha x$, we obtain

$$\lim_{x \to 0} \frac{x^2 - y^2}{x^2 + y^2} = \lim_{x \to 0} \frac{x^2(1 - \alpha^2)}{x^2(1 + \alpha^2)} = \frac{1 - \alpha^2}{1 + \alpha^2}.$$

The limit is obviously not independent of α; it equals 0 if $\alpha = 1$, and 1 if $\alpha = 0$.

The functions in the above three examples are all real-valued. The following theorem shows that the problem of the existence and evaluation of a limit for any function $\mathscr{R}^n \xrightarrow{f} \mathscr{R}^m$ reduces to the same problem for the coordinate functions. The latter are, of course, real-valued.

2.1 Theorem. Given $\mathscr{R}^n \xrightarrow{f} \mathscr{R}^m$, with coordinate functions $f_1, \ldots, f_m$, and a point $\mathbf{y}_0 = (b_1, \ldots, b_m)$ in $\mathscr{R}^m$, then

$$\lim_{\mathbf{x} \to \mathbf{x}_0} f(\mathbf{x}) = \mathbf{y}_0 \tag{2}$$

if and only if

$$\lim_{\mathbf{x} \to \mathbf{x}_0} f_i(\mathbf{x}) = b_i, \qquad i = 1, \ldots, m. \tag{3}$$

Proof. Since the domain of f equals the domain of f_i, $i = 1, \ldots, m$, the vector $\mathbf{x}_0$ is a limit point of the domain of f if and only if it is a limit point of the domain of each f_i. Suppose Equation (2) holds and

$\epsilon > 0$ is given. Then there exists $\delta > 0$ such that if $\mathbf{x}$ is in the domain of f and $0 < |\mathbf{x} - \mathbf{x}_0| < \delta$, then $|f(\mathbf{x}) - \mathbf{y}_0| < \epsilon$. Hence,

$$|f_i(\mathbf{x}) - b_i| \leq |f(\mathbf{x}) - \mathbf{y}_0| < \epsilon, \qquad i = 1, \ldots, m,$$

and so Equation (3) holds. Conversely, assume (3) and let $\epsilon > 0$ be given. Then there exists $\delta_i > 0$ such that if $\mathbf{x}$ is in the domain of f_i and $0 < |\mathbf{x} - \mathbf{x}_0| < \delta_i$, then

$$|f_i(\mathbf{x}) - b_i| < \frac{\epsilon}{\sqrt{m}}.$$

We set $\delta = \min \{\delta_1, \ldots, \delta_m\}$. If $\mathbf{x}$ is in the domain of f and

$$0 < |\mathbf{x} - \mathbf{x}_0| < \delta,$$

then

$$\max \{|f_i(\mathbf{x}) - b_i|\} < \frac{\epsilon}{\sqrt{m}}.$$

We now use the fact that, for any vector $\mathbf{x} = (x_1, \ldots, x_n)$,

$$|\mathbf{x}| \leq \sqrt{n} \max \{|x_1|, \ldots, |x_n|\}.$$

Then

$$|f(\mathbf{x}) - \mathbf{y}_0| \leq \sqrt{m} \max \{|f_i(\mathbf{x}) - b_i|\} < \epsilon.$$

This completes the proof.

EXAMPLE 4. Vector functions f_1 and f_2 are defined by

$$f_1(t) = \begin{pmatrix} t \\ t^2 \\ \sin t \end{pmatrix}, \qquad f_2(t) = \begin{pmatrix} t \\ t^2 \\ \sin \dfrac{1}{t} \end{pmatrix}.$$

Then,

$$\lim_{t \to 0} f_1(t) = \begin{pmatrix} 0 \\ 0 \\ 0 \end{pmatrix},$$

but $\lim f_2(t)$ does not exist because the coordinate function $\sin (1/t)$ has no limit at $t = 0$.

The concept of continuity is essential in calculus. Roughly speaking, a continuous function f is one whose values do not change abruptly. That is, if $\mathbf{x}$ is close to $\mathbf{x}_0$, then $f(\mathbf{x})$ must be close to $f(\mathbf{x}_0)$ This idea is related to the notion of limit, and the definition of continuity is as follows: **A function f is continuous at $\mathbf{x}_0$** if $\mathbf{x}_0$ is in the domain of f and $\lim_{\mathbf{x} \to \mathbf{x}_0} f(\mathbf{x}) = f(\mathbf{x}_0)$. At a non-limit or **isolated** point of the domain of f we cannot ask for a limit, but instead we simply define f to be automatically continuous at such a point. It is an immediate corollary of Theorem 2.1 that

2.2 Theorem. A vector function is continuous at a point if and only if its coordinate functions are continuous there.

EXAMPLE 5. The function

$$f_1(t) = \begin{pmatrix} t \\ t^2 \\ \sin t \end{pmatrix}$$

is continuous at every value of t. On the other hand, the function

$$f_2(t) = \begin{pmatrix} t \\ t^2 \\ \sin \dfrac{1}{t} \end{pmatrix}$$

is continuous except at $t = 0$.

2.3 Theorem. Every linear function $\mathscr{R}^n \xrightarrow{L} \mathscr{R}^m$ is continuous, and for such an L there is a number k such that

$$|L(\mathbf{x})| \le k\,|\mathbf{x}|, \qquad \text{for every } \mathbf{x} \text{ in } \mathscr{R}^n.$$

Proof. We prove the inequality first. Let $\mathbf{e}_1, \ldots, \mathbf{e}_n$ be the natural basis for $\mathscr{R}^n$, so that if $\mathbf{x} = (x_1, \ldots, x_n)$, then $\mathbf{x} = x_1\mathbf{e}_1 + \cdots + x_n\mathbf{e}_n$. Since L is linear,

$$L(\mathbf{x}) = x_1 L(\mathbf{e}_1) + \cdots + x_n L(\mathbf{e}_n).$$

By the homogeneity and triangle properties of the norm, we have

$$|L(\mathbf{x})| \le |x_1|\,|L(\mathbf{e}_1)| + \cdots + |x_n|\,|L(\mathbf{e}_n)|.$$

Setting $k = |L(\mathbf{e}_1)| + \cdots + |L(\mathbf{e}_n)|$, and using the fact that $|x_i| \le |\mathbf{x}|$ for $i = 1, \ldots, n$, gives the desired inequality.

We use the inequality to show that L is continuous. If $\mathbf{x}$ and $\mathbf{x}_0$ are vectors in $\mathscr{R}^n$,

$$|L(\mathbf{x}) - L(\mathbf{x}_0)| = |L(\mathbf{x} - \mathbf{x}_0)|$$
$$\le k\,|\mathbf{x} - \mathbf{x}_0|.$$

This shows that as $\mathbf{x}$ tends to $\mathbf{x}_0$, $L(\mathbf{x})$ tends to $L(\mathbf{x}_0)$.

A function is simply called **continuous** if it is continuous at every point of its domain. From Theorem 2.2 we conclude that a continuous vector-valued function of a single variable, $\mathscr{R} \xrightarrow{f} \mathscr{R}^n$, is precisely one for which the coordinate functions $f_1, \ldots, f_n$ are continuous real-valued functions of a real variable. The latter of course include most of the functions of ordinary calculus, such as x^2, $\sin x$, and, for $x > 0$, $\log x$. These same functions can be used to construct examples of the continuous coordinate functions that go to make up a vector-valued function of a vector variable, $\mathcal{R}^n \xrightarrow{f} \mathcal{R}^m$. For example the coordinate functions of

$$f(x, y) = \left(\frac{\sin xy}{e^{x+y}}, \frac{\cos xy}{e^{x+y}}\right)$$

are continuous. The continuity of these and other examples can be deduced from repeated application of the following three theorems:

2.4 The functions $\mathcal{R}^n \xrightarrow{P_k} \mathcal{R}$, where $P_k(x_1, \ldots, x_n) = x_k$, are continuous for $k = 1, 2, \ldots, n$.

2.5 The functions $\mathcal{R}^2 \xrightarrow{S} \mathcal{R}$ and $\mathcal{R}^2 \xrightarrow{M} \mathcal{R}$, defined by $S(x, y) = x + y$ and $M(x, y) = xy$, are continuous.

2.6 If $\mathcal{R}^n \xrightarrow{f} \mathcal{R}^m$ and $\mathcal{R}^m \xrightarrow{g} \mathcal{R}^p$ are continuous, then the composition $g \circ f$ given by $g \circ f(\mathbf{x}) = g(f(\mathbf{x}))$ is continuous wherever it is defined.

Proving the continuity of P_k, S, and M is left as an exercise.

Proof of 2.6. We assume that $\mathbf{x}_0$ is a limit point of the domain of $g \circ f$ and show that $\lim_{\mathbf{x} \to \mathbf{x}_0} g \circ f(\mathbf{x}) = g \circ f(\mathbf{x}_0)$. If $\epsilon > 0$, we can, by the continuity of g, find a $\delta > 0$ such that $|g(\mathbf{y}) - g(f(\mathbf{x}_0))| < \epsilon$ whenever $|\mathbf{y} - f(\mathbf{x}_0)| < \delta$ and $\mathbf{y}$ is in the domain of g. But since f is also continuous, we can find a $\delta' > 0$ such that $|f(\mathbf{x}) - f(\mathbf{x}_0)| < \delta$ if $|\mathbf{x} - \mathbf{x}_0| < \delta'$ and $\mathbf{x}$ is in the domain of f. It follows that $|g \circ f(\mathbf{x}) - g \circ f(\mathbf{x}_0)| = |g(f(\mathbf{x})) - g(f(\mathbf{x}_0))| < \epsilon$ for these same vectors $\mathbf{x}$, and hence that $g \circ f$ is continuous at $\mathbf{x}_0$. Since $\mathbf{x}_0$ was an arbitrary limit point of the domain of $g \circ f$, the proof is complete.

EXAMPLE 6. The function $f(x, y) = \sqrt{1 - x^2 - y^2}$, defined for $|(x, y)| \leq 1$, is continuous, because it can be written

$$f(x, y) = \sqrt{1 - (P_1(x, y))^2 - (P_2(x, y))^2},$$

and so is a composition of continuous functions. Similarly, $g(x, y) = \log(x + y)$, defined for $x + y > 0$, is continuous. The product of f and g, given by

$$h(x, y) = \sqrt{1 - x^2 - y^2} \log(x + y),$$

is defined on the half-disc which is the intersection of the domains of f and g, and which is shown in Figure 16. The product is a continuous function because it is the com-

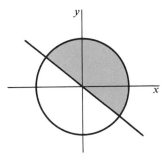

Figure 16

position of the continuous vector function

$$F(x, y) = (f(x, y), g(x, y))$$

with the function M of 2.5.

A vector $\mathbf{x}_0$ is an interior point of a subset of a vector space if all points sufficiently close to $\mathbf{x}_0$ are also in the subset. Consider, for example, the subset S of $\mathscr{R}^2$ consisting of all points (x, y) such that $0 < x \leq 2$ and $-1 \leq y < 1$ (cf. Figure 17). The points $(1, 0)$, $(\frac{1}{2}, \frac{1}{2})$, $(1, -1)$, $(2, 0)$ all belong to S. The first two are interior points and the last two are not. More generally, the interior points of S are precisely those (x, y) that satisfy the inequalities $0 < x < 2$ and $-1 < y < 1$. The formal definition is as follows: $\mathbf{x}_0$ is an **interior point** of a subset S of $\mathscr{R}^n$ if there exists a positive real number δ such that $\mathbf{x}$ belongs to S whenever $|\mathbf{x} - \mathbf{x}_0| < \delta$.

A subset of $\mathscr{R}^n$, all of whose points are interior, is called **open**. Notice that according to this definition the whole space $\mathscr{R}^n$ is an open set. So also is the empty subset ϕ of $\mathscr{R}^n$. Since ϕ contains no points, the condition for openness is vacuously satisfied. An open set containing a particular point is often called a **neighborhood** of that point.

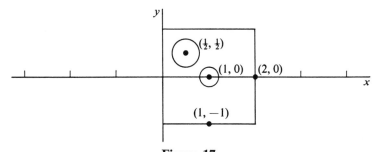

Figure 17

EXAMPLE 6. For any $\epsilon > 0$ and any $\mathbf{x}_0$ in $\mathscr{R}^n$, the set B_ϵ of all vectors $\mathbf{x}$ such that $|\mathbf{x} - \mathbf{x}_0| < \epsilon$ is open. In 3-dimensional space, for example, B_ϵ is the ϵ-ball pictured in Figure 12 for $\epsilon = 0.5$. Let $\mathbf{x}_1$ be an arbitrary point in B_ϵ. Then $|\mathbf{x}_1 - \mathbf{x}_0| < \epsilon$. We must show that every vector sufficiently close to $\mathbf{x}_1$ is in B_ϵ. Set

$$\delta = \epsilon - |\mathbf{x}_1 - \mathbf{x}_0|.$$

Then δ is positive. Suppose $\mathbf{x}$ is any vector such that $|\mathbf{x} - \mathbf{x}_1| < \delta$. By the triangle inequality,

$$\begin{aligned}
|\mathbf{x} - \mathbf{x}_0| &= |(\mathbf{x} - \mathbf{x}_1) + (\mathbf{x}_1 - \mathbf{x}_0)| \\
&\leq |\mathbf{x} - \mathbf{x}_1| + |\mathbf{x}_1 - \mathbf{x}_0| \\
&< \delta + (\epsilon - \delta) = \epsilon.
\end{aligned}$$

Hence, $\mathbf{x}$ is in B_ϵ, and the proof is complete.

EXAMPLE 7. Let I be a finite set of points in $\mathscr{R}^n$. Then the set consisting of all points in $\mathscr{R}^n$ that are not in I is open. Thus a vector function that is defined at all points of $\mathscr{R}^n$ except for some finite set has for its domain an open subset of $\mathscr{R}^n$.

Two basic properties of open sets are described in the following simple theorems. The proof of the first is left as an exercise.

2.7 Theorem. The union of an arbitrary collection of open subsets of $\mathscr{R}^n$ is open.

2.8 Theorem. The intersection of two open subsets of $\mathscr{R}^n$ is open.

Proof (of Theorem 2.8). Consider a point $\mathbf{x}_0$ belonging to both of two open subsets S_1 and S_2 of $\mathscr{R}^n$. Since S_i is open, $i = 1, 2$, there exists $\delta_i > 0$ such that if $|\mathbf{x} - \mathbf{x}_0| < \delta_i$, then $\mathbf{x}$ is in S_i. Set $\delta = \min\{\delta_1, \delta_2\}$. Clearly, if $|\mathbf{x} - \mathbf{x}_0| < \delta$ then $\mathbf{x}$ belongs to $S_1 \cap S_2$.

Theorem 2.8 of course implies that the intersection of any finite number of open subsets of $\mathscr{R}^n$ is open.

A set S is **closed** if it contains all its limit points, and the **closure** of S is the set S together with its limit points. The **boundary** of S is the closure of S with the interior of S deleted. Thus an interval $a \leq x \leq b$, denoted $[a, b]$, is called a closed interval and is in fact a closed set in the above sense. An open interval $a < x < b$, denoted (a, b), is on the other hand an open set.

EXERCISES

In Exercises 1 and 2 take the domains of the functions to be as large as possible.

1. At which points do the following functions fail to have limits?

(a) $f\begin{pmatrix} x \\ y \end{pmatrix} = \begin{pmatrix} y + \tan x \\ \ln (x + y) \end{pmatrix}$.

(b) $f\begin{pmatrix} x \\ y \end{pmatrix} = \begin{pmatrix} \dfrac{y}{x^2 + 1} \\ \dfrac{x}{y^2 - 1} \end{pmatrix}$.

(c) $f(x, y) = \dfrac{x}{\sin x} + y$.

(d) $f(x, y) = \begin{cases} \dfrac{x}{\sin x} + y, & \text{if } x \neq 0. \\ 2 + y, & \text{if } x = 0. \end{cases}$

(e) $f(t) = \begin{pmatrix} \sin t \\ \cos t \\ \sin \dfrac{1}{t^2} \end{pmatrix}$

2. At which points do the following functions fail to be continuous?

(a) $f\begin{pmatrix} x \\ y \end{pmatrix} = \begin{pmatrix} \dfrac{1}{x^2} + \dfrac{1}{y^2} \\ x^2 + y^2 \end{pmatrix}$

(b) $f\begin{pmatrix} u \\ v \end{pmatrix} = \begin{pmatrix} 3u - 4v \\ u + 8v \end{pmatrix}$

(c) $f(x, y) = \begin{cases} \dfrac{\sin x}{x} + y, & \text{if } x \neq 0. \\ 1 + y, & \text{if } x = 0. \end{cases}$

(d) $f\begin{pmatrix} x \\ y \end{pmatrix} = \begin{cases} \dfrac{x^2 - y^2}{x^2 + y^2}, & \text{if } x^2 + y^2 \neq 0 \\ 0, & \text{if } x^2 + y^2 = 0 \end{cases}$

(e) $f\begin{pmatrix} u \\ v \end{pmatrix} = \begin{pmatrix} v \tan u \\ u \sec v \\ v \end{pmatrix}$

(f) $f(\mathbf{x}) = \dfrac{|\mathbf{x}|}{1 - |\mathbf{x}|^2}$

3. When $\mathbf{x}_0 = (1, 2)$, draw the set of all vectors $\mathbf{x}$ in $\mathscr{R}^2$ such that

(a) $|\mathbf{x} - \mathbf{x}_0| \leq 3$
(b) $|\mathbf{x} - \mathbf{x}_0| = 3$
(c) $|\mathbf{x} - \mathbf{x}_0| < 3$

4. Identify as open, closed, both, or neither, the subset of $\mathscr{R}^2$ consisting of all vectors $\mathbf{x} = (x, y)$ such that

(a) $|\mathbf{x} - (1, 2)| \leq 0.5$.
(b) $|\mathbf{x} - (1, 2)| < 0.5$.
(c) $|\mathbf{x} - (1, 2)| < -0.5$.
(d) $0 < x < 3$ and $0 < y < 2$.
(e) $2 \leq x < 3$ and $0 < y < 2$.
(f) $\dfrac{x^2}{a^2} + \dfrac{y^2}{b^2} < 1$.
(g) $\mathbf{x} \neq (0, 2)$ or $(1, 2)$.
(h) $x^2 + y^2 > 0$.
(i) $x > 0$.
(j) $x > y$.

5. Let the set S consist of the points (x, y) in $\mathscr{R}^2$ satisfying $0 < x^2 + y^2 < 1$, together with the interval $1 \leq x < 2$ of the x-axis.

(a) Describe the boundary of S.
(b) What are the interior points of S?
(c) Describe the closure of S.

6. Prove Theorem 2.7.

7. Prove that $\mathbf{x}$ is a boundary point of a set S if and only if every neighborhood of $\mathbf{x}$ contains a point of S and a point of the complement of S.

8. A vector function f is said to have a **removable discontinuity** at $\mathbf{x}_0$ if (a) f is not continuous at $\mathbf{x}_0$, (b) there is a vector $\mathbf{y}_0$ such that $\lim_{\mathbf{x} \to \mathbf{x}_0} f(\mathbf{x}) = \mathbf{y}_0$. Give an example of a function f and a point $\mathbf{x}_0$ such that f is not continuous at $\mathbf{x}_0$ and (1) f has a removable discontinuity at $\mathbf{x}_0$, (2) f does not have a removable discontinuity at $\mathbf{x}_0$.

9. Prove that every translation is a continuous vector function. A vector function $\mathscr{R}^n \xrightarrow{t} \mathscr{R}^n$ is a **translation** if there exists a vector $\mathbf{y}_0$ in $\mathscr{R}^n$ such that $t(\mathbf{x}) = \mathbf{x} + \mathbf{y}_0$ for all $\mathbf{x}$ in $\mathscr{R}^n$.

10. Prove 2.4 and 2.5 of the text.

11. If f and g are vector functions with the same domain and same range space, prove

$$\lim_{\mathbf{x} \to \mathbf{x}_0} (f(\mathbf{x}) + g(\mathbf{x})) = \lim_{\mathbf{x} \to \mathbf{x}_0} f(\mathbf{x}) + \lim_{\mathbf{x} \to \mathbf{x}_0} g(\mathbf{x}),$$

provided that $\lim_{\mathbf{x} \to \mathbf{x}_0} f(\mathbf{x})$ and $\lim_{\mathbf{x} \to \mathbf{x}_0} g(\mathbf{x})$ exist.

12. Let $\mathscr{L}$ be a line and $\mathscr{P}$ a plane in $\mathscr{R}^3$. Is either $\mathscr{P}$ or $\mathscr{L}$ an open subset?

13. Let S be a closed subset of $\mathscr{R}^n$. Prove that the complement of S in $\mathscr{R}^n$ is open.

14. Converse of Exercise 13: If S is an open subset of $\mathscr{R}^n$, show that the complement of S in $\mathscr{R}^n$ is closed.

15. Show that $\sqrt{a^2 + b^2} \leq |a| + |b|$.

16. Show that $|(x_1, \ldots, x_n)| \leq \sqrt{n} \max \{|x_1|, \ldots, |x_n|\}$.

3. DERIVATIVES OF FUNCTIONS OF ONE VARIABLE

A continuous function $\mathscr{R} \xrightarrow{g} \mathscr{R}^n$, with $g(t)$ defined for $a < t < b$, determines parametrically a curve γ in $\mathscr{R}^n$. Several 2 and 3-dimensional examples are given in Section 1. In the next three sections we shall look at some ways in which the characteristics of a particular function g that is used to represent γ can be translated into geometric statements about γ. First we shall define the derivative of g and show how it leads to the definition of tangent vector and tangent line to γ.

The function g has a **derivative** $g'(t)$ at a point t in the interval (a, b) if

$$g'(t) = \lim_{h \to 0} \frac{g(t + h) - g(t)}{h}.$$

If the limit exists for each t in (a, b), then $g'(t)$ determines a new function $\mathscr{R} \xrightarrow{g'} \mathscr{R}^n$, just as in the case $n = 1$. The derivative is often written dg/dt.

EXAMPLE 1. Let $g(t) = (t^2, t^3)$. Then

$$\lim_{h \to 0} \frac{g(t + h) - g(t)}{h} = \lim_{h \to 0} \frac{1}{h} \begin{pmatrix} (t + h)^2 - t^2 \\ (t + h)^3 - t^3 \end{pmatrix}$$

$$= \lim_{h \to 0} \begin{pmatrix} \dfrac{(t + h)^2 - t^2}{h} \\ \dfrac{(t + h)^3 - t^3}{h} \end{pmatrix}.$$

Since $\lim_{h \to 0} ((t + h)^2 - t^2)/h = 2t$ and $\lim_{h \to 0} ((t + h)^3 - t^3)/h = 3t^2$, the limit $g'(t)$ exists by Theorem 2.1, and $g'(t) = (2t, 3t^2)$.

The previous example suggests that a function $\mathscr{R} \xrightarrow{g} \mathscr{R}^n$ has a derivative at a point t if and only if each coordinate function of g has a derivative there. This is true, and in fact we have

3.1   If $g(t) = \begin{pmatrix} g_1(t) \\ \cdot \\ \cdot \\ \cdot \\ g_n(t) \end{pmatrix}$, then $g'(t) = \begin{pmatrix} g_1'(t) \\ \cdot \\ \cdot \\ \cdot \\ g_n'(t) \end{pmatrix}$ where the derivatives $g_k'(t)$ are

ordinary derivatives of real-valued functions of a real variable. The result is an immediate consequence of Theorem 2.1, relating the limit of a vector function to the limits of its coordinate functions.

EXAMPLE 2. If

$$g(t) = \begin{pmatrix} \cos t \\ \sin t \end{pmatrix}, \quad \text{then} \quad g'(t) = \begin{pmatrix} -\sin t \\ \cos t \end{pmatrix}.$$

If

$$h(t) = \begin{pmatrix} t \\ t^2 \\ t^3 \end{pmatrix}, \quad \text{then} \quad h'(t) = \begin{pmatrix} 1 \\ 2t \\ 3t^2 \end{pmatrix}.$$

It is clear from Figure 18 that the vector $g(t + h) - g(t)$ has a direction which, as h tends to 0, should tend to what we would like to call the tangent direction to the curve γ at $g(t)$. However, since g is assumed continuous,

$$\lim_{h \to 0} g(t + h) - g(t) = 0,$$

and the zero vector that we get as a limit has no direction. This difficulty is overcome in most examples by dividing by h before letting h tend to zero. Observe that division by h will not change the direction of $g(t + h) - g(t)$ if h is positive, and will reverse it if h is negative. A glance at Figure 18 shows that this reversal is desirable for our purposes. (What would be wrong with

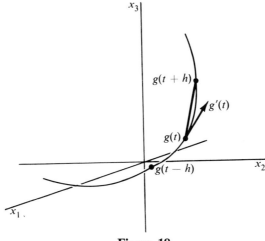

Figure 18

dividing by $|h|$?) The derivative $g'(t)$, if it exists and is not zero, is called the **tangent vector** to γ at $g(t)$. Of course, any nonzero multiple of $g'(t)$ is then called *a* tangent vector, and the line with direction vector $g'(t)$, and passing through $g(t)$, is called the **tangent line** to γ at $g(t)$. Thus, if $g(t_0)$ is a particular point on a curve, the tangent line at $g(t_0)$ will have a parametric representation of the form

$$tg'(t_0) + g(t_0).$$

The tangent vector $g'(t_0)$ is usually pictured with its tail at $g(t_0)$ as in Figure 18.

EXAMPLE 3. The circle defined parametrically by $g(t) = (\cos t,\ \sin t)$ has a tangent vector at $g(t_0)$ given by $g'(t_0) = (-\sin t_0,\ \cos t_0)$. In particular, the tangent vector at $g(\pi/4) = (1/\sqrt{2},\ 1/\sqrt{2})$ is $g'(\pi/4) = (-1/\sqrt{2},\ 1/\sqrt{2})$. Hence the tangent line to the circle at $(1/\sqrt{2},\ 1/\sqrt{2})$ has a parametric representation $(x, y) = t(-1/\sqrt{2},\ 1/\sqrt{2}) + (1/\sqrt{2},\ 1/\sqrt{2})$. The line is shown in Figure 19, together with some tangent vectors, each of which has length $|g'(t_0)| = 1$.

For the spiral curve given by $f(t) = (\cos t,\ \sin t,\ t)$, we have $f'(0) = (0, 1, 1)$. The tangent line to the spiral at $(1, 0, 0)$ can be represented by

$$\begin{pmatrix} x \\ y \\ z \end{pmatrix} = t\begin{pmatrix} 0 \\ 1 \\ 1 \end{pmatrix} + \begin{pmatrix} 1 \\ 0 \\ 0 \end{pmatrix},$$

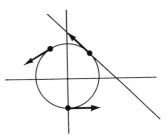

and in this case the tangent vector $f'(0)$ has length $\sqrt{2}$.

Figure 19

One reason for singling out $g'(t)$ for special attention as *the* tangent vector, rather than some multiple of it, is that we often want to consider the parameter t as a time variable, and $g(t)$ as representing the path of a point moving in $\mathscr{R}^n$. Under this interpretation, the euclidean length $|g'(t)|$ is the natural definition for the speed of motion along the path γ described by $g(t)$ as t varies. To justify the use of the term "speed", we observe that, for small h, the number $|g(t+h) - g(t)|/|h|$ is close to the average rate of traversal of γ over the interval from t to $t+h$. In addition, if $g'(t)$ exists, it is easy to show that

$$\lim_{h \to 0} \frac{|g(t+h) - g(t)|}{|h|} = |g'(t)|.$$

In fact,

$$\left| \frac{|g(t+h) - g(t)|}{|h|} - |g'(t)| \right| \leq \left| \frac{g(t+h) - g(t)}{h} - g'(t) \right|,$$

which tends to zero as h tends to zero. Thus $|g'(t)|$ is a limit of average rates over arbitrarily small time intervals. For this reason the real-valued function v defined by $v(t) = |g'(t)|$ is called the **speed** of g, and the vector $\mathbf{v}(t) = g'(t)$ is called its **velocity vector** at the point $g(t)$. The vector $\mathbf{v}(t)$ is, of course, the same as what we have called the tangent vector to γ at $g(t)$, provided $\mathbf{v}(t) \neq 0$.

EXAMPLE 4. If a point moves in the plane so that at time t its position is $g(t) = (t^2, t^3)$, then the velocity vector is $\mathbf{v}(t) = (2t, 3t^2)$, and $v(t) = \sqrt{4t^2 + 9t^4}$. In particular, $\mathbf{v}(0) = 0$. The path traced by g is shown in Figure 20 for $-1 \leq t \leq 1$, and in drawing the picture it is helpful to observe that the coordinates of a point on the path satisfy the equation $y^2 = x^3$.

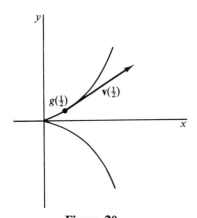

The fact that the tangent vector shrinks to zero in this example as $g(t)$ approaches the origin is a reflection of the fact that if the velocity vector varies continuously, the speed must be zero at an abrupt change in the direction of motion. In this way the parametrization describes the physical situation well. However, for the purpose of assigning a tangent line to the path at the origin, the given parametrization is not useful.

Figure 20

EXAMPLE 5. Let $f(t) = (\cos t, \sin t, t)$, as in the second part of Example 3. Then $\mathbf{v}(t) = (-\sin t, \cos t, 1)$. It follows that the velocity vector is always perpendicular to the vector $(\cos t, \sin t, 0)$ that points from the axis of the spiral to $f(t)$. The speed at any time t is $v(t) = |\mathbf{v}(t)| = \sqrt{2}$.

We list here some useful formulas that hold if f and g each has a vector derivative on an interval (a, b) and φ is real-valued and differentiable there.

3.2 $(f + g)' = f' + g'$, $(cf)' = cf'$, c constant.

3.3 $(\varphi f)' = \varphi f' + \varphi' f$.

3.4 $(f \cdot g)' = f \cdot g' + f' \cdot g$.

3.5 $(f(u))' = u'f'(u)$, where u is a real-valued, differentiable function of one variable, with its range in (a, b).

These can all be proved by writing f and g in terms of their coordinate functions and then applying the corresponding differentiation formulas for real-valued functions, together with Formula 3.1. For example, the proof of 3.5, a version of the chain rule for differentiation, goes like this:

$$(f(u))' = (f_1(u), \ldots, f_n(u))'$$
$$= ([f_1(u)]', \ldots, [f_n(u)]')$$
$$= (f_1'(u)u', \ldots, f_n'(u)u') = u'f'(u).$$

If $\mathscr{R} \xrightarrow{g} \mathscr{R}^n$ has a derivative $\mathscr{R} \xrightarrow{g'} \mathscr{R}^n$, then we can ask for the derivative of g', which we denote by g''. Thus we have $\mathscr{R} \xrightarrow{g''} \mathscr{R}^n$, though g'' may be defined at fewer points than g or even g'. We also write d^2g/dt^2 for g'', and so on for higher order derivatives.

EXAMPLE 6. Let $\mathscr{R} \xrightarrow{g} \mathscr{R}^3$ describe a path in $\mathscr{R}^3$ with velocity vector $\mathbf{v}(t)$ and speed $v(t)$ at each point $g(t)$. Then $\mathbf{t}(t) = (1/v(t))\mathbf{v}(t)$ is a tangent vector of length 1, provided $v(t) \neq 0$. In any case, we can write $g'(t) = v(t)\mathbf{t}(t)$. If we assume that g' has a derivative, we define the **acceleration vector** at $g(t)$ by $\mathbf{a}(t) = g''(t)$. The physical significance of $\mathbf{a}(t)$ is that if $g(t)$ describes the motion of a particle of constant mass m, then $m\mathbf{a}(t)$ is the **force vector** $F(t)$ acting on the particle. If we denote by $a(t)$ the length of $\mathbf{a}(t)$, then $a(t)$ is the **magnitude of the acceleration**, and $ma(t)$ is the **magnitude of the force** acting on the particle.

If $\mathbf{t}(t)$ is a unit tangent vector at $g(t)$, the equation $g'(t) = v(t)\mathbf{t}(t)$ implies that $\mathbf{a} = (v\mathbf{t})'$. Applying Formula 3.3, we get $\mathbf{a} = v'\mathbf{t} + v\mathbf{t}'$. Thus if $\mathbf{t}'(t) = 0$, the acceleration vector, and hence the force vector at $g(t)$, has either the same or else the opposite direction to the motion. On the other hand, if $\mathbf{t}'(t) \neq 0$, we can define the unit vector $\mathbf{n}$ by $\mathbf{n}(t) = \mathbf{t}'(t)/|\mathbf{t}'(t)|$, and so the acceleration vector can be written

$$\mathbf{a} = v'\mathbf{t} + v|\mathbf{t}'|\mathbf{n}.$$

This equation expresses the acceleration $\mathbf{a}(t)$ at each point $g(t)$ in terms of an orthonormal pair of vectors $\mathbf{t}(t)$ and $\mathbf{n}(t)$. For we have $|\mathbf{t}| = |\mathbf{n}| = 1$

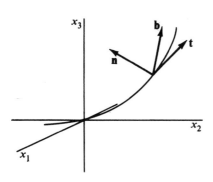

Figure 21

by the definition of these vectors, and application of Formula 3.4 to the equation $\mathbf{t} \cdot \mathbf{t} = 1$ gives $\mathbf{t} \cdot \mathbf{t'} = 0$. But by the definition of $\mathbf{n}$, this implies $\mathbf{t} \cdot \mathbf{n} = 0$.

The pair $\mathbf{t}(t)$, $\mathbf{n}(t)$ should be pictured at $g(t)$ as in Figure 21. The third unit vector $\mathbf{b}(t)$ shown there is defined by $\mathbf{b} = \mathbf{t} \times \mathbf{n}$, and is called the **binormal vector** to the path, while $\mathbf{n}$ is called the **principal normal**. Thus any vector naturally associated with the point $g(t)$ on the path can be written as a linear combination of the triple $\{\mathbf{t}(t), \mathbf{n}(t), \mathbf{b}(t)\}$, which changes as we go from point to point along the path.

EXERCISES

1. If $g(t) = (e^t, t)$ for all real t, sketch in $\mathscr{R}^2$ the curve described by g together with the tangent vectors $g'(0)$ and $g'(1)$.

2. Let $f(t) = (t, t^2, t^3)$ for $0 \leq t \leq 1$.
    (a) Sketch the curve described by f in $\mathscr{R}^3$ and the tangent line at $(\frac{1}{2}, \frac{1}{4}, \frac{1}{8})$.
    (b) Find $|f'(t)|$.
    (c) If $f(t) = (t, t^2, t^3)$ for all real t, find all points of the curve described by f at which the tangent vector is parallel to the vector $(4, 4, 3)$. Are there any points at which the tangent is perpendicular to $(4, 4, 3)$?

3. Sketch the curve represented by $(x, y) = (t^3, t^5)$, and show that the parametrization fails to assign a tangent vector at the origin. Find a parametrization of the curve that does assign a tangent at the origin.

4. Show that the curve described by $g(t) = (\sin 2t, 2 \sin^2 t, 2 \cos t)$ lies on a sphere centered at the origin in $\mathscr{R}^3$. Find the length of the velocity vector $\mathbf{v}(t)$ and show that the projection of this vector into the x, y-plane has a constant length.

5. (a) Show that if $\mathscr{R} \xrightarrow{\mathbf{v}} \mathscr{R}^3$ is continuous for $0 \leq t$, then there is a unique path g through a given point $g(0)$ in $\mathscr{R}^3$, having $\mathbf{v}(t)$ as its velocity vector at $g(t)$.
    (b) Show that a continuous function $\mathscr{R} \xrightarrow{\mathbf{a}} \mathscr{R}^3$ defined for $0 \leq t$, determines a unique path in $\mathscr{R}^3$, having $\mathbf{a}(t)$ as its acceleration vector, provided the initial point $g(0)$ and initial velocity $\mathbf{v}(0)$ are specified.

6. Suppose a target moves with constant speed $v > 0$ on a circular path of radius r, and that a missile, also having constant speed v, pursues the target by starting from the center of the circle, always remaining between the center and the target. When does the missile hit the target?

7. Prove (a) 3.2, (b) 3.3, (c) 3.4 of the text.

8. Show that if f is vector valued, differentiable, and never zero for $a < t < b$, then

(a) $f \cdot \dfrac{df}{dt} = |f| \dfrac{d|f|}{dt}$.

(b) $|f|$ is constant if and only if $f \cdot f' = 0$.

(c) (If $f(t)$ is in $\mathscr{R}^3$) $f(t)$ has a constant direction if and only if $f \times f' \equiv 0$.

9. Consider the vector differential equation

$$\mathbf{x}'' + a\mathbf{x}' + b\mathbf{x} = 0,$$

to be solved for a function $\mathbf{x}(t)$ taking values in $\mathscr{R}^n$ and defined on some interval. We assume that a and b are constants. Show that if the real equation $r^2 + ar + b = 0$ has distinct roots r_1 and r_2, then the differential equation has a solution of the form

$$\mathbf{x}(t) = \mathbf{c}_1 e^{r_1 t} + \mathbf{c}_2 e^{r_2 t},$$

where $\mathbf{c}_1$ and $\mathbf{c}_2$ are constant vectors in $\mathscr{R}^n$. What happens if $r_1 = r_2$?

10. Prove that $(f \times g)' = (f \times g') + (f' \times g)$, where f and g take values in $\mathscr{R}^3$ and are differentiable on an interval.

11. Show that if $\mathscr{R} \xrightarrow{g} \mathscr{R}^n$ has a derivative and $g'(t) = 0$ for $a < t < b$, then $g(t)$ is a constant vector on that interval. [*Hint.* Apply the mean-value theorem to each coordinate function.]

12. Let a differentiable function $g(t)$ represent the position in $\mathscr{R}^3$ at time t of a particle of possibly varying mass $m(t)$. The vector function $P(t) = m(t)\mathbf{v}(t)$ is called the **linear momentum** of the particle. The **force vector** is $F(t) = (m(t)\mathbf{v}(t))'$. The **angular momentum** about the origin is $L(t) = g(t) \times P(t)$, and the **torque** about the origin is $N(t) = g(t) \times F(t)$.

(a) Show that if F is identically zero, then P is constant. This is called the law of conservation of linear momentum.

(b) Show that $L'(t) = N(t)$, and hence that if N is identically zero, then L is constant. This is called the law of conservation of angular momentum.

13. Show that if a particle has an acceleration vector $\mathbf{a}(t)$ at time t and $v(t) \neq 0$, then $v' = \mathbf{t} \cdot \mathbf{a}$, where $\mathbf{t}$ is the unit vector $(1/v)\mathbf{v}$.

14. Let $\mathscr{R} \xrightarrow{f} \mathscr{R}^n$ be a function defined for $a \leq t \leq b$. If the coordinate functions $f_1, \ldots, f_n$ of f are integrable, we can define the integral of f over the interval $[a, b]$ by

$$\int_a^b f(t)\, dt = \left(\int_a^b f_1(t)\, dt, \ldots, \int_a^b f_n(t)\, dt \right).$$

(a) If $f(t) = (\cos t, \sin t)$ for $0 \leq t \leq \pi/2$, compute $\int_0^{\pi/2} f(t)\, dt$.

(b) If $g(t) = (t, t^2, t^3)$ for $0 \leq t \leq 1$, compute $\int_0^1 g(t)\, dt$.

15. If $\mathscr{R} \xrightarrow{f} \mathscr{R}^n$ and $\mathscr{R} \xrightarrow{g} \mathscr{R}^n$ are both integrable over $[a, b]$, show by using the corresponding properties of integrals of real-valued functions that:

$$\int_a^b kf(t)\, dt = k \int_a^b f(t)\, dt, \qquad k \text{ any real number.}$$

$$\int_a^b (f(t) + g(t))\, dt = \int_a^b f(t)\, dt + \int_a^b g(t)\, dt,$$

where the integrals are as defined in the previous exercise.

16. If $\mathscr{R} \xrightarrow{f} \mathscr{R}^n$ is defined for $a \leq t \leq b$, and f' is continuous there, prove the following extension of the fundamental theorem of calculus:

$$\int_a^b f'(t)\, dt = f(b) - f(a).$$

17. If $\mathscr{R} \xrightarrow{f} \mathscr{R}^n$ is continuous over $[a, b]$,

(a) Show that

$$\int_a^b \mathbf{k} \cdot f(t)\, dt = \mathbf{k} \cdot \int_a^b f(t)\, dt,$$

where $\mathbf{k}$ is a constant vector.

(b) Show that

$$\left| \int_a^b f(t)\, dt \right| \leq \int_a^b |f(t)|\, dt.$$

[*Hint.* By the Cauchy-Schwarz inequality

$$f(u) \cdot \int_a^b f(t)\, dt \leq |f(u)| \left| \int_a^b f(t)\, dt \right|, \qquad \text{for each } u.$$

Integrate with respect to u, and apply the result of Part (a).]

4. ARC LENGTH

The definition of length for vectors can be used to define the length of a parametrized curve γ. We assume that γ is described by a continuous function $\mathscr{R} \xrightarrow{g} \mathscr{R}^n$, where the domain of g is a closed interval $a \leq t \leq b$. Thus γ is the image of $[a, b]$ under g. Corresponding to any finite set P of numbers $a = t_0 < t_1 < \ldots < t_K = b$, there are points $g(t_k)$, $k = 0, \ldots, K$, on γ. We join these points in order by a polygonal path as shown in Figure 22. The length of the kth segment of the polygonal approximation to γ is $|g(t_k) - g(t_{k-1})|$, and the total length of the polygon is

$$l(P) = \sum_{k=1}^K |g(t_k) - g(t_{k-1})|.$$

Let $l(\gamma)$ denote the least upper bound of the numbers $l(P)$. This will, of course, be infinite if the set of numbers $l(P)$ is unbounded. If $l(\gamma)$ is finite, then γ is said to be **rectifiable**, and $l(\gamma)$ is called its **length**. It is clear from the definition that $l(\gamma)$ depends on the function g that describes γ and not just on γ itself.

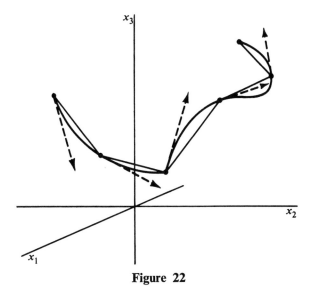

Figure 22

This is reasonable if we want to take into account the fact that some part of γ may be traced more than once by g. In practice this is very often what is wanted. If it should happen that g is not one-to-one, then we may write $l(g)$ instead of $l(\gamma)$ to emphasize the dependence on g.

The length of a path is usually awkward to compute directly from the definition. However, if γ is parametrized by a function g such that the tangent vector $g'(t)$ varies continuously with t, then $l(\gamma)$ is finite and equal to $\int_a^b |g'(t)|\, dt$. In fact, it is enough to assume that g is **piecewise smooth**, that is g' is continuously extendable to finitely many closed intervals with union $[a, b]$. This allows us to find the length of some curves for which the tangent has an abrupt change, as in Figure 22.

4.1 Theorem: Let a curve γ be parametrized by a piecewise smooth function $\mathcal{R} \xrightarrow{g} \mathcal{R}^n$, defined for $a \leq t \leq b$. Then $l(\gamma)$ is finite and

$$l(\gamma) = \int_a^b |g'(t)|\, dt.$$

The proof of this theorem is given in Appendix 3, and we shall give here only an argument that makes the integral formula plausible. Since by definition the existence of $g'(t_{k-1})$ means

$$\lim_{t_k \to t_{k-1}} \frac{g(t_k) - g(t_{k-1})}{t_k - t_{k-1}} = g'(t_{k-1}),$$

we have

$$g(t_k) - g(t_{k-1}) - (t_k - t_{k-1})g'(t_{k-1}) = (t_k - t_{k-1})Z(t_k - t_{k-1}),$$

where $Z(t_k - t_{k-1})$ satisfies

$$\lim_{t_k \to t_{k-1}} Z(t_k - t_{k-1}) = 0.$$

Thus $(t_k - t_{k-1})g'(t_{k-1})$ becomes a better approximation to $g(t_k) - g(t_{k-1})$ as $(t_k - t_{k-1})$ is made small. We are led to approximate

$$l(P) = \sum_{k=1}^{K} |g(t_k) - g(t_{k-1})|$$

by

$$\sum_{k=1}^{K} |g'(t_{k-1})| (t_k - t_{k-1}).$$

(Some of the tangent vectors $(t_k - t_{k-1})g'(t_{k-1})$ are shown in Figure 22.) But if g' is continuous, so is $|g'|$, and, letting $m(P) = \max_{1 \le k \le K} (t_k - t_{k-1})$, we have, to conclude the argument,

$$\lim_{m(P) \to 0} \sum_{k=1}^{K} |g'(t_{k-1})| (t_k - t_{k-1}) = \int_a^b |g'(t)| \, dt.$$

A curve in $\mathscr{R}^n$ will usually be described by coordinate functions. Thus, if γ is defined for $a \le t \le b$ by $g(t) = (g_1(t), g_2(t), g_3(t))$, then $|g'(t)| = \sqrt{(g_1'(t))^2 + (g_2'(t))^2 + (g_3'(t))^2}$, and so

$$l(g) = \int_a^b \sqrt{(g_1'(t))^2 + (g_2'(t))^2 + (g_3'(t))^2} \, dt,$$

with a similar formula holding in $\mathscr{R}^n$. For example, the spiral curve in $\mathscr{R}^3$ defined by $g(t) = (\cos t, \sin t, t)$ for $0 \le t \le 1$ has length

$$l(g) = \int_0^1 \sqrt{(-\sin t)^2 + (\cos t)^2 + 1} \, dt$$
$$= \sqrt{2}.$$

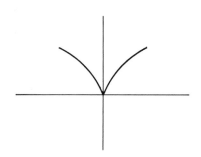

EXAMPLE 1. The plane curve defined by $g(t) = (t^2, |t|)$ for $-1 \le t \le 1$ is shown in Figure 23. Since g is piecewise smooth, $l(g)$ is finite. We have

Figure 23

$$g'(t) = \begin{cases} (2t, -1), -1 \le t < 0 \\ (2t, 1), 0 < t \le 1, \end{cases}$$

so $|g'(t)| = \sqrt{4t^2 + 1}$ for $-1 \le t \le 1$, $t \ne 0$. Then

$$l(g) = \int_{-1}^{1} \sqrt{4t^2 + 1} \, dt$$
$$= \sqrt{5} + (1/2) \log (2 + \sqrt{5}).$$

EXAMPLE 2. The graph γ of a real-valued continuous function f, defined for $a \le x \le b$, is a curve in $\mathscr{R}^2$ that can be described parametrically by the one-to-one function

$$g(x) = \begin{pmatrix} x \\ f(x) \end{pmatrix}, \qquad a \le x \le b.$$

If f' is continuous, then so is $|g'(x)| = \sqrt{1 + (f'(x))^2}$, and the formula for finding $l(\gamma)$ becomes in this case

$$l(\gamma) = \int_a^b \sqrt{1 + (f'(x))^2}\, dx.$$

If γ is a piecewise smooth curve described by a one-to-one function $g(t)$, $a \le t \le b$, we can think of $l(\gamma)$ as representing the total mass of γ, assuming γ has a uniform density equal to 1 at each point. More generally, if p is a real-valued function defined on γ, we can form the integral

$$\int_a^b p(g(t))\,|g'(t)|\, dt,$$

and, if it exists, call it the integral of p over γ. In particular, if p is a non-negative function that can be interpreted as the density per unit of length of a mass distribution over γ, the integral becomes the definition of the **total mass** m of the distribution.

EXAMPLE 3. Consider a full turn of the spiral curve described by $g(t) = (\cos t, \sin t, t)$ for $0 \le t \le 2\pi$. Suppose that the density of the curve at a point is equal to the square of the distance of that point from the midpoint $\mathbf{q}$ of the axis of the spiral. Relative to our description of the curve, this midpoint has coordinates $(0, 0, \pi)$. Thus the density at $g(t)$ is equal to

$$|g(t) - \mathbf{q}|^2 = \cos^2 t + \sin^2 t + (t - \pi)^2$$
$$= 1 + (t - \pi)^2.$$

Also, we have seen that $|g'(t)| = \sqrt{2}$. Hence, the total mass of the distribution is given by

$$m = \int_0^{2\pi} [1 + (t - \pi)^2]\sqrt{2}\, dt$$
$$= \sqrt{2} \int_{-\pi}^{\pi} (1 + t^2)\, dt = (\tfrac{2}{3})\sqrt{2}\,(3\pi + \pi^3).$$

If $g(t)$, with $a \le t \le b$, defines a smooth curve γ having a nonzero tangent at every point, then the function $s(t)$ defined by

4.2
$$s(t) = \int_a^t |g'(u)|\, du$$

is the length of the part of γ corresponding to the interval from a to t. Since $|g'(t)|$ is positive, the function $s(t)$ is strictly increasing. Thus $s(t)$ is a one-to-one function from the interval $a \le t \le b$ to the interval $0 \le s \le l(\gamma)$, and so has an inverse function. We denote this inverse simply by $t(s)$. We now form the vector function $h(s) = g(t(s))$, which describes the same curve γ that $g(t)$ does, but with a new parametrization in which the variable s, with

$0 \leq s \leq l(\gamma)$, represents the length of the path along γ from $h(0)$ to $h(s)$. The curve γ is then said to be parametrized by arc-length.

EXAMPLE 4. Let $g(t) = (t, t^2)$ for $0 \leq t \leq 1$. Then

$$s(t) = \int_0^t \sqrt{1 + 4u^2}\, du$$

$$= \tfrac{1}{2} t \sqrt{1 + 4t^2} + \tfrac{1}{4} \log{(2t + \sqrt{1 + 4t^2})}.$$

Since $s'(t) = \sqrt{1 + 4t^2} > 0$, $s(t)$ is strictly increasing and so has an inverse.

The previous example shows that $t(s)$, the inverse of $s(t)$, may be awkward to compute explicitly. However, its use has several theoretical advantages. For example, if a curve γ is parametrized by arc-length, then the integral of a real-valued function p over γ takes a simpler form. For suppose γ is given originally by a function $g(t)$, with $a \leq t \leq b$. Then the new parametrization is given by a function $h(s)$ defined for $0 \leq s \leq l(\gamma)$, where $h(s) = g(t(s))$. Changing variable in the integral of p over γ we get, because $s'(t) = |g'(t)|$,

$$\int_a^b p(g(t))\, |g'(t)|\, dt = \int_a^b p(g(t)) s'(t)\, dt$$

$$= \int_0^{l(\gamma)} p(h(s))\, ds.$$

The expression $|g'(t)|\, dt$, or its simpler counterpart ds, is sometimes called the **element of arc-length** on the curve γ.

If a curve is parametrized by a function $g(t)$, and $G(t)$ is some vector-valued function, for instance velocity, associated with points on the curve, we are led, in making an arc-length parametrization, to consider the function F defined by $F(s) = G(t(s))$. Using Equation 3.5 to differentiate with respect to s, we get $F'(s) = G'(t(s))t'(s)$. But since the functions $t(s)$ and $s(t)$ are inverse to one another, and since $s'(t) = v(t)$, the speed along the curve as described by g, we find that $G'(t(s)) = v(t(s))F'(s)$, or

4.3 $$G'(t(s)) = v(t(s)) \frac{d}{ds} G(t(s)).$$

This equation expresses the relation between the derivatives of F and G at the same point on the curve.

EXAMPLE 5. The equation

$$\mathbf{a}(t) = v'(t)\mathbf{t}(t) + v(t)\,|\mathbf{t}'(t)|\,\mathbf{n}(t), \tag{1}$$

derived in Example 6 of the previous section, can be given a more geometric interpretation if it is rewritten with arc-length as the parameter. Replacing t by $t(s)$, and using Equation 4.3 we get

$$\mathbf{t}'(t(s)) = v(t(s)) \frac{d}{ds} \mathbf{t}(t(s)).$$

Since $v > 0$, when we take the norm of each side, v can be taken outside the norm giving

$$|\mathbf{t}'(t(s))| = v(t(s)) \left| \frac{d}{ds} \mathbf{t}(t(s)) \right|.$$

The factor $|(d/ds)\mathbf{t}(t(s))|$ is called the **curvature** of the curve at the point corresponding to $t(s)$, and it is denoted $\kappa(s)$. Thus Equation (1) above becomes

4.4 $$\mathbf{a} = v'\mathbf{t} + v^2\kappa\mathbf{n}.$$

The terms in the sum are called the **tangential** and **normal** (or **centripetal**) **components** of the acceleration respectively, and the numerical factors are sometimes denoted $a_t = v'$ and $a_n = v^2\kappa$.

From Equation 4.4 we can immediately conclude several things about **a**, the acceleration vector. If the speed v is a constant v_0, then $v' = 0$, and $\mathbf{a}(t) = v_0^2\kappa(t)\mathbf{n}(t)$. This means that **a** is perpendicular to the curve and that its length, $v_0^2\kappa(t)$, varies only with the curvature κ. At the other extreme, if the path of motion is a straight line, then the unit tangent vector **t** is a constant vector so $(d/ds)\mathbf{t}(t(s)) = 0$. Thus $\kappa = 0$, and we have $\mathbf{a}(t) = v'(t)\mathbf{t}(t)$, which shows that the acceleration vector has either the same direction as the tangent or the opposite direction, depending on the sign of v'. Exercise 10 shows that κ, the curvature of the path, is a measure of how rapidly the tangent vector **t** is turning.

EXERCISES

1. Find the length of the following curves.
   (a) $(x, y) = (t, \log \cos t), 0 \leq t \leq 1$.   [*Ans.* $\log (\sec 1 + \tan 1)$].
   (b) $(x, y) = (t^2, \frac{2}{3}t^3 - \frac{1}{2}t), 0 \leq t \leq 2$.   [*Ans.* $\frac{19}{3}$].
   (c) $y = x^{3/2}, 0 \leq x \leq 5$.
   (d) $g(t) = (6t^2, 4\sqrt{2}\, t^3, 3t^4), -1 \leq t \leq 2$.   [*Ans.* 81].

2. (a) Set up the integral for the arc-length of the ellipse $(x, y) = (a \cos t, b \sin t), 0 \leq t \leq 2\pi$.
   (b) Show that the computation of the integral in part (a) can be reduced to the computation of a standard elliptic integral of the form
   $$\int_0^{\pi/2} \sqrt{1 - k^2 \sin^2 \theta}\, d\theta.$$
   (c) By using a table of elliptic integrals or by direct numerical calculation find an approximate value for the arc-length of an ellipse with $a = 1$ and $b = 2$.   [*Ans.* 9.689.]

3. Suppose a curve γ is parametrically defined by two continuously differentiable functions
   $$f(t), \qquad a \leq t \leq b,$$
   $$g(u), \qquad \alpha \leq u \leq \beta.$$

These functions are called **equivalent** parametrizations of γ if there is a continuously differentiable function φ such that

$$a = \varphi(\alpha) \quad \text{and} \quad b = \varphi(\beta),$$
$$f(\varphi(u)) = g(u), \qquad \alpha \le u \le \beta,$$
$$\varphi'(u) > 0, \qquad \alpha < u < \beta.$$

(a) Show that equivalent parametrizations of γ assign the same length to γ.

(b) Show that

$$(x, y) = (\cos t, \sin t), \qquad 0 \le t \le \frac{\pi}{2},$$

and

$$(x, y) = \left(\frac{1 - u^2}{1 + u^2}, \frac{2u}{1 + u^2} \right), \qquad 0 \le u \le 1,$$

are equivalent parametrizations of a quarter circle.

(c) Find a pair of nonequivalent parametrizations of some curve.

4. Show that the curve

$$(x, y) = (\cos s, \sin s), \qquad 0 \le s \le 2\pi$$

is parametrized by arc-length, and sketch the velocity and acceleration vectors, together with the curve, at $s = \pi/2$.

5. Let γ be a continuously differentiable curve with end-points $\mathbf{p}_1$ and $\mathbf{p}_2$. Let λ be the line segment $\mathbf{p}_1 + t(\mathbf{p}_2 - \mathbf{p}_1)$, $0 \le t \le 1$. Prove that $l(\lambda) \le l(\gamma)$.

6. Consider the spiral curve

$$\begin{pmatrix} x \\ y \\ z \end{pmatrix} = \begin{pmatrix} a \cos \omega t \\ a \sin \omega t \\ bt \end{pmatrix}, \qquad 0 \le t.$$

(a) Find explicitly the arc-length parametrization of the curve.

(b) Find the unit tangent and principal normal vectors at an arbitrary point.

(c) Find the curvature at an arbitrary point.

7. (a) Show that for a line given by $g(t) = t\mathbf{x}_1 + \mathbf{x}_0$, the curvature is identically zero.

(b) Show that if a curve γ, parametrized by arc-length and given by a function $f(s)$, has a tangent at every point and has curvature identically zero, then γ is a straight line.

8. Find the total mass of the spiral given by $g(t) = (a \cos t, a \sin t, bt)$, $0 \le t \le 2\pi$, if its density per unit of length at (x, y, z) is equal to $x^2 + y^2 + z^2$.

9. Show that if γ is the *graph* of a function $\mathscr{R} \xrightarrow{f} \mathscr{R}^2$, defined for $a \le x \le b$, then

$$l(\gamma) = \int_a^b \sqrt{1 + (f_1'(x))^2 + (f_2'(x))^2} \, dx,$$

where f_1 and f_2 are the coordinate functions of γ, assumed continuously differentiable.

10. If a curve is parametrized by arc-length, its curvature is $\kappa(s) = |(d/ds)\mathbf{t}(s)|$. Show that if $\theta(s, h)$ is the angle between $\mathbf{t}(s)$ and $\mathbf{t}(s + h)$, which tends to zero as h tends to zero, then

$$\kappa(s) = \lim_{h \to 0} \left| \frac{\theta(s, h)}{h} \right|.$$

[*Hint.* Show that $|\mathbf{t}(s + h) - \mathbf{t}(s)| = \sqrt{2 - 2 \cos \theta(s, h)}$.]

11. Show that if a curve is given parametrically by a function $g(t)$, then in terms of derivatives with respect to t, the curvature at $g(t)$ is

$$\frac{\sqrt{|g'(t)|^2 |g''(t)|^2 - (g'(t) \cdot g''(t))^2}}{|g'(t)|^3}.$$

[*Hint.* Use Equation 4.4 to show that $g'' \cdot \mathbf{n} = v^2 \kappa$, then dot both sides of 4.4 with g''.]

12. Let γ be a continuously differentiable curve having a mass distribution of density $p(\mathbf{x})$ at each point $\mathbf{x}$ of γ. Let m be the total mass of γ. If γ is given by $\mathcal{R} \xrightarrow{g} \mathcal{R}^n$, $a \le t \le b$, the **center of mass** of the distribution is the vector

$$\mathbf{z} = \frac{1}{m} \int_a^b g(t) p(g(t)) |g'(t)| \, dt.$$

(See Problem 14 of the previous section for the definition of the vector integral.)

(a) Find the center of mass of the spiral $g(t) = (a \cos t, a \sin t, bt)$, $0 \le t \le 2\pi$, with density at (x, y, z) equal to $x^2 + y^2 + z^2$.

(b) Show that if γ has uniform density 1 and is parametrized by arc length, then

$$\mathbf{z} = \frac{1}{m} \int_0^{l(\gamma)} g(s) \, ds.$$

(c) Use the result of Problem 17(b) of the previous section to show that the center of mass then satisfies

$$|\mathbf{z}| \le \frac{1}{m} \int_0^{l(\gamma)} |g(s)| \, ds.$$

5. LINE INTEGRALS

The integral $\int_a^b f(x) \, dx$ of a real-valued function f of a real variable can be generalized as follows. Let $\mathcal{R}^3 \xrightarrow{F} \mathcal{R}^3$ be a continuous vector field defined in a region D of $\mathcal{R}^3$. Let γ be a curve lying in D and parametrized by a function $\mathcal{R} \xrightarrow{g} \mathcal{R}^3$ with $g(t)$ defined and continuously differentiable for $a \le t \le b$. To say that γ lies in D means simply that the range of g lies in D. A typical situation is shown in Figure 24. At each point $g(t)$ of γ we picture the tangent vector $g'(t)$ as an arrow with its initial point at $g(t)$. Also at $g(t)$ we locate the arrow describing the vector field F at $g(t)$. The dot product $F(g(t)) \cdot g'(t)$ is then a continuous real-valued function of t for $a \le t \le b$, and the integral

$$\int_a^b F(g(t)) \cdot g'(t) \, dt \qquad (1)$$

is called the **line integral** of F over γ.

EXAMPLE 1. If a vector field is given in $\mathcal{R}^3$ by $F(x, y, z) = (x^2, y^2, z^2)$ and γ is given by $g(t) = (t, t^2, t^3)$ for $0 \le t \le 1$, then the integral of F over γ is

$$\int_0^1 (t^2, t^4, t^6) \cdot (1, 2t, 3t^2) \, dt = \int_0^1 (t^2 + 2t^5 + 3t^8) \, dt = 1.$$

The line integral can be interpreted in qualitative terms as follows. The dot product

$$F(g(t)) \cdot \frac{g'(t)}{|g'(t)|}$$

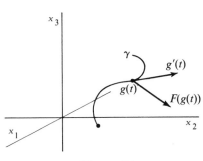

Figure 24

is the coordinate of $F(g(t))$ in the direction of the unit tangent vector to γ at $g(t)$. Then $F(g(t)) \cdot g'(t)$, the integrand in Formula (1), is the tangential coordinate of $F(g(t))$ times $|g'(t)|$, the speed of traversal of γ at $g(t)$. In particular, if $F(g(t))$ is always perpendicular to γ at $g(t)$, the integrand, and hence the integral will be zero. At the other extreme, for a given field F, if the speed $|g'(t)|$ is prescribed at each point of the curve, then the integrand will be maximized by choosing a curve γ that at each point has the same direction as the field there. Thus the integrand in the line integral can be thought of as a measure of the effect of the vector field along γ.

Formula (1) can be generalized to any number of dimensions. Thus if $\mathcal{R}^n \xrightarrow{F} \mathcal{R}^n$, and $\mathcal{R} \xrightarrow{g} \mathcal{R}^n$ describes for $a \le t \le b$ a smooth curve, γ, lying in D, the line integral of F over γ is still defined by Formula (1), in which the dot product is now formed in $\mathcal{R}^n$.

EXAMPLE 2. Let $F(x, y) = (x, y)$ define a vector field in $\mathcal{R}^2$. The curve given by $g(t) = (\cos t, \sin t)$ for $0 \le t \le \pi/2$ is a quarter circle shown in Figure 25 together with some tangent vectors and some vectors of the field. Because the field is perpendicular to the curve at each point, we expect the integral to be zero and in fact we have

$$\int_0^{\pi/2} F(g(t)) \cdot g'(t) \, dt = \int_0^{\pi/2} (\cos t, \sin t) \cdot (-\sin t, \cos t) \, dt = 0.$$

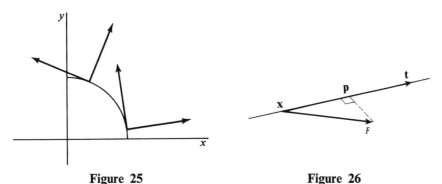

Figure 25   **Figure 26**

EXAMPLE 3. An important physical interpretation of the line integral arises as follows: Suppose that the function $\mathscr{R}^3 \xrightarrow{F} \mathscr{R}^3$ determines a continuous force field in a region D in $\mathscr{R}^3$. To define W, the work done in moving a particle along a curve γ in D, we use the definition that for linear motion in a constant field

$$W = (F_t)(s),$$

where s is the distance traversed and F_t is the coordinate of the force in the direction of motion. In Figure 26 a particle moves along a line having direction vector $\mathbf{t}$ with $|\mathbf{t}| = 1$, and is subject at each point $\mathbf{x}$ to the same force vector $F(\mathbf{x})$. The coordinate of F in the direction of motion is $F_t = F \cdot \mathbf{t}$. Then $W = (F \cdot \mathbf{t})s$.

For motion along a continuously differentiable curve, we begin by approximating the curve by tangent vectors, as is done in defining arc-length. If the curve γ is given parametrically by $\mathscr{R} \xrightarrow{g} \mathscr{R}^3$ with $g(t)$ defined for $a \leq t \leq b$, then the arrows representing the tangent vectors $g'(t_{k-1})(t_k - t_{k-1})$, $t_0 < t_1 < \ldots < t_K$, will approximate γ as shown in Figure 27. Let us fix a point $\mathbf{x}_k = g(t_k)$ on γ, and near $\mathbf{x}_k$ approximate F by the constant field $F(\mathbf{x}_k)$. The tangential coordinate of $F(\mathbf{x}_k)$ is $F(\mathbf{x}_k) \cdot \mathbf{t}(t_k)$ where $\mathbf{t}(t) = g'(t)/|g'(t)|$.

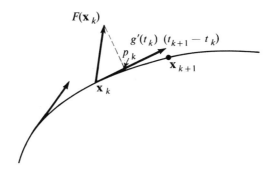

Figure 27

Thus the work done in moving a particle along γ from $\mathbf{x}_k$ to $\mathbf{x}_{k+1}$ is approximately

$$W_k = [F(\mathbf{x}_k) \cdot \mathbf{t}(t_k)] \, |g'(t_k)| \, (t_{k+1} - t_k)$$
$$= F(g(t_k)) \cdot g'(t_k)(t_{k+1} - t_k).$$

Letting $m(P) = \max_{1 \leq k \leq K} (t_k - t_{k-1})$, we get

$$\lim_{m(P) \to 0} \sum_{k=0}^{K-1} W_k = \int_a^b F(g(t)) \cdot g'(t) \, dt,$$

which we define to be the **work** done in moving the particle through the domain of F along γ.

The assumptions made in the previous example that F be continuous and that g' be continuous assured that the integrand $F(g(t)) \cdot g'(t)$ would be continuous and hence that the line integral would exist. However these conditions are stronger than necessary. It is enough to assume that the path of integration is piecewise smooth and then that the vector field F is sufficiently regular so that the integral in Formula (1) exists. Thus the derivative g' may be discontinuous at finitely many points, so that γ has sharp corners as shown in Figure 28.

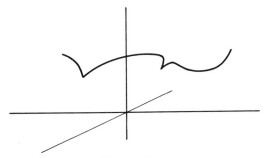

Figure 28

EXAMPLE 4. Let a vector field be defined in $\mathscr{R}^3$ by $F(x, y, z) = (x, y, z)$. Let $g(t) = (\cos t, \sin t, |t - \pi/2|)$ describe a curve γ in $\mathscr{R}^3$ for $0 \leq t \leq \pi$. Then γ has a corner at $(0, 1, 0)$, where $t = \pi/2$. Indeed g is not differentiable there, and in fact $\lim_{t \to \pi/2-} g'(t) = (-1, 0, -1)$ and $\lim_{t \to \pi/2+} g'(t) = (-1, 0, 1)$, showing that the direction of the tangent jumps abruptly at $t = \pi/2$. Nevertheless, the integral of F over γ exists. To compute it, the interval of integration would ordinarily be broken at $t = \pi/2$. However, in this particular case $F(g(t)) \cdot g'(t) = t - \pi/2$ unless $t = \pi/2$, and the line integral is easily seen to have the value zero over the interval $0 \leq t \leq \pi$.

A convenient notation for line integrals arises if we denote the parametrization of γ by $g(t) = (x(t), y(t), z(t))$ for $a \leq t \leq b$. Denoting the coordinate functions of F by F_1, F_2, and F_3, and suppressing the variable t in the integrand, we get

$$\int_a^b F(g(t)) \cdot g'(t)\, dt = \int_a^b \left[F_1(x, y, z)\frac{dx}{dt} + F_2(x, y, z)\frac{dy}{dt} + F_3(x, y, z)\frac{dz}{dt} \right] dt.$$

The last integral can be abbreviated

$$\int_\gamma F_1\, dx + F_2\, dy + F_3\, dz,$$

and can be still further shortened by writing $dx = (dx, dy, dz)$. Then the formula becomes

$$\int_\gamma F \cdot dx.$$

The meaning of this notation is developed further in Chapter 5, Section 7. In the meantime we shall simply use it as a shorthand.

EXAMPLE 5. Let $\mathscr{R}^4 \xrightarrow{F} \mathscr{R}^4$ be given by

$$F(x, y, z, w) = (x - y, y - z, z - w, w - x).$$

The curve γ, given by $g(t) = (t, -t, t^2, -t^2)$ for $0 \leq t \leq 1$, passes through the field. The integral of F over γ is

$$\int_\gamma F \cdot dx = \int_0^1 [(2t)(1) + (-t - t^2)(-1) + (2t^2)(2t) + (-t^2 - t)(-2t)]\, dt$$
$$= 4.$$

Let γ be a differentiable curve in $\mathscr{R}^n$ given by $\mathscr{R} \xrightarrow{g} \mathscr{R}^n$ for $a \leq t \leq b$. The integral over γ of a real-valued function p, with its domain containing γ, is defined to be

$$\int_a^b p(g(t))\, |g'(t)|\, dt. \tag{2}$$

The function p can be thought of as the density per unit of length of a mass distribution over γ, in which case the integral represents the total mass distributed along γ. If we write the line integral of a vector field over γ in the form

$$\int_a^b F(g(t)) \cdot \frac{g'(t)}{|g'(t)|}\, |g'(t)|\, dt, \tag{3}$$

the relationship between Formulas (2) and (3) becomes clear. The integral of the vector field over γ depends on the direction of the tangent to γ at each point and not just the length of the tangent as in the case of the integral of a real-valued function over γ. If the curve γ is parametrized by arc-length, then the two integrals take the respective forms

$$\int_0^{l(\gamma)} p(g(s))\, ds \quad \text{and} \quad \int_0^{l(\gamma)} F(g(s)) \cdot t(s)\, ds,$$

where $t(s) = (dg/ds)(s)$ is a tangent vector to γ of length 1.

It is clear from the definition of the line integral that, in general, the value depends on the parametrization of the curve γ. The extent to which the value is independent of parametrization is taken up in the exercises.

EXERCISES

1. Compute the following line integrals.

   (a) $\int_L x \, dx + x^2 \, dy + y \, dz$, where L is given by $g(t) = (t, t, t)$, for $0 \le t \le 1$.

   (b) $\int_P (x + y) \, dx + dy$, where P is given by $g(t) = (t, t^2)$, $0 \le t \le 1$.

   (c) $\int_{\gamma_1} x \, dy$ and $\int_{\gamma_2} x \, dy$, where γ_1 is given by $g(t) = (\cos t, \sin t)$ for $0 \le t \le 2\pi$, and where γ_2 is given by $h(t) = (\cos t, \sin t)$ for $0 \le t \le 4\pi$.

   (d) $\int_{\gamma_1} (dx + dy)$, where γ_1 is given by $(x, y) = (\cos t, \sin t)$, $0 \le t \le 2\pi$.

   (e) $\int_{\gamma_1} \dfrac{dx + dy}{x^2 + y^2}$, where γ_1 is the curve in part (d).

   (f) $\int_\gamma (e^x \, dx + z \, dy + \sin z \, dz)$, where γ is given by $(x, y, z) = (t, t^2, t^3)$, $0 \le t \le 1$.

   (g) $\int_\gamma F \cdot d\mathbf{x}$, where $F(x, y, z, w) = (x, x, y, xw)$ and γ is given by $(x, y, z, w) = (t, 1, t, t)$, $0 \le t \le 2$.

2. Let γ_1 be given by $(x, y) = (\cos t, \sin t)$, $0 \le t \le \pi/2$, and γ_2 be given by $(x, y) = (1 - u, u)$, $0 \le u \le 1$. Compute $\int_{\gamma_1} (f \, dx + g \, dy)$ and $\int_{\gamma_2} (f \, dx + g \, dy)$ for the choices of f and g given below.

   (a) $f(x, y) = x$, $g(x, y) = x + 1$.

   (b) $f(x, y) = x + y$, $g(x, y) = 1$.

   (c) $f(x, y) = \dfrac{1}{x^2 + y^2}$, $g(x, y) = \dfrac{1}{x^2 + y^2}$.

3. Find the work done in moving a particle along the curve $(x, y, z) = (t, t, t^2)$, $0 \le t \le 2$, under the influence of the field $F(x, y, z) = (x + y, y, y)$.

4. Prove that if γ is a curve given parametrically by a function $\mathscr{R} \xrightarrow{f} \mathscr{R}^n$ with

$$\mathbf{x} = f(t), \qquad 0 \le t \le 1$$

and if $-\gamma$ is the curve described by

$$\mathbf{x} = f(1 - t), \qquad 0 \le t \le 1,$$

then

$$\int_{-\gamma} F \cdot d\mathbf{x} = -\int_\gamma F \cdot d\mathbf{x}.$$

5. Let $F(x, y) = (y, x)$ describe a vector field in $\mathscr{R}^2$. Find a curve γ_1 passing through the field and starting at the point $(2, 1)$ such that γ_1 has length 1 and the integral of F over γ_1 is zero.

6. Prove that if γ is given by $\mathscr{R} \xrightarrow{g} \mathscr{R}^n$ for $a \leq t \leq b$ and γ is then reparametrized by arc-length s so that $t = t(s)$, then

$$\int_a^b F(g(t)) \cdot g'(t)\, dt = \int_0^{l(\gamma)} F(h(s)) \cdot t(s)\, ds,$$

where $h(s) = g(t(s))$ and $t(s) = (dh/ds)(s)$. [*Hint.* Use the change of variable theorem for integrals.]

7. Let $\mathscr{R}^n \xrightarrow{F} \mathscr{R}^n$ be a vector field and γ a curve such that the line integral $\int_\gamma F \cdot dx$ exists. Prove that if $|F(x)| \leq M$, a constant, on γ, then $|\int_\gamma F \cdot dx| \leq Ml(\gamma)$.

8. (a) If $g(t)$ and $h(u)$ are equivalent parametrizations of γ as defined in Exercise 3 of the previous section on arc-length, show that $\int_\gamma F \cdot dx$ has the same value when computed with either parametrization.
(b) Find nonequivalent parametrizations of the circle $x^2 + y^2 = 1$ in $\mathscr{R}^2$ and a vector field F such that the integrals of F with respect to the two parametrizations are different.

9. Find the total mass of the wire $\begin{pmatrix} x \\ y \\ z \end{pmatrix} = \begin{pmatrix} 6t^2 \\ 4\sqrt{2}\, t^3 \\ 3t^4 \end{pmatrix}$, $0 \leq t \leq 1$:

(a) If the density at the point corresponding to t is t^2.
(b) If the density s units from the origin measured along the curve is $(s + 1)$.
(c) If the density at a point is equal to its distance from the origin measured in $\mathscr{R}^3$.

10. Show that if $\int_\gamma F \cdot dx$ and $\int_\gamma G \cdot dx$ exist, then $\int_\gamma (aF + bG) \cdot dx = a \int_\gamma F \cdot dx + b \int_\gamma G \cdot dx$, where a and b are any constants.

11. Show that if γ and η are smooth curves described by functions $\mathscr{R} \xrightarrow{g} \mathscr{R}^n$ defined on $[a, b]$, and $\mathscr{R} \xrightarrow{h} \mathscr{R}^n$ defined on $[b, c]$, with $g(b) = h(b)$, then

$$\int_\delta F \cdot dx = \int_\gamma F \cdot dx + \int_\eta F \cdot dx,$$

where δ is the curve given by

$$f(t) = \begin{cases} g(t), & a \leq t \leq b \\ h(t), & b \leq t \leq c, \end{cases}$$

and F is a continuous vector field on $\gamma \cup \eta$.

12. Let a function $g(t)$ represent the position of a particle of varying mass $m(t)$ in $\mathscr{R}^3$ at time t. Then the velocity vector of the particle is $v(t) = g'(t)$, and the force vector acting on the particle at $g(t)$ is $F(g(t)) = [m(t)v(t)]'$.

(a) Show that $F(g(t)) \cdot g'(t) = m'(t)v^2(t) + m(t)v(t)v'(t)$, where v is the speed of the particle.
(b) Show that if $m(t)$ is constant, then the work done in moving the particle over its path between times $t = a$ and $t = b$ is $w = (m/2)(v^2(b) - v^2(a))$. (The function $(\frac{1}{2})mv^2(t)$ is the kinetic energy of the particle.)

6. PARTIAL DERIVATIVES

Let f be a real-valued function with domain space $\mathscr{R}^n$. For each $i = 1$, $\ldots, n$, we define a new real-valued function called the **partial derivative of** f **with respect to the** i**th variable** and denoted by $\partial f / \partial x_i$. For each $\mathbf{x} = (x_1, \ldots, x_n)$ in the domain of f, the number $(\partial f / \partial x_i)(\mathbf{x})$ is by definition

$$\frac{\partial f}{\partial x_i}(\mathbf{x}) = \lim_{t \to 0} \frac{f(x_1, \ldots, x_i + t, \ldots, x_n) - f(x_1, \ldots, x_i, \ldots, x_n)}{t}. \quad (1)$$

The domain space of $\partial f / \partial x_i$ is $\mathscr{R}^n$, and the domain of $\partial f / \partial x_i$ is the subset of the domain of f consisting of all $\mathbf{x}$ for which the above limit exists. Thus the domain of $\partial f / \partial x_i$ could conceivably be the empty set. The number $(\partial f / \partial x_i)(\mathbf{x})$ is simply the derivative at x_i of the function of one variable obtained by holding $x_1, \ldots, x_{i-1}, x_{i+1}, \ldots, x_n$ fixed and by considering f to be a function of the ith variable only.

EXAMPLE 1. Let $f(x, y, z) = x^2 y + y^2 z + z^2 x$. Then,

$$\frac{\partial f}{\partial x}(x, y, z) = 2xy + z^2,$$

$$\frac{\partial f}{\partial y}(x, y, z) = x^2 + 2yz,$$

$$\frac{\partial f}{\partial z}(x, y, z) = y^2 + 2zx.$$

The partial derivatives at $\mathbf{x} = (1, 2, 3)$ are

$$\frac{\partial f}{\partial x}(1, 2, 3) = 4 + 9 = 13,$$

$$\frac{\partial f}{\partial y}(1, 2, 3) = 1 + 12 = 13,$$

$$\frac{\partial f}{\partial z}(1, 2, 3) = 4 + 6 = 10.$$

EXAMPLE 2. Let $f(u, v) = \sin u \cos v$. Then

$$\frac{\partial f}{\partial u} = \frac{\partial \sin u \cos v}{\partial u} = \cos u \cos v,$$

$$\frac{\partial f}{\partial v} = \frac{\partial \sin u \cos v}{\partial v} = -\sin u \sin v,$$

$$\frac{\partial f}{\partial u}(0, 0) = \frac{\partial \sin u \cos v}{\partial u}(0, 0) = \cos 0 \cos 0 = 1,$$

$$\frac{\partial f}{\partial v}\left(\frac{\pi}{2}, \frac{\pi}{2}\right) = \frac{\partial \sin u \cos v}{\partial v}\left(\frac{\pi}{2}, \frac{\pi}{2}\right) = -\sin \frac{\pi}{2} \sin \frac{\pi}{2} = -1.$$

One can repeat the operation of taking partial derivative. The partial derivative of $\partial f/\partial x_i$ with respect to the jth variable is $\partial/\partial x_j \, (\partial f/\partial x_i)$ and is denoted by $\partial^2 f/\partial x_j \partial x_i$. This can be repeated indefinitely, provided the derivatives exist. An alternative notation for higher-order partial derivatives is illustrated below.

$$\frac{\partial f}{\partial x_i} = f_{x_i}$$

$$\frac{\partial}{\partial x_j}\left(\frac{\partial f}{\partial x_i}\right) = \frac{\partial^2 f}{\partial x_j \, \partial x_i} = f_{x_i x_j}$$

$$\frac{\partial}{\partial x_i}\left(\frac{\partial f}{\partial x_i}\right) = \frac{\partial^2 f}{\partial x_i^2} = f_{x_i x_i}$$

$$\frac{\partial}{\partial x_i}\left(\frac{\partial^2 f}{\partial x_j \, \partial x_i}\right) = \frac{\partial^3 f}{\partial x_i \, \partial x_j \, \partial x_i} = f_{x_i x_j x_i}.$$

EXAMPLE 3. Consider $f(x, y) = xy - x^2$.

$$f_x = \frac{\partial f}{\partial x} = y - 2x$$

$$f_{xy} = \frac{\partial^2 f}{\partial y \, \partial x} = 1$$

$$f_{xx} = \frac{\partial^2 f}{\partial x^2} = -2$$

$$f_{yxx} = \frac{\partial^3 f}{\partial x^2 \, \partial y} = 0.$$

Look at the graph in 3-dimensional euclidean space of a function $f(x, y)$. A typical example is shown in Figure 29. The intersection of the surface with the plane $y = b$ is a curve, defined implicitly by the equations

$$z = f(x, y), \qquad y = b.$$

Consider as a subset of 2-dimensional space the curve defined by the function $g(x) = f(x, b)$. Its slope at $x = a$ is

$$g'(a) = \frac{\partial f}{\partial x}(a, b).$$

Similarly, at $y = b$ the curve defined by $h(y) = f(a, y)$ has slope equal to

$$h'(b) = \frac{\partial f}{\partial y}(a, b).$$

The angles α and β shown in Figure 29 therefore satisfy

$$\tan \alpha = \frac{\partial f}{\partial x}(a, b), \quad \tan \beta = \frac{\partial f}{\partial y}(a, b).$$

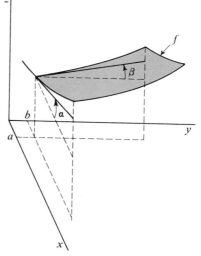

Figure 29

The numbers $\tan \alpha$ and $\tan \beta$ computed above are the slopes of tangent lines to two curves contained in the graph of the function f. For this reason it is natural to define the tangent plane to the graph of f to be the plane containing the two tangent lines. (If f satisfies the condition of differentiability defined in the next section, this is what is done.) We see easily that the set of points (x, y, z) satisfying the equation

$$z = f(a, b) + \frac{\partial f}{\partial x}(a, b)(x - a) + \frac{\partial f}{\partial y}(a, b)(y - b) \tag{2}$$

is a plane containing the tangent lines found above. (Set $y = b$ and $x = a$ respectively.)

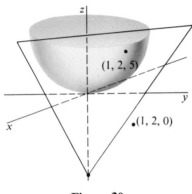

Figure 30

EXAMPLE 4. The graph of the function $f(x, y) = x^2 + y^2$, shown in Figure 30 has partial derivatives at $(1, 2)$ given by

$$\frac{\partial f}{\partial x}(1, 2) = 2, \qquad \frac{\partial f}{\partial y}(1, 2) = 4.$$

Then Equation (2) becomes

$$z = 5 + 2(x - 1) + 4(y - 2)$$
$$= 2x + 4y - 5,$$

so that the tangent plane at $(1, 2, 5)$ is the graph in $\mathscr{R}^3$ of the function defined by $2x + 4y - 5$.

It is an important theorem that if certain continuity conditions are satisfied, then the higher-order partial derivatives of $\mathscr{R}^n \xrightarrow{f} \mathscr{R}$ are independent of the order of differentiation. A precise statement is

6.1 Theorem. Let $f(x, y)$ be a real-valued function such that f_x, f_y, and f_{xy}(or f_{yx}) are continuous at every point of an open subset S of $\mathscr{R}^2$. Then, at every point of S, the derivative f_{yx} (or f_{xy}) exists and $f_{xy} = f_{yx}$.

This theorem is a simple consequence of the possibility of changing order of integration. See Exercise 8 of Chapter 4, Section 2.

The theorem can be applied successively to still higher-order partial derivatives, provided the analogous differentiability and continuity requirements are satisfied. Moreover, by considering only two variables at a time, we can apply it to functions $\mathscr{R}^n \xrightarrow{f} \mathscr{R}$ where $n > 2$. Thus, for the commonly encountered functions, which have partial derivatives of arbitrarily high order, we have typically

$$\frac{\partial^2 f}{\partial x \, \partial y} = \frac{\partial^2 f}{\partial y \, \partial x}$$

$$\frac{\partial^3 g}{\partial x \, \partial y \, \partial x} = \frac{\partial^3 g}{\partial x^2 \, \partial y}$$

$$\frac{\partial^4 h}{\partial z \, \partial x \, \partial y \, \partial z} = \frac{\partial^4 h}{\partial x \, \partial y \, \partial z^2}, \text{ etc.}$$

So far we have considered the partial derivatives only of real-valued functions. If $\mathscr{R}^n \xrightarrow{f} \mathscr{R}^m$ is a vector-valued function, then $\partial f/\partial x_i$ is still defined by Equation (1). The difference is that, in that equation, the quotient, and hence the limit, is now a vector. It follows immediately from Theorem 2.1 that

if $\qquad f(\mathbf{x}) = \begin{pmatrix} f_1(\mathbf{x}) \\ \vdots \\ f_m(\mathbf{x}) \end{pmatrix}, \qquad$ then $\quad \dfrac{\partial f}{\partial x_i}(\mathbf{x}) = \begin{pmatrix} \dfrac{\partial f_1}{\partial x_i}(\mathbf{x}) \\ \vdots \\ \dfrac{\partial f_m}{\partial x_i}(\mathbf{x}) \end{pmatrix}.$

The geometric significance of this partial derivative is that if all the variables but one in the domain space $\mathscr{R}^n$ are held fixed, and x_i alone is allowed to vary, then $f(\mathbf{x})$ traces a curve in $\mathscr{R}^m$, and $\partial f/\partial x_i(\mathbf{x})$ is a tangent vector to the curve, as defined in Section 3.

EXAMPLE 5. Let

$$f(u, v) = \begin{pmatrix} u \cos v \\ u \sin v \\ v \end{pmatrix}.$$

Then

$$\frac{\partial f}{\partial u}(u_0, v_0) = \begin{pmatrix} \cos v_0 \\ \sin v_0 \\ 0 \end{pmatrix}, \qquad \frac{\partial f}{\partial v}(u_0, v_0) = \begin{pmatrix} -u_0 \sin v_0 \\ u_0 \cos v_0 \\ 1 \end{pmatrix}.$$

The curves represented parametrically by the restricted functions $f(u, v_0)$ and $f(u_0, v)$ have the partial derivatives $(\partial f/\partial u)(u_0, v_0)$ and $(\partial f/\partial v)(u_0, v_0)$ as tangent vectors at $f(u_0, v_0)$. An example is shown in Figure 31.

If $\mathscr{R}^2 \xrightarrow{f} \mathscr{R}^3$ is differentiable, and the tangent vectors to parameter curves given by $\partial f/\partial u$ and $\partial f/\partial v$ at a point $f(u_0, v_0)$ span a plane, then this plane serves to define the tangent plane at $f(u_0, v_0)$ to the surface represented parametrically by f. Thus, in general, the tangent plane would be the set of points representable in the form

$$f(u_0, v_0) + u \frac{\partial f}{\partial u}(u_0, v_0) + v \frac{\partial f}{\partial v}(u_0, v_0)$$

as u and v vary over all real numbers.

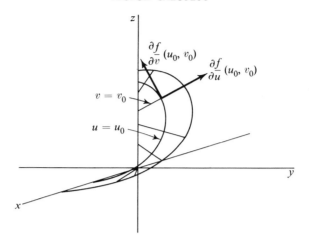

Figure 31

EXAMPLE 6. Continuing with the function of Example 5, at $f(1, \pi/2)$ $= (0, 1, \pi/2)$, the tangent vectors

$$\frac{\partial f}{\partial u}\left(1, \frac{\pi}{2}\right) = \begin{pmatrix} 0 \\ 1 \\ 0 \end{pmatrix}, \qquad \frac{\partial f}{\partial v}\left(1, \frac{\pi}{2}\right) = \begin{pmatrix} -1 \\ 0 \\ 1 \end{pmatrix}$$

span a plane through the origin. The tangent plane to the range of f at $f(1, \pi/2)$ consists of the vectors

$$\begin{pmatrix} 0 \\ 1 \\ \pi/2 \end{pmatrix} + u \begin{pmatrix} 0 \\ 1 \\ 0 \end{pmatrix} + v \begin{pmatrix} -1 \\ 0 \\ 1 \end{pmatrix},$$

for all (u, v) in $\mathscr{R}^2$.

EXERCISES

1. Find $\dfrac{\partial f}{\partial x}$ and $\dfrac{\partial f}{\partial y}$, where $f(x, y)$ is:

(a) $x^2 + x \sin (x + y)$.   (b) $\sin x \cos (x + y)$.
(c) e^{x+y+1}.   (d) $\arctan (y/x)$.
(e) x^y.   (f) $\log_x y$.

$$\left[Ans. \ \frac{\partial f}{\partial x} = -\frac{\ln y}{x(\ln x)^2}. \right]$$

2. Find $\dfrac{\partial^2 f}{\partial y \, \partial x}$ and $\dfrac{\partial^2 f}{\partial x \, \partial y}$, where f is

(a) $xy + x^2 y^3$.   (b) $\sin (x^2 + y^2)$.   (c) $\dfrac{1}{x^2 + y^2}$.

3. Find the first-order partial derivatives of the following functions:

(a) $f(x, y, z) = x^2 e^{x+y+z} \cos y$.

(b) $f(x, y, z, w) = \dfrac{x^2 - y^2}{z^2 + w^2}$.

(c) $f(x, y, z) = x^{(y^z)}$.

4. Find $\dfrac{\partial^3 f(x, y)}{\partial x^2 \partial y}$ if $f(x, y) = \log(x + y)$.

5. Show that $\dfrac{\partial^2 f}{\partial x^2} + \dfrac{\partial^2 f}{\partial y^2} = 0$ is satisfied by

(a) $\log(x^2 + y^2)$. (b) $x^3 - 3xy^2$.

6. If $f(x, y, z) = 1/(x^2 + y^2 + z^2)^{1/2}$, show that

$$f_{xx} + f_{yy} + f_{zz} = 0.$$

7. If $f(x_1, x_2, \ldots, x_n) = 1/(x_1^2 + x_2^2 + \cdots + x_n^2)^{(n-2)/2}$, show that

$$f_{x_1 x_1} + f_{x_2 x_2} + \cdots + f_{x_n x_n} = 0.$$

8. Prove directly that if $f(x, y)$ is a polynomial, then

$$\frac{\partial^2 f}{\partial x \, \partial y} = \frac{\partial^2 f}{\partial y \, \partial x}.$$

9. If

$$f(x, y) = \begin{cases} 2xy \dfrac{x^2 - y^2}{x^2 + y^2}, & \text{for} \quad x^2 + y^2 \neq 0 \\ 0 & , & \text{for} \quad x = y = 0, \end{cases}$$

show that $f_{xy}(0, 0) = -2$ and $f_{yx}(0, 0) = 2$.

10. For each of the following functions find an explicit representation for the tangent plane to the graph at the indicated point. Also, sketch the graph of the given function together with the tangent plane.

(a) $\sqrt{1 - x^2 - y^2}$ at $(\tfrac{1}{2}, \tfrac{1}{2}, 1/\sqrt{2})$.

(b) e^{x+y} at $(1, 2, e^3)$.

(c) $\sin(x^2 + y^2)$ at $(0, 0, 0)$.

11. Find a parametric representation for the line perpendicular to the tangent plane found in Exercise 10(a) and passing through the point of tangency.

12. For each of the following functions find the vector partial derivatives at the indicated point. Sketch the coordinate curves for which these vectors are the tangents at the given point and sketch the tangent plane at that point.

(a) $f(u, v) = (u, v, u^2 + v^2)$ at $(1, 1, 2)$.

(b) $f(u, v) = (\cos u \sin v, \sin u \sin v, \cos v)$ for $(u, v) = (\pi/4, \pi/4)$.

13. Find a parametric representation for the tangent plane of Exercise 12(a) and also one for the line perpendicular to the tangent plane and passing through the point of tangency.

7. THE DIFFERENTIAL

The simplest vector functions with domain space $\mathscr{R}^n$ and range space $\mathscr{R}^m$ are the constant functions: For a fixed $\mathbf{y}_0$ in $\mathscr{R}^m$,

$$f(\mathbf{x}) = \mathbf{y}_0, \qquad \text{for every } \mathbf{x} \text{ in } \mathscr{R}^n.$$

Next in complexity are the linear functions $\mathscr{R}^n \xrightarrow{L} \mathscr{R}^m$. Recall that the sum of a constant function and a linear function is called an **affine function**. Thus a function $\mathscr{R}^n \xrightarrow{A} \mathscr{R}^m$ is affine if there exists a linear function $\mathscr{R}^n \xrightarrow{L} \mathscr{R}^m$ and a vector $\mathbf{y}_0$ in $\mathscr{R}^m$ such that

$$A(\mathbf{x}) = L(\mathbf{x}) + \mathbf{y}_0, \qquad \text{for every } \mathbf{x} \text{ in } \mathscr{R}^n.$$

We shall see that affine functions form the basis of the differential calculus of vector functions.

EXAMPLE 1. In terms of coordinate variables an affine function is defined by linear equations. For example, consider the point

$$\mathbf{y}_0 = \begin{pmatrix} 1 \\ 2 \\ 0 \end{pmatrix}$$

and the linear function $\mathscr{R}^4 \xrightarrow{L} \mathscr{R}^3$ defined by the matrix

$$\begin{pmatrix} 2 & 3 & 0 & 1 \\ 1 & 0 & 5 & 2 \\ 1 & 2 & 0 & 3 \end{pmatrix}.$$

The affine function $A(\mathbf{x}) = L(\mathbf{x}) + \mathbf{y}_0$, where

$$\mathbf{x} = \begin{pmatrix} x \\ y \\ z \\ t \end{pmatrix}$$

is described by the equations

$$u = 2x + 3y + t + 1$$
$$v = x + 5z + 2t + 2$$
$$w = x + 2y + 3t.$$

Since any system of linear equations can be systematically solved, any affine function can be completely analyzed.

We shall now study the possibility of approximating an arbitrary vector function f near a point $\mathbf{x}_0$ of its domain by an affine function A. The general idea is the possibility of replacing near $\mathbf{x}_0$ what may be a very complicated function by a simple one. Before trying to decide whether or not an approximation exists, we first have to say what we shall mean by an approximation. We begin by requiring that $f(\mathbf{x}_0) = A(\mathbf{x}_0)$. Since $A(\mathbf{x}) = L(\mathbf{x}) + \mathbf{y}_0$, where L is linear, we obtain $f(\mathbf{x}_0) = L(\mathbf{x}_0) + \mathbf{y}_0$, and so

$$A(\mathbf{x}) = L(\mathbf{x} - \mathbf{x}_0) + f(\mathbf{x}_0). \tag{1}$$

The next requirement is that

$$\lim_{\mathbf{x} \to \mathbf{x}_0} (f(\mathbf{x}) - A(\mathbf{x})) = 0. \tag{2}$$

At first glance, Equation (2) may appear to say more than it really does. From (1) we obtain

$$f(\mathbf{x}) - A(\mathbf{x}) = f(\mathbf{x}) - f(\mathbf{x}_0) - L(\mathbf{x} - \mathbf{x}_0).$$

Now every linear function is continuous, so $\lim_{\mathbf{x} \to \mathbf{x}_0} L(\mathbf{x} - \mathbf{x}_0) = L(0) = 0.$ Hence,

$$\lim_{\mathbf{x} \to \mathbf{x}_0} (f(\mathbf{x}) - A(\mathbf{x})) = \lim_{\mathbf{x} \to \mathbf{x}_0} (f(\mathbf{x}) - f(\mathbf{x}_0)).$$

It follows that Equation (2) is precisely the statement that the vector function f is continuous at $\mathbf{x}_0$. This is significant, but it says nothing whatever about how good an approximation to f the affine function A is. In fact, it says nothing about L at all. Thus, in order for our notion of approximation to distinguish one affine function from another or to measure in any way how well A approximates f, some additional requirement is necessary. A natural condition, and the one we shall require, is that $f(\mathbf{x}) - A(\mathbf{x})$ approach 0 faster than $\mathbf{x}$ approaches $\mathbf{x}_0$. That is, we demand that

$$\lim_{\mathbf{x} \to \mathbf{x}_0} \frac{f(\mathbf{x}) - f(\mathbf{x}_0) - L(\mathbf{x} - \mathbf{x}_0)}{|\mathbf{x} - \mathbf{x}_0|} = 0,$$

or, equivalently, that f be representable in the form

$$f(\mathbf{x}) = f(\mathbf{x}_0) + L(\mathbf{x} - \mathbf{x}_0) + |\mathbf{x} - \mathbf{x}_0| Z(\mathbf{x} - \mathbf{x}_0),$$

where $Z(\mathbf{y})$ is some function that tends to zero as $\mathbf{y}$ tends to zero.

A function $\mathscr{R}^n \xrightarrow{f} \mathscr{R}^m$ will be called **differentiable** at $\mathbf{x}_0$ if

1. $\mathbf{x}_0$ is an interior point of the domain of f.
2. There is an affine function that approximates f near $\mathbf{x}_0$. That is, there exists a linear function $\mathscr{R}^n \xrightarrow{L} \mathscr{R}^m$ such that

$$\lim_{\mathbf{x} \to \mathbf{x}_0} \frac{f(\mathbf{x}) - f(\mathbf{x}_0) - L(\mathbf{x} - \mathbf{x}_0)}{|\mathbf{x} - \mathbf{x}_0|} = 0.$$

The linear function L is called the **differential** of f at $\mathbf{x}_0$. The function f is said simply to be **differentiable** if it is differentiable at every point of its domain.

According to the definition, the domain of a differentiable function is an open set. It is, however, convenient to extend the definition sufficiently to speak of a differentiable function f defined on an arbitrary subset S of the domain space. By such an f we shall mean the restriction to S of a differentiable function whose domain is open.

EXAMPLE 2. The function f defined by $f(x, y) = \sqrt{1 - x^2 - y^2}$ has for its domain the disc $x^2 + y^2 \leq 1$. Its graph is shown in Figure 32. The interior points of the domain are those (x, y) such that $x^2 + y^2 < 1$. We shall see that this function is differentiable at every interior point of its domain.

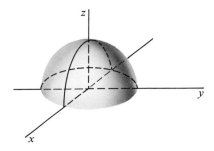

Figure 32

In dimension 1 an affine function has the form $ax + b$. Hence a real-valued function $f(x)$ of a real variable x that is differentiable at x_0 can be approximated near x_0 by a function $A(x) = ax + b$. Since $f(x_0) = A(x_0) = ax_0 + b$, we obtain

$$A(x) = ax + b = a(x - x_0) + f(x_0).$$

The linear part of A (denoted earlier by L) is in this case just multiplication by the real number a. The euclidean norm of a real number is its absolute value, so condition (2) of the definition of differentiability becomes

$$\lim_{x \to x_0} \frac{f(x) - f(x_0) - a(x - x_0)}{|x - x_0|} = 0.$$

This is equivalent to

$$\lim_{x \to x_0} \frac{f(x) - f(x_0)}{x - x_0} = a.$$

The number a is commonly denoted by $f'(x_0)$ and is called the **derivative of f** at x_0. The affine function A is therefore given by

$$A(x) = f(x_0) + f'(x_0)(x - x_0).$$

Its graph is the **tangent line** to the graph of f at x_0, and a typical example is drawn in Figure 33. Thus we have seen that the general definition of differentiability for vector functions reduces in dimension 1 to the definition usually encountered in a one-variable calculus course.

A linear function $\mathscr{R}^n \xrightarrow{L} \mathscr{R}^m$ must be representable by an m-by-n matrix. We shall see below that the matrix of any L satisfying conditions (1) and (2) of the definition of differentiability can be computed in terms of partial derivatives of f. It follows that L is *uniquely* determined by f at each

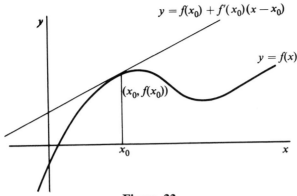

Figure 33

interior point of the domain of f. Thus we can speak of *the* differential of f at $\mathbf{x}_0$ and denote it by $d_{\mathbf{x}_0} f$.

To find the matrix of $d_{\mathbf{x}_0} f$ if $\mathscr{R}^n \xrightarrow{f} \mathscr{R}^m$, we consider the natural basis $(\mathbf{e}_1, \ldots, \mathbf{e}_n)$ for the domain space $\mathscr{R}^n$. If $\mathbf{x}_0$ is an interior point of the domain of f, the vectors

$$\mathbf{x}_j = \mathbf{x}_0 + t\mathbf{e}_j, \qquad j = 1, \ldots, n,$$

are all in the domain of f for sufficiently small t. (Why?) By condition (2) of the definition of the differential, we have

$$\lim_{t \to 0} \frac{f(\mathbf{x}_j) - f(\mathbf{x}_0) - d_{\mathbf{x}_0} f(t\mathbf{e}_j)}{t} = 0,$$

for $j = 1, \ldots, n$. Since $d_{\mathbf{x}_0} f$ is a linear function, this means that

$$\lim_{t \to 0} \frac{f(\mathbf{x}_j) - f(\mathbf{x}_0)}{t} = d_{\mathbf{x}_0} f(\mathbf{e}_j),$$

for $j = 1, \ldots, n$. But, by Theorem 4.2 of Chapter 1, $d_{\mathbf{x}_0} f(\mathbf{e}_j)$ is the jth column of the matrix of $d_{\mathbf{x}_0} f$. On the other hand, the vector $\mathbf{x}_j$ differs from $\mathbf{x}_0$ only in the jth coordinate, and in that coordinate the difference is just the number t. Therefore, the left side of the last equation is precisely the partial derivative $(\partial f / \partial x_j)(\mathbf{x}_0)$. Thus it is this vector which is the jth column of the matrix of $d_{\mathbf{x}_0} f$. If the coordinate functions of f are $f_1, \ldots, f_m$, then

$$\frac{\partial f}{\partial x_j}(\mathbf{x}_0) = \begin{pmatrix} \dfrac{\partial f_1}{\partial x_j}(\mathbf{x}_0) \\ \vdots \\ \dfrac{\partial f_m}{\partial x_j}(\mathbf{x}_0) \end{pmatrix},$$

and the entire matrix of $d_{\mathbf{x}_0} f$ has the form

$$\begin{pmatrix} \dfrac{\partial f_1}{\partial x_1}(\mathbf{x}_0) & \dfrac{\partial f_1}{\partial x_2}(\mathbf{x}_0) & \cdots & \dfrac{\partial f_1}{\partial x_n}(\mathbf{x}_0) \\[2mm] \dfrac{\partial f_2}{\partial x_1}(\mathbf{x}_0) & \dfrac{\partial f_2}{\partial x_2}(\mathbf{x}_0) & \cdots & \dfrac{\partial f_2}{\partial x_n}(\mathbf{x}_0) \\[2mm] \cdot & \cdot & & \cdot \\ \cdot & \cdot & & \cdot \\ \cdot & \cdot & & \cdot \\[2mm] \dfrac{\partial f_m}{\partial x_1}(\mathbf{x}_0) & \dfrac{\partial f_m}{\partial x_2}(\mathbf{x}_0) & \cdots & \dfrac{\partial f_m}{\partial x_n}(\mathbf{x}_0) \end{pmatrix}.$$

This matrix is called the **Jacobian matrix** or **derivative** of f at $\mathbf{x}_0$, and is denoted $f'(\mathbf{x}_0)$. We can summarize what we have just proved as follows.

7.1 Theorem. If the function $\mathscr{R}^n \overset{f}{\longrightarrow} \mathscr{R}^m$ is differentiable at $\mathbf{x}_0$, then the differential $d_{\mathbf{x}_0} f$ is uniquely determined, and its matrix is the Jacobian matrix of f. That is, for all vectors $\mathbf{y}$ in $\mathscr{R}^n$,

$$d_{\mathbf{x}_0} f(\mathbf{y}) = f'(\mathbf{x}_0)\mathbf{y}.$$

While the linear transformation $d_{\mathbf{x}_0} f$ and its matrix $f'(\mathbf{x}_0)$ are logically distinct, the last equation shows that they can be identified in practice, provided it is understood that the matrix of $d_{\mathbf{x}_0} f$ is taken with respect to the natural bases in $\mathscr{R}^n$ and $\mathscr{R}^m$.

EXAMPLE 3. The function

$$f(x, y, z) = \begin{pmatrix} x^2 + e^y \\ x + y \sin z \end{pmatrix}$$

has coordinate functions $f_1(x, y, z) = x^2 + e^y$ and $f_2(x, y, z) = x + y \sin z$. The Jacobian matrix at (x, y, z) is by definition

$$f'(x, y, z) = \left(\frac{\partial f}{\partial x}(x, y, z) \quad \frac{\partial f}{\partial y}(x, y, z) \quad \frac{\partial f}{\partial z}(x, y, z) \right),$$

so for this example

$$f'(x, y, z) = \begin{pmatrix} 2x & e^y & 0 \\ 1 & \sin z & y \cos z \end{pmatrix}.$$

Thus the differential of f at $(1, 1, \pi)$ is the linear function whose matrix is

$$\begin{pmatrix} 2 & e & 0 \\ 1 & 0 & -1 \end{pmatrix}.$$

EXAMPLE 4. The function f defined by

$$f(x, y) = (x^2 + 2xy + y^2, \, xy^2 + x^2 y)$$

has differential $d_{\mathbf{x}}f$ at $\mathbf{x} = (x, y)$ represented by the Jacobian matrix

$$f'(x, y) = \begin{pmatrix} 2x + 2y & 2x' + 2y \\ y^2 + 2xy & 2xy + x^2 \end{pmatrix}.$$

How can one tell whether or not a vector function is differentiable? Theorem 7.1 says only that if f is differentiable, then the differential is represented by the Jacobian matrix. It does not go the other way. Thus Examples 3 and 4 are inconclusive to the extent that we have simply assumed that the functions appearing in them are differentiable. Just as the derivative of a real-valued function of one variable may fail to exist, so in general a vector function need not be differentiable at every point. The next theorem is a convenient criterion for differentiability.

7.2 Theorem. If the domain of $\mathscr{R}^n \xrightarrow{f} \mathscr{R}^m$ is an open set D on which the partial derivatives $\partial f_i/\partial x_j$ of the coordinate functions of f are continuous, then f is differentiable at every point of D.

Proof. Let L be the linear function defined by the Jacobian matrix of f. The theorem will have been proved if it can be shown that L satisfies

$$\lim_{\mathbf{x} \to \mathbf{x}_0} \frac{f(\mathbf{x}) - f(\mathbf{x}_0) - L(\mathbf{x} - \mathbf{x}_0)}{|\mathbf{x} - \mathbf{x}_0|} = 0. \qquad (4)$$

Since by Theorem 2.1 a vector function approaches a limit if and only if the coordinate functions approach the coordinates of the limit, it is enough to prove the theorem for the coordinate functions of f, or, what is notationally simpler, to prove it under the assumption that f is real-valued. If

$$\mathbf{x} = (x_1, \ldots, x_n)$$

and

$$\mathbf{x}_0 = (a_1, \ldots, a_n),$$

set

$$\mathbf{y}_k = (x_1, \ldots, x_k, a_{k+1}, \ldots, a_n),$$
$$k = 0, 1, \ldots, n,$$

so that $\mathbf{y}_0 = \mathbf{x}_0$ and $\mathbf{y}_n = \mathbf{x}$. These vectors are illustrated for three dimensions in Figure 34. Then

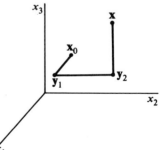

Figure 34

$$f(\mathbf{x}) - f(\mathbf{x}_0) = \sum_{k=1}^{n} (f(\mathbf{y}_k) - f(\mathbf{y}_{k-1})).$$

Because $\mathbf{y}_k$ and $\mathbf{y}_{k-1}$ differ only in their kth coordinates, we can apply the mean-value theorem for real functions of a real variable to get

$$f(\mathbf{y}_k) - f(\mathbf{y}_{k-1}) = (x_k - a_k)\frac{\partial f}{\partial x_k}(\mathbf{z}_k),$$

where $\mathbf{z}_k$ is a point on the segment joining $\mathbf{y}_k$ and $\mathbf{y}_{k-1}$. Then

$$f(\mathbf{x}) - f(\mathbf{x}_0) = \sum_{k=1}^{n}(x_k - a_k)\frac{\partial f}{\partial x_k}(\mathbf{z}_k).$$

We also have

$$L(\mathbf{x} - \mathbf{x}_0) = \left(\frac{\partial f}{\partial x_1}(\mathbf{x}_0) \ldots \frac{\partial f}{\partial x_n}(\mathbf{x}_0)\right)\begin{pmatrix} x_1 - a_1 \\ \vdots \\ \vdots \\ x_n - a_n \end{pmatrix}$$

$$= \sum_{k=1}^{n}(x_k - a_k)\frac{\partial f}{\partial x_k}(\mathbf{x}_0).$$

Hence

$$|f(\mathbf{x}) - f(\mathbf{x}_0) - L(\mathbf{x} - \mathbf{x}_0)| = \left|\sum_{k=1}^{n}\left(\frac{\partial f}{\partial x_k}(\mathbf{z}_k) - \frac{\partial f}{\partial x_k}(\mathbf{x}_0)\right)(x_k - a_k)\right|$$

$$\leq \sum_{k=1}^{n}\left|\frac{\partial f}{\partial x_k}(\mathbf{z}_k) - \frac{\partial f}{\partial x_k}(\mathbf{x}_0)\right||\mathbf{x} - \mathbf{x}_0|,$$

where we have used the triangle inequality and the fact that

$$|x_k - a_k| \leq |\mathbf{x} - \mathbf{x}_0| \quad \text{for} \quad k = 1, 2, \ldots, n.$$

Since the partial derivatives are continuous at $\mathbf{x}_0$, and the $\mathbf{z}_k$ tend to $\mathbf{x}_0$ as $\mathbf{x}$ does, the limit Equation (4) follows immediately.

The entries in the Jacobian matrices that appear in Examples 3 and 4 are continuous functions. As a result of the theorem just proved we conclude that the two functions in those examples are differentiable.

EXAMPLE 5. The function

$$f(x, y) = \sqrt{1 - x^2 - y^2}$$

defined for all (x, y) such that $x^2 + y^2 < 1$ is the same as in Example 2 except that we have removed the boundary of the disc so that the domain is an open set. The Jacobian matrix is

$$(f_x \quad f_y) = \left(\frac{-x}{\sqrt{1 - x^2 - y^2}} \quad \frac{-y}{\sqrt{1 - x^2 - y^2}}\right).$$

The entries are continuous on the open disc, and we conclude, by Theorem 7.2, that f is differentiable there.

EXAMPLE 6. Consider the function

$$f(t) = \begin{pmatrix} \cos t \\ \sin t \end{pmatrix}, \qquad -\infty < t < \infty.$$

The derivative $f'(t_0)$ is the 2-by-1 matrix

$$\begin{pmatrix} -\sin t_0 \\ \cos t_0 \end{pmatrix}.$$

It is instructive to consider the matrix as a vector in the range space of f and to draw it with its tail at the image point $f(t_0)$. For $t_0 = 0$, $\pi/4$, $\pi/3$, $\pi/2$, and π, the respective matrices of the differential $d_{t_0}f$ are

$$\begin{pmatrix} 0 \\ 1 \end{pmatrix}, \quad \begin{pmatrix} -\dfrac{\sqrt{2}}{2} \\ \dfrac{\sqrt{2}}{2} \end{pmatrix}, \quad \begin{pmatrix} -\dfrac{\sqrt{3}}{2} \\ \dfrac{1}{2} \end{pmatrix}, \quad \begin{pmatrix} -1 \\ 0 \end{pmatrix}, \quad \text{and} \quad \begin{pmatrix} 0 \\ -1 \end{pmatrix}.$$

These vectors, drawn with their tails at their corresponding image points under f, are shown in Figure 35. Evidently, for curves at least, the differential is related to the notion of a tangent vector. The affine function that best approximates $f(t)$ in some neighborhood of t_0 is the vector function of t given by

$$f'(t_0)(t - t_0) + f(t_0),$$

which in terms of matrices becomes

$$t\begin{pmatrix} -\sin t_0 \\ \cos t_0 \end{pmatrix} + \begin{pmatrix} \cos t_0 + t_0 \sin t_0 \\ \sin t_0 - t_0 \cos t_0 \end{pmatrix}.$$

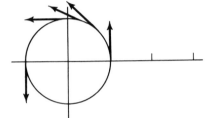

Figure 35

This is the equation of the line tangent to the range of f at $f(t_0)$.

A good geometric picture of the differential of a real-valued function $f(x, y)$ at $\mathbf{x}_0 = (x_0, y_0)$ is obtained by looking at the surface defined explicitly by f, and at the tangent plane to the surface at $(x_0, y_0, f(\mathbf{x}_0))$. An example is shown in Figure 36. The tangent plane is the graph of the affine function defined by

$$A(x, y) = f(x_0, y_0) + f'(x_0, y_0)\begin{pmatrix} x - x_0 \\ y - y_0 \end{pmatrix}, \qquad \text{all } (x, y) \text{ in } \mathscr{R}^2.$$

The difference $A(x, y) - f(x_0, y_0)$ is a good approximation to the increment $f(x, y) - f(x_0, y_0)$, provided (x, y) is close to (x_0, y_0). Figure 36 on page 150 is the analog of a similar picture, included in many one-variable calculus texts, that exhibits the differential for real-valued functions of one variable.

The example given in Exercise 19 below shows that continuity of a derivative f' is not necessary for differentiability of f. It follows that the continuity condition given in Theorem 7.2 is stronger than necessary, and the condition is called continuous differentiability to distinguish it from differentiability.

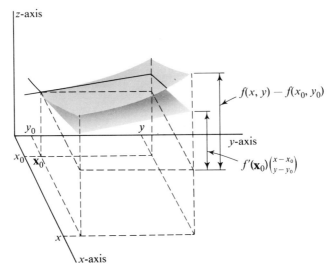

Figure 36

The definition is: A vector function f is **continuously differentiable** on an open set D if the entries in the Jacobian matrix of f are continuous on D. Thus each of the functions of Examples 2–6 is not only differentiable but even continuously differentiable in the interior of its domain.

We finally remark that *if a function f is differentiable, then f is necessarily continuous*, (even though the entries in f' may not be continuous). The proof is very simple and we leave it as an exercise. (See Problem 11.)

EXERCISES

1. A linear function $\mathscr{R}^n \xrightarrow{L} \mathscr{R}^m$ is defined by a matrix (a_{ij}), and

$$
\mathbf{y}_0 = \begin{pmatrix} b_1 \\ \cdot \\ \cdot \\ \cdot \\ b_m \end{pmatrix}
$$

is a vector in $\mathscr{R}^m$. Construct a specific example by choosing m and n, a matrix (a_{ij}), and a vector

$$
\begin{pmatrix} b_1 \\ \cdot \\ \cdot \\ \cdot \\ b_m \end{pmatrix}
$$

so that the affine function

$$
A(\mathbf{x}) = L(\mathbf{x}) + \mathbf{y}_0, \quad \text{all } \mathbf{x} \text{ in } \mathscr{R}^n,
$$

(a) Explicitly defines a line in $\mathscr{R}^2$.

(b) Explicitly defines a line in $\mathscr{R}^3$.

(c) Explicitly defines a plane in $\mathscr{R}^3$.

(d) Parametrically defines a line in $\mathscr{R}^3$.

(e) Parametrically defines a plane in $\mathscr{R}^3$.

What condition must the matrix (a_{ij}) satisfy in order to give an example for (e)?

2. If f is the vector function defined by

$$f\begin{pmatrix} x \\ y \end{pmatrix} = \begin{pmatrix} x^2 - y^2 \\ 2xy \end{pmatrix},$$

find the derivative of f at the following points:

(a) $\begin{pmatrix} x \\ y \end{pmatrix}$,   (b) $\begin{pmatrix} a \\ b \end{pmatrix}$,   (c) $\begin{pmatrix} 1 \\ 0 \end{pmatrix}$,   (d) $\begin{pmatrix} \frac{1}{\sqrt{2}} \\ \frac{1}{\sqrt{2}} \end{pmatrix}$.

$$\left[Ans.\ (c)\ \begin{pmatrix} 2 & 0 \\ 0 & 2 \end{pmatrix}. \right]$$

3. Find the derivative of each of the following functions at the indicated points.

(a) $f\begin{pmatrix} x \\ y \end{pmatrix} = x^2 + y^2$ at $\begin{pmatrix} x \\ y \end{pmatrix} = \begin{pmatrix} 1 \\ 1 \end{pmatrix}$.

(b) $g(x, y, z) = xyz$ at $(x, y, z) = (1, 0, 0)$.

(c) $f(t) = \begin{pmatrix} \sin t \\ \cos t \end{pmatrix}$ at $t = \dfrac{\pi}{4}$. $\left[Ans.\ \begin{pmatrix} \frac{1}{\sqrt{2}} \\ \frac{-1}{\sqrt{2}} \end{pmatrix}. \right]$

(d) $f(t) = \begin{pmatrix} e^t \\ t \\ t^2 \end{pmatrix}$ at $t = 1$.

(e) $g(x, y) = \begin{pmatrix} x + y \\ x^2 + y^2 \end{pmatrix}$ at $(x, y) = (1, 2)$.

(f) $A\begin{pmatrix} u \\ v \end{pmatrix} = \begin{pmatrix} u + v \\ v - v \\ 1 \end{pmatrix}$ at $\begin{pmatrix} u \\ v \end{pmatrix} = \begin{pmatrix} 1 \\ 0 \end{pmatrix}$.

(g) $T\begin{pmatrix} u \\ v \end{pmatrix} = \begin{pmatrix} u \cos v \\ u \sin v \\ v \end{pmatrix}$ at $\begin{pmatrix} u \\ v \end{pmatrix} = \begin{pmatrix} 1 \\ \pi \end{pmatrix}$. $\left[Ans.\ \begin{pmatrix} -1 & 0 \\ 0 & -1 \\ 0 & 1 \end{pmatrix}. \right]$

(h) $f(x, y, z) = (x + y + z, xy + yz + zx, xyz)$ at (x, y, z).

4. Let T be a transformation from three-dimensional to two-dimensional euclidean space defined by

$$T\begin{pmatrix} x \\ y \\ z \end{pmatrix} = \begin{pmatrix} x \\ y \end{pmatrix}.$$

(a) What is the geometric interpretation of this transformation?

(b) Show that T is differentiable at all points and find the matrix of the

differential of T at $\begin{pmatrix} 1 \\ 1 \\ 1 \end{pmatrix}$. $\left[Ans. \begin{pmatrix} 1 & 0 & 0 \\ 0 & 1 & 0 \end{pmatrix} . \right]$

5. (a) Draw the curve in $\mathscr{R}^2$ defined parametrically by the function
$$g(t) = (t - 1, t^2 - 3t + 2), \quad -\infty < t < \infty.$$

(b) Find the affine function that approximates g
   (1) near $t = 0$.   (2) near $t = 2$.   [Ans. $A(t) = (t - 1, t - 2)$.]

(c) Draw the curve defined parametrically by the affine function.

6. Let f be the function given in Exercise 2, and let
$$\mathbf{x_0} = \begin{pmatrix} 1 \\ 0 \end{pmatrix}, \quad \mathbf{y_1} = \begin{pmatrix} 0.1 \\ 0 \end{pmatrix}, \quad \mathbf{y_2} = \begin{pmatrix} 0 \\ 0.1 \end{pmatrix}, \quad \text{and} \quad \mathbf{y_3} = \begin{pmatrix} 0.1 \\ 0.1 \end{pmatrix}.$$

(a) Compute $f(\mathbf{x_0} + \mathbf{y_i})$ for $i = 1, 2, 3$.

(b) Find the affine function A that approximates f near $\mathbf{x_0}$.

(c) Use A to find approximations to the vectors
$$f(\mathbf{x_0} + \mathbf{y_i}), \quad i = 1, 2, 3.$$

7. (a) Sketch the surface in $\mathscr{R}^3$ defined explicitly by the function
$$f(x, y) = 4 - x^2 - y^2.$$

(b) Find the affine function that approximates f
   (1) near $(0, 0)$.   (2) near $(2, 0)$.   [Ans. $A(x, y) = 8 - 4x$.]

(c) Draw the graphs of the affine functions in (b).

8. What is the derivative of the affine function
$$\begin{pmatrix} a_1 & a_2 & a_3 \\ b_1 & b_2 & b_3 \\ c_1 & c_2 & c_3 \end{pmatrix} \begin{pmatrix} x \\ y \\ z \end{pmatrix} + \begin{pmatrix} a_0 \\ b_0 \\ c_0 \end{pmatrix} ?$$

9. Prove that every linear function is its own differential.

10. Prove that if the vector function f is differentiable at $\mathbf{x_0}$, then
$$f'(\mathbf{x_0})\mathbf{x} = \lim_{t \to 0} \frac{f(\mathbf{x_0} + t\mathbf{x}) - f(\mathbf{x_0})}{t}.$$

11. Prove that if a vector function is differentiable at a point, then it is continuous there. [Hint. Multiply the quotient in the definition of differential by $|\mathbf{x} - \mathbf{x_0}|$.]

12. At which points do the following functions fail to be differentiable? Why?

(a) $f\begin{pmatrix} x \\ y \end{pmatrix} = \begin{pmatrix} \dfrac{1}{x^2} + \dfrac{1}{y^2} \\ x^2 + y^2 \end{pmatrix}.$ (b) $g\begin{pmatrix} x \\ y \end{pmatrix} = \begin{pmatrix} \dfrac{\sqrt{x^2 - y^2}}{x + y} \end{pmatrix}.$

(c) $f(u, v) = |u + v|.$

(d) $h(x, y) = \begin{cases} (x \sin (1/x), x^2 + y^2), & \text{if } x \neq 0. \\ (0, x^2 + y^2), & \text{if } x = 0. \end{cases}$

13. Prove that every translation is differentiable. What is the differential?

14. Consider the function $\mathscr{R}^n \xrightarrow{f} \mathscr{R}$ defined by $f(\mathbf{x}) = |\mathbf{x}|^2 = \mathbf{x} \cdot \mathbf{x}$. Prove that $f'(\mathbf{x})\mathbf{y} = 2\mathbf{x} \cdot \mathbf{y}$, for any $\mathbf{x}$ and $\mathbf{y}$ in $\mathscr{R}^n$.

15. Is the function $\mathscr{R}^n \xrightarrow{g} \mathscr{R}$ defined by $g(\mathbf{x}) = |\mathbf{x}|$ differentiable at every point of its domain?

16. Consider the function

$$N(\mathbf{x}) = \max\{|x_1|, \ldots, |x_n|\},$$

for $\mathbf{x} = (x_1, \ldots, x_n)$ in $\mathscr{R}^n$. For what points does the function fail to be differentiable? Answer for (a) $n = 1$, (b) $n = 2$, (c) arbitrary n.

17. Show that if f and g are differentiable at $\mathbf{x}_0$ and a is a real number, then $f + g$ and af are differentiable at $\mathbf{x}_0$ and

(a) $d_{\mathbf{x}_0}(f + g) = d_{\mathbf{x}_0}f + d_{\mathbf{x}_0}g$.
(b) $d_{\mathbf{x}_0}(af) = a(d_{\mathbf{x}_0}f)$.

The domain of $f + g$ is the intersection of the domains of f and g. [*Hint.* Use the uniqueness of the differential.]

18. Verify that the function

$$f(x, y) = \begin{cases} \dfrac{xy}{x^2 - y^2}, & x \neq \pm y, \\ 0, & x = \pm y, \end{cases}$$

has a Jacobian matrix at $(0, 0)$, but that it is not differentiable there.

19. Show that the function defined by

$$f(x) = \begin{cases} x^2 \sin \dfrac{1}{x}, & x \neq 0 \\ 0, & x = 0 \end{cases}$$

is differentiable for all x, but is not continuously differentiable at $x = 0$.

8. DERIVATIVE WITH RESPECT TO A VECTOR

Let $\mathscr{R}^n \xrightarrow{f} \mathscr{R}$ be a real-valued function, and let $\mathbf{y}$ be a vector in the domain space $\mathscr{R}^n$. The **derivative of f with respect to $\mathbf{y}$**, denoted by $\partial f/\partial \mathbf{y}$, is the real-valued function defined by

$$\frac{\partial f}{\partial \mathbf{y}}(\mathbf{x}) = \lim_{t \to 0} \frac{f(\mathbf{x} + t\mathbf{y}) - f(\mathbf{x})}{t}.$$

The domain of $\partial f/\partial \mathbf{y}$ is the subset of the domain of f for which the above limit exists.

The connection between the derivative with respect to a vector and the differential is provided in the following theorem.

8.1 Theorem. If f is differentiable at $\mathbf{x}$, then

$$\frac{\partial f}{\partial \mathbf{y}}(\mathbf{x}) = f'(\mathbf{x})\mathbf{y}, \qquad \text{for every } \mathbf{y} \text{ in } \mathscr{R}^n.$$

Proof. If $\mathbf{y} = 0$, then $(\partial f/\partial \mathbf{y})(\mathbf{x}) = 0 = f'(\mathbf{x})\mathbf{y}$. Hence, in the remainder of the proof we assume that $\mathbf{y} \neq 0$. The existence of the derivative $f'(\mathbf{x})$ implies that

$$\lim_{t \to 0} \frac{f(\mathbf{x} + t\mathbf{y}) - f(\mathbf{x}) - f'(\mathbf{x})(t\mathbf{y})}{|t\mathbf{y}|} = 0,$$

which is equivalent to

$$\lim_{t \to 0} \frac{1}{|\mathbf{y}|} \left| \frac{f(\mathbf{x} + t\mathbf{y}) - f(\mathbf{x})}{t} - f'(\mathbf{x})\mathbf{y} \right| = 0.$$

This in turn is equivalent to

$$\lim_{t \to 0} \frac{f(\mathbf{x} + t\mathbf{y}) - f(\mathbf{x})}{t} = f'(\mathbf{x})\mathbf{y},$$

and the proof is finished.

The equation

$$\frac{\partial f}{\partial \mathbf{y}}(\mathbf{x}) = f'(\mathbf{x})\mathbf{y}$$

shows that for a differentiable function the derivative with respect to a vector involves nothing really new. However, it does represent a change in viewpoint. In a typical discussion of $f'(\mathbf{x})\mathbf{y}$, the vector $\mathbf{y}$ will be regarded as the variable, and $\mathbf{x}$ will be considered fixed. In $(\partial f/\partial \mathbf{y})(\mathbf{x})$ the opposite is true.

EXAMPLE 1. A real-valued function g is defined by

$$g\begin{pmatrix} x \\ y \end{pmatrix} = xy^2 e^{2x}, \qquad \begin{cases} -\infty < x < \infty. \\ -\infty < y < \infty. \end{cases}$$

We take $\mathbf{y} = \begin{pmatrix} a \\ b \end{pmatrix}$. Then, if $\mathbf{x} = \begin{pmatrix} x \\ y \end{pmatrix}$.

$$\frac{\partial g}{\partial \mathbf{y}}\begin{pmatrix} x \\ y \end{pmatrix} = g'(\mathbf{x})\mathbf{y} = (y^2 e^{2x}(1 + 2x) \quad 2xy e^{2x})\begin{pmatrix} a \\ b \end{pmatrix}$$

$$= ye^{2x}(ay + 2axy + 2bx).$$

The derivative with respect to a vector is a natural generalization of the partial derivative. If the domain space of f is $\mathscr{R}^n$ and $\mathbf{e}_j$ is the n-dimensional vector consisting of all zeros except that the jth coordinate is equal to 1, then

$$\frac{\partial f}{\partial \mathbf{e}_j}(\mathbf{x}) = \lim_{t \to 0} \frac{f(\mathbf{x} + t\mathbf{e}_j) - f(\mathbf{x})}{t} = \frac{\partial f}{\partial x_j}(\mathbf{x}).$$

Notice in Example 1 that

$$\frac{\partial g}{\partial \mathbf{y}} = \begin{cases} \dfrac{\partial g}{\partial x} & \text{if } a = 1 \text{ and } b = 0. \\[2mm] \dfrac{\partial g}{\partial y} & \text{if } a = 0 \text{ and } b = 1. \end{cases}$$

For each vector $\mathbf{u}$ in $\mathscr{R}^n$ of length $|\mathbf{u}| = 1$, we define the **directional derivative of f in the direction of u** to be the function $\partial f/\partial \mathbf{u}$. The reason for the name "directional derivative" is that in a euclidean space there is a natural way to associate a vector to each direction, namely, take the unit vector (vector of length 1) in that direction. The number $(\partial f/\partial \mathbf{u})(\mathbf{x})$ is then regarded as a standard measure of the rate of change of the values of f in the direction of $\mathbf{u}$.

EXAMPLE 2. The domain space of the function

$$f(x, y, z) = xyz + e^{2x+y}$$

is assumed to be euclidean 3-dimensional space. Find the directional derivative of f in the direction of $\mathbf{u} = (\frac{1}{2}, \frac{1}{2}, 1/\sqrt{2})$. Setting $\mathbf{x} = (x, y, z)$ and using Theorem 8.1, we obtain

$$\frac{\partial f}{\partial \mathbf{u}}(\mathbf{x}) = f'(\mathbf{x})\mathbf{u} = \begin{pmatrix} yz + 2e^{2x+y} & xz + e^{2x+y} & xy \end{pmatrix} \begin{pmatrix} 1/2 \\ 1/2 \\ 1/\sqrt{2} \end{pmatrix}$$

$$= \frac{yz + xz + \sqrt{2}\,xy}{2} + \frac{3e^{2x+y}}{2}.$$

It follows that the directional derivative of f in the direction of $\mathbf{u}$ has at the origin the value $\partial f/\partial \mathbf{u}\,(0, 0, 0) = \frac{3}{2}$.

Let $\mathscr{R}^2 \xrightarrow{f} \mathscr{R}$ be a function whose graph is a surface in 3-dimensional euclidean space, and let $\mathbf{u}$ be a unit vector in $\mathscr{R}^2$, i.e., $|\mathbf{u}| = 1$. An example is shown in Figure 37. The value of the directional derivative $\partial f/\partial \mathbf{u}$ at $\mathbf{x} = (x, y)$ is by definition

$$\frac{\partial f}{\partial \mathbf{u}}(\mathbf{x}) = \lim_{t \to 0} \frac{f(\mathbf{x} + t\mathbf{u}) - f(\mathbf{x})}{t}.$$

The distance between the points $\mathbf{x} + t\mathbf{u}$ and $\mathbf{x}$ is given by

$$|(\mathbf{x} + t\mathbf{u}) - \mathbf{x}| = |t\mathbf{u}| = |t|.$$

Hence, the ratio

$$\frac{f(\mathbf{x} + t\mathbf{u}) - f(\mathbf{x})}{t}$$

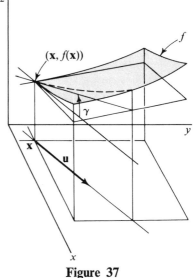

Figure 37

is the slope of the line through the points $f(\mathbf{x} + t\mathbf{u})$ and $f(\mathbf{x})$. It follows that the limit, $(\partial f/\partial \mathbf{u})(\mathbf{x})$, of the ratio is the slope of the tangent line at $(\mathbf{x}, f(\mathbf{x}))$ to the curve formed by the intersection of the graph of f with the plane that contains $\mathbf{x}$ and $\mathbf{x} + \mathbf{u}$, and is parallel to the z-axis. This curve is drawn with a dotted line in the figure. The angle γ shown in Figure 37 therefore satisfies the equation

$$\tan \gamma = \frac{\partial f}{\partial \mathbf{u}}(\mathbf{x}).$$

The situation here is a generalization of that illustrated in Figure 29 of Section 6. If we choose $\mathbf{u} = (1, 0)$, the angle γ becomes the angle α in the earlier figure and

$$\frac{\partial f}{\partial \mathbf{u}} = \frac{\partial f}{\partial x}.$$

On the other hand, if we take $\mathbf{v} = (0, 1)$, then γ is the angle β in Figure 29, and

$$\frac{\partial f}{\partial \mathbf{v}} = \frac{\partial f}{\partial y}.$$

The mean-value theorem for real-valued functions of a real variable can be extended to *real-valued* functions of a vector variable as follows.

8.2 Theorem. Let $\mathscr{R}^n \xrightarrow{f} \mathscr{R}$ be differentiable on an open set containing the segment S joining two vectors $\mathbf{x}$ and $\mathbf{y}$ in $\mathscr{R}^n$. Then there is a point $\mathbf{x}_0$ on S such that

$$f(\mathbf{y}) - f(\mathbf{x}) = f'(\mathbf{x}_0)(\mathbf{y} - \mathbf{x}).$$

Proof. Consider the function $g(t) = f(t(\mathbf{y} - \mathbf{x}) + \mathbf{x})$, defined for $0 \leq t \leq 1$. If we set $\Theta(t) = t(\mathbf{y} - \mathbf{x}) + \mathbf{x}$, then if h is a real number,

$$
\begin{aligned}
g(t + h) - g(t) &= f((t + h)(\mathbf{y} - \mathbf{x}) + \mathbf{x}) - f(t(\mathbf{y} - \mathbf{x}) + \mathbf{x}) \\
&= f'(\Theta(t))h(\mathbf{y} - \mathbf{x}) + |h(\mathbf{y} - \mathbf{x})|Z(h(\mathbf{y} - \mathbf{x})),
\end{aligned}
$$

where $\lim_{h \to 0} Z(h(\mathbf{y} - \mathbf{x})) = 0$. This last relation simply says that f is differentiable at $\Theta(t)$. Dividing by h, we get

$$\frac{g(t + h) - g(t)}{h} = f'(\Theta(t))(\mathbf{y} - \mathbf{x}) \pm |\mathbf{y} - \mathbf{x}|Z(h(\mathbf{y} - \mathbf{x})),$$

whence

$$g'(t) = f'(\Theta(t))(\mathbf{y} - \mathbf{x}). \tag{1}$$

But by the mean-value theorem for functions of one variable,

$$
\begin{aligned}
\frac{g(1) - g(0)}{1 - 0} &= f(\mathbf{y}) - f(\mathbf{x}) \\
&= g'(t_0),
\end{aligned}
$$

for some t_0 satisfying $0 < t_0 < 1$. Setting $t = t_0$ and $\Theta(t_0) = \mathbf{x}_0$ in Equation (1) gives the required formula.

One of the most important conclusions to be drawn from the mean-value theorem for functions of one variable is that a function with zero derivative on an interval is constant. For a function f of a vector variable we shall replace the domain interval by an open set D in $\mathscr{R}^n$ that we assume to be **polygonally connected**. A polygonally connected set S is one such that any two points in it can be joined by a polygon in S, that is, by a finite sequence of line segments lying in S.

8.3 Theorem. If $\mathscr{R}^n \overset{f}{\longrightarrow} \mathscr{R}^m$ is differentiable on a polygonally connected open set D and $f'(\mathbf{x}) = 0$ for every $\mathbf{x}$ in D, then f is constant.

Proof. We need only prove that each coordinate function of f is constant, and so we can assume that f is real-valued. If $\mathbf{x}_1$ and $\mathbf{x}_2$ are points of D joined by a single line segment, then Theorem 8.2 and the assumption that $f'(\mathbf{x}) = 0$ in D together imply that $f(\mathbf{x}_1) = f(\mathbf{x}_2)$. Obviously the same conclusion holds for two points joined by a finite sequence of segments. So f is constant.

EXERCISES

1. Find the value at $\mathbf{x}$ of the derivative of each of the following functions with respect to the vector $\mathbf{y}$.

   (a) $T(x, y, z) = x^2 y\, e^{x+y+2z}$, $\mathbf{x} = \begin{pmatrix} 1 \\ 0 \\ 1 \end{pmatrix}$, and $\mathbf{y} = \begin{pmatrix} a \\ b \\ c \end{pmatrix}$.

   (b) $f(x, y)$, $\mathbf{x} = (x, y)$, and $\mathbf{y} = (\cos \alpha, \sin \alpha)$. (Assume that f is real-valued and differentiable.)

2. For each of the following functions defined on 3-dimensional euclidean space, find the directional derivative in the direction of the unit vector $\mathbf{u}$ at the point $\mathbf{x}$.

   (a) $f(x, y, z) = x^2 + y^2 + z^2$, $\mathbf{u} = (1/\sqrt{3}, 1/\sqrt{3}, 1/\sqrt{3})$, $\mathbf{x} = (1, 0, 1)$.

   (b) $h(x, y, z) = xyz$, $\mathbf{u} = (\cos \alpha \sin \beta, \sin \alpha \sin \beta, \cos \beta)$, $\mathbf{x} = (1, 0, 0)$.

3. For each of the following real-valued functions defined on euclidean space, find the directional derivative at $\mathbf{x}$ in the direction indicated.

   (a) $f(x, y) = x^2 - y^2$ at $\mathbf{x} = (1, 1)$ and in the direction

   $$\left(\frac{1}{\sqrt{5}}, \frac{2}{\sqrt{5}} \right). \qquad \left[Ans.\ \frac{-2}{\sqrt{5}}. \right]$$

   (b) $f(x, y) = e^x \sin y$ at $\mathbf{x} = (1, 0)$ and in the direction $(\cos \alpha, \sin \alpha)$.

(c) $f(x, y) = e^{x+y}$ at $\mathbf{x} = (1, 1)$ in the direction of the curve defined by $g(t) = (t^2, t^3)$ at $g(2)$ for t increasing.

4. Show, using Theorem 8.1, that if $\mathcal{R}^n \xrightarrow{f} \mathcal{R}$ is differentiable and

$$
\mathbf{y} = \begin{pmatrix} y_1 \\ \cdot \\ \cdot \\ \cdot \\ y_n \end{pmatrix},
$$

then

$$
\frac{\partial f}{\partial \mathbf{y}}(\mathbf{x}) = \sum_{j=1}^{n} y_j \frac{\partial f}{\partial x_j}(\mathbf{x}).
$$

5. Show, using Theorem 8.1, that if f is differentiable and a is a real number, then

$$
\frac{\partial f}{\partial a\mathbf{y}} = a\frac{\partial f}{\partial \mathbf{y}}
$$

6. Show that if f is differentiable, then

$$
\frac{\partial f}{\partial (\mathbf{y} + \mathbf{z})} = \frac{\partial f}{\partial \mathbf{y}} + \frac{\partial f}{\partial \mathbf{z}}.
$$

7. Find the absolute value of the directional derivative at $(1, 1, 0)$ of the function $f(x, y, z) = x^2 + ye^z$ in the direction of the tangent line at $g(0)$ to the curve in 3-dimensional euclidean space defined parametrically by $g(t) = (3t^2 + t + 1, 2t, t^2)$.

8. Find the directional derivative at $(1, 0, 0)$ of the function $f(x, y, z) = x^2 + ye^z$ in the direction of increasing t along the curve in euclidean $\mathcal{R}^3$ defined by $g(t) = (t^2 - t + 2, t, t + 2)$ at $g(0)$.   [Ans. $-1/\sqrt{3}$.]

9. Find the absolute value of the directional derivative at $(1, 0, 1)$ of the function $f(x, y, z) = 4x^2y + y^2z$ in the direction of the perpendicular at $(1, 1, 1)$ to the surface in euclidean 3-space defined implicitly by $x^2 + 2y^2 + z^2 = 4$.   [Ans. $8/\sqrt{6}$.]

10. (a) Show that the vector $(y_1z_2 - y_2z_1, z_1x_2 - z_2x_1, x_1y_2 - x_2y_1)$ is perpendicular to (x_1, y_1, z_1) and (x_2, y_2, z_2).
    (b) Find the absolute value of the directional derivative at $(1, 2, 1)$ of the function $f(x, y, z) = x^3 + y^2 + z$ in the direction of the perpendicular at $(1, 2, 1)$ to the surface defined parametrically by $(x, y, z) = (u^2v, u + v, u)$.   [Ans. $2/\sqrt{3}$.]

11. If the temperature at a point (x, y, z) of a solid ball of radius 3 centered at $(0, 0, 0)$ is given by $T(x, y, z) = yz + zx + xy$, find the direction in which T is increasing most rapidly at $(1, 1, 2)$.

12. Show that the mean-value formula of Theorem 8.2 can be written in the form

$$
f(\mathbf{y}) - f(\mathbf{x}) = \frac{\partial f}{\partial (\mathbf{y} - \mathbf{x})}(\mathbf{x}_0).
$$

13. Show that the function f defined by

$$f(x, y) = \begin{cases} \dfrac{x|y|}{\sqrt{x^2 + y^2}}, & (x, y) \neq (0, 0) \\ 0, & (x, y) = (0, 0) \end{cases}$$

has a directional derivative in every direction at $(0, 0)$, but that f is not differentiable at $(0, 0)$.

9. THE GRADIENT

If f is a differentiable real-valued function, $\mathscr{R}^n \xrightarrow{f} \mathscr{R}$, then the function ∇f defined by

$$\nabla f(\mathbf{x}) = \left(\frac{\partial f}{\partial x_1}(\mathbf{x}), \ldots, \frac{\partial f}{\partial x_n}(\mathbf{x}) \right)$$

is called the **gradient** of f. The gradient is evidently a function from $\mathscr{R}^n$ to $\mathscr{R}^n$, and it is most often pictured as a vector field.

EXAMPLE 1. The function $f(x, y) = \frac{1}{6}(x^2 + y^3)$ is differentiable in all of $\mathscr{R}^2$, and so $\nabla f(x, y) = (\frac{1}{3}x, \frac{1}{2}y^2)$ is also defined in $\mathscr{R}^2$. The field is shown in Figure 38 at several points.

The function $g(x, y, z) = x^2 + y^2 + z^2$ has gradient $\nabla g(x, y, z) = (2x, 2y, 2z)$, and the direction of the field is directly away from the origin at each point.

The gradient of a function is important for several reasons. To begin, we remark that the derivative of a real-valued function f with respect to a vector $\mathbf{y}$ can be written in terms of the gradient of f as

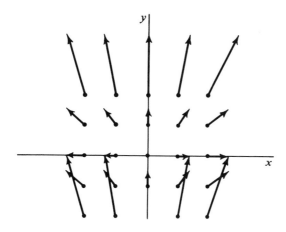

Figure 38

9.1 $$\frac{\partial f}{\partial \mathbf{y}}(\mathbf{x}) = \nabla f(\mathbf{x}) \cdot \mathbf{y}.$$

The reason is that $(\partial f / \partial \mathbf{y})(\mathbf{x}) = f'(\mathbf{x})\mathbf{y}$, and the application of the matrix $f'(\mathbf{x})$ to $\mathbf{y}$ is the same as the dot product $\nabla f(\mathbf{x}) \cdot \mathbf{y}$. Using Equation 9.1, we can easily prove the following theorem, which is the origin of the use of the term gradient.

9.2 **Theorem.** Let $\mathscr{R}^n \xrightarrow{f} \mathscr{R}$ be differentiable in an open set D in $\mathscr{R}^n$. Then at each point $\mathbf{x}$ in D for which $\nabla f(\mathbf{x}) \neq 0$, the vector $\nabla f(\mathbf{x})$ points in the direction of maximum increase for f. The number $|\nabla f(\mathbf{x})|$ is the maximum rate of increase.

Proof. Given a unit vector $\mathbf{u}$, we have, by Equation 9.1 and the Cauchy-Schwarz inequality,

$$\frac{\partial f}{\partial \mathbf{u}}(\mathbf{x}) = \nabla f(\mathbf{x}) \cdot \mathbf{u} \leq |\nabla f(\mathbf{x})|.$$

But when $\mathbf{u} = \nabla f(\mathbf{x})/|\nabla f(\mathbf{x})|$, and only then, we have

$$\frac{\partial f}{\partial \mathbf{u}}(\mathbf{x}) = |\nabla f(\mathbf{x})|.$$

Thus the rate of increase $\partial f / \partial \mathbf{u}(\mathbf{x})$ is never greater than $|\nabla f(\mathbf{x})|$ and is equal to it in the direction of the gradient.

EXAMPLE 2. Let $f(x, y) = e^{xy}$. Then $\nabla f(x, y) = (y e^{xy}, x e^{xy})$, so that at $(1, 2)$ the function f increases most rapidly in the direction $\nabla f(1, 2) = (2e^2, e^2)$, which has the same direction as the unit vector $(2/\sqrt{5}, 1/\sqrt{5})$. The rate of increase in that direction is $|\nabla f(1, 2)| = \sqrt{5}\, e^2$. Similarly $\nabla f(-1, 2) = (2e^{-2}, -e^{-2})$ and has direction $(2/\sqrt{5}, -1/\sqrt{5})$, with maximum rate of increase at $(-1, 2)$ equal to $\sqrt{5}\, e^{-2}$.

Next we shall prove a chain rule for differentiating the composition, $f(F(t))$, of a function $\mathscr{R} \xrightarrow{F} \mathscr{R}^n$ and a function $\mathscr{R}^n \xrightarrow{f} \mathscr{R}$. Thus if $\mathscr{R} \xrightarrow{F} \mathscr{R}^3$ is given by $F(t) = (t, t^2, t)$ and $\mathscr{R}^3 \xrightarrow{f} \mathscr{R}$ by $f(x, y, z) = x \cos(y + z)$, then $f(F(t)) = t \cos(t^2 + t)$. This defines a new function from $\mathscr{R}$ to $\mathscr{R}$. For example, if f is defined in a region D of $\mathscr{R}^3$ and F describes the motion of a point along a path lying in D, we may be interested in finding the rate of change of the composite function with respect to t. The theorem gives a formula for doing this in terms of the gradient of f.

9.3 **Theorem.** Let f be real-valued and continuously differentiable on an open set D in $\mathscr{R}^n$ and let $F(t)$ be defined and differentiable for $a < t < b$, taking its values in D. Then the composite function $g(t) = f(F(t))$ is differentiable for $a < t < b$ and

$$g'(t) = \nabla f(F(t)) \cdot F'(t).$$

Proof. By definition,

$$g'(t) = \lim_{h \to 0} \frac{g(t + h) - g(t)}{h}$$

$$= \lim_{h \to 0} \frac{f(F(t + h)) - f(F(t))}{h},$$

if the limit exists. Since F is differentiable, it is continuous. Then we can choose $\delta > 0$ such that whenever $|h| < \delta$, $F(t + h)$ is always inside an open ball centered at $F(t)$ and contained in D. We now apply the mean-value theorem of the previous section to f, getting

$$f(\mathbf{y}) - f(\mathbf{x}) = f'(\mathbf{x}_0)(\mathbf{y} - \mathbf{x})$$

$$= \nabla f(\mathbf{x}_0) \cdot (\mathbf{y} - \mathbf{x}),$$

where $\mathbf{x}_0$ is some point on the segment joining $\mathbf{y}$ and $\mathbf{x}$. Letting $\mathbf{x} = F(t)$ and $\mathbf{y} = F(t + h)$, with $|h| < \delta$, we have

$$\frac{g(t + h) - g(t)}{h} = \nabla f(\mathbf{x}_0) \cdot \frac{F(t + h) - F(t)}{h}.$$

The vector $\mathbf{x}_0$ is now some point on the segment joining $F(t)$ and $F(t + h)$. (Why is $\mathbf{x}_0$ in the domain of f?) Since f was assumed continuously differentiable, $\nabla f(\mathbf{x})$ is continuous, and so $\nabla f(\mathbf{x}_0)$ tends to $\nabla f(F(t))$ as h tends to zero. The dot product is continuous, so $g'(t)$ exists, with

$$g'(t) = \lim_{h \to 0} \nabla f(\mathbf{x}_0) \cdot \frac{F(t + h) - F(t)}{h}.$$

$$= \nabla f(F(t)) \cdot F'(t).$$

EXAMPLE 3. Let $f(x, y) = x^2y + xy^3$ for (x, y) in $\mathscr{R}^2$. Let $F(t)$ be differentiable in some neighborhood of $t = t_0$ and take its values in $\mathscr{R}^2$. If it is known only that $F(t_0) = (-1, 1)$ and $F'(t_0) = (2, 3)$, then the composition, $g(t) = f(F(t))$, is known only at $t = t_0$, and $g'(t_0)$ cannot be computed by direct differentiation. However, by the previous theorem we have

$$g'(t_0) = \nabla f(F(t_0)) \cdot F'(t_0).$$

We find that $\nabla f(x, y) = (2xy + y^3, x^2 + 3xy^2)$, so $\nabla f(F(t_0)) = (-1, -2)$. Then $g'(t_0) = (-1, -2) \cdot (2, 3) = -8$.

An extension of Theorem 9.3 is proved in the next section.

The idea of a tangent to a level curve or surface is related closely to the gradient. For let S be a level set of a continuously differentiable function $\mathscr{R}^n \xrightarrow{f} \mathscr{R}$. Thus S is the set of points $\mathbf{x}$ satisfying $f(\mathbf{x}) = k$ for some constant k. To say that a point $\mathbf{x}_0$ is on S is to say that $f(\mathbf{x}_0) = k$. Now suppose there is a smooth curve γ lying in S, passing through $\mathbf{x}_0$, and having tangent vector $\mathbf{v}$ at $\mathbf{x}_0$. We parametrize γ by $\mathscr{R} \xrightarrow{g} \mathscr{R}^n$, with $g(t_0) = \mathbf{x}_0$, and $g'(t_0) = \mathbf{v} \neq 0$. Applying the chain rule to the function $h(t) = f(g(t))$ at t_0 gives

$$h'(t_0) = \nabla f(g(t_0)) \cdot g'(t_0)$$
$$= \nabla f(\mathbf{x}_0) \cdot \mathbf{v}.$$

But since γ lies on S, we have $h(t) = f(g(t)) = k$, that is, h is constant. Thus $h'(t_0) = 0$, and

$$\nabla f(\mathbf{x}_0) \cdot \mathbf{v} = 0.$$

This says that $\nabla f(\mathbf{x}_0)$, if it is not zero, is perpendicular to every tangent vector to an arbitrary smooth curve lying on S and passing through $\mathbf{x}_0$. For this reason it is natural to say that $\nabla f(\mathbf{x}_0)$ is perpendicular or **normal** to S at $\mathbf{x}_0$ and to take as the **tangent** plane (or line) to S at $\mathbf{x}_0$ the set of all points $\mathbf{x}$ satisfying

9.4 $$\nabla f(\mathbf{x}_0) \cdot (\mathbf{x} - \mathbf{x}_0) = 0,$$

if $\nabla f(\mathbf{x}_0) \neq 0$. The tangent plane can also be defined to be the set of all points $\mathbf{x}$ satisfying $f'(\mathbf{x}_0)(\mathbf{x} - \mathbf{x}_0) = 0$, if $f'(\mathbf{x}_0) \neq 0$. This is identical with the statement just given in terms of the gradient and is a special case of a general definition given in Section 14.

EXAMPLE 4. The function $f(x, y, z) = x^2 + y^2 - z^2$ has for one of its level surfaces a cone C consisting of all points satisfying $x^2 + y^2 - z^2 = 0$. The point $\mathbf{x}_0 = (1, 1, \sqrt{2})$ lies on C, and to find the tangent plane to C at $\mathbf{x}_0$ we compute $\nabla f(\mathbf{x}_0) = (2, 2, -2\sqrt{2})$. Then

$$\nabla f(\mathbf{x}_0) \cdot (\mathbf{x} - \mathbf{x}_0) = (2, 2, -2\sqrt{2}) \cdot (x - 1, y - 1, z - \sqrt{2}),$$

and the tangent plane is given by $(x - 1) + (y - 1) - \sqrt{2}(z - \sqrt{2}) = 0$, or $x + y - \sqrt{2}z = 0$. This plane is shown in Figure 39. Notice both C and its tangent contain a common line with direction $(2, 2, \sqrt{2})$, and that the normal vector to the tangent is perpendicular to that line.

Putting together Theorem 9.2 with 9.4, we see that the direction of maximum increase of a real-valued differentiable function at a point is perpendicular to the level set of the function through that point.

EXAMPLE 5. The function $f(x, y) = xy$ has level curves $xy = k$. If $k \neq 0$, these curves are all hyperbolas, and each one of them is intersected perpendicularly by every member of the family of hyperbolas $g(x, y) = x^2 - y^2 = k$. (These are shown in Figure 40). To see this, observe that $\nabla f(x, y)$

Figure 39

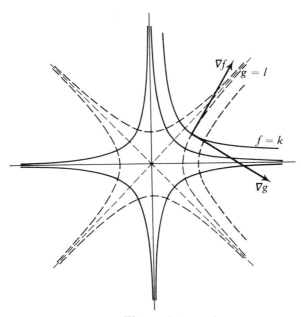

Figure 40

$= (y, x)$ and $\nabla g(x, y) = (2x, -2y)$. Hence, for each (x, y) we have $\nabla f(x, y) \cdot \nabla g(x, y) = 0$. Thus the normal vectors, and hence the tangents, are perpendicular. It also follows that a tangent to a curve from one family points in a direction of maximum increase for the defining function of the other family. The argument fails at $(0, 0)$. See Exercise 6.

As another example of the use of the gradient, we shall prove the following theorem, which is an extension of the familiar formula

$$\int_a^b f'(t)\, dt = f(b) - f(a), \tag{1}$$

the fundamental theorem of calculus.

9.5 Theorem. Let f be a continuously differentiable real-valued function defined in an open set D of $\mathscr{R}^n$. (Thus ∇f is a continuous vector field in D.) If γ is a piecewise smooth curve in D with initial and terminal points $\mathbf{a}$ and $\mathbf{b}$, then

$$\int_\gamma \nabla f \cdot d\mathbf{x} = f(\mathbf{b}) - f(\mathbf{a}).$$

In particular, the value of the line integral of a *gradient* field over a curve depends only on the end-points of the curve and so, in this case, the notation

$$\int_a^b \nabla f \cdot d\mathbf{x} = f(\mathbf{b}) - f(\mathbf{a})$$

is justified.

Proof. Suppose γ is parametrized by $G(t)$ with $a \leq t \leq b$, and $G(a) = \mathbf{a}$, $G(b) = \mathbf{b}$. Using first the definition of the line integral, and then Theorem 9.3, we have

$$\int_\gamma \nabla f \cdot d\mathbf{x} = \int_a^b \nabla f(G(t)) \cdot G'(t) \, dt$$

$$= \int_a^b \frac{d}{dt} f(G(t)) \, dt.$$

But by Equation (1), the fundamental theorem, the last integral is equal to $f(G(b)) - f(G(a)) = f(\mathbf{b}) - f(\mathbf{a})$.

EXAMPLE 6. Consider the field $\nabla f(x, y)$ in $\mathscr{R}^2$, where $f(x, y) = \frac{1}{2}(x^2 + y^2)$. Then $\nabla f(x, y) = (x, y)$. If γ is any continuously differentiable curve with initial and final end-points (x_1, y_1), and (x_2, y_2) then

$$\int_\gamma x \, dx + y \, dy = f(x_2, y_2) - f(x_1, y_1)$$

$$= \frac{1}{2}(x_2^2 - x_1^2) + \frac{1}{2}(y_2^2 - y_1^2).$$

This is what we would expect formally from the fundamental theorem. If, on the other hand, we let $g(x, y) = xy$, we have $\nabla g(x, y) = (y, x)$, and for any curve of the kind previously considered we have

$$\int_\gamma y \, dx + x \, dy = x_2 y_2 - x_1 y_1.$$

EXERCISES

1. Find the gradient, ∇f, of each of the following functions at the indicated points.

(a) $f(x, y, z) = (x - y)e^{xz}$; $(1, 2, -1)$.
(b) $f(x, y) = x^2 - y^2 - \sin y$, for arbitrary (x, y) in $\mathscr{R}^2$.
(c) $f(x, y) = x + y$; $(2, 3)$.
(d) $f(\mathbf{x}) = |\mathbf{x}|^2$, for arbitrary $\mathbf{x}$ in $\mathscr{R}^n$.
(e) $f(\mathbf{x}) = |\mathbf{x}|^\alpha$, for arbitrary nonzero $\mathbf{x}$ in $\mathscr{R}^n$.
(f) $f(x, y) = 0$ identically in $\mathscr{R}^2$; $(1, 1)$.

2. For the functions in the previous problem find the direction and rate of maximum increase at the indicated point.

3. (a) The notation grad f is often used for the gradient ∇f. Show that

$$\frac{\partial f}{\partial \mathbf{y}}(\mathbf{x}) = \text{grad } f(\mathbf{x}) \cdot \mathbf{y}.$$

(b) The notation $\nabla_\mathbf{y} f$ is often used for the derivative $\partial f/\partial \mathbf{y}$. Show that

$$\nabla_\mathbf{y} f(\mathbf{x}) = \nabla f(\mathbf{x}) \cdot \mathbf{y}.$$

4. Find, if possible, a normal vector and the tangent plane to each of the following level curves or surfaces at the indicated points.

(a) $x^2 + y^2 - z^2 = 2$ at $(x, y, z) = (1, 1, 0)$ and at $(x, y, z) = (0, 0, 0)$.
(b) $x \sin y = 0$ at $(x, y) = (0, \pi/2)$ and at $(x, y) = (0, 0)$.
(c) $|\mathbf{x}| = 2$ at $\mathbf{x} = \mathbf{e}_1$, the first natural basis vector in $\mathscr{R}^n$.
(d) $x^2 y + yz + w = 3$ at $(x, y, z, w) = (1, 1, 1, 1)$.
(e) $xyz = 1$ at $(x, y, z) = (1, 1, 1)$.
(f) $xyz = 0$ at $(x, y, z) = (1, 2, 0)$.

5. If $\mathscr{R}^2 \xrightarrow{f} \mathscr{R}$ is continuously differentiable, its graph can be defined implicitly in $\mathscr{R}^3$ as the level surface S of the function $F(x, y, z) = z - f(x, y)$ given by $F(x, y, z) = 0$.

(a) Show that $\nabla F = (-\partial f/\partial x, \ -\partial f/\partial y, \ 1)$, which is never the zero vector.
(b) Find a normal vector and the tangent plane to the graph of $f(x, y) = xy + ye^x$ at $(x, y) = (1, 1)$.

6. (a) The example $f(x, y) = x^2 + y^2$ has $\nabla f(0, 0) = 0$, which fails to indicate that there is a direction of maximum increase for f at $(x, y) = (0, 0)$. Is this reasonable? What happens at $(0, 0)$?
(b) In Example 5 of the text, the point $(x, y) = (0, 0)$ has been avoided. What are the directions of maximum increase for $f(x, y) = xy$ and $g(x, y) = x^2 - y^2$ at $(x, y) = (0, 0)$?

7. If $f(x, y) = e^{x+y}$ and $F'(0) = (1, 2)$, find $g'(0)$, where $g(t) = f(F(t))$ and $F(0) = (1, -1)$.

8. Let γ be a curve in $\mathscr{R}^3$ being traversed at time $t = 1$ with speed 2 and in the direction of $(1, -1, 2)$. If $t = 1$ corresponds to the point $(1, 1, 1)$ on γ, find the rate of change of the function $x + y + xy$ along γ at $t = 1$.

9. If $f(x, y, z) = \sin x$ and $F(t) = (\cos t, \sin t, t)$, find $g'(\pi)$, where $g(t) = f(F(t))$.

10. Let $\mathscr{R} \xrightarrow{F} \mathscr{R}^n$ be differentiable. Let $\mathscr{R}^n \xrightarrow{f} \mathscr{R}$ be continuously differentiable and such that the composition $g(t) = f(F(t))$ exists. If $F'(t_0)$ is tangent to a level surface of f at $F(t_0)$, show that $g'(t_0) = 0$.

11. Given a vector field $\mathscr{R}^n \xrightarrow{F} \mathscr{R}^n$, the problem of finding a function $\mathscr{R}^n \xrightarrow{f} \mathscr{R}$ such that $\nabla f = F$ is equivalent to solving the following system of equations for f, where $F_1, \ldots, F_n$ are the coordinate functions of F:

$$\frac{\partial f}{\partial x_1} = F_1, \ldots, \frac{\partial f}{\partial x_n} = F_n.$$

(a) For the case $n = 2$, show that if the system

$$\frac{\partial f}{\partial x}(x, y) = F_1(x, y), \qquad \frac{\partial f}{\partial y}(x, y) = F_2(x, y)$$

has a solution f, then f must have both of the forms

$$f(x, y) = \int F_1(x, y)\, dx + C_1(y)$$

and

$$f(x, y) = \int F_2(x, y)\, dy + C_2(x),$$

where each indefinite integration is performed with the other variable held fixed.

(b) Find f, if $\nabla f(x, y) = (y^2 + 2xy, 2xy + x^2)$, by using part (a).

(c) Find f, if $\nabla f(x, y, z) = (y + z, z + x, x + y)$, by using an appropriate extension of part (a).

(d) Find f, if $\nabla f(x, y, z) = (yz + z, xz, xy + x)$.

12. (a) Find the function f of Problem 11(b) by direct computation of a line integral of ∇f from $(0, 0)$ to (x, y).

(b) Find the function f of Problem 11(c) by direct computation of a line integral from $(0, 0, 0)$ to (x, y, z).

13. (a) Show that if $F_1, \ldots, F_n$ are continuously differentiable, then a necessary condition for the system of equations

$$\frac{\partial f}{\partial x_1} = F_1, \ldots, \frac{\partial f}{\partial x_n} = F_n$$

to have a solution f is that

$$\frac{\partial F_i}{\partial x_j} = \frac{\partial F_j}{\partial x_i}, \qquad i, j = 1, \ldots, n.$$

(b) Show that the functions $\mathscr{R}^2 \xrightarrow{F} \mathscr{R}^2$ and $\mathscr{R}^3 \xrightarrow{G} \mathscr{R}^3$, given by $F(x, y) = (xy, x^2)$ and $G(x, y, z) = (y, x, -zx)$, are not the gradients of real-valued functions.

14. (a) Compute the line integral $\int_\gamma y\, dx + x\, dy$ along an arbitrary continuously differentiable curve from $(0, 0)$ to $(2, 3)$. [*Hint:* Guess a function $\mathscr{R}^2 \xrightarrow{f} \mathscr{R}$ such that $\nabla f(x, y) = (y, x)$.]

(b) Compute the line integral $\int_\gamma x\, dx + y\, dy + z\, dz$ along an arbitrary continuously differentiable curve from $(0, 0, 0)$ to $(1, 2, 3)$ and from $(0, 0, 0)$ to (x, y, z).

15. Let $F(x, y) = \left(\dfrac{-y}{x^2 + y^2}, \dfrac{x}{x^2 + y^2} \right)$ for $(x, y) \neq (0, 0)$.

(a) If F_1 and F_2 are the coordinate functions of F, show that

$$\frac{\partial F_1}{\partial y} = \frac{\partial F_2}{\partial x}.$$

(b) Show that in any region not meeting the y-axis, F is the gradient of $f(x, y) = \arctan(y/x)$, the principal branch.

(c) Show that F is not the gradient of any function f differentiable in a region completely surrounding the origin—for example, the region defined by $x^2 + y^2 > 0$.

16. Show that if a force field in a region D of $\mathscr{R}^3$ has the form ∇f for some

continuously differentiable function $\mathcal{R}^3 \xrightarrow{f} \mathcal{R}$, then the work done in moving a particle through the field depends only on the level surfaces of f on which the particle starts and finishes.

17. The level surfaces of a function $\mathcal{R}^3 \xrightarrow{f} \mathcal{R}$ are called the **equipotential surfaces** of the vector field ∇f, and f is called the **potential function** of the field.

(a) Show that the equipotential surfaces are orthogonal to the field.

(b) Find the equipotential surfaces of the field $\nabla f(x, y, z) = (x, y, z)$.

(c) Find the field of which $f(x, y, z) = (x^2 + y^2 + z^2)^{-1/2}$ (the **Newtonian potential**) is the potential function.

(d) Find the field of which $f(x, y) = -\frac{1}{2} \log (x^2 + y^2)$ (the **logarithmic potential**) is the potential function.

(e) Show that if $f(\mathbf{x}) = |\mathbf{x}|^{2-n}$ (the generalized Newtonian potential in $\mathcal{R}^n$, $n \geq 3$), then $\nabla f(\mathbf{x}) = (2 - n)|\mathbf{x}|^{-n}\mathbf{x}$.

18. Let $\mathcal{R} \xrightarrow{F} \mathcal{R}^3$ define a smooth curve γ for $a \leq t \leq b$, with γ lying in a region D of $\mathcal{R}^3$ in which $\mathcal{R}^3 \xrightarrow{f} \mathcal{R}$ is continuously differentiable. Show that

$$\frac{d}{dt} \int_{F(a)}^{F(t)} \nabla f \cdot d\mathbf{x} = \nabla f(F(t)) \cdot F'(t).$$

19. Suppose that $\int_{\mathbf{x}_0}^{\mathbf{x}} F(\mathbf{x}) \cdot d\mathbf{x}$ is independent of the piecewise smooth curve γ joining $\mathbf{x}_0$ to $\mathbf{x}$ for all $\mathbf{x}$ in some open set D in $\mathcal{R}^n$. Show that $\nabla f = F$, where $f(\mathbf{x}) = \int_{\mathbf{x}_0}^{\mathbf{x}} F \cdot d\mathbf{x}$. [*Hint:* Look at the integral over a curve γ approaching $\mathbf{x}$ in an arbitrary direction, and apply the fundamental theorem of calculus.]

20. If $T(x, y, z)$ represents the temperature at a point (x, y, z) of a region R in $\mathcal{R}^3$, the vector field ∇T is called the **temperature gradient**. Under certain physical assumptions $\nabla T(x, y, z)$ is proportional to the vector that represents the direction and rate per unit of area of heat flow at (x, y, z). The sets on which T is constant are called **isotherms**. If the isotherms of a temperature function are concentric spheres, prove that the temperature gradient points either toward or away from the center of the spheres.

10. THE CHAIN RULE

If two functions f and g are so related that the range space of f is the same as the domain space of g, we may form the **composite function** $g \circ f$ by first applying f and then g. Thus,

$$g \circ f(\mathbf{x}) = g(f(\mathbf{x}))$$

for every vector $\mathbf{x}$ such that $\mathbf{x}$ is in the domain of f and $f(\mathbf{x})$ is in the domain of g. The domain of $g \circ f$ consists of those vectors $\mathbf{x}$ that are carried by f

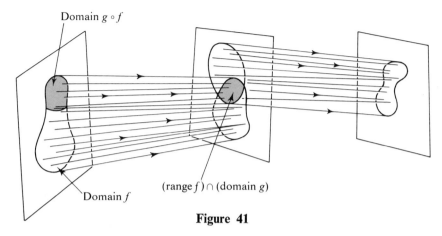

Domain $g \circ f$

(range f) ∩ (domain g)

Domain f

Figure 41

into the domain of g. It is conceivable that there are no such vectors **x**, i.e., that the intersection of the range of f with the domain of g is empty. If this happens, the composition $g \circ f$ is not defined. An abstract picture of the composition of two functions is shown in Figure 41.

EXAMPLE 1. The functions $\mathcal{R}^2 \xrightarrow{f} \mathcal{R}$ and $\mathcal{R} \xrightarrow{g} \mathcal{R}^3$ are defined by

$$f(x, y) = [\ln (x + y)]^2, \qquad g(t) = \begin{pmatrix} t \\ t^2 \\ t^3 \end{pmatrix}, \qquad -1 \leq t \leq 1.$$

The domain of f consists of all vectors (x, y) such that $0 < x + y$, and the range of f is the set of all real numbers t such that $0 \leq t$. The domain of g is the interval $-1 \leq t \leq 1$. The intersection of the last two sets is the interval $0 \leq t \leq 1$. It follows that the domain of the composite function $g \circ f$ is the set of all points (x, y) such that $0 \leq [ln(x + y)]^2 \leq 1$ or, equivalently, such that $e^{-1} \leq x + y \leq e$; see Figure 42. Composing the formulas that define f and g, we obtain

$$g \circ f(x, y) = \begin{pmatrix} [\ln (x + y)]^2 \\ [\ln (x + y)]^4 \\ [\ln (x + y)]^6 \end{pmatrix}, \qquad \frac{1}{e} \leq x + y \leq e.$$

The purpose of this section is the determination of the differential of $g \circ f$ in terms of the differentials of f and g. Suppose $\mathcal{R}^n \xrightarrow{f} \mathcal{R}^m$ is differentiable at $\mathbf{x}_0$ and $\mathcal{R}^m \xrightarrow{g} \mathcal{R}^p$ is differentiable at $\mathbf{y}_0$. Since the range space $\mathcal{R}^m$ of $d_{\mathbf{x}_0} f$ is the domain of $d_{\mathbf{y}_0} g$, the composite function $(d_{\mathbf{y}_0} g) \circ (d_{\mathbf{x}_0} f)$ is defined, and is a linear function with domain $\mathcal{R}^n$ and range space $\mathcal{R}^p$. The chain rule asserts that if $\mathbf{y}_0 = f(\mathbf{x}_0)$, this composite linear function is precisely the differential of $g \circ f$ at $\mathbf{x}_0$. That is, *the differential of a composition is the composition of the differentials.* The theorem is stated below in terms of the matrices of the differentials.

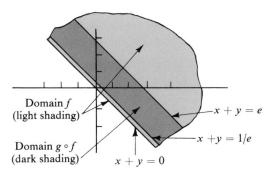

Domain f
(light shading)

Domain $g \circ f$
(dark shading)

$x + y = e$

$x + y = 1/e$

$x + y = 0$

Figure 42

10.1 Theorem. The chain rule. If $\mathscr{R}^n \xrightarrow{f} \mathscr{R}^m$ is differentiable at $\mathbf{x}_0$ and $\mathscr{R}^m \xrightarrow{g} \mathscr{R}^p$ is differentiable at $f(\mathbf{x}_0)$, then $g \circ f$ is differentiable at $\mathbf{x}_0$ and

$$(g \circ f)'(\mathbf{x}_0) = g'(f(\mathbf{x}_0))f'(\mathbf{x}_0).$$

Proof. The first thing to prove is that $\mathbf{x}_0$ is an interior point of the domain of $g \circ f$. Since g is differentiable at $f(\mathbf{x}_0)$, the point $\mathbf{y}_0 = f(\mathbf{x}_0)$ is by definition an interior point of the domain of g. Hence, there exists a positive real number δ' such that a point $\mathbf{y}$ is in the domain of g whenever $|\mathbf{y} - \mathbf{y}_0| < \delta'$. The function f, being differentiable at $\mathbf{x}_0$, is also continuous there (see Exercise 11, Section 7). Furthermore, $\mathbf{x}_0$ is by definition an interior point of the domain of f. It follows that there exists a positive number δ such that if $|\mathbf{x} - \mathbf{x}_0| < \delta$, then $\mathbf{x}$ is in the domain of f and

$$|f(\mathbf{x}) - \mathbf{y}_0| = |f(\mathbf{x}) - f(\mathbf{x}_0)| < \delta'.$$

But δ' has been chosen just so that if the last inequality holds, then $f(\mathbf{x})$ is in the domain of g. Thus any point $\mathbf{x}$ in $\mathscr{R}^n$ that satisfies $|\mathbf{x} - \mathbf{x}_0| < \delta$ lies in the domain of the composite function $g \circ f$, and the vector $\mathbf{x}_0$ is therefore an interior point of that domain.

It remains to prove that the composite linear function with matrix $g'(\mathbf{y}_0)f'(\mathbf{x}_0)$ satisfies the criterion for being the differential of $g \circ f$ at $\mathbf{x}_0$. That is, we must prove that if

$$g \circ f(\mathbf{x}) - g \circ f(\mathbf{x}_0) - g'(\mathbf{y}_0)f'(\mathbf{x}_0)(\mathbf{x} - \mathbf{x}_0) = |\mathbf{x} - \mathbf{x}_0|Z(\mathbf{x} - \mathbf{x}_0), \quad (1)$$

then

$$\lim_{\mathbf{x} \to \mathbf{x}_0} Z(\mathbf{x} - \mathbf{x}_0) = 0.$$

Since f and g are differentiable at $\mathbf{x}_0$ and $\mathbf{y}_0$ respectively, there are functions Z_1 and Z_2 such that

$$f(\mathbf{x}) - f(\mathbf{x}_0) = f'(\mathbf{x}_0)(\mathbf{x} - \mathbf{x}_0) + |\mathbf{x} - \mathbf{x}_0|Z_1(\mathbf{x} - \mathbf{x}_0),$$
$$g(\mathbf{y}) - g(\mathbf{y}_0) = g'(\mathbf{y}_0)(\mathbf{y} - \mathbf{y}_0) + |\mathbf{y} - \mathbf{y}_0|Z_2(\mathbf{y} - \mathbf{y}_0),$$

and

$$\lim_{\mathbf{x} \to \mathbf{x}_0} Z_1(\mathbf{x} - \mathbf{x}_0) = \lim_{\mathbf{y} \to \mathbf{y}_0} Z_2(\mathbf{y} - \mathbf{y}_0) = 0.$$

Using the f-equation to substitute into the g-equation, we get

$$g \circ f(\mathbf{x}) - g \circ f(\mathbf{x}_0)$$
$$= g'(\mathbf{y}_0)(f'(\mathbf{x}_0)(\mathbf{x} - \mathbf{x}_0) + |\mathbf{x} - \mathbf{x}_0| Z_1(\mathbf{x} - \mathbf{x}_0))$$
$$+ |f(\mathbf{x}) - f(\mathbf{x}_0)| Z_2(f(\mathbf{x}) - f(\mathbf{x}_0)).$$

From this it follows, by the linearity of the matrix multiplier $g'(\mathbf{y}_0)$, that

$$g \circ f(\mathbf{x}) - g \circ f(\mathbf{x}_0) - g'(\mathbf{y}_0)f'(\mathbf{x}_0)(\mathbf{x} - \mathbf{x}_0) \qquad (2)$$
$$= |\mathbf{x} - \mathbf{x}_0| g'(\mathbf{y}_0)[Z_1(\mathbf{x} - \mathbf{x}_0)] + |f(\mathbf{x}) - f(\mathbf{x}_0)| Z_2(f(\mathbf{x}) - f(\mathbf{x}_0)).$$

We note that since f is differentiable at $\mathbf{x}_0$

$$|f(\mathbf{x}) - f(\mathbf{x}_0)| = |f'(\mathbf{x}_0)(\mathbf{x} - \mathbf{x}_0) + |\mathbf{x} - \mathbf{x}_0| Z_1(\mathbf{x} - \mathbf{x}_0)|$$
$$\leq k|\mathbf{x} - \mathbf{x}_0| + |Z_1(\mathbf{x} - \mathbf{x}_0)||\mathbf{x} - \mathbf{x}_0|,$$

where in the last step we have used the triangle inequality, and Theorem 2.3 provides the constant k. This inequality enables us to estimate the right-hand side of Equation (2), showing that its norm is less than or equal to $|\mathbf{x} - \mathbf{x}_0|$ multiplied by a function that tends to zero as $\mathbf{x}$ tends to $\mathbf{x}_0$. In fact, we have the upper estimate

$$|\mathbf{x} - \mathbf{x}_0| \{|g'(\mathbf{y}_0)[Z_1(\mathbf{x} - \mathbf{x}_0)]| + [k + |Z_1(\mathbf{x} - \mathbf{x}_0)|]|Z_2(f(\mathbf{x}) - f(\mathbf{x}_0))|\}.$$

But as $\mathbf{x}$ tends to $\mathbf{x}_0$, $f(\mathbf{x})$ tends to $f(\mathbf{x}_0)$, so both $Z_0(\mathbf{x} - \mathbf{x}_0)$ and $Z_2(f(\mathbf{x}) - f(\mathbf{x}_0))$ tend to zero. This shows that $Z(\mathbf{x} - \mathbf{x}_0)$ itself, defined by Equation (1), tends to zero, thus completing the proof.

EXAMPLE 2. Let f and g be the vector functions defined in Example 1, namely,

$$f(x, y) = [\ln(x + y)]^2, \qquad g(t) = \begin{pmatrix} t \\ t^2 \\ t^3 \end{pmatrix}.$$

Using the chain rule, we shall compute the derivative $(g \circ f)'(\mathbf{x}_0)$ at $\mathbf{x}_0 = (1, 1)$. The matrix $f'(\mathbf{x}_0)$ is the Jacobian matrix

$$\left(\frac{2 \ln(x + y)}{x + y} \quad \frac{2 \ln(x + y)}{x + y} \right)_{x = y = 1} = (\ln 2 \quad \ln 2).$$

The point $\mathbf{y}_0 = f(\mathbf{x}_0)$ is the real number $t_0 = (\ln 2)^2$. The Jacobian matrix of g at t_0 is

$$\begin{pmatrix} 1 \\ 2t_0 \\ 3t_0^2 \end{pmatrix} = \begin{pmatrix} 1 \\ 2(\ln 2)^2 \\ 3(\ln 2)^4 \end{pmatrix}.$$

According to the chain rule, $(g \circ f)'(\mathbf{x}_0) = g'(t_0)f'(\mathbf{x}_0)$. The matrix of the composition of two linear functions is the product of their respective matrices. Hence the matrix $(g \circ f)'(\mathbf{x}_0)$ of $d_{\mathbf{x}_0}(g \circ f)$ is

$$\begin{pmatrix} 1 \\ 2(\ln 2)^2 \\ 3(\ln 2)^4 \end{pmatrix} (\ln 2 \quad \ln 2) = \begin{pmatrix} \ln 2 & \ln 2 \\ 2(\ln 2)^3 & 2(\ln 2)^3 \\ 3(\ln 2)^5 & 3(\ln 2)^5 \end{pmatrix}.$$

The same result can be obtained by computing directly the partial derivatives in the matrix of the differential of $g \circ f$.

It is common practice in calculus to denote a function by the same symbol as a typical element of its range. Thus the derivative of a function $\mathscr{R} \xrightarrow{f} \mathscr{R}$ is more often than otherwise denoted, in conjunction with the equation $y = f(x)$, by dy/dx. Similarly, the partial derivatives of a function $\mathscr{R}^3 \xrightarrow{f} \mathscr{R}$ are commonly written as

$$\frac{\partial w}{\partial x}, \qquad \frac{\partial w}{\partial y}, \qquad \text{and} \qquad \frac{\partial w}{\partial z}$$

along with the explanatory equation $w = f(x, y, z)$. For example, if $w = xy^2 e^{x+3z}$, then

$$\frac{\partial w}{\partial x} = y^2 e^{x+3z} + xy^2 e^{x+3z},$$

$$\frac{\partial w}{\partial y} = 2xy e^{x+3z},$$

$$\frac{\partial w}{\partial z} = 3xy^2 e^{x+3z}.$$

This notation has the disadvantage that, because it does not contain specific reference to the function being differentiated, it obscures the fact that *functions are the only mathematical objects that have derivatives and differentials*. On the other hand, it is notationally convenient and is, moreover, the traditional language of calculus. To illustrate its convenience, suppose that the functions g and f are given by

$$w = g(x, y, z), \qquad x = f_1(s, t), \qquad y = f_2(s, t), \qquad z = f_3(s, t).$$

Then, by the chain rule,

$$\left(\frac{\partial w}{\partial s} \quad \frac{\partial w}{\partial t} \right) = \left(\frac{\partial g}{\partial x} \quad \frac{\partial g}{\partial y} \quad \frac{\partial g}{\partial z} \right) \begin{pmatrix} \dfrac{\partial x}{\partial s} & \dfrac{\partial x}{\partial t} \\ \dfrac{\partial y}{\partial s} & \dfrac{\partial y}{\partial t} \\ \dfrac{\partial z}{\partial s} & \dfrac{\partial z}{\partial t} \end{pmatrix}.$$

Matrix multiplication yields

$$\left.\begin{aligned} \frac{\partial w}{\partial s} &= \frac{\partial g}{\partial x}\frac{\partial x}{\partial s} + \frac{\partial g}{\partial y}\frac{\partial y}{\partial s} + \frac{\partial g}{\partial z}\frac{\partial z}{\partial s} \\ \frac{\partial w}{\partial t} &= \frac{\partial g}{\partial x}\frac{\partial x}{\partial t} + \frac{\partial g}{\partial y}\frac{\partial y}{\partial t} + \frac{\partial g}{\partial z}\frac{\partial z}{\partial t} \end{aligned}\right\}. \tag{6}$$

A slightly different-looking application of the chain rule is obtained if the domain space of f is 1-dimensional, that is, if f is a function of one variable. Consider, for example,

$$w = g(u, v), \qquad \begin{pmatrix} u \\ v \end{pmatrix} = f(t) = \begin{pmatrix} f_1(t) \\ f_2(t) \end{pmatrix}.$$

The composition $g \circ f$ is in this case a real-valued function of one variable. Its differential is defined by the 1-by-1 matrix whose entry is the derivative

$$\frac{d(g \circ f)}{dt} = \frac{dw}{dt}.$$

The derivatives of g and f are defined respectively by the Jacobian matrices

$$\begin{pmatrix} \dfrac{\partial w}{\partial u} & \dfrac{\partial w}{\partial v} \end{pmatrix} \quad \text{and} \quad \begin{pmatrix} \dfrac{du}{dt} \\ \dfrac{dv}{dt} \end{pmatrix}.$$

Hence, the chain rule implies that

$$\frac{dw}{dt} = \begin{pmatrix} \frac{\partial w}{\partial u} & \frac{\partial w}{\partial v} \end{pmatrix} \begin{pmatrix} \frac{du}{dt} \\ \frac{dv}{dt} \end{pmatrix} = \frac{\partial w}{\partial u}\frac{du}{dt} + \frac{\partial w}{\partial v}\frac{dv}{dt}. \tag{7}$$

Finally, let us suppose that both f and g are real-valued functions of one variable. This is the situation encountered in one-variable calculus. The derivatives of f at t, of g at $s = f(t)$, and of $g \circ f$ at t are represented by the three 1-by-1 Jacobian matrices $(f'(t))$, $(g'(s))$, and $((g \circ f)'(t))$ respectively. The chain rule implies that

10.2 $(g \circ f)'(t) = g'(s)f'(t).$

If the functions are presented in the form

$$x = g(s), \quad s = f(t),$$

the more explicit Formula 10.2 can be written as the famous equation

$$\frac{dx}{dt} = \frac{dx}{ds}\frac{ds}{dt}. \tag{8}$$

EXAMPLE 3. Given that

$$\begin{cases} x = u^2 + v^3, \\ y = e^{uv}, \end{cases} \quad \text{and} \quad \begin{cases} u = t + 1, \\ v = e^t, \end{cases}$$

find dx/dt and dy/dt at $t = 0$. Let $\mathscr{R} \xrightarrow{f} \mathscr{R}^2$ and $\mathscr{R}^2 \xrightarrow{g} \mathscr{R}^2$ be the functions defined by

$$f(t) = \begin{pmatrix} t+1 \\ e^t \end{pmatrix} = \begin{pmatrix} u \\ v \end{pmatrix}, \qquad -\infty < t < \infty,$$

$$g\begin{pmatrix} u \\ v \end{pmatrix} = \begin{pmatrix} u^2 + v^3 \\ e^{uv} \end{pmatrix} = \begin{pmatrix} x \\ y \end{pmatrix}, \qquad \begin{cases} -\infty < u < \infty. \\ -\infty < v < \infty. \end{cases}$$

The differential of f at t is defined by the 2-by-1 Jacobian matrix

$$\begin{pmatrix} \dfrac{du}{dt} \\ \dfrac{dv}{dt} \end{pmatrix} = \begin{pmatrix} 1 \\ e^t \end{pmatrix}.$$

The matrix of the differential of g at $\begin{pmatrix} u \\ v \end{pmatrix}$ is

$$\begin{pmatrix} \dfrac{\partial x}{\partial u} & \dfrac{\partial x}{\partial v} \\ \dfrac{\partial y}{\partial u} & \dfrac{\partial y}{\partial v} \end{pmatrix} = \begin{pmatrix} 2u & 3v^2 \\ ve^{uv} & ue^{uv} \end{pmatrix}.$$

The dependence of x and y on t is given by

$$\begin{pmatrix} x \\ y \end{pmatrix} = (g \circ f)(t), \qquad -\infty < t < \infty.$$

Hence, the two derivatives dx/dt and dy/dt are the entries in the Jacobian matrix that defines the differential of the composite function $g \circ f$. The chain rule therefore implies that

$$\begin{pmatrix} \dfrac{dx}{dt} \\ \dfrac{dy}{dt} \end{pmatrix} = \begin{pmatrix} \dfrac{\partial x}{\partial u} & \dfrac{\partial x}{\partial v} \\ \dfrac{\partial y}{\partial u} & \dfrac{\partial y}{\partial v} \end{pmatrix} \begin{pmatrix} \dfrac{du}{dt} \\ \dfrac{dv}{dt} \end{pmatrix}.$$

That is,

$$\left. \begin{aligned} \frac{dx}{dt} &= \frac{\partial x}{\partial u}\frac{du}{dt} + \frac{\partial x}{\partial v}\frac{dv}{dt} = 2u + 3v^2 e^t \\ \frac{dy}{dt} &= \frac{\partial y}{\partial u}\frac{du}{dt} + \frac{\partial y}{\partial v}\frac{dv}{dt} = ve^{uv} + ue^{uv+t} \end{aligned} \right\} . \tag{9}$$

If $t = 0$, then $\begin{pmatrix} u \\ v \end{pmatrix} = f(0) = \begin{pmatrix} 1 \\ 1 \end{pmatrix}$, and we get $u = v = 1$. It follows that

$$\frac{dx}{dt}(0) = 2 + 3 = 5,$$

$$\frac{dy}{dt}(0) = e + e = 2e.$$

The definition of matrix multiplication gives the derivative formulas that result from applications of the chain rule a formal pattern that is easy to memorize. The pattern is particularly in evidence when the coordinate functions are denoted by real variables as in Formulas (6), (7), (8), and (9). All formulas of the general form

$$\cdots \frac{\partial z}{\partial x}\frac{\partial x}{\partial t} + \frac{\partial z}{\partial y}\frac{\partial y}{\partial t} + \cdots$$

have the disadvantage, however, of not containing explicit reference to the points at which the various derivatives are evaluated. It is, of course, essential to know this information. It can be found by going to the formula

$$(g \circ f)'(\mathbf{x}) = g'(f(\mathbf{x}))f'(\mathbf{x}).$$

It follows that derivatives appearing in the matrix $f'(\mathbf{x})$ are evaluated at $\mathbf{x}$, and those in the matrix $g'(f(\mathbf{x}))$ are evaluated at $f(\mathbf{x})$. This is the reason for setting $t = 0$ and $u = v = 1$ in Formula (9) to obtain the final answers in Example 3.

EXAMPLE 4. Let

$$z = x^y \quad \text{and} \quad \begin{cases} x = f(u, v). \\ y = g(u, v). \end{cases}$$

Suppose that when $u = 1$ and $v = 2$, we have

$$\frac{\partial x}{\partial u} = -1, \quad \frac{\partial x}{\partial v} = 3, \quad \frac{\partial y}{\partial u} = 5, \quad \frac{\partial y}{\partial v} = 0.$$

Suppose also that $f(1, 2) = 2$ and $g(1, 2) = -2$. What is $(\partial z/\partial u)(1, 2)$? The chain rule implies that

$$\frac{\partial z}{\partial u} = \frac{\partial z}{\partial x}\frac{\partial x}{\partial u} + \frac{\partial z}{\partial y}\frac{\partial y}{\partial u}. \tag{10}$$

When $u = 1$ and $v = 2$, we are given that $x = f(1, 2) = 2$ and $y = g(1, 2) = -2$. Hence

$$\frac{\partial z}{\partial x}(2, -2) = yx^{y-1}|_{x=2, y=-2} = (-2)(2^{-3}) = -\frac{1}{4},$$

$$\frac{\partial z}{\partial y}(2, -2) = x^y \ln x|_{x=2, y=-2} = \frac{1}{4}\ln 2.$$

In order to obtain $\partial z/\partial u$ at $(u, v) = (1, 2)$, it is necessary to know at what points to evaluate the partial derivatives that appear in Equation (10). In greater detail, the chain rule implies that

$$\frac{\partial z}{\partial u}(1, 2) = \frac{\partial z}{\partial x}(2, -2)\frac{\partial x}{\partial u}(1, 2) + \frac{\partial z}{\partial y}(2, -2)\frac{\partial y}{\partial u}(1, 2).$$

Hence

$$\frac{\partial z}{\partial u}(1, 2) = \left(-\frac{1}{4}\right)(-1) + \left(\frac{1}{4}\ln 2\right)5 = \frac{1}{4}(1 + 5\ln 2).$$

EXAMPLE 5. If $w = f(ax^2 + bxy + cy^2)$ and $y = x^2 + x + 1$, find $dw/dx(-1)$. The solution relies on formulas that follow from the chain rule (like (6), (7), (8), and (9)). Set

$$z = ax^2 + bxy + cy^2.$$

Then, $w = f(z)$ and

$$\frac{dz}{dx} = \frac{\partial z}{\partial x} + \frac{\partial z}{\partial y}\frac{dy}{dx}.$$

Hence,

$$\frac{dw}{dx} = \frac{df}{dz}\frac{dz}{dx} = \frac{df}{dz}\left(\frac{\partial z}{\partial x} + \frac{\partial z}{\partial y}\frac{dy}{dx}\right)$$
$$= f'(z)(2ax + by + (bx + 2cy)(2x + 1)).$$

If $x = -1$, then $y = 1$ and so $z = a - b + c$. Thus,

$$\frac{dw}{dx}(-1) = f'(a - b + c)(-2a + 2b - 2c).$$

The Jacobian matrix of a function $\mathscr{R}^n \xrightarrow{f} \mathscr{R}^n$ at a point $\mathbf{x}$ is a square matrix. Its determinant is called **the Jacobian determinant of f at $\mathbf{x}$.** An important corollary of the chain rule and the product rule for determinants is

10.3 Theorem. If $\mathscr{R}^n \xrightarrow{f} \mathscr{R}^n$ is differentiable at $\mathbf{x}_0$ and $\mathscr{R}^n \xrightarrow{g} \mathscr{R}^n$ is differentiable at $\mathbf{y}_0 = f(\mathbf{x}_0)$, then the Jacobian determinant of $g \circ f$ at $\mathbf{x}_0$ is the product of the Jacobian determinant of f at $\mathbf{x}_0$ and that of g at $\mathbf{y}_0$.

If f is defined by

$$f\begin{pmatrix} x_1 \\ \vdots \\ x_n \end{pmatrix} = \begin{pmatrix} f_1(x_1, \ldots, x_n) \\ \vdots \\ f_n(x_1, \ldots, x_n) \end{pmatrix} = \begin{pmatrix} y_1 \\ \vdots \\ y_n \end{pmatrix},$$

then the Jacobian determinant of f is denoted by

$$\frac{\partial(f_1, \ldots, f_n)}{\partial(x_1, \ldots, x_n)}.$$

or equivalently

$$\frac{\partial(y_1, \ldots, y_n)}{\partial(x_1, \ldots, x_n)}.$$

The Jacobian determinant of f is a function of the variable $\mathbf{x}$, and its value at $\mathbf{x}_0 = (a_1, \ldots, a_n)$ will be denoted by

$$\frac{\partial(y_1, \ldots, y_n)}{\partial(x_1, \ldots, x_n)}(\mathbf{x}_0) = \frac{\partial(y_1, \ldots, y_n)}{\partial(x_1, \ldots, x_n)}(a_1, \ldots, a_n).$$

EXAMPLE 6. Let

$$f\binom{r}{\theta} = \binom{r\cos\theta}{r\sin\theta} = \binom{x}{y} \quad \text{and} \quad g\binom{x}{y} = \binom{x^2 - y^2}{2xy} = \binom{w}{z}.$$

Then,

$$\frac{\partial(x, y)}{\partial(r, \theta)} = \det\begin{pmatrix} \cos\theta & -r\sin\theta \\ \sin\theta & r\cos\theta \end{pmatrix} = r(\cos^2\theta + \sin^2\theta) = r,$$

and

$$\frac{\partial(w, z)}{\partial(x, y)} = \det\begin{pmatrix} 2x & -2y \\ 2y & 2x \end{pmatrix} = 4(x^2 + y^2).$$

The Jacobian determinant of the composite function $g \circ f$ is denoted in this case by $\partial(w, z)/\partial(r, \theta)$. If

$$\binom{x_0}{y_0} = \binom{r_0\cos\theta_0}{r_0\sin\theta_0},$$

Theorem 10.3 implies that

$$\frac{\partial(w, z)}{\partial(r, \theta)}(r_0, \theta_0) = \frac{\partial(w, z)}{\partial(x, y)}(x_0, y_0)\frac{\partial(x, y)}{\partial(r, \theta)}(r_0, \theta_0)$$

$$= 4(x_0^2 + y_0^2)r_0 = 4r_0^3.$$

EXERCISES

1. Given that

$$f\binom{x}{y} = \binom{x^2 + xy + 1}{y^2 + 2}, \qquad g\binom{u}{v} = \begin{pmatrix} u + v \\ 2u \\ v^2 \end{pmatrix},$$

find the matrix of the differential of the composite function $g \circ f$ at

$$\mathbf{x}_0 = \binom{1}{1}. \qquad \left[Ans. \begin{pmatrix} 3 & 3 \\ 6 & 2 \\ 0 & 12 \end{pmatrix}. \right]$$

2. Let

$$f(t) = \begin{pmatrix} t \\ t+1 \\ t^2 \end{pmatrix} = \begin{pmatrix} x \\ y \\ z \end{pmatrix}$$

and

$$g\begin{pmatrix} x \\ y \\ z \end{pmatrix} = \binom{x + 2y + z^2}{x^2 - y} = \binom{u}{v}.$$

(a) Find the Jacobian matrix of $g \circ f$ at $t = a$. $\left[Ans. \begin{pmatrix} 3 + 4a^3 \\ 2a - 1 \end{pmatrix}. \right]$

(b) Find du/dt in terms of the derivatives of x, y, z, and the partial derivatives of u.

3. Consider the curve defined parametrically by

$$f(t) = \begin{pmatrix} t \\ t^2 - 4 \\ e^{t-2} \end{pmatrix}, \qquad -\infty < t < \infty.$$

Let g be a real-valued differentiable function with domain $\mathscr{R}^3$. If

$$x_0 = \begin{pmatrix} 2 \\ 0 \\ 1 \end{pmatrix}$$

and

$$\frac{\partial g}{\partial x}(x_0) = 4, \qquad \frac{\partial g}{\partial y}(x_0) = 2, \qquad \frac{\partial g}{\partial z}(x_0) = 2,$$

find $d(g \circ f)/dt$ at $t = 2$. [Ans. 14.]

4. Consider the functions

$$f \begin{pmatrix} u \\ v \end{pmatrix} = \begin{pmatrix} u + v \\ u - v \\ u^2 - v^2 \end{pmatrix} = \begin{pmatrix} x \\ y \\ z \end{pmatrix}$$

and

$$F(x, y, z) = x^2 + y^2 + z^2 = w.$$

(a) Find the matrix that defines the differential of $F \circ f$ at $\begin{pmatrix} a \\ b \end{pmatrix}$.

(b) Find $\dfrac{\partial w}{\partial u}$ and $\dfrac{\partial w}{\partial v}$.

5. Let $u = f(x, y)$. Make the change of variables $x = r \cos \theta$, $y = r \sin \theta$. Given that

$$\frac{\partial f}{\partial x} = x^2 + 2xy - y^2 \text{ and } \frac{\partial f}{\partial y} = x^2 - 2xy + 2,$$

find $\dfrac{\partial f}{\partial \theta}$, when $r = 2$ and $\theta = \dfrac{\pi}{2}$. [Ans. 8.]

6. If $w = \sqrt{x^2 + y^2 + z^2}$ and

$$\begin{pmatrix} x \\ y \\ z \end{pmatrix} = \begin{pmatrix} r \cos \theta \\ r \sin \theta \\ r \end{pmatrix},$$

find $\partial w/\partial r$ and $\partial w/\partial \theta$ using the chain rule. Check the result by direct substitution.

7. Vector functions f and g are defined by

$$f\begin{pmatrix} u \\ v \end{pmatrix} = \begin{pmatrix} u\cos v \\ u\sin v \end{pmatrix}, \quad \begin{cases} 0 < u < \infty, \\ -\pi/2 < v < \pi/2, \end{cases}$$

$$g\begin{pmatrix} x \\ y \end{pmatrix} = \begin{pmatrix} \sqrt{x^2 + y^2} \\ \arctan \dfrac{y}{x} \end{pmatrix}, \quad 0 < x < \infty.$$

(a) Find the Jacobian matrix of $g \circ f$ at $\begin{pmatrix} u \\ v \end{pmatrix}$.

(b) Find the Jacobian matrix of $f \circ g$ at $\begin{pmatrix} x \\ y \end{pmatrix}$.

(c) Are the following statements true or false?
   1. domain of f = domain of $g \circ f$.
   2. domain of g = domain of $f \circ g$.

8. A function I is called an **identity function** if $I(\mathbf{x}) = \mathbf{x}$ for all $\mathbf{x}$ in the domain of I.

(a) Show that if differentiable vector functions f and g are so related that the composite function $g \circ f$ is an identity function, then the transformation $(d_{f(\mathbf{x})}g) \circ (d_{\mathbf{x}}f)$ is also an identity function for $\mathbf{x}$ in the domain of $g \circ f$.

(b) How does this exercise apply to the preceding one?

9. If F and f are differentiable vector functions whose composition $f \circ F$ is defined, show that

$$\frac{\partial f \circ F}{\partial \mathbf{y}}(\mathbf{x}) = \left(\frac{\partial f}{\partial (F'(\mathbf{x})\mathbf{y})} \circ F \right)(\mathbf{x})$$

for every vector $\mathbf{y}$ in the domain space of F and every vector $\mathbf{x}$ in the domain of $f \circ F$.

10. Let $\mathbf{x}_1$ be a tangent vector at $\mathbf{x}_0$ to a curve defined parametrically by a differentiable vector function f. If $\mathbf{x}_0$ is in the domain of a differentiable vector function F, prove that $F'(\mathbf{x}_0)\mathbf{x}_1$, if not zero, is a tangent vector at $F(\mathbf{x}_0)$ to the curve defined parametrically by $F \circ f$.

11. The convention of denoting coordinate functions by real variables has its pitfalls. Resolve the following paradox: Let $w = f(x, y, z)$ and $z = g(x, y)$. By the chain rule

$$\frac{\partial w}{\partial x} = \frac{\partial w}{\partial x}\frac{\partial x}{\partial x} + \frac{\partial w}{\partial y}\frac{\partial y}{\partial x} + \frac{\partial w}{\partial z}\frac{\partial z}{\partial x}.$$

The quantities x and y are unrelated so that $\partial y/\partial x = 0$. Clearly $\partial x/\partial x = 1$. Hence,

$$\frac{\partial w}{\partial x} = \frac{\partial w}{\partial x} + \frac{\partial w}{\partial z}\frac{\partial z}{\partial x},$$

and so

$$0 = \frac{\partial w}{\partial z}\frac{\partial z}{\partial x}.$$

In particular, take $w = 2x + y + 3z$ and $z = 5x + 18$. Then

$$\frac{\partial w}{\partial z} = 3 \quad \text{and} \quad \frac{\partial z}{\partial x} = 5.$$

It follows that

$$0 = 15.$$

12. If $y = f(x - at) + g(x + at)$, where a is constant and f and g are twice differentiable, show that

$$a^2 \frac{\partial^2 y}{\partial x^2} = \frac{\partial^2 y}{\partial t^2}. \qquad \text{(Wave equation)}$$

13. If $z = f(x, y)$ is differentiable and $\begin{pmatrix} x \\ y \end{pmatrix} = \begin{pmatrix} r \cos \theta \\ r \sin \theta \end{pmatrix}$, show that

$$\left(\frac{\partial z}{\partial x}\right)^2 + \left(\frac{\partial z}{\partial y}\right)^2 = \left(\frac{\partial z}{\partial r}\right)^2 + \frac{1}{r^2} \left(\frac{\partial z}{\partial \theta}\right)^2.$$

14. If $f(tx, ty) = t^n f(x, y)$ for some integer n, and for all x, y, and t, show that

$$x \frac{\partial f}{\partial x} + y \frac{\partial f}{\partial y} = nf(x, y).$$

15. Show that for a differentiable real-valued function $g(x, y)$,

$$\frac{dg(x, x)}{dx} = \frac{\partial g}{\partial x}(x, x) + \frac{\partial g}{\partial y}(x, x).$$

Using the function $f(x) = (x, x)$ show that this result is equivalent to the statement $(g \circ f)'(x) = g'(f(x))f'(x)$.

Apply the equation to the function $g(x, y) = x^y$.

16. (a) If

$$w = f(x, y, z, t), \qquad x = g(u, z, t), \qquad \text{and} \quad z = h(u, t),$$

write a formula for dw/dt, where by this symbol is meant the rate of change of w with respect to t, and where all the interrelations of w, x, z, t are taken into account.

(b) If

$$f(x, y, z, t) = 2xy + 3z + t^2,$$
$$g(u, z, t) = ut \sin z,$$
$$h(u, t) = 2u + t,$$

evaluate the above dw/dt at the point $u = 1$, $t = 2$, $y = 3$, by using the formula you derived in part (a) and also by substituting in the functions for x and z and then differentiating.

17. Consider a real-valued function $f(x, y)$ such that

$$f_x(2, 1) = 3, \qquad f_y(2, 1) = -2, \qquad f_{xx}(2, 1) = 0,$$
$$f_{xy}(2, 1) = f_{yx}(2, 1) = 1, \qquad f_{yy}(2, 1) = 2.$$

Let $\mathcal{R}^2 \xrightarrow{g} \mathcal{R}^2$ be defined by

$$g(u, v) = (u + v, uv).$$

Find $\dfrac{\partial^2(f \circ g)}{\partial v\, \partial u}$ at $(1, 1)$.   [*Ans.* 2.]

18. Calculate the Jacobian determinants of the following functions at the points indicated.

(a) $f\begin{pmatrix} u \\ v \end{pmatrix} = \begin{pmatrix} u^2 + 2uv + 3v \\ u - v \end{pmatrix} = \begin{pmatrix} x \\ y \end{pmatrix}$, at $\mathbf{u}_0 = \begin{pmatrix} 0 \\ 2 \end{pmatrix}$.   [*Ans.* -7.]

(b) $g\begin{pmatrix} x \\ y \end{pmatrix} = \begin{pmatrix} x^2 - y^2 \\ 2xy \end{pmatrix} = \begin{pmatrix} z \\ w \end{pmatrix}$, at $\mathbf{x}_0 = \begin{pmatrix} 6 \\ -2 \end{pmatrix}$.   [*Ans.* 160.]

(c) $A\begin{pmatrix} x \\ y \end{pmatrix} = \begin{pmatrix} a & b \\ c & d \end{pmatrix}\begin{pmatrix} x \\ y \end{pmatrix}$, at an arbitary $\begin{pmatrix} x \\ y \end{pmatrix}$.

(d) An affine transformation $\mathscr{R}^n \xrightarrow{A} \mathscr{R}^n$, $A(\mathbf{x}) = L(\mathbf{x}) + \mathbf{y}_0$, at an arbitrary $\mathbf{x}_0$.

(e) $T\begin{pmatrix} r \\ \phi \\ \theta \end{pmatrix} = \begin{pmatrix} r \cos \theta \sin \phi \\ r \sin \theta \sin \phi \\ r \cos \phi \end{pmatrix}$, at $\begin{pmatrix} r \\ \phi \\ \theta \end{pmatrix}$.

19. Using the functions f and g in Exercises 18(a) and (b), compute the Jacobian determinant of the composite function $g \circ f$ at $\begin{pmatrix} 0 \\ 2 \end{pmatrix}$.

[*Ans.* -1120.]

20. In terms of functions $\mathscr{R}^2 \xrightarrow{f} \mathscr{R}^2$ and $\mathscr{R}^2 \xrightarrow{g} \mathscr{R}^2$, what do the following equations say and how do they follow from Theorem 10.3?

(a) $\dfrac{\partial(x, y)}{\partial(u, v)} \dfrac{\partial(u, v)}{\partial(r, \theta)} = \dfrac{\partial(x, y)}{\partial(r, \theta)}$.   (b) $\dfrac{\partial(x, y)}{\partial(u, v)} \dfrac{\partial(u, v)}{\partial(x, y)} = 1$.

11. IMPLICITLY DEFINED FUNCTIONS

For any two functions $\mathscr{R}^2 \xrightarrow{F} \mathscr{R}$ and $\mathscr{R} \xrightarrow{f} \mathscr{R}$, **the equation**

$$F(x, y) = 0 \qquad (1)$$

defines f **implicitly** if $F(x, f(x)) = 0$ for every x in the domain of f. The zero on the right-hand side of Equation (1) can be replaced by any constant c. But since $F(x, y) = c$ is equivalent to $G(x, y) = F(x, y) - c = 0$, it is customary to absorb such a constant into the function F.

EXAMPLE 1. Let $F(x, y) = x^2 + y^2 - 1$. Then the condition that $F(x, f(x)) = x^2 + (f(x))^2 - 1 = 0$, for every x in the domain of f, is satisfied by each of the following choices for f.

$$f_1(x) = \sqrt{1 - x^2}, \qquad -1 \le x \le 1.$$
$$f_2(x) = -\sqrt{1 - x^2}, \qquad -1 \le x \le 1.$$
$$f_3(x) = \begin{cases} \sqrt{1 - x^2}, & -\tfrac{1}{2} \le x < 0. \\ -\sqrt{1 - x^2}, & 0 \le x \le 1. \end{cases}$$

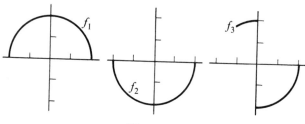

Figure 43

Their graphs are shown in Figure 43. It follows from the definition of an implicitly defined function that all three functions f_1, f_2, f_3 are defined implicitly by the equation $x^2 + y^2 - 1 = 0$.

Consider a function $\mathscr{R}^{n+m} \xrightarrow{F} \mathscr{R}^m$. An arbitrary element in $\mathscr{R}^{n+m}$ can be written as $(x_1, \ldots, x_n, y_1, \ldots, y_m)$ or as a pair $(\mathbf{x}, \mathbf{y})$, where $\mathbf{x} = (x_1, \ldots, x_n)$ and $\mathbf{y} = (y_1, \ldots, y_m)$. In this way F can be thought of either as a function of the two vector variables, $\mathbf{x}$ in $\mathscr{R}^n$ and $\mathbf{y}$ in $\mathscr{R}^m$, or else as a function of the single vector variable $(\mathbf{x}, \mathbf{y})$ in $\mathscr{R}^{n+m}$. **The function $\mathscr{R}^n \xrightarrow{f} \mathscr{R}^m$ is defined implicitly by the equation**

$$F(\mathbf{x}, \mathbf{y}) = 0$$

if $F(\mathbf{x}, f(\mathbf{x})) = 0$ for every $\mathbf{x}$ in the domain of f.

EXAMPLE 2. The equations

$$
\begin{aligned}
x + y + z - 1 &= 0 \\
2x \quad\quad + z + 2 &= 0
\end{aligned}
\tag{2}
$$

determine y and z as functions of x. We get

$$y = x + 3, \qquad z = -2x - 2.$$

In terms of a function $\mathscr{R}^3 \xrightarrow{F} \mathscr{R}^2$, Equations (2) can be written

$$F\left(x, \begin{pmatrix} y \\ z \end{pmatrix}\right) = \begin{pmatrix} x + y + z - 1 \\ 2x \quad\; + z + 2 \end{pmatrix} = \begin{pmatrix} 0 \\ 0 \end{pmatrix}$$

$$= \begin{pmatrix} 1 \\ 2 \end{pmatrix} x + \begin{pmatrix} 1 & 1 \\ 0 & 1 \end{pmatrix}\begin{pmatrix} y \\ z \end{pmatrix} + \begin{pmatrix} -1 \\ 2 \end{pmatrix} = \begin{pmatrix} 0 \\ 0 \end{pmatrix}.$$

The implicitly defined function $\mathscr{R} \xrightarrow{f} \mathscr{R}^2$ is

$$f(x) = \begin{pmatrix} y \\ z \end{pmatrix} = \begin{pmatrix} x + 3 \\ -2x - 2 \end{pmatrix}.$$

Although Example 1 shows that an implicitly defined function need not be continuous, we shall be primarily concerned in this section with functions that are not only continuous but also differentiable. The *implicit function theorem* appearing at the end of Section 13 gives conditions for the existence of a differentiable f defined by an equation $F(\mathbf{x}, f(\mathbf{x})) = 0$.

Before discussing this theorem, however, we consider the problem of finding the differential of f when it is known to exist. Suppose the functions $\mathscr{R}^2 \xrightarrow{F} \mathscr{R}$ and $\mathscr{R} \xrightarrow{f} \mathscr{R}$ are differentiable and that

$$F(x, f(x)) = 0, \qquad \text{for every } x \text{ in the domain of } f.$$

Then the chain rule applied to $F(x, f(x))$ yields

$$F_x(x, f(x)) + F_y(x, f(x))f'(x) = 0.$$

Hence,

11.1 $$f'(x) = -\frac{F_x(x, f(x))}{F_y(x, f(x))}, \qquad \text{if } F_y(x, f(x)) \neq 0.$$

For vector-valued functions a similar computation is possible.

EXAMPLE 3. Given the equations

$$x^2 + y^2 + z^2 - 5 = 0, \qquad xyz + 2 = 0, \tag{3}$$

suppose that x and y are differentiable functions of z, that is, the function defined implicitly by Equations (3) is of the form $(x, y) = f(z)$. To compute dx/dz and dy/dz, we apply the chain rule to the given equations to get

$$2x\frac{dx}{dz} + 2y\frac{dy}{dz} + 2z = 0,$$

$$yz\frac{dx}{dz} + xz\frac{dy}{dz} + xy = 0.$$

These new equations can be solved for $\dfrac{dx}{dz}$ and $\dfrac{dy}{dz}$. The solution is

$$\begin{pmatrix} \dfrac{dx}{dz} \\ \dfrac{dy}{dz} \end{pmatrix} = \begin{pmatrix} \dfrac{x(y^2 - z^2)}{z(x^2 - y^2)} \\ \dfrac{y(z^2 - x^2)}{z(x^2 - y^2)} \end{pmatrix},$$

which is the matrix $f'(z)$. Notice that the corresponding values for x and y have to be known to make the formula completely explicit. That is, from the information given so far there is no possible way of evaluating $(dx/dz)(1)$. On the other hand, given the point $(x, y, z) = (1, -2, 1)$, we have $(dx/dz)(1) = -1$. The reason is that, just as in Example 1, there is more than one function f defined implicitly by Equations (3). By specifying a particular point on its graph, we determine f uniquely in the vicinity of the point.

EXAMPLE 4. Consider

$$xu + yv + zw = 1,$$
$$x + y + z + u + v + w = 0,$$
$$xy + zuv + w = 1.$$

Suppose that each of x, y, and z is a function of u, v, and w. To find the partial derivatives of x, y, and z with respect to w, we differentiate the three equations using the chain rule.

$$u\frac{\partial x}{\partial w} + v\frac{\partial y}{\partial w} + w\frac{\partial z}{\partial w} + z = 0,$$

$$\frac{\partial x}{\partial w} + \frac{\partial y}{\partial w} + \frac{dz}{\partial w} + 1 = 0,$$

$$y\frac{\partial x}{\partial w} + x\frac{\partial y}{\partial w} + uv\frac{\partial z}{\partial w} + 1 = 0.$$

Then,

$$\frac{\partial x}{\partial w} = \frac{uv^2 + xz + w - zuv - xw - v}{u^2v + vy + wx - yw - ux - uv^2}.$$

Similarly, we could solve for $\partial y/\partial w$ and $\partial z/\partial w$. To find partials with respect to u, differentiate the original equations with respect to u and solve for $\partial x/\partial u$, $\partial y/\partial u$, and $\partial z/\partial u$. Partials with respect to v are found by the same method.

The computation indicated in Example 4 leads to the nine entries in the matrix of the differential of an implicitly defined vector function. In order for the computation to work, it is necessary to have the number of given equations equal the number of implicitly defined coordinate functions. To get some insight into the reason for this requirement, suppose we are given a differentiable vector function

$$F(u, v, x, y) = \begin{pmatrix} F_1(u, v, x, y) \\ F_2(u, v, x, y) \end{pmatrix}$$

and that the equations

$$F_1(u, v, x, y) = 0, \qquad F_2(u, v, x, y) = 0 \tag{4}$$

implicitly define a differentiable function $(x, y) = f(u, v)$.
Differentiating Equations (4) with respect to u and v by means of the chain rule, we get

$$\frac{\partial F_1}{\partial u} + \frac{\partial F_1}{\partial x}\frac{\partial x}{\partial u} + \frac{\partial F_1}{\partial y}\frac{\partial y}{\partial u} = 0, \qquad \frac{\partial F_1}{\partial v} + \frac{\partial F_1}{\partial x}\frac{\partial x}{\partial v} + \frac{\partial F_1}{\partial y}\frac{\partial y}{\partial v} = 0,$$

$$\frac{\partial F_2}{\partial u} + \frac{\partial F_2}{\partial x}\frac{\partial x}{\partial u} + \frac{\partial F_2}{\partial y}\frac{\partial y}{\partial u} = 0, \qquad \frac{\partial F_2}{\partial v} + \frac{\partial F_2}{\partial x}\frac{\partial x}{\partial v} + \frac{\partial F_2}{\partial y}\frac{\partial y}{\partial v} = 0.$$

These equations can be written in matrix form as follows:

$$\begin{pmatrix} \dfrac{\partial F_1}{\partial u} & \dfrac{\partial F_1}{\partial v} \\ \dfrac{\partial F_2}{\partial u} & \dfrac{\partial F_2}{\partial v} \end{pmatrix} + \begin{pmatrix} \dfrac{\partial F_1}{\partial x} & \dfrac{\partial F_1}{\partial y} \\ \dfrac{\partial F_2}{\partial x} & \dfrac{\partial F_2}{\partial y} \end{pmatrix}\begin{pmatrix} \dfrac{\partial x}{\partial u} & \dfrac{\partial x}{\partial v} \\ \dfrac{\partial y}{\partial u} & \dfrac{\partial y}{\partial v} \end{pmatrix} = 0. \tag{5}$$

The last matrix on the right is the matrix of the differential of f at (u, v). Solving for it, we get

$$
\begin{pmatrix} \dfrac{\partial x}{\partial u} & \dfrac{\partial x}{\partial v} \\[2ex] \dfrac{\partial y}{\partial u} & \dfrac{\partial y}{\partial v} \end{pmatrix} = - \begin{pmatrix} \dfrac{\partial F_1}{\partial x} & \dfrac{\partial F_1}{\partial y} \\[2ex] \dfrac{\partial F_2}{\partial x} & \dfrac{\partial F_2}{\partial y} \end{pmatrix}^{-1} \begin{pmatrix} \dfrac{\partial F_1}{\partial u} & \dfrac{\partial F_1}{\partial v} \\[2ex] \dfrac{\partial F_2}{\partial u} & \dfrac{\partial F_2}{\partial v} \end{pmatrix}.
\tag{6}
$$

In order to be able to solve Equation (5) uniquely for the matrix $f'(u, v)$, it is essential that the inverse matrix that appears in Equation (6) exist. This implies in particular that the number of equations originally given equals the number of variables implicitly determined, or, equivalently, that the range spaces of F and f must have the same dimension.

The analogue of Equation (6) holds for an arbitrary number of coordinate functions F_i and is proved in exactly the same way. We can summarize the result in the following generalization of 11.1.

11.2 Theorem. If $\mathscr{R}^{n+m} \xrightarrow{F} \mathscr{R}^m$ and $\mathscr{R}^n \xrightarrow{f} \mathscr{R}^m$ are differentiable, and $\mathbf{y} = f(\mathbf{x})$ satisfies $F(\mathbf{x}, \mathbf{y}) = 0$, then

$$
f'(\mathbf{x}) = -F_{\mathbf{y}}^{-1}(\mathbf{x}, f(\mathbf{x})) \, F_{\mathbf{x}}(\mathbf{x}, f(\mathbf{x})),
$$

provided $F_{\mathbf{y}}$ has an inverse. The derivative $F_{\mathbf{y}}$ is computed with $\mathbf{x}$ held fixed, and $F_{\mathbf{x}}$ is computed with $\mathbf{y}$ held fixed.

EXERCISES

1. If

$$
x^2 y + yz = 0, \qquad xyz + 1 = 0,
$$

find $\dfrac{dx}{dz}$ and $\dfrac{dy}{dz}$ at $(x, y, z) = (1, 1, -1)$.

$$
\left[Ans. \ \frac{dx}{dz} = -\frac{1}{2}, \ \frac{dy}{dz} = \frac{3}{2}. \right]
$$

2. If Exercise 1 is expressed in the general vector notation of Theorem 11.2, what are F, $\mathbf{x}$, $\mathbf{y}$, $F_{\mathbf{y}}$, and $F_{\mathbf{x}}$?

3. If

$$
x + y - u - v = 0,
$$
$$
x - y + 2u + v = 0,
$$

find $\dfrac{\partial x}{\partial u}$ and $\dfrac{\partial y}{\partial u}$

(a) By solving for x and y in terms of u and v,
(b) By implicit differentiation.

4. If Exercise 3 is expressed in the vector notation of Theorem 11.2, what is the matrix $f'(\mathbf{x})$?

5. If $x^2 + yu + xv + w = 0$, $x + y + uvw + 1 = 0$, then, regarding x and y as functions of u, v, and w, find

$$\frac{\partial x}{\partial u} \text{ and } \frac{\partial y}{\partial u} \text{ at } (x, y, u, v, w) = (1, -1, 1, 1, -1).$$

$$\left[Ans. \; \frac{\partial x}{\partial u} = 0, \; \frac{\partial y}{\partial u} = 1. \right]$$

6. The equations $2x^3y + yx^2 + t^2 = 0$, $x + y + t - 1 = 0$ implicitly define a curve

$$f(t) = \begin{pmatrix} x(t) \\ y(t) \end{pmatrix}$$

which satisfies

$$f(1) = \begin{pmatrix} -1 \\ 1 \end{pmatrix}.$$

Find the tangent line to f at $t = 1$.

$$\left[Ans. \; t \begin{pmatrix} -\frac{3}{5} \\ -\frac{2}{5} \end{pmatrix} + \begin{pmatrix} -1 \\ 1 \end{pmatrix}. \right]$$

7. Let the equation $x^2/4 + y^2 + z^2/9 - 1 = 0$ define z implicitly as a function $z = f(x, y)$ near the point $x = 1$, $y = \sqrt{11/6}$, $z = 2$. The graph of the function f is a surface. Find its tangent plane at $(1, \sqrt{11/6}, 2)$.

8. Suppose the equation $F(x, y, z) = 0$ implicitly defines $z = f(x, y)$ and that $z_0 = f(x_0, y_0)$. Suppose further that the surface that is the graph of $z = f(x, y)$ has a tangent plane at (x_0, y_0). Show that

$$(x - x_0)\frac{\partial F}{\partial x}(x_0, y_0, z_0) + (y - y_0)\frac{\partial F}{\partial y}(x_0, y_0, z_0)$$

$$+ (z - z_0)\frac{\partial F}{\partial z}(x_0, y_0, z_0) = 0$$

is the equation for this tangent plane.

9. The equations

$$2x + y + 2z + u - v - 1 = 0,$$
$$xy + z - u + 2v - 1 = 0,$$
$$yz + xz + u^2 + v = 0,$$

near $(x, y, z, u, v) = (1, 1, -1, 1, 1)$ define x, y, and z as functions of u and v.

(a) Find the matrix of the differential of the implicitly defined function

$$\begin{pmatrix} x \\ y \\ z \end{pmatrix} = \begin{pmatrix} x(u, v) \\ y(u, v) \\ z(u, v) \end{pmatrix} = f(u, v) \quad \text{at} \quad (u, v) = (1, 1).$$

(b) The function f parametrically defines a surface in the (x, y, z) space. Find the tangent plane to it at the point $(1, 1, -1)$.

12. CURVILINEAR COORDINATES

It is sometimes useful to introduce coordinates in $\mathscr{R}^n$ different from the natural coordinates x_i that appear in the designation of a typical point $(x_1, \ldots, x_n)$. Specifically, to each point $(x_1, \ldots, x_n)$ there will be assigned a new n-tuple $(u_1, \ldots, u_n)$. Clearly, if we are to be able to switch back and forth from one set of coordinates to the other, the assignment described above must be one-one, that is, for each $(x_1, \ldots, x_n)$ there should be just one n-tuple $(u_1, \ldots, u_n)$ and vice versa. In practice the new coordinate assignment is often made for some specific subregion of $\mathscr{R}^n$ rather than for the whole space. The vector space of new coordinates $(u_1, \ldots, u_n)$ will be denoted by $\mathscr{U}^n$ to avoid confusion with $\mathscr{R}^n$, whose points $(x_1, \ldots, x_n)$ are being assigned the new coordinates.

EXAMPLE 1. *Polar coordinates in the plane.* Consider two copies of 2-dimensional space: the xy-plane, denoted by $\mathscr{R}^2$, and the $r\theta$-plane, denoted by $\mathscr{U}^2$. The function $\mathscr{U}^2 \xrightarrow{T} \mathscr{R}^2$ defined by

$$\begin{pmatrix} x \\ y \end{pmatrix} = T\begin{pmatrix} r \\ \theta \end{pmatrix} = \begin{pmatrix} r\cos\theta \\ r\sin\theta \end{pmatrix}, \qquad \begin{cases} 0 < r < \infty \\ -\infty < \theta < \infty \end{cases} \tag{1}$$

has a simple geometric description. The image under T of a point $\begin{pmatrix} r \\ \theta \end{pmatrix}$ is the point

$$\mathbf{x} = \begin{pmatrix} x \\ y \end{pmatrix}$$

whose distance from the origin is r and such that the angle from the positive x-axis to $\mathbf{x}$ in the counterclockwise direction is θ. See Figure 44.

For any two points

$$\begin{pmatrix} r_1 \\ \theta_1 \end{pmatrix} \quad \text{and} \quad \begin{pmatrix} r_2 \\ \theta_2 \end{pmatrix}$$

in the domain of T, it is easy to prove that

$$T\begin{pmatrix} r_1 \\ \theta_1 \end{pmatrix} = T\begin{pmatrix} r_2 \\ \theta_2 \end{pmatrix}$$

if and only if $r_1 = r_2$ and $\theta_1 = \theta_2 + 2\pi m$ for some integer m. The range of T consists of all of $\mathscr{R}^2$ except for the origin. It follows that, for any point

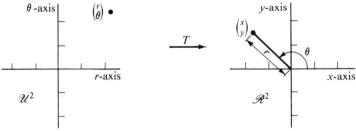

Figure 44

$$\mathbf{x} = \begin{pmatrix} x \\ y \end{pmatrix} \quad \text{in } \mathscr{R}^2 \text{ except } \begin{pmatrix} 0 \\ 0 \end{pmatrix},$$

there exist numbers r and θ, called **polar coordinates** of $\mathbf{x}$, such that

$$T\begin{pmatrix} r \\ \theta \end{pmatrix} = \mathbf{x}.$$

Furthermore, the polar coordinates of $\mathbf{x}$ are uniquely specified up to an integer multiple of 2π in the second coordinate.

From a slightly different point of view, the preceding paragraph says that T is not one-one, but that it becomes so if its domain is restricted to be a subset of a rectangular half-strip in the $r\theta$-plane defined by inequalities

$$0 < r < \infty, \qquad \theta_0 \leq \theta < \theta_0 + 2\pi.$$

So restricted, T has an inverse function. Solving the equations $x = r\cos\theta$, $y = r\sin\theta$ for r and θ, we obtain, for $x \neq 0$,

$$r = \sqrt{x^2 + y^2}, \qquad \theta = \arctan\frac{y}{x} + k\pi.$$

Unless the contrary is explicitly stated, any inverse trigonometric function is the principal branch of the corresponding multiple-valued function. Hence, the range of the function arctan is the interval $-\pi/2 < \theta < \pi/2$. It follows that the function defined by

$$\begin{pmatrix} r \\ \theta \end{pmatrix} = \begin{pmatrix} \sqrt{x^2 + y^2} \\ \arctan\dfrac{y}{x} \end{pmatrix}, \qquad x > 0,$$

is the inverse of the restriction of T to the region $0 < r < \infty$, $-\pi/2 < \theta < \pi/2$. Similarly, the function defined by

$$\begin{pmatrix} r \\ \theta \end{pmatrix} = \begin{pmatrix} \sqrt{x^2 + y^2} \\ \text{arccot}\dfrac{x}{y} \end{pmatrix}, \qquad y > 0,$$

is the inverse of the restriction of T to $0 < r < \infty, 0 < \theta < \pi$.

We have not defined polar coordinates for the origin of the xy-plane simply because

$$\begin{pmatrix} 0\cos\theta \\ 0\sin\theta \end{pmatrix} = \begin{pmatrix} 0 \\ 0 \end{pmatrix} \quad \text{for all } \theta,$$

and so the one-oneness requirement fails at the origin. This fact causes no real difficulty. For example, the equation in rectangular coordinates of the lemniscate,

$$(x^2 + y^2)^2 = 2(x^2 - y^2), \tag{2}$$

becomes, upon introduction of polar coordinates,

$$r^2 = 2\cos 2\theta, \qquad r > 0. \tag{3}$$

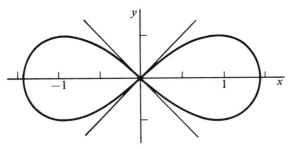

Figure 45

The image under T of the set of pairs (r, θ) that satisfy Equation (3) is precisely the set of pairs (x, y) that satisfy Equation (2), except for the origin. We may simply fill in this one point. See Figure 45.

EXAMPLE 2. *Spherical coordinates in 3-dimensional space.* Consider the function $\mathscr{U}^3 \xrightarrow{\ T\ } \mathscr{R}^3$, defined by

$$T\begin{pmatrix} r \\ \phi \\ \theta \end{pmatrix} = \begin{pmatrix} r \sin \phi \cos \theta \\ r \sin \phi \sin \theta \\ r \cos \phi \end{pmatrix}, \qquad \begin{cases} 0 < r < \infty \\ 0 < \phi < \pi \\ 0 \le \theta < 2\pi. \end{cases} \tag{4}$$

Here for simplicity we have restricted the domain of T from the outset so that it is one-one. Its range is all of $\mathscr{R}^3$ with the exception of the z-axis. Hence, it assigns **spherical coordinates** (r, ϕ, θ) to every point of $\mathscr{R}^3$ except those on the z-axis. As with polar coordinates in the plane, the spherical coordinates (r, ϕ, θ) of a point $\mathbf{x} = (x, y, z)$ have a simple geometric interpretation (see Figure 46): The number r is the distance from $\mathbf{x}$ to the origin.

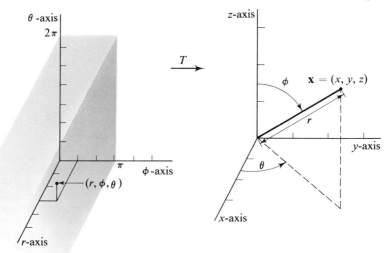

Figure 46

The coordinate ϕ is the angle in radians between the vector $\mathbf{x}$ and the positive z-axis. Finally, θ is the angle in radians from the positive x-axis to the projected image $(x, y, 0)$ of $\mathbf{x}$ on the xy-plane.

We can compute an explicit expression for the inverse function, which we denote by T^{-1}, by solving the equations

$$x = r \sin \phi \cos \theta,$$
$$y = r \sin \phi \sin \theta,$$
$$z = r \cos \phi,$$

for r, θ, and ϕ. We get, for $y \geq 0$,

$$\begin{pmatrix} r \\ \phi \\ \theta \end{pmatrix} = T^{-1}\begin{pmatrix} x \\ y \\ z \end{pmatrix} = \begin{pmatrix} \sqrt{x^2 + y^2 + z^2} \\ \arccos \dfrac{z}{\sqrt{x^2 + y^2 + z^2}} \\ \arccos \dfrac{x}{\sqrt{x^2 + y^2}} \end{pmatrix}, \qquad x^2 + y^2 > 0.$$

Since the range of *arccos* (the principal branch) is the interval $0 \leq \theta \leq \pi$, this function is actually the inverse of the function obtained by restricting the domain of T by the further condition $0 \leq \theta \leq \pi$. In order to get values of θ in the interval $\pi < \theta < 2\pi$, corresponding to $y < 0$, we add π to the third coordinate in the formula above.

Three surfaces in $\mathcal{R}^3$ implicitly defined by spherical coordinate equations $r = 1$, $\phi = \pi/4$, and $\theta = \pi/3$, respectively, are shown in Figure 47. The corresponding rectangular coordinate equations derived from the above expressions for T^{-1} are

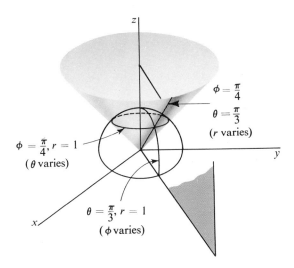

Figure 47

$$x^2 + y^2 + z^2 = 1, \qquad x^2 + y^2 > 0$$

$$z = \frac{\sqrt{2}}{2}\sqrt{x^2 + y^2 + z^2}, \qquad z > 0$$

$$y = \sqrt{3}\,x, \qquad x > 0,$$

respectively.

The name "curvilinear" is applied to coordinates for the reason that, if all but one of the nonrectangular coordinates are held fixed, and the remaining one is varied, the coordinate transformation defines a curve in $\mathcal{R}^n$. Thus in plane polar coordinates the coordinate curves are circles and straight lines as shown in Figure 48. For spherical coordinates, typical coordinate curves are the circle, semicircle, and half-line got as intersections of the pairs of surfaces shown in Figure 47. The curves and surfaces got by varying one or more curvilinear coordinate variables play the same role that the natural coordinate lines and planes of $\mathcal{R}^n$ do. For example, to say that a point in $\mathcal{R}^3$ has rectangular coordinates $(x, y, z) = (1, 2, 1)$ is to say that it lies at the intersection of the coordinate planes $x = 1$, $y = 2$, and $z = 1$. Similarly, to say that a point in $\mathcal{R}^3$ has spherical coordinates $(r, \phi, \theta) = (1, \pi/4, \pi/3)$ is to say that it lies at the intersection of the surfaces shown in Figure 47.

Generalizing from the preceding examples, we see that a system of curvilinear coordinates in $\mathcal{R}^n$ is determined by a function $\mathcal{U}^n \xrightarrow{T} \mathcal{R}^n$. It is assumed that for some open subset N in the domain of T, the restriction of T to N is one-one and therefore has an inverse T^{-1}. The **curvilinear coordinates**, determined by T and N, of a point $\mathbf{x}$ lying in the image set $T(N)$ are

$$\begin{pmatrix} u_1 \\ \cdot \\ \cdot \\ \cdot \\ u_n \end{pmatrix} = T^{-1}\begin{pmatrix} x_1 \\ \cdot \\ \cdot \\ \cdot \\ x_n \end{pmatrix}.$$

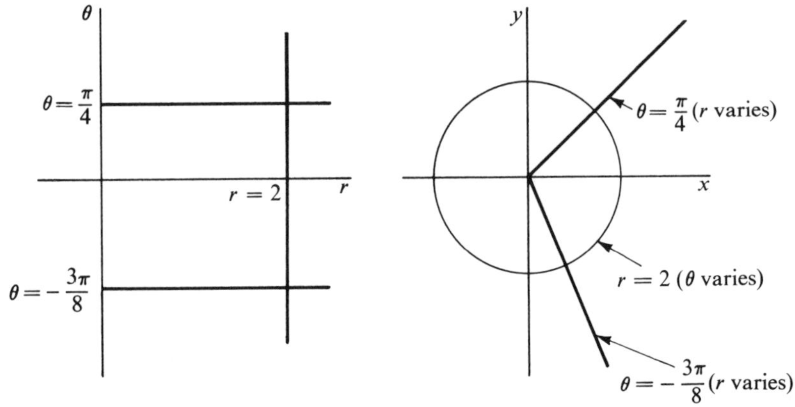

Figure 48

It is convenient to impose fairly stringent regularity conditions on a coordinate transformation. Specifically, we shall assume that at every point $\mathbf{u}$ of N, the function T is continuously differentiable and $d_{\mathbf{u}}T$ is one-one.

The polar and spherical coordinate changes represented by

$$\begin{pmatrix} x \\ y \end{pmatrix} = \begin{pmatrix} r\cos\theta \\ r\sin\theta \end{pmatrix}$$

and

$$\begin{pmatrix} x \\ y \\ z \end{pmatrix} = \begin{pmatrix} r\sin\phi\cos\theta \\ r\sin\phi\sin\theta \\ r\cos\phi \end{pmatrix}$$

have Jacobian matrices

$$\begin{pmatrix} \cos\theta & -r\sin\theta \\ \sin\theta & r\cos\theta \end{pmatrix} \tag{5}$$

and

$$\begin{pmatrix} \sin\phi\cos\theta & r\cos\phi\cos\theta & -r\sin\phi\sin\theta \\ \sin\phi\sin\theta & r\cos\phi\sin\theta & r\sin\phi\cos\theta \\ \cos\phi & -r\sin\phi & 0 \end{pmatrix}, \tag{6}$$

respectively. The matrices (5) and (6), and more generally the Jacobian matrices of differentiable coordinate transformations, have a simple geometric interpretation. Each column of the Jacobian is obtained by differentiation of the coordinate functions with respect to a single variable, while holding the other variables fixed. This means that the jth column of the matrix represents a tangent vector to the curvilinear coordinate curve for which the jth coordinate is allowed to vary. That is, if the coordinate transformation is given by $\mathcal{U}^n \xrightarrow{T} \mathcal{R}^n$, then the jth column of the matrix of the differential $T'(\mathbf{u}_0)$ is a tangent vector, which we shall denote by $\mathbf{c}_j$, at $\mathbf{x}_0 = T(\mathbf{u}_0)$, to the curvilinear coordinate curve formed by allowing only the jth coordinate of $\mathbf{u}_0$ to vary. Tangent vectors are shown (with their initial points translated to the point $\mathbf{x}_0$) in Figure 49 for some polar and spherical coordinate curves. Since the coordinate curves lie in the cartesian space, the coordinates of the tangent vectors $\mathbf{c}_1, \ldots, \mathbf{c}_n$ are rectangular coordinates, not curvilinear coordinates.

We shall show that the Jacobian matrix itself of a coordinate transformation can be interpreted as the matrix of a certain linear change of coordinates. To see this, consider curvilinear coordinates in $\mathcal{R}^n$ given by $\mathbf{x} = T(\mathbf{u})$, where $\mathbf{u}$ is the curvilinear coordinate variable. Fix a point $\mathbf{x}_0$ having curvilinear coordinates $\mathbf{u}_0$. At $\mathbf{x}_0$ we can introduce a new origin and new unit vectors $\mathbf{e}_1, \ldots, \mathbf{e}_n$ with the same directions as the natural basis vectors for $\mathcal{R}^n$. Then, the matrix $T'(\mathbf{u}_0)$ is the matrix of the change of basis to the vectors $\mathbf{e}_1, \ldots, \mathbf{e}_n$

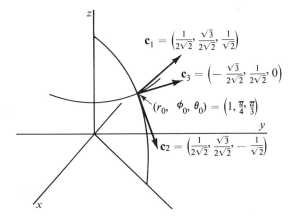

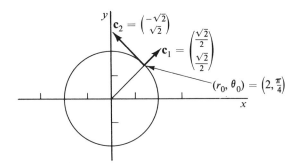

Figure 49

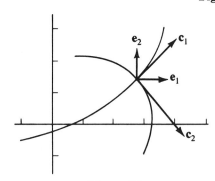

Figure 50

from the vectors $c_1, \ldots, c_n$ that are the tangent vectors to the curvilinear coordinate curves. Figure 50 illustrates the relation between the e_i and the c_i. Notice that the vectors $c_1, \ldots, c_n$ will be linearly independent if and only if $d_{u_0}T$ is one-one. This is one reason for requiring not only that a coordinate transformation be one-one in a neighborhood of a point, but also that its differential be one-one.

EXAMPLE 3. *Cylindrical coordinates in $\mathscr{R}^3$.* The coordinate transformation is defined by

$$\begin{pmatrix} x \\ y \\ z \end{pmatrix} = \begin{pmatrix} r\cos\theta \\ r\sin\theta \\ z \end{pmatrix}, \qquad \begin{cases} 0 < r < \infty. \\ -\pi < \theta \leq \pi. \\ -\infty < z < \infty. \end{cases}$$

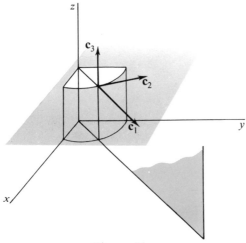

Figure 51

The Jacobian matrix is

$$\begin{pmatrix} \cos\theta & -r\sin\theta & 0 \\ \sin\theta & r\cos\theta & 0 \\ 0 & 0 & 1 \end{pmatrix}.$$

Curvilinear coordinate surfaces and tangent vectors to curvilinear coordinate curves are shown in Figure 51. Notice that the Jacobian determinant is

$$\frac{\partial(x, y, z)}{\partial(r, \theta, z)} = r.$$

Computations involving curvilinear coordinates are much simpler if the coordinate curves, and the vectors c_k, are orthogonal. (This is so in the examples we have considered.) In this case it is customary to replace the c_k by unit vectors having the same direction. Thus, letting $h_1 = |c_1|, \ldots, h_n = |c_n|$, we have a local orthonormal basis $(1/h_1 c_1, \ldots, 1/h_n c_n)$. The result is that the matrix H, whose columns are the rectangular coordinates of $1/h_1 c_1, \ldots, 1/h_n c_n$, is an orthogonal matrix whose inverse is equal to its transpose. Thus H and its inverse have a clear advantage over the Jacobian matrix when changing local basis from $(e_1, \ldots, e_n)$ to $(1/h_1 c_1, \ldots, 1/h_n c_n)$ and back again.

EXAMPLE 4. For spherical coordinates in $\mathscr{R}^3$ we have $h_1 = 1, h_2 = r$, $h_3 = r\sin\phi$, so that the matrix H is given by

$$H = \begin{pmatrix} \sin\phi\cos\theta & \cos\phi\cos\theta & -\sin\theta \\ \sin\phi\sin\theta & \cos\phi\sin\theta & \cos\theta \\ \cos\phi & -\sin\phi & 0 \end{pmatrix}.$$

We have assumed $0 < \phi < \pi$, so that $\sin \phi > 0$. Then, because the matrix H is orthogonal, $H^{-1} = H^t$ and

$$H^{-1} = \begin{pmatrix} \sin \phi \cos \theta & \sin \phi \sin \theta & \cos \phi \\ \cos \phi \cos \theta & \cos \phi \sin \theta & -\sin \phi \\ -\sin \theta & \cos \theta & 0 \end{pmatrix}.$$

Thus, if $\mathbf{x} = x_1 \mathbf{e}_1 + x_2 \mathbf{e}_2 + x_3 \mathbf{e}_3$, then the triple

$$H^{-1} \begin{pmatrix} x_1 \\ x_2 \\ x_3 \end{pmatrix}$$

has as entries the coordinates of $\mathbf{x}$ with respect to the basis $(1/h_1 \mathbf{c}_1, 1/h_2 \mathbf{c}_2, 1/h_3 \mathbf{c}_3)$.

We have seen that the vectors $\mathbf{c}_1, \ldots, \mathbf{c}_n$, tangent to coordinate curves, describe approximately the nature of a curvilinear coordinate system. The inner products of these vectors among themselves occur sufficiently often so that there is a special notation for them:

$$\mathbf{c}_i \cdot \mathbf{c}_j = g_{ij}, \qquad i, j = 1, \ldots, n.$$

Since $\mathbf{c}_i \cdot \mathbf{c}_j = \mathbf{c}_j \cdot \mathbf{c}_i$, we have $g_{ij} = g_{ji}$. If the vectors $\mathbf{c}_1, \ldots, \mathbf{c}_n$ are orthogonal, as is often the case in practice, then only the inner products $\mathbf{c}_i \cdot \mathbf{c}_i = g_{ii}$ will be different from zero. A number of important formulas can be expressed in curvilinear coordinates entirely in terms of the functions g_{ij} and without explicit reference to the particular curvilinear coordinate functions being used.

In the xy-plane suppose curvilinear coordinates are given by

$$\begin{pmatrix} x \\ y \end{pmatrix} = \begin{pmatrix} x(u, v) \\ y(u, v) \end{pmatrix}.$$

The Jacobian of the coordinate transformation is

$$\begin{pmatrix} \dfrac{\partial x}{\partial u} & \dfrac{\partial x}{\partial v} \\ \dfrac{\partial y}{\partial u} & \dfrac{\partial y}{\partial v} \end{pmatrix},$$

whence

$$g_{11} = \left(\frac{\partial x}{\partial u}\right)^2 + \left(\frac{\partial y}{\partial u}\right)^2,$$

$$g_{12} = g_{21} = \frac{\partial x}{\partial u}\frac{\partial x}{\partial v} + \frac{\partial y}{\partial u}\frac{\partial y}{\partial v},$$

$$g_{22} = \left(\frac{\partial x}{\partial v}\right)^2 + \left(\frac{\partial y}{\partial v}\right)^2.$$

Now suppose that

$$\begin{pmatrix} u(t) \\ v(t) \end{pmatrix}$$

is a differentiable function from an interval $[a, b]$ to $\mathcal{U}^2$. Then the equation

$$f(t) = \begin{pmatrix} x(u(t), v(t)) \\ y(u(t), v(t)) \end{pmatrix}, \qquad a \le t \le b,$$

is the parametric representation of a curve in $\mathcal{R}^2$. The tangent vector to the curve can be computed by the chain rule to be

$$\frac{df}{dt} = \begin{pmatrix} \dfrac{dx}{dt} \\[2mm] \dfrac{dy}{dt} \end{pmatrix} = \begin{pmatrix} \dfrac{\partial x}{\partial u}\dfrac{du}{dt} + \dfrac{\partial x}{\partial v}\dfrac{dv}{dt} \\[3mm] \dfrac{\partial y}{\partial u}\dfrac{du}{dt} + \dfrac{\partial y}{\partial v}\dfrac{dv}{dt} \end{pmatrix}.$$

The length of the tangent vector df/dt is then

$$\left|\frac{df}{dt}\right| = \left(\left(\frac{dx}{dt}\right)^2 + \left(\frac{dy}{dt}\right)^2\right)^{1/2}$$

$$= \left(\left[\left(\frac{\partial x}{\partial u}\right)^2 + \left(\frac{\partial y}{\partial u}\right)^2\right]\left(\frac{du}{dt}\right)^2 + 2\left[\frac{\partial x}{\partial u}\frac{\partial x}{\partial v} + \frac{\partial y}{\partial u}\frac{\partial y}{\partial v}\right]\frac{du}{dt}\frac{dv}{dt}\right.$$

$$\left. + \left[\left(\frac{\partial x}{\partial v}\right)^2 + \left(\frac{\partial y}{\partial v}\right)^2\right]\left(\frac{dv}{dt}\right)^2\right)^{1/2}$$

$$= \left(g_{11}\left(\frac{du}{dt}\right)^2 + 2g_{12}\frac{du}{dt}\frac{dv}{dt} + g_{22}\left(\frac{dv}{dt}\right)^2\right)^{1/2}.$$

A similar computation in $\mathcal{R}^n$ leads to the formula

$$\left|\frac{df}{dt}\right| = \left(\sum_{i,j=1}^{n} g_{ij}\frac{du_i}{dt}\frac{du_j}{dt}\right)^{1/2}, \tag{7}$$

where $f(t) = [x_1(u_1(t), \ldots, u_n(t)), \ldots, x_n(u_1(t), \ldots, u_n(t))]$.

Once the g_{ij} have been computed for the particular coordinate system, the above formula can be used for any differentiable curve by substituting in the components of the vector

$$\begin{pmatrix} \dfrac{du}{dt} \\[2mm] \dfrac{dv}{dt} \end{pmatrix}.$$

To be more specific, suppose we are given plane polar coordinates

$$\begin{pmatrix} x \\ y \end{pmatrix} = \begin{pmatrix} r\cos\theta \\ r\sin\theta \end{pmatrix}.$$

The Jacobian matrix is

$$\begin{pmatrix} \cos\theta & -r\sin\theta \\ \sin\theta & r\cos\theta \end{pmatrix}.$$

Hence

$$g_{11} = 1, \qquad g_{12} = g_{21} = 0, \qquad g_{22} = r^2.$$

A curve $f(\theta) = \begin{pmatrix} r(\theta) \cos \theta \\ r(\theta) \sin \theta \end{pmatrix}$ has a tangent vector $df/d\theta$ of length

$$\left| \frac{df}{d\theta} \right| = \left(\left(\frac{dr}{d\theta} \right)^2 + r^2 \right)^{1/2}.$$

EXAMPLE 5. If (r, ϕ, θ) are spherical coordinates in $\mathscr{R}^3$, the length of a curve γ defined by an equation

$$\begin{pmatrix} r \\ \phi \\ \theta \end{pmatrix} = \begin{pmatrix} r(t) \\ \phi(t) \\ \theta(t) \end{pmatrix}, \qquad a \le t \le b,$$

can be computed from (7). The differential of the coordinate transformation

$$\begin{pmatrix} x \\ y \\ z \end{pmatrix} = \begin{pmatrix} r \sin \phi \cos \theta \\ r \sin \phi \sin \theta \\ r \cos \phi \end{pmatrix}$$

is defined by the matrix

$$\begin{pmatrix} \sin \phi \cos \theta & r \cos \phi \cos \theta & -r \sin \phi \sin \theta \\ \sin \phi \sin \theta & r \cos \phi \sin \theta & r \sin \phi \cos \theta \\ \cos \phi & -r \sin \phi & 0 \end{pmatrix}.$$

The function g_{ij} is the inner product of the ith and the jth column of the preceding matrix. Hence

$$\begin{pmatrix} g_{11} & g_{12} & g_{13} \\ g_{21} & g_{22} & g_{23} \\ g_{31} & g_{32} & g_{33} \end{pmatrix} = \begin{pmatrix} 1 & 0 & 0 \\ 0 & r^2 & 0 \\ 0 & 0 & r^2 \sin^2 \phi \end{pmatrix}.$$

And so Equation (7) yields

$$l(\gamma) = \int_a^b \sqrt{\left(\frac{dr}{dt} \right)^2 + r^2 \left(\frac{d\phi}{dt} \right)^2 + r^2 \sin^2 \phi \left(\frac{d\theta}{dt} \right)^2} \, dt.$$

In particular, the curve λ defined by

$$\begin{pmatrix} r \\ \phi \\ \theta \end{pmatrix} = \begin{pmatrix} 1 \\ t \\ t \end{pmatrix}, \qquad 0 \le t \le \frac{\pi}{2}$$

has length

$$l(\lambda) = \int_0^{\pi/2} \sqrt{1 + \sin^2 t} \, dt.$$

This integral cannot be computed by means of an elementary indefinite integral. It can, however, be approximated by simple methods. Or it can be reduced to a standard elliptic integral as follows. Replacing t by $\pi/2 - \theta$, and using $\cos^2 \theta = 1 - \sin^2 \theta$, we get

$$\int_0^{\pi/2} \sqrt{1 + \sin^2 t}\, dt = \sqrt{2} \int_0^{\pi/2} \sqrt{1 - \tfrac{1}{2}\sin^2 \theta}\, d\theta.$$

The latter integral has been tabulated,* and we estimate

$$l(\lambda) \approx \sqrt{2}\,(1.35) \approx 1.91.$$

EXERCISES

1. Sketch the three curves given below in polar coordinates.

    (a) $r = \theta$, $0 \le \theta \le \pi/2$.
    (b) $r(\sin \theta - \cos \theta) = \pi/2$, $\pi/2 \le \theta \le \pi$.
    (c) $r = \pi/2 \cos \theta$, $\pi \le \theta \le 3\pi/2$.

2. In $\mathscr{R}^3$, sketch the curves and surfaces given below in spherical coordinates.

    (a) $r = 2$, $0 \le \theta \le \pi/4$, $\pi/4 \le \phi \le \pi/2$.
    (b) $1 \le r \le 2$, $\theta = \pi/2$, $\phi = \pi/4$.
    (c) $0 \le r \le 1$, $0 \le \theta \le \pi/2$, $\phi = \pi/4$.
    (d) $0 \le r \le 1$, $\theta = \pi/4$, $0 \le \phi \le \pi/4$.

3. Use cylindrical coordinates in $\mathscr{R}^3$ to describe the region defined in rectangular coordinates by $0 \le x$, $x^2 + y^2 \le 1$.

4. Let (r, θ) be polar coordinates in $\mathscr{R}^2$. The equation

$$\begin{pmatrix} r \\ \theta \end{pmatrix} = \begin{pmatrix} \sin t \\ t \end{pmatrix}, \qquad 0 \le t \le \frac{\pi}{2},$$

describes a curve in $\mathscr{U}^2$. Sketch this curve, and sketch its image in $\mathscr{R}^2$ under the polar coordinate transformation.

5. Let (r, ϕ, θ) be spherical coordinates in $\mathscr{R}^3$. The equation

$$\begin{pmatrix} r \\ \phi \\ \theta \end{pmatrix} = \begin{pmatrix} 1 \\ t \\ t \end{pmatrix}$$

determines a curve in $\mathscr{R}^3$ (as well as in the $r\phi\theta$-space $\mathscr{U}^3$). Sketch the curve in $\mathscr{R}^3$. [*Suggestion.* The curve lies on a sphere.]

6. Prove that the Jacobian matrices (5) and (6) of the polar and spherical coordinate transformations given in Examples 2 and 3 have inverses.

7. The equations

$$\left.\begin{aligned} x &= ar \sin \phi \cos \theta \\ y &= br \sin \phi \sin \theta \\ z &= cr \cos \phi \end{aligned}\right\}, \qquad a, b, c > 0,$$

*See, for example, R.S. Burington, *Handbook of Mathematical Tables*, Handbook Publishers, Inc., Sandusky, Ohio, 1965.

define ellipsoidal coordinates in $\mathcal{R}^3$. For $a = 1$, $b = c = 2$, sketch a typical example of each of the three kinds of coordinate surface.

8. Compute the cartesian components of the tangent vectors to the coordinate curves for the general ellipsoidal coordinates given in Exercise 7, when $a = b = 1$, $c = 2$, and $r = \frac{1}{2}$, $\phi = \theta = \pi/2$.

9. Let r, ϕ, and θ be spherical coordinates in $\mathcal{R}^3$. The equation

$$\begin{pmatrix} r \\ \phi \\ \theta \end{pmatrix} = \begin{pmatrix} 1 \\ t \\ t^2 \end{pmatrix}$$

determines a curve in $\mathcal{R}^3$. Compute the cartesian components of the tangent vector to the curve.

10. Prove that in the 3-dimensional spherical coordinates of Example 2 in the text, the sphere $x_1^2 + x_2^2 + x_3^2 = 1$ has the equation $r = 1$.

11. Let "elliptic" coordinates in the plane be determined by

$$\begin{pmatrix} x \\ y \end{pmatrix} = \begin{pmatrix} ar \cos \theta \\ br \sin \theta \end{pmatrix}, \qquad a > 0, \quad b > 0.$$

(a) Compute the coefficients g_{ij} for this coordinate system.
(b) For what choices of a and b will it always be true that $g_{ij} = 0$ for $i \neq j$?

12. Verify the assertion made in the text that the jth column of the Jacobian matrix at $\mathbf{u}_0$ of a coordinate transformation $\mathcal{U}^n \xrightarrow{\ T\ } \mathcal{R}^n$ is a tangent vector at $\mathbf{x}_0 = T(\mathbf{u}_0)$ to the curvilinear coordinate curve obtained by letting the jth coordinate of $\mathbf{u}_0$ vary.

13. Show that if $z = f(x, y)$ and $\begin{pmatrix} x \\ y \end{pmatrix} = \begin{pmatrix} r \cos \theta \\ r \sin \theta \end{pmatrix}$, then

$$\frac{\partial^2 z}{\partial x^2} + \frac{\partial^2 z}{\partial y^2} = \frac{\partial^2 z}{\partial r^2} + \frac{1}{r^2} \frac{\partial^2 z}{\partial \theta^2} + \frac{1}{r} \frac{\partial z}{\partial r}.$$

14. (a) Find the formula for the arc length of a curve determined in plane polar coordinates by an equation of the form

$$\begin{pmatrix} r \\ \theta \end{pmatrix} = \begin{pmatrix} r(t) \\ \theta(t) \end{pmatrix}, \qquad a \leq t \leq b.$$

(b) Compute the length of the curve $\begin{pmatrix} r \\ \theta \end{pmatrix} = \begin{pmatrix} 2t \\ t \end{pmatrix}$, $0 \leq t \leq 2$.

$$[Ans.\ 2\sqrt{5} + \log(2 + \sqrt{5}).]$$

(c) Sketch the curve.

15. An equation

$$\begin{pmatrix} u \\ v \end{pmatrix} = \begin{pmatrix} u(t) \\ v(t) \end{pmatrix}, \qquad a \leq t \leq b,$$

determines a curve γ on the conical surface in $\mathcal{R}^3$

$$\begin{pmatrix} x \\ y \\ z \end{pmatrix} = \begin{pmatrix} u \cos v \sin \alpha \\ u \sin v \sin \alpha \\ u \cos \alpha \end{pmatrix}, \qquad \begin{cases} 0 \leq u \leq \infty, \\ 0 \leq v \leq 2\pi, \end{cases}$$

where α is fixed, $0 < \alpha < \pi/2$. Find the general formula for the arc length of γ.

16. Let $T(u_1, \ldots, u_n) = (x_1, \ldots, x_n)$ define a curvilinear coordinate system in a region D of $\mathscr{R}^n$.

(a) Show that $g_{ij} = \sum\limits_{k=1}^{n} \dfrac{\partial x_k}{\partial u_i} \dfrac{\partial x_k}{\partial u_j}$,   for $i, j = 1, \ldots, n$.

(b) If (g^{ij}) is the matrix inverse to (g_{ij}), show that

$$g^{ij} = \sum_{k=1}^{n} \frac{\partial u_i}{\partial x_k} \frac{\partial u_j}{\partial x_k}, \qquad i, j = 1, \ldots, n.$$

(c) Show that if $f(u_1, \ldots, u_n)$ represents a function differentiable in a region D of $\mathscr{R}^n$, then

$$\nabla f = \sum_{j=1}^{n} \left[\sum_{i=1}^{n} \frac{\partial f}{\partial u_i} g^{ij} \right] \mathbf{c}_j.$$

(d) Show that if T defines an orthogonal coordinate system in D, then

$$\nabla f = \sum_{i=1}^{n} \frac{1}{h_i^2} \frac{\partial f}{\partial u_i} \mathbf{c}_i.$$

13. INVERSE AND IMPLICIT FUNCTION THEOREMS

Let f be a function. If there exists a function f^{-1} with the property

$$f^{-1}(\mathbf{y}) = \mathbf{x} \quad \text{if and only if} \quad f(\mathbf{x}) = \mathbf{y},$$

then f^{-1} is called the **inverse function** of f. It follows that the domain of f^{-1} is the range of f and that the range of f^{-1} is the domain of f. Some familiar examples of functions and their inverses are

$$\begin{cases} f(x) = x^2, & x \geq 0. \\ f^{-1}(y) = \sqrt{y}, & y \geq 0. \end{cases}$$

$$\begin{cases} f(x) = e^x, & -\infty < x < \infty. \\ f^{-1}(y) = \ln y, & y > 0. \end{cases}$$

$$\begin{cases} f(x) = \sin x, & -\dfrac{\pi}{2} \leq x \leq \dfrac{\pi}{2}. \\ f^{-1}(y) = \arcsin y, & -1 \leq y \leq 1. \end{cases}$$

The inverse function f^{-1} should not be confused with the reciprocal $1/f$. For example, if $f(x) = x^2$, then $f^{-1}(2) = \sqrt{2}$, whereas $(f(2))^{-1} = 1/f(2) = \frac{1}{4}$.

We recall that a function is one-one if each element in the range is the image of precisely one element in the domain. A fact that is used repeatedly is that a function f has an inverse if and only if it is one-one.

The inverse function L^{-1} of every invertible linear function $\mathcal{R}^n \xrightarrow{L} \mathcal{R}^m$ is itself linear. That is, by applying L to both sides, we see that

$$L^{-1}(a\mathbf{y}_1 + b\mathbf{y}_2) = aL^{-1}(\mathbf{y}_1) + bL^{-1}(\mathbf{y}_2),$$

whenever $\mathbf{y}_1$ and $\mathbf{y}_2$ are in the range of L. If the dimension of $\mathcal{R}^n$ is less than that of $\mathcal{R}^m$, the range of L is a proper subspace of $\mathcal{R}^m$. In this case, L^{-1} is not defined on all of $\mathcal{R}^m$. On the other hand, if $\mathcal{R}^n$ and $\mathcal{R}^m$ have the same dimension, the domain of L^{-1} is all of $\mathcal{R}^m$. Thus the inverse function of every one-one linear transformation $\mathcal{R}^n \xrightarrow{L} \mathcal{R}^n$ is a linear transformation $\mathcal{R}^n \xrightarrow{L^{-1}} \mathcal{R}^n$.

EXAMPLE 1. Consider the affine function $\mathcal{R}^3 \xrightarrow{A} \mathcal{R}^3$ defined by

$$A\begin{pmatrix} x \\ y \\ z \end{pmatrix} = \begin{pmatrix} 4 & 0 & 5 \\ 0 & 1 & -6 \\ 3 & 0 & 4 \end{pmatrix}\begin{pmatrix} x-1 \\ y-0 \\ z-1 \end{pmatrix} + \begin{pmatrix} 1 \\ 5 \\ 2 \end{pmatrix}.$$

It is obvious that any affine function $A(\mathbf{x}) = L(\mathbf{x} - \mathbf{x}_0) + \mathbf{y}_0$ is one-one if and only if the linear function L is one-one also. In this example,

$$\mathbf{x}_0 = \begin{pmatrix} 1 \\ 0 \\ 1 \end{pmatrix} \quad \text{and} \quad L(\mathbf{x}) = \begin{pmatrix} 4 & 0 & 5 \\ 0 & 1 & -6 \\ 3 & 0 & 4 \end{pmatrix}\begin{pmatrix} x \\ y \\ z \end{pmatrix}.$$

The inverse matrix of

$$\begin{pmatrix} 4 & 0 & 5 \\ 0 & 1 & -6 \\ 3 & 0 & 4 \end{pmatrix}$$

can be computed to be

$$\begin{pmatrix} 4 & 0 & -5 \\ -18 & 1 & 24 \\ -3 & 0 & 4 \end{pmatrix}.$$

It follows that L, and therefore A, has an inverse. In fact, if $A(\mathbf{x}) = \mathbf{y}$, then

$$A(\mathbf{x}) = L(\mathbf{x} - \mathbf{x}_0) + \mathbf{y}_0,$$

and

$$A^{-1}(\mathbf{y}) = L^{-1}(\mathbf{y} - \mathbf{y}_0) + \mathbf{x}_0. \tag{1}$$

That this is the correct expression for A^{-1} may be checked by substituting $A(\mathbf{x})$ for $\mathbf{y}$. We get

$$A^{-1}(A(\mathbf{x})) = L^{-1}(L(\mathbf{x} - \mathbf{x}_0)) + \mathbf{x}_0 = \mathbf{x}.$$

Hence

$$A^{-1}\begin{pmatrix} u \\ v \\ w \end{pmatrix} = \begin{pmatrix} 4 & 0 & -5 \\ -18 & 1 & 24 \\ -3 & 0 & 4 \end{pmatrix}\begin{pmatrix} u-1 \\ v-5 \\ w-2 \end{pmatrix} + \begin{pmatrix} 1 \\ 0 \\ 1 \end{pmatrix}.$$

Obviously this method will enable us to find the inverse of any affine transformation $\mathscr{R}^n \xrightarrow{A} \mathscr{R}^n$ if the inverse exists.

We have the following criteria for deciding whether a linear function $\mathscr{R}^n \xrightarrow{L} \mathscr{R}^m$ has an inverse. If M is the matrix of L, then by Theorem 4.2 the columns of M are the vectors $L(e_j)$ and so span the range of L. Hence L is one-to-one, and has an inverse, if and only if the columns of M are linearly independent. Alternatively, *if M is a square matrix*, then L has an inverse if and only if the inverse matrix M^{-1} exists. We recall that M^{-1} exists if and only if det $M \neq 0$.

The principal purpose of this section is the study of inverses of non-linear vector functions. Given a function $\mathscr{R}^n \xrightarrow{f} \mathscr{R}^n$ one may ask (1) Does it have an inverse? and (2) If it does, what are its properties? In general it is not easy to answer these questions just by looking at the function. On the other hand, we do know how to tell whether or not an affine transformation has an inverse and, what is more, how to compute it explicitly when it does exist. Furthermore, if f is differentiable at a point $\mathbf{x}_0$, it can be approximated near that point by an affine transformation A. For this reason, one might conjecture that if the domain of f is restricted to points close to $\mathbf{x}_0$, then f will have an inverse if A does. In addition, one might guess that A^{-1} is the approximating affine transformation to f^{-1} near $f(\mathbf{x}_0)$. Except for details, these statements are correct and are the content of the inverse function theorem.

13.1 The inverse function theorem. Let $\mathscr{R}^n \xrightarrow{f} \mathscr{R}^n$ be a continuously differentiable function such that $f'(\mathbf{x}_0)$ has an inverse. Then there is an open set N containing $\mathbf{x}_0$ such that f, when restricted to N, has a continuously differentiable inverse f^{-1}. The image set $f(N)$ is open. In addition,

$$[f^{-1}]'(\mathbf{y}_0) = [f'(\mathbf{x}_0)]^{-1}, \qquad \text{where} \quad \mathbf{y}_0 = f(\mathbf{x}_0).$$

That is, the differential of the inverse function at $\mathbf{y}_0$ is the inverse of the differential of f at $\mathbf{x}_0$.

The existence of f^{-1} is proved in the Appendix. Once the existence has been established, we can write $f^{-1} \circ f = I$, where $\mathscr{R}^n \xrightarrow{I} \mathscr{R}^n$ is the identity transformation on the neighborhood N. Then by the chain rule we have, since the identity transformation is its own differential,

$$[f^{-1}]'(\mathbf{y}_0)f'(\mathbf{x}_0) = I, \qquad \text{or} \quad [f^{-1}]'(\mathbf{y}_0) = [f'(\mathbf{x}_0)]^{-1}.$$

For real-valued functions of one variable, the existence of an inverse function is not hard to prove. Let $\mathscr{R} \xrightarrow{f} \mathscr{R}$ satisfy the differentiability condition of the theorem, and suppose that $f'(x_0)$ has a matrix inverse. Since the inverse matrix exists whenever $f'(x_0) \neq 0$, the geometric meaning of the condition that $f'(x_0)$ have an inverse is that the graph of f should not have a horizontal tangent. To be specific, suppose that $f'(x_0) > 0$. Since f' is continuous, we have $f'(x) > 0$ for every x in some interval $a < x < b$ that contains x_0, as shown in Figure 52. We contend that f restricted to this interval is one-one. For suppose x_1 and x_2 are any two points in the interval such that $x_1 < x_2$. By the mean-value theorem it follows that

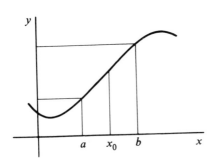

Figure 52

$$\frac{f(x_2) - f(x_1)}{x_2 - x_1} = f'(x_0),$$

for some x_0 in the interval $x_1 < x < x_2$. Since $f'(x_0) > 0$, and $x_2 - x_1 > 0$, we obtain

$$f(x_2) - f(x_1) > 0.$$

Thus, f is strictly increasing in the interval $a < x < b$, and our contention is proved. It follows that f restricted to this interval has an inverse. The other conclusions of the inverse function theorem can also be obtained in a straightforward way for this special case.

EXAMPLE 2. Consider the function f defined by

$$f\begin{pmatrix} x \\ y \end{pmatrix} = \begin{pmatrix} x^3 - 2xy^2 \\ x + y \end{pmatrix}, \qquad \begin{cases} -\infty < x < \infty. \\ -\infty < y < \infty. \end{cases}$$

At the point

$$\mathbf{x}_0 = \begin{pmatrix} 1 \\ -1 \end{pmatrix}$$

the differential $d_{\mathbf{x}_0} f$ is defined by the Jacobian matrix

$$\begin{pmatrix} 3x^2 - 2y^2 & -4xy \\ 1 & 1 \end{pmatrix}_{x=1,\, y=-1} = \begin{pmatrix} 1 & 4 \\ 1 & 1 \end{pmatrix}.$$

The inverse of this matrix is

$$\begin{pmatrix} -\frac{1}{3} & \frac{4}{3} \\ \frac{1}{3} & -\frac{1}{3} \end{pmatrix}.$$

Since f is obviously continuously differentiable, we conclude from the inverse function theorem that in some open set containing $\mathbf{x}_0$ the function f has an inverse f^{-1}. Moreover, if

$$\mathbf{y}_0 = f(\mathbf{x}_0) = \begin{pmatrix} -1 \\ 0 \end{pmatrix},$$

the matrix of the differential $d_{\mathbf{y}_0} f^{-1}$ is

$$\begin{pmatrix} -\frac{1}{3} & \frac{4}{3} \\ \frac{1}{3} & -\frac{1}{3} \end{pmatrix}.$$

Although it would be difficult to evaluate f^{-1} explicitly, it is easy to write down the affine transformation that approximates f^{-1} in the vicinity of the point $\mathbf{y}_0$. It is the inverse A^{-1} of the affine transformation A that approximates f near $\mathbf{x}_0$. We have, either by the inverse function theorem or by formula (1) of Example 1,

$$A(\mathbf{x}) = f(\mathbf{x}_0) + f'(\mathbf{x}_0)(\mathbf{x} - \mathbf{x}_0)$$
$$= \mathbf{y}_0 + f'(\mathbf{x}_0)(\mathbf{x} - \mathbf{x}_0).$$
$$A^{-1}(\mathbf{y}) = f^{-1}(\mathbf{y}_0) + [f^{-1}]'(\mathbf{y}_0)(\mathbf{y} - \mathbf{y}_0)$$
$$= \mathbf{x}_0 + [f'(\mathbf{x}_0)]^{-1}(\mathbf{y} - \mathbf{y}_0).$$

Hence, if we set $\mathbf{y} = \begin{pmatrix} u \\ v \end{pmatrix}$,

$$A^{-1}\begin{pmatrix} u \\ v \end{pmatrix} = \begin{pmatrix} 1 \\ -1 \end{pmatrix} + \begin{pmatrix} -\frac{1}{3} & \frac{4}{3} \\ \frac{1}{3} & -\frac{1}{3} \end{pmatrix}\begin{pmatrix} u + 1 \\ v - 0 \end{pmatrix}$$
$$= \begin{pmatrix} -\frac{1}{3} & \frac{4}{3} \\ \frac{1}{3} & -\frac{1}{3} \end{pmatrix}\begin{pmatrix} u \\ v \end{pmatrix} + \begin{pmatrix} \frac{2}{3} \\ -\frac{2}{3} \end{pmatrix}.$$

EXAMPLE 3. The equations

$$u = x^4 y + x, \qquad v = x + y^3$$

define a transformation from $\mathscr{R}^2$ to $\mathscr{R}^2$. The matrix of the differential of the transformation at $(x, y) = (1, 1)$ is

$$\begin{pmatrix} 4x^3 y + 1 & x^4 \\ 1 & 3y^2 \end{pmatrix}_{(x,y)=(1,1)} = \begin{pmatrix} 5 & 1 \\ 1 & 3 \end{pmatrix}.$$

Since the columns of this matrix are independent, the differential has an inverse, and according to the inverse function theorem the transformation has an inverse also, in an open neighborhood of $(x, y) = (1, 1)$. The inverse transformation would be given by equations of the form

$$x = F(u, v), \qquad y = G(u, v).$$

The actual computation of F and G is difficult, but we can easily compute the partial derivatives of F and G with respect to u and v at the point (u, v)

$= (2, 2)$ that corresponds to $(x, y) = (1, 1)$. These partial derivatives occur in the Jacobian matrix of F and G or, equivalently, in the inverse matrix of the differential of the given functions. We have

$$\begin{pmatrix} \dfrac{\partial F}{\partial u}(2, 2) & \dfrac{\partial F}{\partial v}(2, 2) \\ \dfrac{\partial G}{\partial u}(2, 2) & \dfrac{\partial G}{\partial v}(2, 2) \end{pmatrix} = \begin{pmatrix} 5 & 1 \\ 1 & 3 \end{pmatrix}^{-1} = \begin{pmatrix} \dfrac{3}{14} & -\dfrac{1}{14} \\ -\dfrac{1}{14} & \dfrac{5}{14} \end{pmatrix}.$$

Suppose $\mathscr{R}^n \xrightarrow{f} \mathscr{R}^n$ is a function for which the hypotheses of the inverse function theorem are satisfied at some point $\mathbf{x}_0$. It is important to realize that the theorem does not settle the question of the existence of an inverse for the whole function f, but only for f restricted to some open set containing $\mathbf{x}_0$. For example, the transformation

$$\begin{pmatrix} x \\ y \end{pmatrix} = \begin{pmatrix} u \cos v \\ u \sin v \end{pmatrix}, \qquad 0 < u$$

has Jacobian matrix

$$\begin{pmatrix} \cos v & -u \sin v \\ \sin v & u \cos v \end{pmatrix}$$

with inverse matrix

$$\begin{pmatrix} \cos v & \sin v \\ -\dfrac{1}{u} \sin v & \dfrac{1}{u} \cos v \end{pmatrix}.$$

The inverse matrix exists for all (u, v) satisfying $u > 0$. However, the otherwise unrestricted transformation clearly has no inverse, for the same image point is obtained whenever v increases by 2π. Two corresponding regions are shown in Figure 53. If the transformation is restricted so that, for instance, $0 < v < 2\pi$, then it becomes one-one and has an inverse.

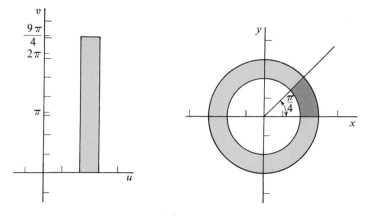

Figure 53

In Section 11 we considered the problem of finding derivatives of an implicitly defined function f under the assumption that f satisfied an equation $F(\mathbf{x}, f(\mathbf{x})) = 0$, with both f and F differentiable. We saw that in order to solve for $f'(\mathbf{x}_0)$ by matrix methods it was necessary for $F_y(\mathbf{x}_0, f(\mathbf{x}_0))$ to have an inverse. It is natural that the same condition occur in the next theorem, which treats the question whether there exists a differentiable f defined implicitly by F.

13.2 Implicit function theorem. Let $\mathscr{R}^{n+m} \xrightarrow{F} \mathscr{R}^m$ be a continuously differentiable function. Suppose that for some $\mathbf{x}_0$ in $\mathscr{R}^n$ and $\mathbf{y}_0$ in $\mathscr{R}^m$

(i) $F(\mathbf{x}_0, \mathbf{y}_0) = 0$,

(ii) $F_y(\mathbf{x}_0, \mathbf{y}_0)$ has an inverse.

Then there exists a continuously differentiable function $\mathscr{R}^n \xrightarrow{f} \mathscr{R}^m$ defined on some neighborhood N of $\mathbf{x}_0$ such that $f(\mathbf{x}_0) = \mathbf{y}_0$ and $F(\mathbf{x}, f(\mathbf{x})) = 0$, for all $\mathbf{x}$ in N.

Proof. The proof consists in reducing the theorem to an application of the inverse function theorem. For that purpose we extend F to a function $\mathscr{R}^{n+m} \xrightarrow{H} \mathscr{R}^{n+m}$ by setting $H(\mathbf{x}, \mathbf{y}) = (\mathbf{x}, F(\mathbf{x}, \mathbf{y}))$. In terms of the coordinate functions $F_1, \ldots, F_m$ of F, the coordinate functions of H are given by

$$
\begin{aligned}
H_1(\mathbf{x}, \mathbf{y}) &= x_1, \\
H_2(\mathbf{x}, \mathbf{y}) &= x_2, \\
&\ \ \vdots \\
H_n(\mathbf{x}, \mathbf{y}) &= x_n, \\
H_{n+1}(\mathbf{x}, \mathbf{y}) &= F_1(x_1, \ldots, x_n, y_1, \ldots, y_m), \\
&\ \ \vdots \\
H_{n+m}(\mathbf{x}, \mathbf{y}) &= F_m(x_1, \ldots, x_n, y_1, \ldots, y_m).
\end{aligned}
$$

The Jacobian matrix of H at $(\mathbf{x}_0, \mathbf{y}_0)$ is

$$
\begin{bmatrix}
1 & 0 & \cdots & 0 & 0 & \cdots & 0 \\
0 & 1 & \cdots & 0 & 0 & \cdots & 0 \\
\vdots & & \ddots & & & & \\
0 & 0 & \cdot & 1 & 0 & & 0 \\
\dfrac{\partial F_1}{\partial x_1} & \dfrac{\partial F_1}{\partial x_2} & \cdots & \dfrac{\partial F_1}{\partial x_n} & \dfrac{\partial F_1}{\partial y_1} & \cdots & \dfrac{\partial F_1}{\partial y_m} \\
\vdots & & & & & & \\
\dfrac{\partial F_m}{\partial x_1} & \dfrac{\partial F_m}{\partial x_2} & \cdots & \dfrac{\partial F_m}{\partial x_n} & \dfrac{\partial F_m}{\partial y_1} & \cdots & \dfrac{\partial F_m}{\partial y_m}
\end{bmatrix}
$$

where all the partial derivatives are evaluated at $(\mathbf{x}_0, \mathbf{y}_0)$. By assumption (ii), the m columns on the right of the matrix are independent. Since they are also independent of the n independent columns on the left, all columns of the matrix are independent, and therefore the differential of H at $(\mathbf{x}_0, \mathbf{y}_0)$ has an inverse.

The function H is certainly continuously differentiable, so we can apply the inverse function theorem at the point $(\mathbf{x}_0, \mathbf{y}_0)$ to get a function H^{-1} that is inverse to H from some open set N' in $\mathcal{R}^{n+m}$ containing $H(\mathbf{x}_0, \mathbf{y}_0)$ to an open set about $(\mathbf{x}_0, \mathbf{y}_0)$. Since $H(\mathbf{x}_0, \mathbf{y}_0) = (\mathbf{x}_0, F(\mathbf{x}_0, \mathbf{y}_0)) = (\mathbf{x}_0, 0)$, the set N of all points $\mathbf{x}$ in $\mathcal{R}^n$ such that $(\mathbf{x}, 0)$ is in N' is an open set (see Exercise 22) and contains $\mathbf{x}_0$.

Let G_1 be the function that selects the first n variables of a point in $\mathcal{R}^{n+m}$, and G_2 the function that selects the last m variables. Thus, $G_1(\mathbf{x}, \mathbf{y}) = \mathbf{x}$ and $G_2(\mathbf{x}, \mathbf{y}) = \mathbf{y}$. Since $H(\mathbf{x}, \mathbf{y}) = (\mathbf{x}, F(\mathbf{x}, \mathbf{y}))$, the function H is the identity on $\mathbf{x}$. The same must therefore be true of H^{-1}. Hence,

$$G_1 = G_1 \circ H^{-1}.$$

We define f by

$$f(\mathbf{x}) = G_2 H^{-1}(\mathbf{x}, 0), \qquad \text{for every} \quad \mathbf{x} \text{ in } N.$$

Then

$$H^{-1}(\mathbf{x}, 0) = (G_1 H^{-1}(\mathbf{x}, 0), G_2 H^{-1}(\mathbf{x}, 0)) = (\mathbf{x}, f(\mathbf{x})).$$

Applying H to both sides, we get

$$(\mathbf{x}, 0) = H(\mathbf{x}, f(\mathbf{x})) = (\mathbf{x}, F(\mathbf{x}, f(\mathbf{x}))),$$

for every $\mathbf{x}$ in N. The two parts of the first and last pairs must be equal. Hence,

$$0 = F(\mathbf{x}, f(\mathbf{x})), \qquad \text{for every } \mathbf{x} \text{ in } N.$$

Finally, f, being the composition of two continuously differentiable functions, is itself continuously differentiable by the chain rule.

EXAMPLE 4. The equation $x^3 y + y^3 x - 2 = 0$ defines $y = f(x)$ implicitly in a neighborhood of $x = 1$ if $f(1) = 1$. As a function of y, $x^3 y + y^3 x - 2$ has Jacobian $(1 + 3y^2)$ at $x = 1$, and the latter is invertible at $y = 1$, that is,

$$1 + 3y^2 \big|_{y=1} = 4 \neq 0.$$

The solution can be computed by standard methods to be

$$y = \sqrt[3]{\frac{1}{x} + \frac{1}{x}\sqrt{\frac{x^{10} + 27}{27}}} + \sqrt[3]{\frac{1}{x} - \frac{1}{x}\sqrt{\frac{x^{10} + 27}{27}}}.*$$

*See R. S. Burington, *Mathematical Tables and Formulas*, Handbook Publishers, Inc., Sandusky, Ohio, 1965.

EXAMPLE 5. The equations

$$z^3 x + w^2 y^3 + 2xy = 0, \qquad xyzw - 1 = 0 \qquad (2)$$

can be written in the form $F(\mathbf{x}, \mathbf{y}) = 0$, where $\mathbf{x} = \begin{pmatrix} x \\ y \end{pmatrix}$, $\mathbf{y} = \begin{pmatrix} z \\ w \end{pmatrix}$ and,

$$F(\mathbf{x}, \mathbf{y}) = \begin{pmatrix} z^3 x + w^2 y^3 + 2xy \\ xyzw - 1 \end{pmatrix}.$$

Let $\mathbf{x}_0 = \begin{pmatrix} -1 \\ -1 \end{pmatrix}$ and $\mathbf{y}_0 = \begin{pmatrix} 1 \\ 1 \end{pmatrix}$. Then

$$F(\mathbf{x}_0, \mathbf{y}) = \begin{pmatrix} -z^3 - w^2 + 2 \\ zw - 1 \end{pmatrix}$$

and the matrix $F_{\mathbf{y}}(1, 1)$ is

$$\begin{pmatrix} -3z^2 & -2w \\ w & z \end{pmatrix}_{\left(\begin{smallmatrix} z \\ w \end{smallmatrix}\right) = \left(\begin{smallmatrix} 1 \\ 1 \end{smallmatrix}\right)} = \begin{pmatrix} -3 & -2 \\ 1 & 1 \end{pmatrix}.$$

The inverse exists and is the matrix

$$\begin{pmatrix} -1 & -2 \\ 1 & 3 \end{pmatrix}.$$

It is then a consequence of the implicit function theorem that Equations (2) implicitly define a function f in an open set about $\mathbf{x}_0$ such that $f(\mathbf{x}_0) = \mathbf{y}_0$. That is, we have

$$\begin{pmatrix} z \\ w \end{pmatrix} = f\begin{pmatrix} x \\ y \end{pmatrix},$$

and so each of z and w is a function of x and y near

$$\begin{pmatrix} -1 \\ -1 \end{pmatrix}.$$

EXERCISES

1. Can a function have two different inverses?

2. Show that $(f^{-1})^{-1} = f$.

3. Which of the following functions have inverses?

    (a) $y = \cosh x$, $-\infty < x < \infty$.
    (b) $y = \cosh x$, $0 \le x < \infty$.
    (c) $f(x) = \tan x$, $\begin{cases} \dfrac{7}{4}\pi \le x < \dfrac{11}{4}\pi, \\ x \ne \dfrac{10\pi}{4}. \end{cases}$
    (d) $f(x) = \tan x$, $0 \le x \le \pi/4$.

(e) $y = x^2 - 2x + 1, 1 \le x < \infty$.

(f) $y = x^2 - 3x + 2, 0 \le x < \infty$.

4. Compute A^{-1} for the following affine functions:

(a) $A(x) = 7x + 2$.

(b) $A\begin{pmatrix} u \\ v \end{pmatrix} = \begin{pmatrix} 1 & 3 \\ 2 & 4 \end{pmatrix} \begin{pmatrix} u - 1 \\ v - 2 \end{pmatrix} + \begin{pmatrix} 3 \\ 4 \end{pmatrix}$.

$$\left[Ans. \ A^{-1}\begin{pmatrix} x \\ y \end{pmatrix} = \begin{pmatrix} -2 & \frac{3}{2} \\ 1 & -\frac{1}{2} \end{pmatrix} \begin{pmatrix} x - 3 \\ y - 4 \end{pmatrix} + \begin{pmatrix} 1 \\ 2 \end{pmatrix}. \right]$$

5. Using the inverse function theorem, show that the following functions have inverses when restricted to some open set containing x_0.

(a) $f(x) = \tan x, x_0 = \pi/6$.

(b) $y = x^2 - 3x + 2, x_0 = 4$.

(c) $y = x^3 - 7x + 6, x_0 = 4$.

(d) $f(x) = \int_{-\infty}^x e^{-t^2} dt, x_0 = 0$.

6. Let $f\begin{pmatrix} x \\ y \end{pmatrix} = \begin{pmatrix} x^2 - y^2 \\ 2xy \end{pmatrix}$.

(a) Show that for every point x_0 except

$$x_0 = \begin{pmatrix} 0 \\ 0 \end{pmatrix},$$

the restriction of f to some open set containing x_0 has an inverse.

(b) Show that with domain unrestricted, f has no inverse.

(c) If f^{-1} is the inverse of f in a neighborhood of the point $\begin{pmatrix} 1 \\ 2 \end{pmatrix}$, compute the affine transformation that approximates f^{-1} close to

$$f\begin{pmatrix} 1 \\ 2 \end{pmatrix} = \begin{pmatrix} -3 \\ 4 \end{pmatrix}. \qquad \left[Ans. \ \begin{pmatrix} \frac{1}{10} & \frac{1}{5} \\ -\frac{1}{5} & \frac{1}{10} \end{pmatrix} \begin{pmatrix} u \\ v \end{pmatrix} + \begin{pmatrix} \frac{1}{2} \\ 1 \end{pmatrix}. \right]$$

7. Find the affine function that best approximates the inverse of the function

$$f\begin{pmatrix} x \\ y \end{pmatrix} = \begin{pmatrix} x^3 + 2xy + y^2 \\ x^2 + y \end{pmatrix}$$

near the point $f\begin{pmatrix} 1 \\ 1 \end{pmatrix}$. Notice that to find the precise inverse would be difficult.

$$\left[Ans. \ \begin{pmatrix} -\frac{1}{3} & \frac{4}{3} \\ \frac{2}{3} & -\frac{5}{3} \end{pmatrix} \begin{pmatrix} u \\ v \end{pmatrix} + \begin{pmatrix} -\frac{1}{3} \\ \frac{5}{3} \end{pmatrix}. \right]$$

8. (a) Let T be defined by

$$\begin{pmatrix} x \\ y \end{pmatrix} = T\begin{pmatrix} r \\ \theta \end{pmatrix} = \begin{pmatrix} r \cos \theta \\ r \sin \theta \end{pmatrix}, \qquad \begin{cases} 0 < r. \\ 0 \le \theta < 2\pi. \end{cases}$$

Find $d_u T$ and its inverse for those points

$$\mathbf{u} = \begin{pmatrix} r \\ \theta \end{pmatrix}$$

for which they exist.

(b) Compute an explicit representation for T^{-1}, and compare $d_x T^{-1}$ with $(d_u T)^{-1}$ at corresponding points.

(c) Let S be defined by

$$\begin{pmatrix} x \\ y \\ z \end{pmatrix} = S \begin{pmatrix} r \\ \phi \\ \theta \end{pmatrix} = \begin{pmatrix} r \sin \phi \cos \theta \\ r \sin \phi \sin \theta \\ r \cos \phi \end{pmatrix}, \qquad \begin{cases} 0 < r. \\ 0 < \phi < \pi/2. \\ 0 < \theta < 2\pi. \end{cases}$$

Find $d_u S$ and its inverse for those points

$$\mathbf{u} = \begin{pmatrix} r \\ \phi \\ \theta \end{pmatrix}$$

for which they exist.

(d) Compute an explicit representation for S^{-1}.

9. Suppose that the function T defined by

$$\begin{pmatrix} u \\ v \end{pmatrix} = T \begin{pmatrix} x \\ y \end{pmatrix} = \begin{pmatrix} f(x, y) \\ g(x, y) \end{pmatrix}$$

has a differentiable inverse function S defined by

$$\begin{pmatrix} x \\ y \end{pmatrix} = S \begin{pmatrix} u \\ v \end{pmatrix} = \begin{pmatrix} h(u, v) \\ k(u, v) \end{pmatrix}.$$

If $f(1, 2) = 3, g(1, 2) = 4$, and $T'(1, 2)$ equals

$$\begin{pmatrix} 3 & 5 \\ 4 & 7 \end{pmatrix}, \qquad \text{find } \frac{\partial h}{\partial v}(3, 4). \qquad \qquad [Ans. \ -5.]$$

10. If

$$\begin{cases} x = u + v + w, \\ y = u^2 + v^2 + w^2, \\ z = u^3 + v^3 + w^3, \end{cases}$$

compute $\partial v/\partial y$ at the image of $(u, v, w) = (1, 2, -1)$, namely $(x, y, z) = (2, 6, 8)$. $\qquad \qquad \qquad \qquad \qquad \qquad \qquad \qquad$ [Ans. 0.]

11. Let

$$f \begin{pmatrix} u \\ v \end{pmatrix} = \begin{pmatrix} u^2 + u^2 v + 10v \\ u + v^3 \end{pmatrix}.$$

(a) Show that f has an inverse f^{-1} in the vicinity of the point $\begin{pmatrix} 1 \\ 1 \end{pmatrix}$.

(b) Find an approximate value of $f^{-1} \begin{pmatrix} 11.8 \\ 2.2 \end{pmatrix}$.

12. Does $f(t) = \begin{pmatrix} t \\ t \\ t \end{pmatrix}$ have an inverse?

13. Show that the differentiable function

$$F(x, y, z) = \begin{pmatrix} f(x, y, z) \\ g(x, y, z) \\ f(x, y, z) + g(x, y, z) \end{pmatrix}$$

can never have a differentiable inverse.

14. Although the condition that the differential $d_{x_0}f$ have an inverse is needed for the proof of the inverse function theorem, it is perfectly possible for this condition to fail even though an inverse exists. Verify this fact with the example $f(x) = x^3$.

15. The inverse function theorem is the correct modification of the simple, but false, assertion that if $d_x f$ has an inverse, then f has an inverse. The converse—namely, if f has an inverse, then $d_x f$ has an inverse—is also false (see Exercise 14). It too, however, is almost true. Using the chain rule, prove the corrected form: *If f is differentiable and has a differentiable inverse, then $d_x f$ is one-one.*

16. Consider the function $\mathcal{R} \xrightarrow{f} \mathcal{R}$ defined by

$$f(x) = \begin{cases} \dfrac{x}{2} + x^2 \sin \dfrac{1}{x}, & \text{if } x \neq 0. \\ 0, & \text{if } x = 0. \end{cases}$$

Show that $d_0 f$ is one-one but that f has no inverse in the vicinity of $x = 0$. What is wrong?

17. What is the inverse function of the linear function

$$L\begin{pmatrix} u \\ v \end{pmatrix} = \begin{pmatrix} u + v \\ u - v \\ u \end{pmatrix}?$$

18. The inverse function theorem can be generalized as follows:

Let $\mathcal{R}^n \xrightarrow{f} \mathcal{R}^m$, where $n < m$, be continuously differentiable. If $d_{x_0}f$ is one-one, there is an open set N containing $\mathbf{x}_0$ such that f, restricted to N, has an inverse f^{-1}.

An important difference between this theorem and the inverse function theorem as we have stated it is that here the image $f(N)$ is not an open subset of $\mathcal{R}^m$. One consequence of this is that f^{-1} is not differentiable at $f(\mathbf{x}_0)$.

(a) If

$$f\begin{pmatrix} u \\ v \end{pmatrix} = \begin{pmatrix} u + v \\ (u + v)^2 \\ (u + v)^3 \end{pmatrix},$$

for what points (u_0, v_0) does f have an inverse in a neighborhood of $f(u_0, v_0)$?

(b) Prove the generalized inverse function theorem. [*Hint.* Let the vectors $y_1, \ldots, y_n$ be a basis for the range of $d_{x_0}f$. Extend to a basis $y_1, \ldots, y_n, y_{n+1}, \ldots, y_m$ for all of $\mathscr{R}^m$, and define $\mathscr{R}^m \overset{g}{\longrightarrow} \mathscr{R}^n$ by

$$g(\sum_{i=1}^{m} a_i y_i) = (a_1, \ldots, a_n).$$

Show that $(g \circ f)$ and $d_{x_0}(g \circ f) = (d_{f(x_0)}g) \circ (d_{x_0}f)$ satisfy the conditions of the inverse function theorem.]

19. Consider the equation $(x - 2)^3 y + xe^{y-1} = 0$.

   (a) Is y defined implicitly as a function of x in a neighborhood of $(x, y) = (1, 1)$?
   (b) In a neighborhood of $(0, 0)$?
   (c) In a neighborhood of $(2, 1)$?

20. The point $(x, y, t) = (0, 1, -1)$ satisfies the equations

$$xyt + \sin xyt = 0, \qquad x + y + t = 0.$$

Are x and y defined implicitly as functions of t in a neighborhood of $(0, 1, -1)$?

21. Requirement (ii) in the implicit function theorem that $F_y(x_0, y_0)$ have an inverse is not a necessary condition for the equation $F(x, y) = 0$ to define a unique differentiable function f such that $f(x_0) = y_0$. Show this by taking $F(x, y) = x^9 - y^3$ and $(x_0, y_0) = (0, 0)$.

22. Show that if N' is an open subset of $\mathscr{R}^{n+m}$ containing the point (x_0, y_0), then the subset N of all x in $\mathscr{R}^n$ such that (x, y_0) is in N' is an open subset of $\mathscr{R}^n$.

23. Prove that under the assumptions of Theorem 13.2 there is only one function f defined by $F(x, f(x)) = 0$ in a neighborhood of x_0, and satisfying $f(x_0) = y_0$. [*Hint*: Use the function $H(x, y) = (x, F(x, y))$.]

14. SURFACES AND TANGENTS

While explicit, implicit, and parametric representations of surfaces have so far been used for illustrative purposes, a precise definition of the term "surface" has not been given. In this section we shall define smooth surface in terms of each of the three representations, give a unified definition of tangent for each mode of representation, and show how the three are related. In particular, we shall see that for each of the three ways of representing a surface—as an image, as a graph, or as a level set—a representation for a tangent is obtained by taking the image, graph, or level set of the affine approximation to the given function.

An n-dimensional **plane** in $\mathscr{R}^m$ is either an n-dimensional linear subspace (that is, a plane containing the origin) or else an affine subspace (that is, the translation of a linear subspace by a fixed vector y_0). When $n = 1$ or $n = 2$ we get a line or an ordinary plane. A parametric representation of an

n-dimensional plane in $\mathscr{R}^m$ is obtained by looking at the range of an affine function $\mathscr{R}^n \xrightarrow{A} \mathscr{R}^m$, where $A(\mathbf{x}) = L(\mathbf{x}) + \mathbf{y}_0$, and L is a linear function defined on $\mathscr{R}^n$. To ensure that the range of A is n-dimensional, we can require that the matrix of L have n linearly independent columns, since the columns $L(\mathbf{e}_j)$ span the range of L.

Parametrically defined surfaces. Let a set S be defined parametrically by a function $\mathscr{R}^n \xrightarrow{f} \mathscr{R}^m$. According to the definition of Section 1, this means that S is the image under f of the domain of f. Next we restrict f to a neighborhood of some point $\mathbf{x}_0$ on which f is one-one. If f is differentiable at $\mathbf{x}_0$, then the affine function A that approximates f near $\mathbf{x}_0$ is given by $A(\mathbf{x}) = f(\mathbf{x}_0) + f'(\mathbf{x}_0)(\mathbf{x} - \mathbf{x}_0)$, for all $\mathbf{x}$ in $\mathscr{R}^n$. Then, if A defines parametrically an n-dimensional plane, this plane is called the **tangent plane** to S at $f(\mathbf{x}_0)$. Notice that n, the dimension of the plane, is required to be the same as the dimension of the domain space of f. If, in addition, f is continuously differentiable on its domain, then the set S is called a **smooth surface** (or **smooth curve** if $n = 1$) at every point at which there is a tangent.

EXAMPLE 1. Consider the surface S in 3-dimensional space $\mathscr{R}^3$ defined parametrically by

$$f\begin{pmatrix} u \\ v \end{pmatrix} = \begin{pmatrix} u\cos v \\ u\sin v \\ v \end{pmatrix}, \qquad \begin{cases} 0 \le u \le 4, \\ 0 \le v \le 2\pi. \end{cases}$$

This function is discussed in Example 7, Section 1, and its range, which is the surface S, is pictured in Figure 6. At $(u_0, v_0) = (2, \pi/2)$ the matrix of the differential is

$$\begin{pmatrix} \cos v_0 & -u_0\sin v_0 \\ \sin v_0 & u_0\cos v_0 \\ 0 & 1 \end{pmatrix} = \begin{pmatrix} 0 & -2 \\ 1 & 0 \\ 0 & 1 \end{pmatrix}.$$

The affine function $A(\mathbf{x}) = f(\mathbf{x}_0) + f'(\mathbf{x}_0)(\mathbf{x} - \mathbf{x}_0)$ that approximates f near $\mathbf{x}_0$ is therefore given by

$$A\begin{pmatrix} u \\ v \end{pmatrix} = \begin{pmatrix} 0 \\ 2 \\ \pi/2 \end{pmatrix} + \begin{pmatrix} 0 & -2 \\ 1 & 0 \\ 0 & 1 \end{pmatrix}\begin{pmatrix} u - 2 \\ v - \pi/2 \end{pmatrix}$$

$$= u\begin{pmatrix} 0 \\ 1 \\ 0 \end{pmatrix} + v\begin{pmatrix} -2 \\ 0 \\ 1 \end{pmatrix} + \begin{pmatrix} \pi \\ 0 \\ 0 \end{pmatrix},$$

for all u and v. Since the vectors

$$\begin{pmatrix} 0 \\ 1 \\ 0 \end{pmatrix} \quad \text{and} \quad \begin{pmatrix} -2 \\ 0 \\ 1 \end{pmatrix}$$

are linearly independent, we conclude that the range of A is a plane. Hence, the surface S has a tangent plane at $(0, 2, \pi/2)$. Eliminating u and v from the equations

$$x = \quad -2v + \pi$$
$$y = u$$
$$z = \quad v$$

we obtain

$$x = -2z + \pi$$

as the equation that implicitly defines the tangent plane to S at $(0, 2, \pi/2)$. See Figure 54.

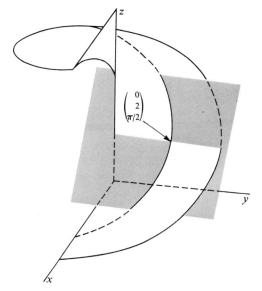

Figure 54

EXAMPLE 2. The function of t defined by

$$f(t) = \begin{pmatrix} x \\ y \\ z \end{pmatrix} = \begin{pmatrix} t \\ t^2 \\ t^3 \end{pmatrix}, \qquad -\infty < t < \infty,$$

and discussed in Example 6, Section 1, parametrically defines the curve shown in Figure 55. The differential of f at t_0 is defined by the Jacobian matrix

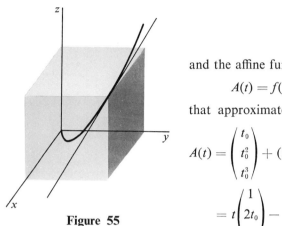

Figure 55

$$\begin{pmatrix} 1 \\ 2t_0 \\ 3t_0^2 \end{pmatrix},$$

and the affine function

$$A(t) = f(t_0) + f'(t_0)(t - t_0)$$

that approximates f near t_0 is given by

$$A(t) = \begin{pmatrix} t_0 \\ t_0^2 \\ t_0^3 \end{pmatrix} + (t - t_0)\begin{pmatrix} 1 \\ 2t_0 \\ 3t_0^2 \end{pmatrix}$$

$$= t\begin{pmatrix} 1 \\ 2t_0 \\ 3t_0^2 \end{pmatrix} - \begin{pmatrix} 0 \\ t_0^2 \\ 2t_0^3 \end{pmatrix}, \qquad -\infty < t < \infty.$$

Since $(1, 2t_0, 3t_0^2) \neq 0$, it follows that the range of A is the tangent line to the curve at $f(t_0)$. Figure 55 shows the curve and the tangent line to it at $f(1) = (1, 1, 1)$.

The condition that the affine approximation to $\mathscr{R}^n \xrightarrow{f} \mathscr{R}^m$ define an n-dimensional plane is important both because of the restriction it places on the tangent and because of the smoothness that it requires of the surface if f is continuously differentiable. As far as the tangent goes, it is clear that its dimension at $f(\mathbf{x}_0)$ is the same as the dimension of the range of the differential of f at $\mathbf{x}_0$. But because the columns of the m-by-n Jacobian matrix $f'(\mathbf{x}_0)$ span the range of the differential, it is enough to require this matrix to have n linearly independent columns. That is,

14.1 Theorem. Let $\mathscr{R}^n \xrightarrow{f} \mathscr{R}^m$ be differentiable. Then the tangent to the range of f at $f(\mathbf{x}_0)$ exists (and has dimension n) if and only if the matrix $f'(\mathbf{x}_0)$ has n linearly independent columns.

The requirement that f be continuously differentiable signifies for a smooth surface S that the tangent varies continuously from point to point on S. To see the effect of the dimension requirement for a smooth surface, we consider the following example.

EXAMPLE 3. The function $\mathscr{R}^2 \xrightarrow{f} \mathscr{R}^3$ defined by

$$f(u, v) = \begin{pmatrix} u \cos v \\ u \sin v \\ u \end{pmatrix}, \qquad \text{for } (u, v) \text{ in } \mathscr{R}^2,$$

is continuously differentiable, because the Jacobian matrix

$$f'(u, v) = \begin{pmatrix} \cos v & -u \sin v \\ \sin v & u \cos v \\ 1 & 0 \end{pmatrix}$$

has continuous entries. The range of f is a cone shown in Figure 56. Points of the cone not at the vertex correspond to values of $u \neq 0$, and it is easy to check that for $u \neq 0$ the columns of $f'(u, v)$ are linearly independent.

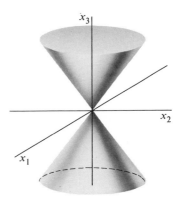

Thus the tangent plane at such a point has the expected dimension, namely 2. However, at the vertex, $u = 0$, so that $f'(0, v)$ has only one nonzero column. Thus any attempt to use the affine approximation to f to define a tangent at the vertex leads to a 1-dimensional tangent. Indeed, it seems natural to say that the cone has no tangent at its vertex. However, the cone satisfies the definition of smooth surface at every other point. The lack of smoothness at the vertex is not associated with a lack of differentiability in f, but rather with the failure of the tangent to exist.

Figure 56

Explicitly defined surfaces. Suppose a set S is defined explicitly by a function $\mathscr{R}^n \xrightarrow{f} \mathscr{R}^m$. This means that S is the graph of f in $\mathscr{R}^{n+m}$, consisting of the points of the form $(\mathbf{x}, f(\mathbf{x}))$, for all $\mathbf{x}$ in the domain of f. If f is differentiable at $\mathbf{x}_0$, the affine function

$$A(\mathbf{x}) = f(\mathbf{x}_0) + f'(\mathbf{x}_0)(\mathbf{x} - \mathbf{x}_0)$$

explicitly defines an n-dimensional plane, and this plane is called the tangent to S at $\mathbf{x}_0$. If in addition f is continuously differentiable, then S is a smooth surface.

The complication in the parametric theory that requires checking that the differential has n-dimensional range does not occur here. If $f'(\mathbf{x}_0)$ exists, then A always has as its graph an n-dimensional plane.

14.2 Theorem. The graph of every affine function $\mathscr{R}^n \xrightarrow{A} \mathscr{R}^m$ is an n-dimensional plane.

Proof. By the definition of an affine function, there exists a linear function $\mathscr{R}^n \xrightarrow{L} \mathscr{R}^m$ and a vector $\mathbf{y}_0$ in $\mathscr{R}^m$ such that

$$A(\mathbf{x}) = L(\mathbf{x}) + \mathbf{y}_0, \qquad \text{for all } \mathbf{x} \text{ in } \mathscr{R}^n.$$

The graph of A is the set of all points

$$(\mathbf{x}, A(\mathbf{x})) = (\mathbf{x}, L(\mathbf{x})) + (0, \mathbf{y}_0), \qquad \mathbf{x} \text{ in } \mathscr{R}^n.$$

It is therefore the image under translation by $(0, \mathbf{y}_0)$ of the graph of L. Hence, the graph of A is an n-dimensional plane if and only if the graph of L, which is a subspace of $\mathscr{R}^{n+m}$, has dimension n. But if $(\mathbf{e}_1, \ldots, \mathbf{e}_n)$ is the natural basis for $\mathscr{R}^n$, then any point $(\mathbf{x}, L(\mathbf{x}))$ on the graph of L can be written

$$(\mathbf{x}, L(\mathbf{x})) = x_1(\mathbf{e}_1, L(\mathbf{e}_1)) + \ldots + x_n(\mathbf{e}_n, L(\mathbf{e}_n)).$$

Clearly the n vectors $(\mathbf{e}_j, L(\mathbf{e}_j))$ are linearly independent, and since they span the graph of L, that graph has dimension n.

EXAMPLE 4. The hemisphere shown in Figure 57 is defined explicitly by

$$g\begin{pmatrix} x \\ y \end{pmatrix} = \sqrt{9 - x^2 - y^2}.$$

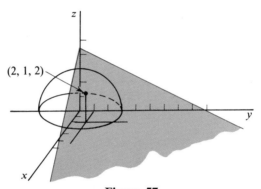

Figure 57

The differential of g at $\mathbf{x}_0 = \begin{pmatrix} 2 \\ 1 \end{pmatrix}$ is defined by the Jacobian matrix

$$\left(\frac{-x}{\sqrt{9 - x^2 - y^2}} \quad \frac{-y}{\sqrt{9 - x^2 - y^2}} \right)_{x=2, y=1} = \left(-1 \quad -\frac{1}{2} \right).$$

The tangent plane to the hemisphere at $(2, 1, 2)$ is the graph of the approximating affine function

$$A(\mathbf{x}) = g(\mathbf{x}_0) + g'(\mathbf{x}_0)(\mathbf{x} - \mathbf{x}_0)$$

$$= 2 + \left(-1 \quad -\frac{1}{2} \right)\begin{pmatrix} x - 2 \\ y - 1 \end{pmatrix}$$

$$= \frac{9}{2} - x - \frac{1}{2}y.$$

The plane is implicitly defined by the equation $z = A(\mathbf{x})$, that is, by

$$2x + y + 2z = 9.$$

The graph of any function $\mathscr{R}^n \xrightarrow{f} \mathscr{R}^m$ can always be represented parametrically by a function $\mathscr{R}^n \xrightarrow{g} \mathscr{R}^{n+m}$ of the form $g(\mathbf{x}) = (\mathbf{x}, f(\mathbf{x}))$. This raises the question of whether the sets S that can be represented in both ways have the same tangents and of whether the notion of smooth surface is the same in both representations. It is clear that g is continuously differentiable if and only if f is, because $g'(\mathbf{x}_0)$ has the form

$$g'(\mathbf{x}_0) = \begin{pmatrix} I \\ f'(\mathbf{x}_0) \end{pmatrix},$$

where I is the n-by-n identity matrix. Thus

$$g(\mathbf{x}_0) + g'(\mathbf{x}_0)(\mathbf{x} - \mathbf{x}_0) = (\mathbf{x}_0, f(\mathbf{x}_0)) + (\mathbf{x} - \mathbf{x}_0, f'(\mathbf{x}_0)(\mathbf{x} - \mathbf{x}_0))$$
$$= (\mathbf{x}, f(\mathbf{x}_0) + f'(\mathbf{x}_0)(\mathbf{x} - \mathbf{x}_0)),$$

and this shows that the graph of the affine approximation to f is the same as the range of the affine approximation to g. Hence the two definitions of tangent and of smooth surface are the same where they overlap.

We recall that the null-space of a linear function $\mathscr{R}^{n+m} \xrightarrow{L} \mathscr{R}^m$ is a subspace of $\mathscr{R}^{n+m}$. Then, for a fixed vector $\mathbf{x}_0$, the set of all $\mathbf{x}$ such that $\mathbf{x} - \mathbf{x}_0$ is in the null-space of L is a plane in $\mathscr{R}^{n+m}$. Clearly the plane passes through $\mathbf{x}_0$.

Implicitly defined surfaces. Consider a function $\mathscr{R}^{n+m} \xrightarrow{F} \mathscr{R}^m$ and a fixed vector $\mathbf{z}_0$ in $\mathscr{R}^m$. Let S be the level set defined by the equation $F(\mathbf{x}) = \mathbf{z}_0$. If F is differentiable at a point $\mathbf{x}_0$ in $\mathscr{R}^{n+m}$ and the affine approximation $A(\mathbf{x}) = F(\mathbf{x}_0) + F'(\mathbf{x}_0)(\mathbf{x} - \mathbf{x}_0)$ determines an n-dimensional plane implicitly by $A(\mathbf{x}) = \mathbf{z}_0$, then this plane is called the tangent to S at $\mathbf{x}_0$. Since $F(\mathbf{x}_0) = \mathbf{z}_0$, the defining equation of the plane reduces to

$$F'(\mathbf{x}_0)(\mathbf{x} - \mathbf{x}_0) = 0. \tag{1}$$

If in addition F is continuously differentiable on its domain, then S is representable as a smooth surface near every point at which there is a tangent.

EXAMPLE 5. The equation $x^2 + y^2 + z^2 = 9$ implicitly defines a sphere of radius 3 with center at the origin in 3-dimensional euclidean space. An equation of the tangent plane to the sphere at

$$\mathbf{x}_0 = (x_0, y_0, z_0) = (2, 1, 2)$$

is determined as follows: If $F(x, y, z) = x^2 + y^2 + z^2$, the Jacobian matrix $F'(\mathbf{x}_0)$ is

$$(2x_0 \quad 2y_0 \quad 2z_0) = (4 \quad 2 \quad 4).$$

Equation (1), which implicitly defines the tangent plane, is therefore

$$(4 \quad 2 \quad 4) \begin{pmatrix} x - 2 \\ y - 1 \\ z - 2 \end{pmatrix} = 0.$$

This is equivalent to $4x + 2y + 4z = 18$ and thence to $2x + y + 2z = 9$. Notice that we have found the same equation as that obtained for the tangent plane in Example 4.

If the plane determined by the equation $F'(\mathbf{x}_0)(\mathbf{x} - \mathbf{x}_0) = 0$ is not n-dimensional, then, according to the definition, the function $\mathscr{R}^{n+m} \xrightarrow{F} \mathscr{R}^m$ does not assign a tangent to the level set $F(\mathbf{x}) = \mathbf{z}_0$ at $\mathbf{x} = \mathbf{x}_0$. This is similar to the complication that occurs in the parametric theory and that gave rise to Theorem 14.1. In the present case we need to know that n is the dimension of the null space of the linear transformation with matrix $F'(\mathbf{x}_0)$. Since the dimension of the null space is equal to the dimension of the domain minus the dimension of the range, we want the dimension of the range to be m. (Theorem 8.7, Chapter 1) Hence

14.3 Theorem. Let $\mathscr{R}^{n+m} \xrightarrow{F} \mathscr{R}^m$ be differentiable. Then the tangent to the level set $F(\mathbf{x}) = \mathbf{z}_0$ at $\mathbf{x}_0$ exists (and has dimension n) if and only if $F'(\mathbf{x}_0)$ has m linearly independent columns.

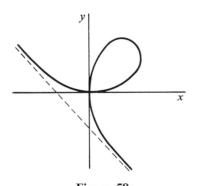

Figure 58

Example 3 shows that in the parametric case a surface may fail to be smoothly represented because the dimension of the tangent is too small. The following example is fairly typical of the way in which the standard method of assigning tangents in the implicit case may fail.

EXAMPLE 6. Figure 58 shows the folium of Descartes, which is the level set determined by $x^3 + y^3 - 3xy = 0$. The function $F(x, y) = x^3 + y^3 - 3xy$ is continuously differentiable with derivative

$$F'(x, y) = (3x^2 - 3y, \quad 3y^2 - 3x).$$

The criterion of Theorem 14.3 requires that one or another of the two entries be different from zero, in which case the tangent at a point (x_0, y_0) satisfies

$$(x_0^2 - y_0)(x - x_0) + (y_0^2 - x_0)(y - y_0) = 0.$$

The one point at which the differential fails to assign a tangent is $(x, y) = (0, 0)$. There the null space of the differential has dimension 2.

The function $\mathscr{R} \xrightarrow{f} \mathscr{R}^2$ given by

$$f(t) = \left(\frac{3t}{1 + t^3}, \quad \frac{3t^2}{1 + t^3} \right), \qquad -1 < t < \infty$$

is a parametrization of the part of the curve that lies in the first and second quadrants, and it assigns the curve a horizontal tangent at the origin. Interchanging the coordinate functions of f gives a parametrization of the part of the curve in the first and fourth quadrants.

If $\mathscr{R}^{n+m} \xrightarrow{F} \mathscr{R}^m$ is continuously differentiable and its level set $F(\mathbf{x}) = 0$ has an implicitly determined tangent at a point $\mathbf{x}_0$, then according to Theorem 14.3 the m-by-$(n + m)$ matrix $F'(\mathbf{x}_0)$ has m linearly independent columns. Denote the variables corresponding to these columns by the vector $\mathbf{y}$ and observe that the implicit function theorem applies. The conclusion is that, writing $\mathbf{x} = (\mathbf{v}, \mathbf{y})$, there is a continuously differentiable function $\mathscr{R}^n \xrightarrow{f} \mathscr{R}^m$ satisfying $F(\mathbf{v}, f(\mathbf{v})) = 0$ in some neighborhood of $\mathbf{x}_0$. The significance of this result is that, restricted to a neighborhood of $\mathbf{x}_0$, the level set $F(\mathbf{x}) = 0$ can be represented as the graph of the function f. It is routine to show that we get the same tangent by using the explicit or the implicit representation, and we leave the computation as Exercise 12.

To complete the ideas of this section, consider a real-valued function $f(x, y)$. The surface S defined explicitly by f is the same as that defined implicitly by the equation $z = f(x, y)$. The tangent plane to S at $\mathbf{x}_0 = (x_0, y_0, z_0)$, where $z_0 = f(x_0, y_0)$, can be found as follows. Set $F(x, y, z) = f(x, y) - z$. The differential $F'(\mathbf{x}_0)$ is defined by the Jacobian matrix

$$F'(x_0, y_0, z_0) = \left(\frac{\partial f}{\partial x}(x_0, y_0) \quad \frac{\partial f}{\partial y}(x_0, y_0) \quad -1 \right).$$

The equation of the tangent plane is therefore $F'(\mathbf{x}_0)(\mathbf{x} - \mathbf{x}_0) = 0$, which is equivalent to

$$z - z_0 = (x - x_0)\frac{\partial f}{\partial x}(x_0, y_0) + (y - y_0)\frac{\partial f}{\partial y}(x_0, y_0).$$

The points (x, y, z) that satisfy this equation are, of course, precisely the graph of the affine transformation that approximates f near (x_0, y_0). Thus both the implicit and explicit approach to the tangent plane have led to the same result.

A **normal**, or perpendicular, vector to a set S at a point $\mathbf{x}_0$ is any vector $\mathbf{y}_0$ that is perpendicular to the tangent plane to S at $\mathbf{x}_0$. Notice that, while the notion of perpendicularity is used in the definition of normal, it is not used in the definition of tangent.

EXAMPLE 7. Let the surface S in $\mathscr{R}^3$ be defined implicitly with respect to a function $\mathscr{R}^3 \xrightarrow{F} \mathscr{R}$ by the equation $F(\mathbf{x}) = 0$. If S has a tangent plane at $\mathbf{x}_0$, it is implicitly defined by

$$F'(\mathbf{x}_0)(\mathbf{x} - \mathbf{x}_0) = 0.$$

The vector

$$\mathbf{y}_0 = \left(\frac{\partial F}{\partial x}(\mathbf{x}_0), \frac{\partial F}{\partial y}(\mathbf{x}_0), \frac{\partial F}{\partial z}(\mathbf{x}_0) \right)$$

is perpendicular to the tangent plane and is therefore a normal to S at $\mathbf{x}_0$.

EXERCISES

1. Find a parametric representation $t\mathbf{x}_1 + \mathbf{x}_2$ for the tangent line to each of the curves defined parametrically by the following functions at the points indicated. Sketch the curve and the tangent line.

(a) $f(t) = \begin{pmatrix} t \\ e^t \end{pmatrix}$, at $f(0)$. $\left[Ans. \ t\begin{pmatrix} 1 \\ 1 \end{pmatrix} + \begin{pmatrix} 0 \\ 1 \end{pmatrix}. \right]$

(b) $g(t) = \begin{pmatrix} x \\ y \\ z \end{pmatrix} = \begin{pmatrix} t^2 + 1 \\ t - 1 \\ t^2 \end{pmatrix}$, at $\begin{pmatrix} 2 \\ 0 \\ 1 \end{pmatrix}$.

2. Find the tangent plane to each of the surfaces defined parametrically by the following functions at the points indicated. Sketch the surface and the tangent plane in (a) and (b).

(a) $f\begin{pmatrix} u \\ v \end{pmatrix} = \begin{pmatrix} u + v \\ u - v \\ u^2 - v^2 \end{pmatrix}$, $\begin{Bmatrix} 0 \le u \le 2 \\ 0 \le v \le 2 \end{Bmatrix}$ at $f\begin{pmatrix} 1 \\ 1 \end{pmatrix}$.

$\left[Ans. \ \begin{pmatrix} u + v + 2 \\ u - v \\ 2u - 2v \end{pmatrix}. \right]$

(b) $g\begin{pmatrix} u \\ v \end{pmatrix} = \begin{pmatrix} x \\ y \\ z \end{pmatrix} = \begin{pmatrix} \cos u \sin v \\ \sin u \sin v \\ \cos v \end{pmatrix}$, $\begin{Bmatrix} 0 \le u \le 2\pi \\ 0 \le v \le \pi/2 \end{Bmatrix}$ at $g\begin{pmatrix} \pi \\ \pi/4 \end{pmatrix}$.

(c) $\begin{pmatrix} x \\ y \\ z \end{pmatrix} = \begin{pmatrix} u + v + 1 \\ 2u + 3v \\ u + 2v - 2 \end{pmatrix}$, at $\begin{pmatrix} 3 \\ 5 \\ 1 \end{pmatrix}$.

3. Find the tangent plane or tangent line to each of the following explicitly defined curves and surfaces at the points indicated.

(a) $f(x) = (x - 1)(x - 2)(x - 3)$, at $(0, -6)$.

(b) $f(x, y) = \dfrac{1}{x^2 + y^2}$, at $(x_0, y_0, f(x_0, y_0)) = \left(0, 2, \dfrac{1}{4} \right)$.

(c) $g(t) = \begin{pmatrix} t \\ e^t \end{pmatrix}$, at $\begin{pmatrix} 1 \\ 1 \\ e \end{pmatrix}$. $\left[Ans. \ L(t) = t\begin{pmatrix} 1 \\ e \end{pmatrix}. \right]$

(d) $g(x, y) = \cosh (x^2 + y^2)$, at $(x_0, y_0, g(x_0, y_0)) = (1, 2, \cosh 5)$.

4. Find the tangent line or tangent plane to each of the following implicitly defined curves and surfaces at the points indicated. Sketch the curve or surface and the tangent in (b), (d), and (e).

(a) $xy + yz + zx = 1$, at $\mathbf{x}_0 = (2, -1, 3)$.
  (Cf. Section 1, Example 8.)

(b) $\dfrac{x^2}{4} + \dfrac{y^2}{9} + z^2 = 1$, at $\mathbf{x}_0 = \left(1, \ 0, \ \dfrac{\sqrt{3}}{2} \right)$.

$\left[Ans. \ \dfrac{x}{2} + \sqrt{3}\, z = 2. \right]$

(c) $5x + 5y + 2z = 8$, at $(1, 1, -1)$.

(d) $\dfrac{x^2}{a^2} + \dfrac{y^2}{b^2} = 1$, at $(x_0, y_0) = \left(\dfrac{\sqrt{3}\,a}{2}, \dfrac{b}{2} \right)$.

(e) $F \begin{pmatrix} x \\ y \\ z \end{pmatrix} = \begin{pmatrix} x^2 + y^2 + z^2 \\ x + y \end{pmatrix} = \begin{pmatrix} 9 \\ 3 \end{pmatrix}$, at $\mathbf{x}_0 = \begin{pmatrix} 2 \\ 1 \\ 2 \end{pmatrix}$.

$$\left[Ans. \; \begin{pmatrix} 4 & 2 & 4 \\ 1 & 1 & 0 \end{pmatrix} \begin{pmatrix} x \\ y \\ z \end{pmatrix} = \begin{pmatrix} 18 \\ 3 \end{pmatrix}. \right]$$

5. In each of Exercises 1(a), 2(a), 2(b), and 4(b), find a normal to the given curve or surface at the point indicated. $\left[Ans. \; 1(a)\begin{pmatrix} 1 \\ -1 \end{pmatrix}. \right]$

6. Each of the following curves and surfaces fails, according to our definitions, to have a tangent line or plane at the indicated point. Why?

(a) $f(t) = \begin{pmatrix} t \\ |t| \\ t^2 \end{pmatrix}$, at $f(0)$.

(b) $g(t) = \begin{pmatrix} t^2 - 2t \\ t^3 - 3t \\ t^4 - t^3 - t \end{pmatrix}$, at $\begin{pmatrix} -1 \\ -2 \\ -1 \end{pmatrix}$.

(c) $f\begin{pmatrix} u \\ v \end{pmatrix} = \begin{pmatrix} u^2 v^4 \\ uv^2 \\ u^2 + v^4 \end{pmatrix}$, at $f\begin{pmatrix} 1 \\ 1 \end{pmatrix}$.

(d) $f(x, y) = \sqrt{1 - x^2 - y^2}$, at $\left(\dfrac{\sqrt{2}}{2}, \dfrac{\sqrt{2}}{2}, 0 \right)$

(e) $F \begin{pmatrix} x \\ y \\ z \end{pmatrix} = \begin{pmatrix} z^2 e^{x+y} \\ 2xyz^2 \end{pmatrix} = \begin{pmatrix} 4e^2 \\ 8 \end{pmatrix}$, at $\mathbf{x}_0 = \begin{pmatrix} 1 \\ 1 \\ 2 \end{pmatrix}$.

7. Find all points at which the surface defined parametrically by the function

$$f\begin{pmatrix} u \\ v \end{pmatrix} = \begin{pmatrix} u^2 v^2 \\ uv \\ uv + 1 \end{pmatrix}$$

fails to have a tangent plane.

8. Different vector functions can define the same curve or surface. Show that the functions

$$f_1(t) = (\cos t, \sin t), \qquad 0 < t < 2\pi,$$

$$f_2(s) = \left(\dfrac{s^2 - 1}{s^2 + 1}, \dfrac{2s}{s^2 + 1} \right) \quad -\infty < s < \infty,$$

parametrically define the same curve in 2-dimensional euclidean space.

9. Consider the vector functions

$$f(t) = \begin{pmatrix} t^3 \\ t^3 \\ t^3 \end{pmatrix}, \qquad -\infty < t < \infty,$$

$$g\begin{pmatrix} u \\ v \end{pmatrix} = \begin{pmatrix} u^3 \\ v^3 \\ 0 \end{pmatrix}, \qquad \begin{cases} -\infty < u < \infty, \\ -\infty < v < \infty. \end{cases}$$

(a) What curve and what surface are parametrically defined by f and g, respectively?

(b) Show that according to our definition the curve does not have a tangent line and the surface does not have a tangent plane at $(0, 0, 0)$.

10. Let

$$f(t) = \begin{pmatrix} t^3 \\ t^3 \end{pmatrix}, \qquad -\infty < t < \infty.$$

(a) Show that the curve in $\mathcal{R}^3$ defined explicitly by f has a tangent line at every point.

(b) Show that the curve in $\mathcal{R}^2$ defined parametrically by f fails to have a tangent line at one point.

(c) Interpret (a) and (b) geometrically. What is the relation between the tangent line in (a) and in (b)?

11. Let $y_0 = 0$ lie in the range of a function $\mathcal{R}^n \xrightarrow{F} \mathcal{R}^m$. The surface S defined implicitly by the equation $F(\mathbf{x}) = 0$ is assumed to have a tangent $\mathcal{T}$ at $\mathbf{x}_0$.

(a) Check that the surface S' in $\mathcal{R}^{n+m}$ defined explicitly by F has a tangent $\mathcal{T}'$ at $(\mathbf{x}_0, \mathbf{y}_0)$.

(b) Let $\mathcal{P}$ be the plane in $\mathcal{R}^{n+m}$ defined by the equation $\mathbf{y} = 0$, and show that $S = S' \cap \mathcal{P}$.

(c) Prove that $\mathcal{T} = \mathcal{T}' \cap \mathcal{P}$.

(d) Using the equation $F(x, y) = x^2 + y^2 - 2 = 0$ and the point $\mathbf{x}_0 = (1, 1)$, draw a picture illustrating S, $\mathcal{T}$, S', $\mathcal{T}'$, and $\mathcal{P}$.

(e) Using the equation $F(x, y) = 4x^2 - 4xy + y^2 = 0$ and the point $\mathbf{x}_0 = (1, 2)$, draw a picture illustrating S, S', $\mathcal{T}'$, and $\mathcal{P}$. What happens to $\mathcal{T}$?

12. Show that if $\mathcal{R}^{n+m} \xrightarrow{F} \mathcal{R}^m$ determines a smooth surface S, then the tangent to S at $\mathbf{x}_0$ determined by $F'(\mathbf{x}_0)(\mathbf{x} - \mathbf{x}_0) = 0$ is the same as the tangent to the graph of the function $\mathcal{R}^n \xrightarrow{f} \mathcal{R}^m$ which satisfies $F(\mathbf{v}, f(\mathbf{v})) = 0$, and whose existence is guaranteed by the implicit function theorem.

13. Verify that the two parametrically defined tangents at the origin that are described in Example 6 of the text are horizontal and vertical, respectively.

14. Show that if $\mathcal{P}$ is an n-dimensional plane through the origin in $\mathcal{R}^{m+n}$, then $\mathcal{P}$ is precisely the null-space of some linear function taking values in $\mathcal{R}^m$.

REAL-VALUED FUNCTIONS 3

1. EXTREME VALUES

A real-valued function f has an **absolute maximum value at x_0** if, for all x in the domain of f,

$$f(x) \leq f(x_0),$$

and an **absolute minimum value** if instead

$$f(x_0) \leq f(x).$$

The number $f(x_0)$ is called a **local maximum value** or a **local minimum value** if there is a neighborhood N of x_0 such that, respectively,

$$f(x) \leq f(x_0) \quad \text{or} \quad f(x_0) \leq f(x),$$

for all x in N. A maximum or minimum value of f is called an **extreme value**. A point x_0 at which an extreme value occurs is called an **extreme point**.

EXAMPLE 1. Consider the function $f(x, y) = x^2 + y^2$ whose domain is the set of points (x, y) that lie inside or on the ellipse $x^2 + 2y^2 = 1$. The graph of f is shown in Figure 1. Suppose that f has an extreme value (i.e., maximum or minimum) at a point (x_0, y_0) in the interior of the ellipse. Then obviously, both functions f_1 and f_2 defined by

$$f_1(x) = f(x, y_0), \qquad f_2(y) = f(x_0, y)$$

must also have extreme values at x_0 and y_0, respectively. Applying the familiar criterion for functions of one variable, we have

$$f_1'(x_0) = f_2'(y_0) = 0.$$

Since

$$f_1'(x_0) = \frac{\partial f}{\partial x}(x_0, y_0)$$

and

$$f_2'(y_0) = \frac{\partial f}{\partial y}(x_0, y_0),$$

a necessary condition for f to have an extreme value at (x_0, y_0) is

$$\frac{\partial f}{\partial x}(x_0, y_0) = \frac{\partial f}{\partial y}(x_0, y_0) = 0.$$

In this example,

$$\frac{\partial f}{\partial x}(x, y) = 2x \quad \text{and} \quad \frac{\partial f}{\partial y}(x, y) = 2y,$$

and so the only extreme value of f in the interior of the ellipse occurs at $(x_0, y_0) = (0, 0)$. It is obvious from the graph of f, shown in Figure 1, that this value is a minimum. The ellipse itself can be defined parametrically by the function

$$g(t) = (x, y) = \left(\cos t, \frac{1}{\sqrt{2}} \sin t \right), \qquad 0 \leq t < 2\pi.$$

Thus, the values of f on the ellipse are given as the values of the composition

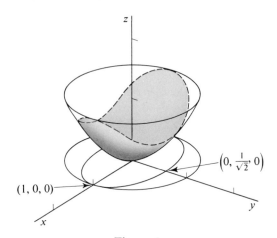

Figure 1

$f \circ g$. Any extreme values of f on the ellipse will be extreme for $f \circ g$. The latter is a real-valued function of one variable, and we treat it in the usual way—that is, by setting its derivative equal to zero. By the chain rule, we obtain

$$\frac{d}{dt}(f \circ g) = \left(2\cos t \quad \frac{2}{\sqrt{2}}\sin t\right)\begin{pmatrix} -\sin t \\ \frac{1}{\sqrt{2}}\cos t \end{pmatrix}$$

$$= -2 \cos t \sin t + \sin t \cos t$$

$$= -\frac{1}{2}\sin 2t.$$

Extreme values therefore may occur at $t = 0$, $\pi/2$, π, and $3\pi/2$. The corresponding values of (x, y) are $(1, 0)$, $(0, 1/\sqrt{2})$, $(-1, 0)$, and $(0, -1/\sqrt{2})$, and those of f are 1, $\frac{1}{2}$, 1, and $\frac{1}{2}$ respectively. We see that the absolute minimum of f is 0 at $(0, 0)$ and that the absolute maximum of f occurs at the two points $(1, 0)$ and $(-1, 0)$. Notice that the two extreme values of $f \circ g$ that occur at $t = \pi/2$ and $3\pi/2$ are not extreme for f, as can be seen by looking at Figure 1.

The methods used in the preceding example are valid in any number of dimensions. The next theorem is the principal criterion used in this extension, and while it can be proved by reducing it to the one-variable method, we give an independent proof that at the same time re-examines the basis of that method.

1.1 Theorem. If a differentiable function $\mathcal{R}^n \xrightarrow{f} \mathcal{R}$ has a local extreme value at a point $\mathbf{x}_0$ interior to its domain, then $f'(\mathbf{x}_0) = 0$.

Proof. Suppose f has a local minimum at $\mathbf{x}_0$. For any $\mathbf{y}$ in $\mathcal{R}^n$, there is an $\epsilon > 0$ such that if $-\epsilon < t < \epsilon$, then $f(\mathbf{x}_0) \le f(\mathbf{x}_0 + t\mathbf{y})$. Hence, for $0 < t < \epsilon$,

$$0 \le \frac{f(\mathbf{x}_0 + t\mathbf{y}) - f(\mathbf{x}_0)}{t},$$

$$0 \le \frac{f(\mathbf{x}_0 - t\mathbf{y}) - f(\mathbf{x}_0)}{t}.$$

It follows by Theorem 8.1 of Chapter 2 that

$$\frac{\partial f}{\partial \mathbf{y}}(\mathbf{x}_0) = f'(\mathbf{x}_0)\mathbf{y}.$$

Therefore,

$$0 \le \lim_{t \to 0+} \frac{f(\mathbf{x}_0 + t\mathbf{y}) - f(\mathbf{x}_0)}{t} = f'(\mathbf{x}_0)\mathbf{y},$$

$$0 \le \lim_{t \to 0+} \frac{f(\mathbf{x}_0 - t\mathbf{y}) - f(\mathbf{x}_0)}{t} = f'(\mathbf{x}_0)(-\mathbf{y}) = -f'(\mathbf{x}_0)\mathbf{y}.$$

We conclude that $f'(\mathbf{x}_0)\mathbf{y} = 0$. Because $\mathbf{y}$ is arbitrary, $f'(\mathbf{x}_0) = 0$. The argument for a maximum value is analogous.

The above result is what we should expect. Recall that

$$\frac{\partial f}{\partial \mathbf{y}}(\mathbf{x}_0) = f'(\mathbf{x}_0)\mathbf{y},$$

and that the derivative with respect to $\mathbf{y}$ measures the rate of change of f in the direction of $\mathbf{y}$. At an extreme point in the interior of the domain of f, this rate should be zero in every direction. The importance of the theorem is that of all the interior points $\mathbf{x}$ of the domain of f we need to look for extreme points only among those for which $f'(\mathbf{x}) = 0$. Points $\mathbf{x}$ for which $f'(\mathbf{x}) = 0$ are called **critical points** of f.

In practice we are often given a function f that is differentiable on an open set and want to find the extreme points of f when it is restricted to some subset S of the domain of f. In the next example the following two remarks are illustrated: (1) *a point $\mathbf{x}$ such that $f'(\mathbf{x}) = 0$ is not necessarily an extreme point for f;* (2) *f may have an extreme point $\mathbf{x}$ when restricted to a set S without having $f'(\mathbf{x}) = 0$.*

EXAMPLE 2. Let $f(x, y, z) = xyz$ in the region defined by $|x| \leq 1$, $|y| \leq 1, |z| \leq 1$. Thus the domain of f is the cube with each edge of length 2 illustrated in Figure 2. The condition for critical points, $f'(\mathbf{x}) = 0$, is equivalent to $(yz, xz, xy) = (0, 0, 0)$. The solutions of this equation are the points

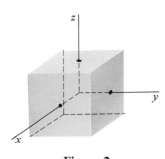

satisfying $x = y = 0$, or $x = z = 0$, or $y = z = 0$; in other words, the coordinate axes. Since f has the value zero at any one of its critical points, and since f has both positive and negative values in the neighborhood of any one of these points, no critical point can be an extreme point. Furthermore, a little thought shows that f has maximum value 1 and minimum value -1. These values occur at the corners of the cube, none of which is a critical point.

Figure 2

The problem of finding the extreme values of a function f on the boundary of a subregion R of $\mathscr{R}^n$ is one in which f has been restricted to a set S of lower dimension than that of R. Then, as we have seen in Example 2, it is not sufficient just to examine the critical points of f as a function on R. More generally, we may be interested in f when it is restricted to a lower-dimensional set S that is not necessarily the boundary of any region at all.

EXAMPLE 3. The function $f(x, y, z) = y^2 - z - x$ has a differential defined by the matrix

$$(-1 \quad 2y \quad -1),$$

so f has no critical points as a function defined on $\mathscr{R}^3$. Suppose, however, that f is restricted to the curve γ defined parametrically by

$$\begin{pmatrix} x \\ y \\ z \end{pmatrix} = \begin{pmatrix} t \\ t^2 \\ t^3 \end{pmatrix}, \qquad -\infty < t < \infty.$$

On γ, f takes the values $F(t) = f(t, t^2, t^3) = t^4 - t^3 - t$ while t varies over $(-\infty, \infty)$. We have

$$F'(t) = 4t^3 - 3t^2 - 1 = (t - 1)(4t^2 + t + 1).$$

Then $F'(t)$ is zero only at $t = 1$. Furthermore, since $F''(t) = 12t^2 - 6t$, we have $F''(1) > 0$. It follows that the point $(1, 1, 1)$ is a relative minimum for f restricted to the curve γ. The minimum value of f on γ is -1, and there are no other extreme values.

EXAMPLE 4. Suppose the function $f(x, y, z) = x + y + z$ is restricted to the intersection of the two surfaces

$$x^2 + y^2 = 1, \qquad z = 2$$

shown in Figure 3. The curve C of intersection can be parametrized by

$$\begin{pmatrix} x \\ y \\ z \end{pmatrix} = \begin{pmatrix} \cos t \\ \sin t \\ 2 \end{pmatrix}, \qquad 0 \le t < 2\pi.$$

The function f on C takes the value $F(t) = \cos t + \sin t + 2$. We have $F'(t) = -\sin t + \cos t$, so $F'(t) = 0$ at $t = \pi/4$ and $t = 5\pi/4$. Since $F''(\pi/4) < 0$ and $F''(5\pi/4) > 0$,

$$f(\sqrt{2}/2, \sqrt{2}/2, 2) = \sqrt{2} + 2$$

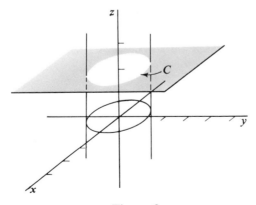

Figure 3

is the maximum and

$$f(-\sqrt{2}/2, -\sqrt{2}/2, 2) = -\sqrt{2} + 2$$

is the minimum value for f on C.

The solution of the previous problem depended on our being able to find a concrete parametric representation for the curve of intersection of the cylinder $x^2 + y^2 - 1 = 0$ and the plane $z - 2 = 0$. When a specific parametrization is not readily available, we can still sometimes apply the method of **Lagrange multipliers** to be described below. The method consists in verifying the pure existence of a parametric representation and then deriving necessary conditions for there to be an extreme point for a function f when restricted to the parametrized curve or surface.

1.2 **Theorem. Lagrange multiplier method.** Let the function $\mathscr{R}^n \xrightarrow{G} \mathscr{R}^m$, $n > m$, be continuously differentiable and have coordinate functions G_1, $G_2, \ldots, G_m$. Suppose the equations

$$G_1(x_1, \ldots, x_n) = 0$$
$$G_2(x_1, \ldots, x_n) = 0$$
$$\cdot \qquad \cdot$$
$$\cdot \qquad \cdot$$
$$\cdot \qquad \cdot$$
$$G_m(x_1, \ldots, x_n) = 0$$

implicitly define a surface S in $\mathscr{R}^n$, and that at a point $\mathbf{x}_0$ of S the matrix $G'(\mathbf{x}_0)$ has some m columns linearly independent.

If $\mathbf{x}_0$ is an extreme point of a differentiable function $\mathscr{R}^n \xrightarrow{f} \mathscr{R}$, when restricted to S, then $\mathbf{x}_0$ is a critical point of the function

$$f + \lambda_1 G_1 + \ldots + \lambda_m G_m$$

for some constants $\lambda_1 \ldots, \lambda_m$.

Proof. The implicit function theorem ensures that there is a parametric representation for S in a neighborhood of $\mathbf{x}_0$. For suppose that for some choice of m variables, say $x_1, \ldots, x_m$, the columns of the matrix

$$\begin{bmatrix} \dfrac{\partial G_1}{\partial x_1} & \dfrac{\partial G_1}{\partial x_2} & \cdots & \dfrac{\partial G_1}{\partial x_n} \\ \cdot & & & \cdot \\ \cdot & & & \cdot \\ \cdot & & & \cdot \\ \dfrac{\partial G_m}{\partial x_1} & \dfrac{\partial G_m}{\partial x_2} & \cdots & \dfrac{\partial G_m}{\partial x_n} \end{bmatrix}_{\mathbf{x}_0} \tag{1}$$

are independent. Then the matrix has an inverse. Write $\mathbf{x}_0 = (a_1, \ldots, a_n)$, and set $\mathbf{u}_0 = (a_1, \ldots, a_m)$ and $\mathbf{v}_0 = (a_{m+1}, \ldots, a_n)$. By the implicit function theorem, there is a differentiable function $\mathscr{R}^{n-m} \xrightarrow{h} \mathscr{R}^m$ defined on a neighborhood N of $\mathbf{v}_0$ such that $h(\mathbf{v}_0) = \mathbf{u}_0$ and $G(h(\mathbf{v}), \mathbf{v}) = 0$ for all $\mathbf{v}$ in N. The function $\mathscr{R}^{n-m} \xrightarrow{H} \mathscr{R}^n$ defined by

$$H(\mathbf{v}) = (h(\mathbf{v}), \mathbf{v}), \qquad \text{for all } \mathbf{v} \text{ in } N,$$

is a parametric representation of a part of S containing $\mathbf{x}_0 = H(\mathbf{v}_0)$. The surface S has a tangent $\mathscr{T}$ of dimension $n - m$ at $\mathbf{x}_0$, because the Jacobian of H at $\mathbf{v}_0$ is

$$\begin{bmatrix} \dfrac{\partial h_1}{\partial x_{m+1}} & \dfrac{\partial h_1}{\partial x_{m+2}} & \cdots & \dfrac{\partial h_1}{\partial x_n} \\[1em] \vdots & & & \\[0.5em] \dfrac{\partial h_m}{\partial x_{m+1}} & \cdots & & \dfrac{\partial h_m}{\partial x_n} \\[1em] 1 & 0 & \cdots & 0 \\ 0 & 1 & \cdots & 0 \\ \cdots & & & \\ 0 & 0 & \cdots & 1 \end{bmatrix}_{\mathbf{v}_0},$$

where $h_1, \ldots, h_m$ are the coordinate functions of h, and the columns of this matrix are clearly independent.

Now compose H with f. Since $\mathbf{x}_0$ is an extreme point of f in S, the point $\mathbf{v}$ is an extreme point of $f \circ H$. Hence,

$$(f \circ H)'(\mathbf{v}_0) = f'(\mathbf{x}_0)H'(\mathbf{v}_0) = 0. \tag{2}$$

Because G is constantly zero on S,

$$(G \circ H)'(\mathbf{v}_0) = G'(\mathbf{x}_0)H'(\mathbf{v}_0) = 0. \tag{3}$$

Looking at (2) and (3) together, we see that $d_{\mathbf{x}_0} f$ and $d_{\mathbf{x}_0} G$ are both zero on the range of $d_{\mathbf{v}_0} H$, which set is the tangent $\mathscr{T}$. Thus the matrix

$$\begin{bmatrix} \dfrac{\partial f}{\partial x_1} & \cdots & \dfrac{\partial f}{\partial x_n} \\[1em] \dfrac{\partial G_1}{\partial x_1} & \cdots & \dfrac{\partial G_1}{\partial x_n} \\[1em] \vdots & & \vdots \\[0.5em] \dfrac{\partial G_m}{\partial x_1} & \cdots & \dfrac{\partial G_m}{\partial x_n} \end{bmatrix}_{\mathbf{x}_0}$$

defines a linear function $\mathscr{R}^n \xrightarrow{L} \mathscr{R}^{m+1}$ that is identically zero on $\mathscr{T}$. Since the dimension of $\mathscr{T}$ is $n - m$, we have

$$n - m \leq \text{dimension of null space of } L.$$

It is always true for a linear function L that

$n =$ dimension of null-space of $L +$ dimension of range of L,

so

$$n \geq n - m + \text{dimension of range of } L,$$

that is,

$$m \geq \text{dimension of range of } L.$$

Then there is a linear function $\mathscr{R}^{m+1} \xrightarrow{\Lambda} \mathscr{R}$ such that Λ is zero on the range of L, but not identically zero on $\mathscr{R}^{m+1}$. In other words, there is a nonzero Λ such that $\Lambda \circ L = 0$. In matrix form $\Lambda = (\lambda_0, \lambda_1, \ldots, \lambda_m)$, and so

$$(\lambda_0, \lambda_1, \ldots, \lambda_m) \begin{bmatrix} \dfrac{\partial f}{\partial x_1} & \cdots & \dfrac{\partial f}{\partial x_n} \\[2mm] \dfrac{\partial G_1}{\partial x_1} & & \dfrac{\partial G_1}{\partial x_n} \\[2mm] . & & . \\ . & & . \\ . & & . \\[2mm] \dfrac{\partial G_m}{\partial x_1} & \cdots & \dfrac{\partial G_m}{\partial x_n} \end{bmatrix}_{\mathbf{x}_0} = 0. \tag{4}$$

It cannot happen that $\lambda_0 = 0$, for then the rows of (1) are dependent, contradicting the fact that (1) has an inverse. Taking $\lambda_0 = 1$ (if $\lambda_0 \neq 1$, divide through by λ_0), the condition (4) becomes

$$\frac{\partial f}{\partial x_j}(\mathbf{x}_0) + \lambda_1 \frac{\partial G_1}{\partial x_j}(\mathbf{x}_0) + \ldots + \lambda_m \frac{\partial G_m}{\partial x_j}(\mathbf{x}_0) = 0,$$

for $j = 1, \ldots, m$. In other words, $(f + \lambda_1 G_1 + \ldots + \lambda_m G_m)'(\mathbf{x}_0) = 0$. This completes the proof.

In applying the theorem it is important to verify that some m columns of $G'(\mathbf{x})$ are independent for $\mathbf{x}$ in S. Points for which this condition fails must be examined separately in looking for extreme points. All extreme points $\mathbf{x}_0$ for which the condition is satisfied are such that there are constants $\lambda_1, \ldots, \lambda_m$ for which

$$f + \lambda_1 G_1 + \ldots + \lambda_m G_m$$

has $\mathbf{x}_0$ as a critical point, or in other words,

$$f'(\mathbf{x}_0) + \lambda_1 G_1'(\mathbf{x}_0) + \ldots + \lambda_m G_m'(\mathbf{x}_0) = 0. \tag{5}$$

EXAMPLE 5. The problem of Example 4 is that of finding the extreme points of $f(x, y, z) = x + y + z$ subject to the conditions

$$x^2 + y^2 - 1 = 0, \qquad z - 2 = 0. \tag{6}$$

We write down
$$(x + y + z) + \lambda_1(x^2 + y^2 - 1) + \lambda_2(z - 2).$$
The critical points of this function occur when
$$1 + 2\lambda_1 x = 0, \qquad 1 + 2\lambda_1 y = 0, \qquad 1 + \lambda_2 = 0.$$
In addition, we must satisfy Equations (6). Solving for λ_1 and λ_2, as well as x, y, and z, we get
$$\lambda_2 = -1, \qquad \lambda_1 = \pm\frac{1}{\sqrt{2}}, \qquad x = y = \pm\frac{1}{\sqrt{2}}, \qquad z = 2.$$
That is, the critical points are
$$\left(\frac{1}{\sqrt{2}}, \frac{1}{\sqrt{2}}, 2\right) \quad \text{and} \quad \left(-\frac{1}{\sqrt{2}}, -\frac{1}{\sqrt{2}}, 2\right).$$
As in Example 4, we easily see that f has its maximum value, $\sqrt{2} + 2$, at the first of these points and its minimum value, $-\sqrt{2} + 2$, at the other. Notice that while the λ's are not needed in the final answer it is necessary to consider all values of the λ's for which the equations can be satisfied.

EXAMPLE 6. Find the maximum value of $f(x, y, z) = x - y + z$, subject to the condition $x^2 + y^2 + z^2 = 1$. The function
$$x - y + z + \lambda(x^2 + y^2 + z^2 - 1)$$
has critical points satisfying
$$1 + 2\lambda x = 0, \qquad -1 + 2\lambda y = 0, \qquad 1 + 2\lambda z = 0,$$
and
$$x^2 + y^2 + z^2 = 1.$$
The solutions of these equations are
$$\lambda = \pm\sqrt{3}/2, \quad x = -y = z = \pm 1/\sqrt{3}.$$
The maximum of f occurs at $\left(\frac{1}{\sqrt{3}}, -\frac{1}{\sqrt{3}}, \frac{1}{\sqrt{3}}\right)$. The maximum value is $\sqrt{3}$.

EXAMPLE 7. Let $g(x_1, x_2, \ldots, x_n) = 0$ implicitly define a surface S in $\mathscr{R}^n$ and let $\mathbf{a} = (a_1, a_2, \ldots, a_n)$ be a fixed point. Minimizing the distance from S to $\mathbf{a}$ is the same thing as minimizing the square of the distance. Thus $\mathbf{p}$, the nearest point to $\mathbf{a}$ on S, must be among the critical points of
$$\sum_{k=1}^{n} (x_k - a_k)^2 + \lambda g(x_1, \ldots, x_n)$$
for some λ. The critical points satisfy, in addition to $g(x_1, \ldots, x_n) = 0$, the equations

$$2(x_1 - a_1) + \lambda \frac{\partial g}{\partial x_1}(x_1, \cdots, x_n) = 0$$

$$\vdots$$

$$2(x_n - a_n) + \lambda \frac{\partial g}{\partial x_n}(x_1, \cdots, x_n) = 0.$$

In vector form these equations reduce at the critical point $\mathbf{p}$ to

$$\begin{pmatrix} p_1 - a_1 \\ \vdots \\ \vdots \\ p_n - a_n \end{pmatrix} = -\frac{\lambda}{2} \begin{bmatrix} \frac{\partial g}{\partial x_1}(\mathbf{p}) \\ \vdots \\ \vdots \\ \frac{\partial g}{\partial x_n}(\mathbf{p}) \end{bmatrix},$$

where $\mathbf{p} = (p_1, \ldots, p_n)$. The vector $\mathbf{p} - \mathbf{a}$ on the left is then parallel to the normal vector to S at $\mathbf{p}$, which appears on the right side of the equation. In other words, $\mathbf{p} - \mathbf{a}$ is perpendicular to S. A two-dimensional example is illustrated in Figure 4.

If f is a differentiable real-valued function, $\mathscr{R}^n \xrightarrow{f} \mathscr{R}$, then the vector

$$\left(\frac{\partial f}{\partial x_1}(\mathbf{x}), \ldots, \frac{\partial f}{\partial x_n}(\mathbf{x}) \right) = \nabla f(\mathbf{x})$$

is called the gradient vector of f at $\mathbf{x}$. We have shown in Theorem 9.2 of Chapter 2 that *the direction of the gradient vector of f at $\mathbf{x}$ is a direction of maximum rate of increase for f at $\mathbf{x}$.*

In terms of the gradient the Lagrange condition (5) can be written

$$\nabla f(\mathbf{x}_0) + \lambda_1 \nabla G_1(\mathbf{x}_0) + \ldots + \lambda_m \nabla G_m(\mathbf{x}_0) = 0. \tag{7}$$

Furthermore, for each $i = 1, \ldots, m$, the vector

$$\nabla G_i(\mathbf{x}_0) = \left(\frac{\partial G_i}{\partial x_1}(\mathbf{x}_0), \ldots, \frac{\partial G_i}{\partial x_n}(\mathbf{x}_0) \right)$$

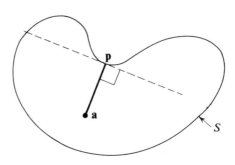

Figure 4

is perpendicular to the tangent to the surface S_i at $\mathbf{x}_0$ determined by $G_i(\mathbf{x}) = 0$. It follows that each vector $\nabla G_i(\mathbf{x}_0)$ is perpendicular to the tangent to S at $\mathbf{x}_0$, because the tangent to S is the intersection of the tangents to the S_i. Since by (7) $\nabla f(\mathbf{x}_0)$ is a linear combination of the vectors $\nabla G_i(\mathbf{x}_0)$, the gradient of f itself is perpendicular to S. In other words, if $\mathbf{x}_0$ is an extreme point of f restricted to S, the direction of greatest increase for f must be perpendicular to S.

EXAMPLE 8. The planes

$$x + y + z - 1 = 0 \quad \text{and} \quad x + y - z = 0$$

intersect in a line S as shown in Figure 5. Let $f(x, y) = xy$, and restrict f to S. Using the Lagrange method, we consider

$$xy + \lambda(x + y + z - 1) + \mu(x + y - z).$$

Its critical points occur when

$$y + \lambda + \mu = 0, \qquad x + \lambda + \mu = 0, \qquad \lambda - \mu = 0.$$

The only point that satisfies these conditions, together with the condition that it lie on S, is $\mathbf{x}_0 = (\frac{1}{4}, \frac{1}{4}, \frac{1}{2})$. We have $\nabla f(\mathbf{x}_0) = (\frac{1}{4}, \frac{1}{4}, 0)$, which is perpendicular to S. The unit vector $\mathbf{u}$ in the direction of $\nabla f(\mathbf{x}_0)$ is shown in Figure 5 with its initial point moved to $\mathbf{x}_0$.

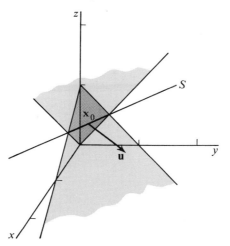

Figure 5

EXERCISES

1. Find the critical points of $x^2 + 4xy - y^2 - 8x - 6y$.   [*Ans.* (2, 1)]

2. Find the points at which the largest and smallest values are attained by the following functions.

(a) $x + y$ in the square with corners $(\pm 1, \pm 1)$.
[*Ans.* Max. $(1, 1)$, min $(-1, -1)$.]

(b) $x + y + z$ in the region $x^2 + y^2 + z^2 \leq 1$.
[*Ans.* Max. $(1/\sqrt{3}, 1/\sqrt{3}, 1/\sqrt{3})$,
min. $(-1/\sqrt{3}, -1/\sqrt{3}, -1/\sqrt{3})$.]

(c) $x^2 + 24xy + 8y^2$ in the region $x^2 + y^2 \leq 25$.
[*Ans.* Max. $\pm(3, 4)$, min. $\pm(4, -3)$.]

(d) $1/(x^2 + y^2)$ in the region $(x - 2)^2 + y^2 \leq 1$.
[*Ans.* Max $(1, 0)$, min. $(3, 0)$.]

(e) $x^2 + y^2 + (2\sqrt{2}/3)xy$ in the ellipse $x^2 + 2y^2 \leq 1$.
[*Ans.* Max. $(\pm 2/\sqrt{5}, \pm 1/\sqrt{10})$, min. $(0, 0)$.]

3. Find the point on the curve

$$\begin{pmatrix} x \\ y \\ z \end{pmatrix} = \begin{pmatrix} \cos t \\ \sin t \\ \sin t/2 \end{pmatrix}$$

that is farthest from the origin.   [*Ans.* $(-1, 0, 1)$.]

4. Find the critical points of the following functions.
(a) $x + y \sin x$.   (b) $xy + xz$.   (c) $x^2 + y^2 + z^2 - 1$.

5. Find the maximum value of the function $x(y + z)$, given that $x^2 + y^2 = 1$ and $xz = 1$.   [*Ans.* $3/2$.]

6. Find the minimum value of $x + y^2$, subject to the condition $2x^2 + y^2 = 1$.   [*Ans.* $-1/\sqrt{2}$.]

7. Let $f(x, y)$ and $g(x, y)$ be continuously differentiable, and suppose that, subject to the condition $g(x, y) = 0, f(x, y)$ attains its maximum value M at (x_0, y_0). Show that the level curve $f(x, y) = M$ is tangent to the curve $g(x, y) = 0$ at (x_0, y_0).

8. A rectangular box with no top is to have surface area 32 square units. Find the dimensions that will give it the maximum volume.

9. Find the minimum distance in $\mathcal{R}^2$ from the ellipse $x^2 + 2y^2 = 1$ to the line $x + y = 4$. [*Hint.* Treat the square of the distance as a function of four variables.]

10. (a) Find the maximum value of $x^2 + xy + y^2 + yz + z^2$, subject to the condition $x^2 + y^2 + z^2 = 1$.   [*Ans.* $1 + 1/\sqrt{2}$.]

(b) Find the maximum value of the same function subject to the conditions $x^2 + y^2 + z^2 = 1$ and $ax + by + cz = 0$, where (a, b, c) is a point at which the maximum is attained in (a).   [*Ans.* 1.]

11. Consider a differentiable function $\mathcal{R}^n \xrightarrow{f} \mathcal{R}$ and a continuously differentiable function $\mathcal{R}^n \xrightarrow{G} \mathcal{R}^m$, $m < n$. Suppose the surface S defined by $G(\mathbf{x}) = 0$ has a tangent $\mathcal{T}$ of dimension $n - m$ at $\mathbf{x}_0$, and that the function f restricted to S has an extreme value at $\mathbf{x}_0$. Show that $\mathcal{T}$ is parallel to the tangent to the surface defined explicitly by f at the point $(\mathbf{x}_0, f(\mathbf{x}_0))$.

12. (a) Find the points $\mathbf{x}_0$ at which $f(x, y) = x^2 - y^2 - y$ attains its maximum on the circle $x^2 + y^2 = 1$.   [*Ans.* $(\pm\sqrt{15}/4, -\frac{1}{4})$.]

(b) Find the directions in which f increases most rapidly at $\mathbf{x}_0$.

[*Ans.* $(\pm\sqrt{15}/4, -\tfrac{1}{4})$.]

13. The planes $x + y - z - 2w = 1$ and $x - y + z + w = 2$ intersect in a set $\mathscr{F}$ in $\mathscr{R}^4$. Find the point on $\mathscr{F}$ that is nearest to the origin.

[*Ans.* $(\tfrac{27}{19}, -\tfrac{7}{19}, \tfrac{7}{19}, -\tfrac{3}{19})$.]

14. Let $\mathbf{x}_1, \ldots, \mathbf{x}_N$ be points in $\mathscr{R}^n$, and let

$$f(\mathbf{x}) = \sum_{k=1}^{N} |\mathbf{x} - \mathbf{x}_k|^2.$$

Find the point at which f attains its minimum and find the minimum value.

15. Prove by solving an appropriate minimum problem that if $a_k > 0$, $k = 1, \ldots, n$, then

$$(a_1 \, a_2 \quad \cdots \quad a_n)^{1/n} \le \frac{a_1 + a_2 + \ldots + a_n}{n}$$

2. QUADRATIC POLYNOMIALS

Let $F(\mathbf{x}, \mathbf{y}) = \mathbf{x} \cdot \mathbf{y}$, be the euclidean dot product of two vectors $\mathbf{x}$ and $\mathbf{y}$ in $\mathscr{R}^n$. In addition to having the property $F(\mathbf{x}, \mathbf{x}) \ge 0$, the function F satisfies

$$F(\mathbf{x}, \mathbf{y}) = F(\mathbf{y}, \mathbf{x}) \tag{1}$$

$$F(\mathbf{x} + \mathbf{x}', \mathbf{y}) = F(\mathbf{x}, \mathbf{y}) + F(\mathbf{x}', \mathbf{y}) \tag{2}$$

$$F(a\mathbf{x}, \mathbf{y}) = aF(\mathbf{x}, \mathbf{y}), \tag{3}$$

where a is any real number. As a consequence of the definition of F, or of the above three properties, F is linear in the second variable also. Because of the symmetry property (1) and the linearity in both variables, a real-valued function F satisfying (1)–(3) for all pairs of vectors $\mathbf{x}$ and $\mathbf{y}$ in $\mathscr{R}^n$ is called a **symmetric bilinear function**. Such a function can be written in terms of coordinates as follows. Let $\mathbf{x} = (x_1, \ldots, x_n)$ and $\mathbf{y} = (y_1, \ldots, y_n)$. Then,

$$\mathbf{x} = \sum_{i=1}^{n} x_i \mathbf{e}_i, \qquad \mathbf{y} = \sum_{j=1}^{n} y_j \mathbf{e}_j,$$

where $\mathbf{e}_k$, $k = 1, 2, \ldots, n$, are the natural basis vectors

$$\begin{pmatrix} 1 \\ 0 \\ \cdot \\ \cdot \\ \cdot \\ 0 \end{pmatrix}, \quad \begin{pmatrix} 0 \\ 1 \\ \cdot \\ \cdot \\ \cdot \\ 0 \end{pmatrix}, \quad \cdots, \quad \begin{pmatrix} 0 \\ 0 \\ \cdot \\ \cdot \\ \cdot \\ 1 \end{pmatrix},$$

of $\mathscr{R}^n$. We have from (2) and (3)

$$F(\mathbf{x}, \mathbf{y}) = F\left(\sum_{1}^{n} x_i \mathbf{e}_i, \sum_{1}^{n} y_j \mathbf{e}_j \right) = \sum_{i=1}^{n} \sum_{j=1}^{n} F(\mathbf{e}_i, \mathbf{e}_j) x_i y_j,$$

where, by (1) $F(\mathbf{e}_i, \mathbf{e}_j) = F(\mathbf{e}_j, \mathbf{e}_i)$. Conversely, an arbitrary choice of the numbers $F(\mathbf{e}_i, \mathbf{e}_j) = a_{ij}$, consistent with $a_{ij} = a_{ji}$, determines the most general symmetric bilinear function. In summary, symmetric bilinear functions are just those that in terms of coordinates have the form

$$F(\mathbf{x}, \mathbf{y}) = \sum_{i,j=1}^{n} a_{ij} x_i y_j, \qquad a_{ij} = a_{ji}. \tag{4}$$

In particular, if $a_{ii} = 1$ and $a_{ij} = 0$ for $i \neq j$, we get our original example

$$\mathbf{x} \cdot \mathbf{y} = \sum_{i=1}^{n} x_i y_i.$$

If F is a symmetric bilinear function on $\mathscr{R}^n$, the real-valued function of a single vector defined by

$$Q(\mathbf{x}) = F(\mathbf{x}, \mathbf{x}) \quad \text{for all} \quad \mathbf{x} \text{ in } \mathscr{R}^n$$

is called a **homogeneous quadratic polynomial**, or sometimes a **quadratic form**. Thus, by definition, every Q is associated with some bilinear F, and vice versa. From (4) it follows that in coordinate form,

$$Q(\mathbf{x}) = \sum_{i,j=1}^{n} a_{ij} x_i x_j, \qquad a_{ij} = a_{ji}. \tag{5}$$

For example, if F is the euclidean dot product, we have associated with it the quadratic polynomial

$$\mathbf{x} \cdot \mathbf{x} = \sum_{i=1}^{n} x_i^2.$$

The word **homogeneous**, applied to a polynomial, means that all terms have the same degree in the coordinate variables x_i. Throughout this section the phrase "quadratic polynomial" will be understood to mean "homogeneous quadratic polynomial."

Equation (4) can be written as a matrix product as follows:

$$F(\mathbf{x}, \mathbf{y}) = (x_1 \quad x_1 \quad \ldots \quad x_n) \begin{pmatrix} a_{11} & a_{12} & \ldots & a_{1n} \\ a_{21} & & & \\ \vdots & & & \\ a_{n1} & \ldots & & a_{nn} \end{pmatrix} \begin{pmatrix} y_1 \\ y_2 \\ \vdots \\ y_n \end{pmatrix}$$

or

$$F(\mathbf{x}, \mathbf{y}) = \mathbf{x}^t A \mathbf{y} = \mathbf{x} \cdot A \mathbf{y}.$$

This follows immediately from the definition of matrix multiplication. The condition $a_{ji} = a_{ij}$ means that the matrix $A = (a_{ij})$ is symmetric about its principal diagonal.

In the matrix notation, (5) becomes

$$Q(\mathbf{x}) = \mathbf{x}^t A \mathbf{x},$$

and we have as a familiar special case

$$Q(\mathbf{x}) = \mathbf{x}^t I \mathbf{x} = \mathbf{x} \cdot \mathbf{x}.$$

In case $a_{ij} = 0$ for $i \neq j$, A is a diagonal matrix and Q is said to be represented in **diagonal form**.

EXAMPLE 1. We give some examples of quadratic polynomials.

$$(x \quad y) \begin{pmatrix} 1 & 2 \\ 2 & 4 \end{pmatrix} \begin{pmatrix} x \\ y \end{pmatrix} = x^2 + 4xy + y^2,$$

$$(x \quad y \quad z) \begin{pmatrix} 1 & 0 & 1 \\ 0 & 1 & 0 \\ 1 & 0 & 1 \end{pmatrix} \begin{pmatrix} x \\ y \\ z \end{pmatrix} = x^2 + y^2 + z^2 + 2xz,$$

$$(x_1 \quad x_2 \quad x_3 \quad x_4) \begin{pmatrix} 1 & 0 & 0 & 0 \\ 0 & 2 & 0 & 0 \\ 0 & 0 & 3 & 0 \\ 0 & 0 & 0 & 4 \end{pmatrix} \begin{pmatrix} x_1 \\ x_2 \\ x_3 \\ x_4 \end{pmatrix} = x_1^2 + 2x_2^2 + 3x_3^2 + 4x_4^2.$$

A quadratic polynomial Q is called **positive definite** if $Q(\mathbf{x}) > 0$ except for $\mathbf{x} = 0$. We remark that if Q is positive definite and F is its associated bilinear function, then F is an inner product in $\mathscr{R}^n$. This is so because (1)–(3) together with the positive definiteness condition are the characteristic properties of an inner product.

EXAMPLE 2. The graphs of two quadratic polynomials are shown in Figure 6. The one on the left is positive definite. The other one is not; its graph is called a **hyperbolic paraboloid**.

EXAMPLE 3. The quadratic polynomial

$$Q_1(x, y, z) = (x - y - z)^2 = x^2 + y^2 + z^2 - 2xy - 2xz + 2yz$$

is nonnegative. However, it is not positive definite because it is zero on the plane $x - y - z = 0$.

The polynomial

$$Q_2(x, y, z) = (x + y + z)^2 - (x - y - z)^2 = 4xy + 4xz$$

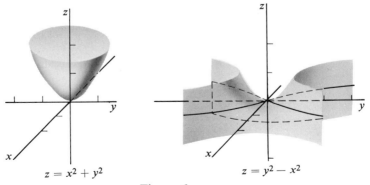

$$z = x^2 + y^2 \qquad\qquad z = y^2 - x^2$$

Figure 6

changes sign. In fact, Q_2 is negative on the plane $x + y + z = 0$ and positive on the plane $x - y - z = 0$, except along the line of intersection of the two planes, where Q_2 is zero.

The polynomial

$$Q_3(x, y, z) = x^2 + y^2$$

is nonnegative, but not positive definite, because $Q_3(0, 0, z) = 0$ for arbitrary z.

In the examples just given, we have seen illustrations of the fact that if a quadratic polynomial can be written, say, in the diagonal form

$$Q(x, y, z) = a_1 x^2 + a_2 y^2 + a_3 z^2,$$

then Q is positive definite if and only if all the coefficients a_i are positive. Furthermore, in the event that some coefficients are negative or zero, it is possible to determine regions for which Q is positive or negative. In the next examples we consider one way in which a polynomial $Q(x, y)$ can be written in diagonal form.

EXAMPLE 4. In $\mathscr{R}^2$ we get the most general symmetric bilinear function by choosing a, b, and c arbitrarily in

$$F((x, y), (x', y')) = (x \quad y) \begin{pmatrix} a & b \\ b & c \end{pmatrix} \begin{pmatrix} x' \\ y' \end{pmatrix}.$$

The general quadratic polynomial is then

$$Q(x, y) = ax^2 + 2bxy + cy^2.$$

To determine conditions under which Q is positive definite, notice first that we could not have both $a = 0$ and $c = 0$. For then $Q(x, y) = 2bxy$, and, if $b \neq 0$, this polynomial assumes both positive and negative values. Suppose then that $a \neq 0$. Completing the square, we have

$$Q(x, y) = \frac{1}{a}\left[a^2\left(x + \frac{b}{a}y\right)^2 + (ac - b^2)y^2 \right]. \tag{6}$$

Similarly, if $c \neq 0$,

$$Q(x, y) = \frac{1}{c}\left[c^2\left(y + \frac{b}{c}x\right)^2 + (ac - b^2)x^2 \right]. \tag{7}$$

We see directly that Q is positive definite if and only if $ac - b^2 > 0$ and either $a > 0$ or $c > 0$.

EXAMPLE 5. Having written Q in one of the above two forms (6) or (7), an obvious change of variable can be used to simplify the polynomial. To be specific, suppose $a \neq 0$ and that (6) holds. Letting

$$u = x + \frac{b}{a}y, \qquad v = 0x + y,$$

we can write Q in the form

$$au^2 + \frac{1}{a}(ac - b^2)v^2.$$

This transformation of coordinates corresponds to a change of basis in which the natural basis of $\mathscr{R}^2$ is replaced by the basis

$$\mathbf{x}_1 = (1, 0), \qquad \mathbf{x}_2 = \left(-\frac{b}{a}, 1\right).$$

The coordinate relations between x, y and u, v can be written in matrix form as

$$\begin{pmatrix} u \\ v \end{pmatrix} = \begin{pmatrix} 1 & \frac{b}{a} \\ 0 & 1 \end{pmatrix} \begin{pmatrix} x \\ y \end{pmatrix}, \qquad \begin{pmatrix} x \\ y \end{pmatrix} = \begin{pmatrix} 1 & -\frac{b}{a} \\ 0 & 1 \end{pmatrix} \begin{pmatrix} u \\ v \end{pmatrix}.$$

In order to see concretely the geometric significance of the choice of new basis, we consider a numerical example. Let

$$Q(\mathbf{x}) = Q(x, y) = x^2 + 2xy + 3y^2.$$

Then $a = b = 1$ and $c = 3$. The new basis consists of the vectors $x_1 = (1, 0)$ and $\mathbf{x}_2 = (-1, 1)$. With respect to the new coordinates

$$Q(\mathbf{x}) = u^2 + 2v^2.$$

where

$$\begin{pmatrix} u \\ v \end{pmatrix} = \begin{pmatrix} 1 & 1 \\ 0 & 1 \end{pmatrix} \begin{pmatrix} x \\ y \end{pmatrix}, \qquad \begin{pmatrix} x \\ y \end{pmatrix} = \begin{pmatrix} 1 & -1 \\ 0 & 1 \end{pmatrix} \begin{pmatrix} u \\ v \end{pmatrix}.$$

Clearly Q is positive definite. The vectors $\mathbf{x}_1$ and $\mathbf{x}_2$, together with the level curve $Q(\mathbf{x}) = 1$, are shown in Figure 7.

We have seen in Example 5 that a quadratic polynomial can be reduced to diagonal form by writing it in terms of the coordinates of an appropriately

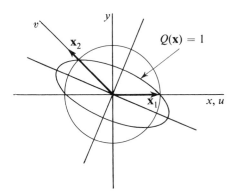

Figure 7

chosen basis. However, this was done with basis vectors that were not necessarily perpendicular. The next theorem shows that we can always find a diagonalizing basis consisting of perpendicular vectors of length 1.

2.1 Theorem. Let Q be a quadratic polynomial on $\mathscr{R}^n$. There exists an orthonormal basis $x_1, \ldots, x_n$ such that if $y_1, \ldots, y_n$ are the coordinates of a vector x with respect to this basis, then

$$Q(x) = \lambda_1 y_1^2 + \ldots + \lambda_n y_n^2.$$

As a result,

$$Q(x_k) = \lambda_k, \qquad k = 1, \ldots, n.$$

Proof. The basis vectors $x_1, \ldots, x_n$ will be chosen successively as follows. Let S^{n-1} be the set of unit vectors in $\mathscr{R}^n$, that is, the set of all x such that $|x| = 1$.* Let x_1 be a maximum point on S^{n-1} for the function Q restricted to S^{n-1}. (See the introduction to Appendix II.) By its choice, x_1 is a unit vector. Let $\mathscr{V}_{n-1}$ be the $(n-1)$-dimensional subspace of $\mathscr{R}^n$ consisting of the vectors x of $\mathscr{R}^n$ that are perpendicular to x_1, and let S^{n-2} be the unit sphere in $\mathscr{V}_{n-1}$. Restrict x to S^{n-2}, and let x_2 be a vector on S^{n-2} such that $Q(x)$ assumes its maximum, for x on S^{n-2}, at x_2. By its choice, x_2 is a unit vector perpendicular to x_1. Assuming that $x_1, \ldots, x_k$, $k < n$, have been chosen in this way, let $\mathscr{V}_{n-k}$ be the subspace of $\mathscr{R}^n$ consisting of all vectors perpendicular to $x_1, \ldots, x_k$. Let S^{n-k-1} be the unit sphere in $\mathscr{V}_{n-k}$, and let Q assume its maximum on S^{n-k-1} at the point x_{k+1}. Continue the process until n unit vectors have been chosen in this way, each perpendicular to those already chosen.

The vectors $x_1, \ldots, x_n$ clearly form an orthonormal basis for $\mathscr{R}^n$. We now show that this basis is a diagonalizing basis for Q. Since Q has a maximum at x_1 when restricted to the unit sphere $|x|^2 - 1 = 0$, by Lagrange's theorem, (Theorem 1.2), the function f defined by

$$f(x) = Q(x) - \lambda(|x|^2 - 1)$$

must have a critical point at x_1 for some λ. That is $f'(x_1) = 0$. Direct computation shows that every quadratic polynomial Q on $\mathscr{R}^n$ and its associated bilinear function F satisfy the equation

$$Q'(x)y = 2F(x, y), \qquad \text{for any } x \text{ and } y \text{ in } \mathscr{R}^n.$$

(See Exercise 10.) Hence, at the critical point x_1,

$$0 = f'(x_1)y = 2F(x_1, y) - 2\lambda x_1 \cdot y,$$

and we conclude that

$$F(x_1, y) = \lambda x_1 \cdot y, \qquad \text{for any } y \text{ in } \mathscr{R}^n.$$

*The set of all unit vectors in $\mathscr{R}^n$ is an $(n-1)$-dimensional surface implicitly defined by the equation $|x| = 1$. For this reason, we write the index $n-1$ on S^{n-1}.

It follows that

$$F(\mathbf{x}_1, \mathbf{x}_k) = 0, \qquad k = 2, \ldots, n, \qquad F(\mathbf{x}_1, \mathbf{x}_1) = \lambda = Q(\mathbf{x}_1).$$

By restricting Q to $\mathscr{V}_{n-1}$ the subspace of $\mathscr{R}^n$ perpendicular to $\mathbf{x}_1$, we can repeat the same argument and obtain

$$F(\mathbf{x}_2, \mathbf{x}_k) = 0, \qquad k = 3, \ldots, n.$$

Continuing in this way, we obtain finally

$$F(\mathbf{x}_i, \mathbf{x}_k) = 0, \qquad \text{if } i \neq k.$$

If an arbitrary vector $\mathbf{x}$ is written in terms of the basis $\mathbf{x}_1, \ldots, \mathbf{x}_n$ as $\mathbf{x} = y_1\mathbf{x}_1 + \ldots + y_n\mathbf{x}_n$, we obtain

$$Q(\mathbf{x}) = \sum_{j,k=1}^{n} F(\mathbf{x}_j, \mathbf{x}_k) y_j y_k$$

$$= \sum_{k=1}^{n} F(\mathbf{x}_k, \mathbf{x}_k) y_k^2 = \sum_{k=1}^{n} Q(\mathbf{x}_k) y_k^2.$$

This completes the proof.

A further consequence of the proof just given can be stated as follows.

2.2 **Theorem.** The basis vectors $\mathbf{x}_1, \ldots, \mathbf{x}_n$ with respect to which a quardratic polynomial Q has the form

$$Q(\mathbf{x}) = \sum_{k=1}^{n} \lambda_k y_k^2$$

can be chosen by requiring that $Q(\mathbf{x}_k)$ be the maximum value of Q restricted to the unit sphere of the subspace of $\mathscr{R}^n$ perpendicular to $\mathbf{x}_1, \mathbf{x}_2, \ldots, \mathbf{x}_{k-1}$.

The maximum value property of the basis vectors $\mathbf{x}_k$ can be used to compute them, as in the next example.

EXAMPLE 6. Suppose the quadratic polynomial

$$Q(x, y) = 3x^2 + 2xy + 3y^2$$

is expressed using the coordinates of the natural basis for $\mathscr{R}^2$. We restrict Q to the unit circle

$$x^2 + y^2 - 1 = 0.$$

By Lagrange's theorem, (Theorem 1.2), Q will have its maximum at the critical points of

$$3x^2 + 2xy + 3y^2 - \lambda(x^2 + y^2 - 1),$$

for some λ. That is, for some λ, the vector (x, y) must satisfy

$$(3 - \lambda)x + \qquad y = 0$$
$$x + (3 - \lambda)y = 0$$

in addition to $x^2 + y^2 = 1$. (λ has been replaced by $-\lambda$.) Nonzero solutions to these equations will exist only if the columns of the matrix

$$\begin{pmatrix} 3 - \lambda & 1 \\ 1 & 3 - \lambda \end{pmatrix}$$

are dependent. Since dependence is equivalent to

$$\begin{vmatrix} 3 - \lambda & 1 \\ 1 & 3 - \lambda \end{vmatrix} = 0,$$

we must have $(3 - \lambda)^2 - 1 = 0$ or $\lambda = 2, 4$. The corresponding solutions for (x, y) are

$$\lambda = 2: \quad (x, y) = \left(\pm \frac{1}{\sqrt{2}}, \mp \frac{1}{\sqrt{2}} \right).$$

$$\lambda = 4: \quad (x, y) = \left(\pm \frac{1}{\sqrt{2}}, \pm \frac{1}{\sqrt{2}} \right).$$

The maximum of Q occurs at $(\pm 1/\sqrt{2}, \pm 1/\sqrt{2})$, so we can choose $\mathbf{x}_1 = (1/\sqrt{2}, 1/\sqrt{2})$. For $\mathbf{x}_2$ we can take either of the two vectors $(\pm 1/\sqrt{2}, \mp 1/\sqrt{2})$. Let $\mathbf{x}_2 = (-1/\sqrt{2}, 1/\sqrt{2})$.

The change of coordinate equation is then

$$\begin{pmatrix} x \\ y \end{pmatrix} = \begin{pmatrix} \dfrac{1}{\sqrt{2}} & \dfrac{-1}{\sqrt{2}} \\ \dfrac{1}{\sqrt{2}} & \dfrac{1}{\sqrt{2}} \end{pmatrix} \begin{pmatrix} u \\ v \end{pmatrix}.$$

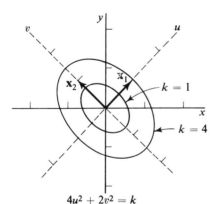

$$4u^2 + 2v^2 = k$$

Figure 8

In terms of the new variables we have

$$Q(\mathbf{x}) = 4u^2 + 2v^2.$$

In Figure 8, level curves of Q are shown in their relation to the new and to the original basis vectors.

For some purposes it is unnecessary to compute the orthonormal basis vectors $\mathbf{x}$ of Theorem 2.1 provided that the numbers λ can be found. For example, it is clear just from knowing the λ_k whether Q is positive definite or not. The following theorem enables us to compute, or estimate, the λ_k.

2.3 Theorem. Let Q be a quadratic polynomial in $\mathscr{R}^n$ given by

$$Q(\mathbf{x}) = \mathbf{x}^t A \mathbf{x},$$

where A is a symmetric matrix. Suppose that, with respect to the coordinates of the orthonormal basis $\mathbf{x}_1, \ldots, \mathbf{x}_n$, Q has the form

$$Q(\mathbf{x}) = \sum_{k=1}^{n} \lambda_k y_k^2, \tag{8}$$

where $Q(\mathbf{x}_k) = \lambda_k$. Then the numbers λ_k are the roots of the equation

$$\det(A - \lambda I) = 0. \tag{9}$$

Although the existence of the basis vectors, $\mathbf{x}_1, \ldots, \mathbf{x}_k$ has been proved in Theorem 2.1, it is not necessary to know what they are in order to find the λ_k. The λ_k can be computed by solving Equation (9). Equation (9) is called the **characteristic equation** of Q, and the roots λ_k are called **characteristic roots** or **eigenvalues**. The next theorem provides another method for computing the basis vectors $\mathbf{x}_1, \ldots, \mathbf{x}_n$.

2.4 Theorem. Let $\mathbf{z}_1, \ldots, \mathbf{z}_n$ be any orthonormal basis such that, for each $k = 1, \ldots, n$, the vector $\mathbf{z}_k$ satisfies the matrix equation

$$(A - \lambda_k I)\mathbf{z}_k = 0. \tag{10}$$

Then, with respect to this basis, Q has the diagonal form (8).

Vectors $\mathbf{z}_k$ that satisfy Equation (10) are called **characteristic vectors** or **eigenvectors corresponding to** λ_k.

Proof (of Theorem 2.3). Suppose that the orthonormal basis vectors $\mathbf{x}_1, \ldots, \mathbf{x}_n$ that diagonalize Q are

$$\mathbf{x}_1 = \begin{pmatrix} b_{11} \\ \cdot \\ \cdot \\ \cdot \\ b_{n1} \end{pmatrix}, \quad \mathbf{x}_2 = \begin{pmatrix} b_{12} \\ \cdot \\ \cdot \\ \cdot \\ b_{n2} \end{pmatrix}, \quad \cdots, \quad \mathbf{x}_n = \begin{pmatrix} b_{1n} \\ \cdot \\ \cdot \\ \cdot \\ b_{nn} \end{pmatrix}.$$

Let B be the n by n matrix with columns $\mathbf{x}_1, \ldots, \mathbf{x}_n$. According to Chapter 1, Section 10, coordinates of the same point are related by the equation $\mathbf{x} = B\mathbf{y}$, where

$$\mathbf{x} = \begin{pmatrix} x_1 \\ \cdot \\ \cdot \\ \cdot \\ x_n \end{pmatrix} \quad \text{and} \quad \mathbf{y} = \begin{pmatrix} y_1 \\ \cdot \\ \cdot \\ \cdot \\ y_n \end{pmatrix},$$

where $y_1, \ldots, y_n$ are the coordinates with respect to $\mathbf{x}_1, \ldots, \mathbf{x}_n$. Then substituting $B\mathbf{y}$ for $\mathbf{x}$ gives

$$\begin{aligned} Q(\mathbf{x}) &= (B\mathbf{y})^t A(B\mathbf{y}) \\ &= \mathbf{y}^t (B^t A B)\mathbf{y} \\ &= \mathbf{y}^t \Lambda \mathbf{y}. \end{aligned}$$

By the choice of the columns of B, the matrix $\Lambda = B^t A B$ is a diagonal matrix with diagonal entries $\lambda_1, \ldots, \lambda_n$. Furthermore, since the columns of B are the coordinates of perpendicular unit vectors with respect to an orthonormal basis, we have directly, by matrix multiplication, $B^t B = I$. In other words, $B^t = B^{-1}$. Then $\Lambda = B^{-1}AB$. Subtracting λI from both sides of this equation and factoring the right-hand member, we get

$$\Lambda - \lambda I = B^{-1}AB - \lambda I$$
$$= B^{-1}(A - \lambda I)B.$$

But $\Lambda - \lambda I$ is a diagonal matrix with diagonal entries $\lambda_k - \lambda$, so

$$(\lambda_1 - \lambda)(\lambda_2 - \lambda) \ldots (\lambda_n - \lambda) = \det (\Lambda - \lambda I)$$
$$= \det B^{-1} \det (A - \lambda I) \det B$$
$$= \det (A - \lambda I).$$

This shows that the roots of $\det (A - \lambda I) = 0$ are $\lambda_1, \ldots, \lambda_n$.

Proof (of Theorem 2.4). Let $\mathbf{z}_1, \ldots, \mathbf{z}_n$ be an orthonormal basis satisfying $A\mathbf{z}_k = \lambda_k \mathbf{z}_k$, for $k = 1, 2, \ldots, n$. Let C be the matrix with columns $\mathbf{z}_1, \mathbf{z}_2, \ldots, \mathbf{z}_n$. The equation

$$\mathbf{x} = C\mathbf{z}$$

gives the relation between the coordinates of the basis $\mathbf{z}_1, \ldots, \mathbf{z}_n$ in $\mathscr{R}^n$ and the natural coordinates. Then

$$Q(\mathbf{x}) = \mathbf{x}^t A \mathbf{x} = (C\mathbf{z})^t A (C\mathbf{z}) = \mathbf{z}^t (C^t A C)\mathbf{z}.$$

All we have to do is verify that the matrix $C^t A C$ is diagonal with diagonal entries $\lambda_1, \ldots, \lambda_n$. Schematically, we write

$$C^t A C = \begin{pmatrix} \mathbf{z}_1^t \\ \cdot \\ \cdot \\ \cdot \\ \mathbf{z}_n^t \end{pmatrix} A(\mathbf{z}_1 \quad \ldots \quad \mathbf{z}_n)$$

$$= \begin{pmatrix} \mathbf{z}_1^t \\ \cdot \\ \cdot \\ \cdot \\ \mathbf{z}_n^t \end{pmatrix} (A\mathbf{z}_1 \quad \ldots \quad A\mathbf{z}_n)$$

$$= \begin{pmatrix} \mathbf{z}_1^t \\ \cdot \\ \cdot \\ \cdot \\ \mathbf{z}_n^t \end{pmatrix} (\lambda_1 \mathbf{z}_1 \quad \ldots \quad \lambda_n \mathbf{z}_n).$$

Using the fact that

$$\mathbf{z}_i^t \mathbf{z}_j = \mathbf{z}_i \cdot \mathbf{z}_j = \begin{cases} 1, & \text{if } i = j, \\ 0, & \text{if } i \neq j, \end{cases}$$

we get

$$C^t A C = \begin{pmatrix} \lambda_1 & 0 & \cdots & 0 \\ 0 & \lambda_2 & & \cdot \\ \cdot & & & \cdot \\ \cdot & & & \cdot \\ 0 & & \cdots & \lambda_n \end{pmatrix}.$$

This completes the proof.

EXAMPLE 7. Let $Q(x, y, z) = xy + yz + zx$. The matrix of Q is

$$\begin{pmatrix} 0 & \frac{1}{2} & \frac{1}{2} \\ \frac{1}{2} & 0 & \frac{1}{2} \\ \frac{1}{2} & \frac{1}{2} & 0 \end{pmatrix}$$

and the characteristic equation is

$$\begin{vmatrix} -\lambda & \frac{1}{2} & \frac{1}{2} \\ \frac{1}{2} & -\lambda & \frac{1}{2} \\ \frac{1}{2} & \frac{1}{2} & -\lambda \end{vmatrix} = 0$$

or

$$-\lambda^3 + \tfrac{3}{4}\lambda + \tfrac{1}{4} = 0.$$

The characteristic roots are $\lambda = 1, -\frac{1}{2}, -\frac{1}{2}$. So there is an orthonormal system of coordinates (u, v, w) with respect to which Q has the form

$$u^2 - \tfrac{1}{2}v^2 - \tfrac{1}{2}w^2.$$

To find the related basis vectors we look for the unit vector solutions of the equations

$$\begin{pmatrix} -\lambda & \frac{1}{2} & \frac{1}{2} \\ \frac{1}{2} & -\lambda & \frac{1}{2} \\ \frac{1}{2} & \frac{1}{2} & -\lambda \end{pmatrix} \begin{pmatrix} x \\ y \\ z \end{pmatrix} = 0,$$

with $\lambda = 1$ and $\lambda = -\frac{1}{2}$. With $\lambda = 1$ we get $x = y = z$ for a solution, so we can choose $\mathbf{x}_1 = (1/\sqrt{3}, 1/\sqrt{3}, 1/\sqrt{3})$. When $\lambda = -\frac{1}{2}$, the matrix equation simply requires that the two remaining basis vectors lie in the plane $x + y + z = 0$, perpendicular to $\mathbf{x}_1$. Then $\mathbf{x}_2$ and $\mathbf{x}_3$ can be chosen to be arbitrary perpendicular vectors in that plane, for example,

$$\left(\frac{1}{\sqrt{2}}, -\frac{1}{\sqrt{2}}, 0\right) \quad \text{and} \quad \left(\frac{1}{\sqrt{6}}, \frac{1}{\sqrt{6}}, -\frac{2}{\sqrt{6}}\right).$$

A level surface of a quadratic polynomial is called a **quadratic surface**. Since every quadratic polynomial can be diagonalized with respect to some orthonormal basis, it is sufficient to be able to picture the level surfaces of

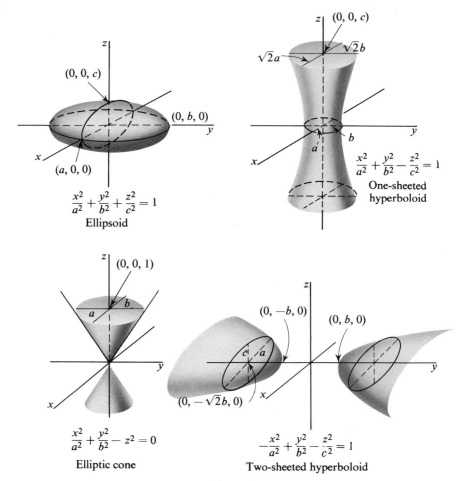

$$\frac{x^2}{a^2} + \frac{y^2}{b^2} + \frac{z^2}{c^2} = 1$$
Ellipsoid

$$\frac{x^2}{a^2} + \frac{y^2}{b^2} - \frac{z^2}{c^2} = 1$$
One-sheeted
hyperboloid

$$\frac{x^2}{a^2} + \frac{y^2}{b^2} - z^2 = 0$$
Elliptic cone

$$-\frac{x^2}{a^2} + \frac{y^2}{b^2} - \frac{z^2}{c^2} = 1$$
Two-sheeted hyperboloid

Figure 9

some standard quadratic polynomials in order to be able to picture a more general quadratic suface. Figure 9 shows some illustrations of quadratic surfaces in $\mathcal{R}^3$.

EXAMPLE 8. The quadratic polynomial $xy + yz$ can be represented by a symmetric matrix as

$$xy + yz = (x \ \ y \ \ z)\begin{pmatrix} 0 & \frac{1}{2} & 0 \\ \frac{1}{2} & 0 & \frac{1}{2} \\ 0 & \frac{1}{2} & 0 \end{pmatrix}\begin{pmatrix} x \\ y \\ z \end{pmatrix}.$$

The characteristic equation is $-\lambda^3 + \frac{1}{2}\lambda = 0$, and this equation has roots $\lambda = 1/\sqrt{2}, 0, -1/\sqrt{2}$. The corresponding characteristic vector equations, together with their unit vector solutions, are as follows:

$$\lambda = \frac{1}{\sqrt{2}}: \quad \begin{pmatrix} -\dfrac{1}{\sqrt{2}} & \dfrac{1}{2} & 0 \\[2mm] \dfrac{1}{2} & -\dfrac{1}{\sqrt{2}} & \dfrac{1}{2} \\[2mm] 0 & \dfrac{1}{2} & -\dfrac{1}{\sqrt{2}} \end{pmatrix} \begin{pmatrix} x \\ y \\ z \end{pmatrix} = 0,$$

$$(x, y, z) = \pm\left(\frac{1}{2}, \frac{1}{\sqrt{2}}, \frac{1}{2}\right)$$

$$\lambda = 0: \quad \begin{pmatrix} 0 & \dfrac{1}{2} & 0 \\[2mm] \dfrac{1}{2} & 0 & \dfrac{1}{2} \\[2mm] 0 & \dfrac{1}{2} & 0 \end{pmatrix} \begin{pmatrix} x \\ y \\ z \end{pmatrix} = 0, \quad (x, y, z) = \pm\left(\frac{1}{\sqrt{2}}, 0, -\frac{1}{\sqrt{2}}\right)$$

$$\lambda = -\frac{1}{\sqrt{2}}: \quad \begin{pmatrix} \dfrac{1}{\sqrt{2}} & \dfrac{1}{2} & 0 \\[2mm] \dfrac{1}{2} & \dfrac{1}{\sqrt{2}} & \dfrac{1}{2} \\[2mm] 0 & \dfrac{1}{2} & \dfrac{1}{\sqrt{2}} \end{pmatrix} \begin{pmatrix} x \\ y \\ z \end{pmatrix} = 0,$$

$$(x, y, z) = \pm\left(\frac{1}{2}, -\frac{1}{\sqrt{2}}, \frac{1}{2}\right).$$

We choose the diagonalizing basis

$$\mathbf{x}_1 = \left(\frac{1}{2}, \frac{1}{\sqrt{2}}, \frac{1}{2}\right), \quad \mathbf{x}_2 = \left(\frac{1}{\sqrt{2}}, 0, -\frac{1}{\sqrt{2}}\right), \quad \mathbf{x}_3 = \left(\frac{1}{2}, -\frac{1}{\sqrt{2}}, \frac{1}{2}\right).$$

If u, v, and w are the coordinates with respect to the new basis, then the polynomial will have the form $(1/\sqrt{2})u^2 - (1/\sqrt{2})w^2$. The level surface

$$\frac{1}{\sqrt{2}}u^2 - \frac{1}{\sqrt{2}}w^2 = 1$$

is the hyperbolic cylinder one sheet of which is shown in Figure 10.

Homogeneous polynomials of degree $N > 2$ can be defined in very much the same way as quadratic polynomials. We can start with a real-valued function $F(\mathbf{x}_1, \ldots, \mathbf{x}_N)$ that is symmetric in its N vector variables, and linear in each of them, and defined for every N vectors $\mathbf{x}_1, \ldots, \mathbf{x}_N$. Then

$$P(\mathbf{x}) = F(\mathbf{x}, \mathbf{x}, \ldots, \mathbf{x})$$

will be a polynomial of degree N. Alternatively, we can consider functions of $\mathbf{x} = (x_1, x_2, \ldots, x_n)$ having the form

$$P(\mathbf{x}) = \sum_{i_1, \ldots, i_N = 1}^{n} a_{i_1 \cdots i_N} x_{i_1} \cdots x_{i_N},$$

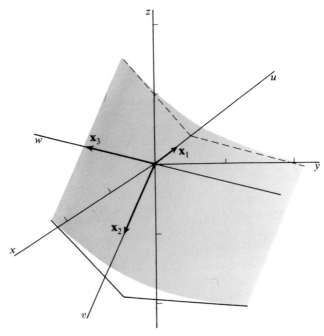

Figure 10

where the coefficients $a_{i_1 \cdots i_N}$ are symmetric in the subscripts. In both cases we get the same class of functions. The symmetry condition on the coefficients or on F is a convenience, and if it were not assumed, it could be obtained simply by averaging the nonsymmetric coefficients. The details are left as an exercise (Exercise 12).

EXERCISES

1. By changing coordinates, write each of the following quadratic polynomials as a sum of squares. In each problem exhibit an orthonormal basis that does the job, and write the coordinate transformation.

   (a) $3x^2 + 2\sqrt{2}\,xy + 4y^2$.

   $$\left[Ans.\ Q(\mathbf{x}) = 2u^2 + 5v^2;\ \mathbf{x}_1 = \left(\frac{\sqrt{2}}{\sqrt{3}}, -\frac{1}{\sqrt{3}} \right),\ \mathbf{x}_2 = \left(\frac{1}{\sqrt{3}}, \frac{\sqrt{2}}{\sqrt{3}} \right). \right]$$

   (b) $3x^2 + 2\sqrt{3}\,xy + 5y^2$.

   $$\left[Ans.\ Q(\mathbf{x}) = 2u^2 + 6v^2;\ \mathbf{x}_1 = \left(-\frac{\sqrt{3}}{2}, \frac{1}{2} \right),\ \mathbf{x}_2 = \left(\frac{1}{2}, \frac{\sqrt{3}}{2} \right). \right]$$

   (c) $(x \quad y)\begin{pmatrix} 2 & 2 \\ 2 & 5 \end{pmatrix}\begin{pmatrix} x \\ y \end{pmatrix}$.

(d) $2x^2 - 5xy + 2y^2 - 2xz - 4z^2 - 2yz$.

$$\left[\text{Ans. } Q(\mathbf{x}) = \frac{9}{2}u^2 - \frac{9}{2}v^2 + 0w^2; \qquad \mathbf{x}_1 = \left(\frac{1}{\sqrt{2}}, -\frac{1}{\sqrt{2}}, 0\right),\right.$$
$$\left.\mathbf{x}_2 = \left(\frac{1}{3\sqrt{2}}, \frac{1}{3\sqrt{2}}, \frac{4}{3\sqrt{2}}\right), \qquad \mathbf{x}_3 = \left(\frac{2}{3}, \frac{2}{3}, -\frac{1}{3}\right).\right]$$

(e) $(x \quad y \quad z) \begin{pmatrix} -1 & 2 & 0 \\ 2 & 0 & 2 \\ 0 & 2 & 1 \end{pmatrix} \begin{pmatrix} x \\ y \\ z \end{pmatrix}$.

2. (a) For each polynomial Q in Exercise 1, find the maximum of Q when Q is restricted to the unit sphere, $|\mathbf{x}| = 1$, of the euclidean space on which Q is defined. [*Hint*. See Theorem 2.2.]

   (b) Find the maximum of the polynomial in 1 (a), restricted to the circle $x^2 + y^2 = 3$. [*Ans.* 15].

3. Classify the following quadratic polynomials as positive definite, negative definite, or neither. Give reasons. (Q is **negative definite** if $Q < 0$ except for $Q(0) = 0$.)

   (a) $2x^2 - 7xy + 5y^2$.   [*Ans.* Neither.]

   (b) $2x^2 - 3xy + 5y^2$.   [*Ans.* Positive definite.]

   (c) $-x^2 + 2xy - 6y^2$.   [*Ans.* Negative definite.]

   (d) $3x^2 + xy + 3y^2 + 5z^2$.   [*Ans.* Positive definite.]

   (e) $(x \quad y \quad z) \begin{pmatrix} 1 & 3 & 0 \\ 3 & 1 & 1 \\ 0 & 1 & 3 \end{pmatrix} \begin{pmatrix} x \\ y \\ z \end{pmatrix}$.

                                                                 [*Ans.* Neither.]

4. Prove that $x^2 + y^2 + z^2 - xy - xz - yz$ is not positive definite, but becomes so when restricted to the plane $x + y + z = 0$.

5. Sketch the level curves $Q(\mathbf{x}) = 1$ and $Q(\mathbf{x}) = 0$ for each of the following polynomials in $\mathscr{R}^2$.

   (a) xy.   (b) $x^2 + xy + y^2$.   (c) $x^2 + xy - 2y^2$.

6. Sketch the level surfaces $Q(\mathbf{x}) = 1$ and $Q(\mathbf{x}) = 0$ for the following polynomials in $\mathscr{R}^3$.

   (a) $x^2 - xy + y^2 + z^2$.   (b) $x^2 + xy$.   (c) $x^2 - 2xy + y^2 - z^2$.

7. Show that every quadratic polynomial Q satisfies

$$Q(a\mathbf{x}) = a^2 Q(\mathbf{x}),$$

   for every real number a.

8. Let Q be an arbitrary quadratic polynomial on $\mathscr{R}^n$, and F its associated symmetric bilinear function. Prove that

$$F(\mathbf{x}, \mathbf{y}) = \tfrac{1}{2}[Q(\mathbf{x} + \mathbf{y}) - Q(\mathbf{x}) - Q(\mathbf{y})],$$

for all vectors $\mathbf{x}$ and $\mathbf{y}$ in $\mathscr{R}^n$. This equation proves that F is uniquely determined by Q.

9. Prove that every quadratic polynomial Q on $\mathscr{R}^n$ is a continuous function.

10. Let Q be an arbitrary quadratic polynomial on $\mathscr{R}^n$, and F its associated symmetric bilinear function, that is, $Q(\mathbf{x}) = F(\mathbf{x}, \mathbf{x})$. Prove that Q is a differentiable vector function, or more explicitly, that

$$Q'(\mathbf{x})\mathbf{y} = 2F(\mathbf{x}, \mathbf{y}).$$

11. Prove that every quadratic polynomial Q is a continuously differentiable function.

12. What follows illustrates the fact that the condition of symmetry on a bilinear function can be obtained by averaging out the nonsymmetry. Let G be a real-valued function defined for all pairs of vectors $\mathbf{x}$ and $\mathbf{y}$ and linear in each variable (we do *not* assume symmetry). Show that the function F defined by

$$F(\mathbf{x}, \mathbf{y}) = \tfrac{1}{2}(G(\mathbf{x}, \mathbf{y}) + G(\mathbf{y}, \mathbf{x}))$$

is a symmetric bilinear function. Show that $G(\mathbf{x}, \mathbf{x}) = F(\mathbf{x}, \mathbf{x})$, and hence that G and F define the same quadratic polynomial.

13. Let Q be a quadratic polynomial on $\mathscr{R}^n$. Prove that there exists a basis $(\mathbf{x}_1, \ldots, \mathbf{x}_n)$ for $\mathscr{R}^n$ such that, for any vector $\mathbf{x} = y_1\mathbf{x}_1 + \ldots + y_n\mathbf{x}_n$,

$$Q(\mathbf{x}) = \sum_{i=1}^n \lambda_i y_i^2, \quad \text{with } \lambda_i = 0, 1, \text{ or } -1.$$

14. Prove that if Q is a positive-definite quadratic polynomial on $\mathscr{R}^n$, there exists a positive real number m such that

$$Q(\mathbf{x}) \geq m|\mathbf{x}|^2, \quad \text{for all } \mathbf{x} \text{ in } \mathscr{R}^n.$$

[*Suggestion.* Diagonalize Q.] A corollary is that the values of Q on the unit sphere $|\mathbf{x}| = 1$ are bounded away from zero.

15. Let Q be a positive-definite quadratic polynomial in $\mathscr{R}^2$, and let λ_1 and λ_2 be its characteristic roots. Show that $\lambda_1^{-1/2}$ and $\lambda_2^{-1/2}$ are the lengths of the principal axes of the ellipse $Q(\mathbf{x}) = 1$.

16. Verify that if $a \neq 0$ and $ab - f^2 \neq 0$,

$$(x \ \ y \ \ z)\begin{pmatrix} a & f & e \\ f & b & d \\ e & d & c \end{pmatrix}\begin{pmatrix} x \\ y \\ z \end{pmatrix} = a\left(x + \frac{f}{a}y + \frac{e}{a}z\right)^2$$

$$+ \frac{\begin{vmatrix} a & f \\ f & b \end{vmatrix}}{a}\left(y + \frac{\begin{vmatrix} a & f \\ e & d \end{vmatrix}}{\begin{vmatrix} a & f \\ f & b \end{vmatrix}}z\right)^2 + \frac{\begin{vmatrix} a & f & e \\ f & b & d \\ e & d & c \end{vmatrix}}{\begin{vmatrix} a & f \\ f & b \end{vmatrix}}z^2.$$

Conclude that the above polynomial is positive definite if and only if the three determinants are positive:

$$\begin{vmatrix} a & f & e \\ f & b & d \\ e & d & c \end{vmatrix}.$$

What is the condition for negative definiteness? The criterion can be extended to quadratic polynomials in $\mathscr{R}^n$. See R. M. Thrall and L. Tornheim, *Vector Spaces and Matrices*, Wiley, 1957, p. 170.

17. Show that the linear transformation $\mathscr{R}^n \xrightarrow{L} \mathscr{R}^n$ determined by a symmetric matrix A has the property that

$$L(\mathbf{x}) \cdot \mathbf{y} = \mathbf{x} \cdot L(\mathbf{y})$$

for all $\mathbf{x}$ and $\mathbf{y}$ in $\mathscr{R}^n$. Conversely, show that if this equation is satisfied, then A is a symmetric matrix.

18. A transformation $\mathscr{R}^n \xrightarrow{L} \mathscr{R}^n$ for which the equation in Exercise 17 holds is called a symmetric transformation. Show that for a given symmetric transformation there is an orthonormal basis such that with respect to this basis the matrix of the transformation is diagonal.

19. (a) Give a geometric description of the action on $\mathscr{R}^3$ of the symmetric transformations with matrices

$$\begin{pmatrix} \lambda_1 & 0 & 0 \\ 0 & 1 & 0 \\ 0 & 0 & 1 \end{pmatrix}, \quad \begin{pmatrix} 1 & 0 & 0 \\ 0 & \lambda_2 & 0 \\ 0 & 0 & 1 \end{pmatrix}, \quad \text{and} \quad \begin{pmatrix} 1 & 0 & 0 \\ 0 & 1 & 0 \\ 0 & 0 & \lambda_3 \end{pmatrix}.$$

(b) Use the result of Exercise 18 to give a geometric description of the action of a symmetric transformation in $\mathscr{R}^3$.

20. The proof of Theorem 2.1 works just as well when the euclidean inner product is replaced by an arbitrary one. Use this fact to prove the following theorem: If Q_1 and Q_2 are quadratic polynomials in $\mathscr{R}^n$, and Q_1 is positive definite, then there is an orthonormal basis for $\mathscr{R}^n$ with respect to which Q_1 and Q_2 both have diagonal form.

21. Prove the converse of Theorem 2.4, namely, that if $\mathbf{x}_1, \ldots, \mathbf{x}_n$ is an orthonormal diagonalizing basis for $Q(\mathbf{x}) = \mathbf{x}^t A \mathbf{x}$, then $(A - \lambda_k I)\mathbf{x}_k = 0$, where $\lambda_k = Q(\mathbf{x}_k)$.

3. TAYLOR EXPANSIONS

We begin by reviewing the definition and the simplest properties of the Taylor expansion for functions of one variable. If $f(x)$ has an Nth derivative at x_0, its **Taylor expansion of degree N about x_0** is the polynomial

$$f(x_0) + \frac{1}{1!}f'(x_0)(x - x_0) + \frac{1}{2!}f''(x_0)(x - x_0)^2$$

$$+ \ldots + \frac{1}{N!}f^{(N)}(x_0)(x - x_0)^N.$$

The relation between f and its Taylor expansion can be expressed conveniently by the following **integral remainder formula**.

3.1 Theorem. If f has a continuous Nth derivative in a neighborhood of x_0, then in that neighborhood

$$f(x) = f(x_0) + \frac{1}{1!}f'(x_0)(x - x_0) + \ldots + \frac{1}{N!}f^{(N)}(x_0)(x - x_0)^N + R_N,$$

$$(1)$$

where

$$R_N = \frac{1}{(N-1)!} \int_{x_0}^{x} (x - t)^{N-1} [f^{(N)}(t) - f^{(N)}(x_0)] \, dt.$$

Proof. The remainder can be written as the difference

$$R_N = \frac{1}{(N-1)!} \int_{x_0}^{x} (x - t)^{N-1} f^{(N)}(t) \, dt - \frac{f^{(N)}(x_0)}{(N-1)!} \int_{x_0}^{x} (x - t)^{N-1} dt.$$

The second of these integrals is directly computed to be

$$\frac{1}{N!} f^{(N)}(x_0)(x - x_0)^N,$$

which is just the last term of the Taylor expansion. The first integral can be integrated by parts to give

$$\frac{1}{(N-2)!} \int_{x_0}^{x} (x - t)^{N-2} [f^{(N-1)}(t) - f^{(N-1)}(x_0)] \, dt = R_{N-1}.$$

We therefore obtain

$$R_N = -\frac{1}{N!} f^{(N)}(x_0)(x - x_0)^N + R_{N-1}.$$

If we substitute the preceding equation into (1), we get (1) back again with N replaced by $N - 1$. The induction is completed by noticing that for $N = 1$, Equation (1) is just

$$f(x) = f(x_0) + f'(x_0)(x - x_0) + \int_{x_0}^{x} [f'(t) - f'(x_0)] \, dt,$$

and that this is a valid equation.

It follows from the remainder formula that a polynomial of degree N is equal to its Taylor expansion of degree N. For if f is of degree N, $f^{(N)}$ is a constant function and so the remainder is identically zero. We list some common examples. It is only in the first one that we have equality. The expansions are all about $x = 0$.

$$(1 + x)^N = \sum_{k=0}^{N} \binom{N}{k} x^k,$$

$$\frac{1}{(1 - x)^M}: \quad \sum_{k=0}^{N} \binom{M + k - 1}{M - 1} x^k,$$

$$e^x: \quad 1 + \frac{1}{1!}x + \frac{1}{2!}x^2 + \ldots + \frac{1}{N!}x^N,$$

$$\log(1 - x): \quad -x - \frac{1}{2}x^2 - \frac{1}{3}x^3 - \ldots - \frac{1}{N}x^N, \tag{2}$$

$$\cos x: \quad 1 - \frac{x^2}{2!} + \frac{x^4}{4!} - \ldots + (-1)^k \frac{x^{2k}}{(2k)!},$$

$$\sin x: \quad x - \frac{x^3}{3!} + \frac{x^5}{5!} - \ldots + (-1)^k \frac{x^{2k+1}}{(2k + 1)!}.$$

Figure 11 shows the graphical relationship between the functions e^x and $\cos x$, and their second-degree Taylor expansions.

For a function $f(x, y)$ of two variables having continuous Nth-order partial derivatives in a neighborhood of (x_0, y_0) the **Taylor expansion of degree N about** (x_0, y_0) is the polynomial

$$f(x_0, y_0) + \frac{1}{1!}((x - x_0)f_x(x_0, y_0) + (y - y_0)f_y(x_0, y_0))$$

$$+ \frac{1}{2!}((x - x_0)^2 f_{xx}(x_0, y_0) + 2(x - x_0)(y - y_0)f_{xy}(x_0, y_0)$$

$$+ (y - y_0)^2 f_{yy}(x_0, y_0)) \tag{3}$$

$$\vdots$$

$$+ \frac{1}{N!} \sum_{k=0}^{N} \binom{N}{k} (x - x_0)^k (y - y_0)^{N-k} f_{x^k y^{N-k}}(x_0, y_0).$$

EXAMPLE 1. Let $f(x, y) = \sqrt{1 + x^2 + y^2}$. To expand about $(0, 0)$ through the second degree, we compute

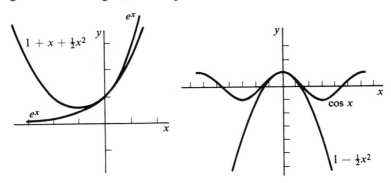

Figure 11

$$f_x(0, 0) = f_y(0, 0) = 0,$$
$$f_{xx}(0, 0) = f_{yy}(0, 0) = 1 \quad \text{and} \quad f_{xy}(0, 0) = 0.$$

Then Formula (3) reduces to the second-degree polynomial $1 + \frac{1}{2}(x^2 + y^2)$. The graphs of f and its second-degree Taylor expansion are shown in Figure 12.

To simplify the writing of the terms of the Taylor expansion, we can use the following notation. The differential operator

$$\left(x\frac{\partial}{\partial x} + y\frac{\partial}{\partial y} \right)$$

applied to f and evaluated at $\mathbf{x}_0 = (x_0, y_0)$ is by definition the first-degree polynomial

$$(d_{\mathbf{x}_0} f)\binom{x}{y} = \left(x\frac{\partial}{\partial x} + y\frac{\partial}{\partial y} \right)_{\mathbf{x}_0} f = x\frac{\partial f}{\partial x}(\mathbf{x}_0) + y\frac{\partial f}{\partial y}(\mathbf{x}_0).$$

Differentials of order k, $k > 1$, can also be defined. They are homogeneous polynomials of degree k. If f has the required derivatives, the definition is

$$(d_{\mathbf{x}_0}^k f)\binom{x}{y} = \left(x\frac{\partial}{\partial x} + y\frac{\partial}{\partial y} \right)_{\mathbf{x}_0}^k f$$
$$= \sum_{j=0}^{k} \binom{k}{j} x^j y^{k-j} \frac{\partial^k f}{\partial x^j \partial y^{k-j}}(\mathbf{x}_0).$$

Here the operator

$$\left(x\frac{\partial}{\partial x} + y\frac{\partial}{\partial y} \right)^k$$

has been multiplied out according to the binomial expansion. The operator is applied to f, and the partial derivatives are then evaluated at $\mathbf{x}_0 = (x_0, y_0)$. Notice that x and y are the only variables that appear in the preceding equation, since

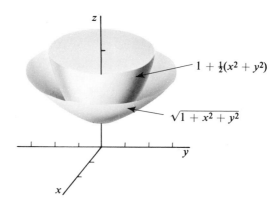

$$1 + \frac{1}{2}(x^2 + y^2)$$

$$\sqrt{1 + x^2 + y^2}$$

Figure 12

$$\binom{k}{j}\frac{\partial^k f}{\partial x^j \partial y^{k-j}}(\mathbf{x}_0)$$

is a constant for a fixed $\mathbf{x}_0$. The Nth-degree Taylor expansion of f at $\mathbf{x}_0$ can now be written

$$f(x_0, y_0) + \frac{1}{1!}(d_{\mathbf{x}_0}f)\binom{x - x_0}{y - y_0} + \ldots + \frac{1}{N!}(d_{\mathbf{x}_0}^N f)\binom{x - x_0}{y - y_0}.$$

EXAMPLE 2. If $f(x, y) = x^2 e^y$, then the differential of order 3 at $(1, 1)$ evaluated at $(x - 1, y - 1)$ is the polynomial

$$(d_{(1,1)}^3 f)\binom{x - 1}{y - 1} = \left((x - 1)\frac{\partial}{\partial x} + (y - 1)\frac{\partial}{\partial y}\right)^3_{(1,1)} f$$

$$= (x - 1)^3 \frac{\partial^3 f}{\partial x^3}(1, 1) + 3(x - 1)^2 (y - 1)\frac{\partial^3 f}{\partial x^2 \partial y}(1, 1)$$

$$+ 3(x - 1)(y - 1)^2 \frac{\partial^3 f}{\partial x \partial y^2}(1, 1) + (y - 1)^3 \frac{\partial^3 f}{\partial y^3}(1, 1).$$

EXAMPLE 3. When the polynomial $(x_1 + x_2 + \ldots + x_n)^N$ is multiplied out, each term will consist of a constant times a factor of the form $x_1^{k_1} x_2^{k_2} \ldots x_n^{k_n}$ where the nonnegative integers k_i satisfy $k_1 + \ldots + k_n = N$. The **multinomial expansion** has the form

$$(x_1 + \ldots + x_n)^N = \sum_{k_1 + \cdots + k_n = N} \binom{N}{k_1 \ldots k_n} x_1^{k_1} \ldots x_n^{k_n}.$$

The **multinomial coefficients** can be computed to be

$$\binom{N}{k_1 \ldots k_n} = \frac{N!}{k_1! \ldots k_n!}.$$

This computation will be done later using Taylor's theorem (Theorem 3.2). The coefficients can also be computed by counting.*

For a function of n variables, the kth-**order differential at** $\mathbf{x}_0 = (a_1, \ldots, a_n)$ is defined to be the following polynomial in $\mathbf{x} = (x_1, \ldots, x_n)$:

$$d_{\mathbf{x}_0}^k f(\mathbf{x}) = \left(x_1 \frac{\partial}{\partial x_1} + \ldots + x_n \frac{\partial}{\partial x_n}\right)^k_{\mathbf{x}_0} f$$

$$= \sum_{k_1 + \cdots + k_n = k} \binom{k}{k_1 \ldots k_n} x_1^{k_1} \ldots x_n^{k_n} \frac{\partial^k f}{\partial x_1^{k_1} \ldots \partial x_n^{k_n}}(a_1, \ldots, a_n).$$

In terms of differentials the Taylor expansion about $\mathbf{x}_0$ is defined to be

$$f(\mathbf{x}_0) + \frac{1}{1!}(d_{\mathbf{x}_0}f)(\mathbf{x} - \mathbf{x}_0) + \frac{1}{2!}(d_{\mathbf{x}_0}^2 f)(\mathbf{x} - \mathbf{x}_0)$$

$$+ \ldots + \frac{1}{N!}(d_{\mathbf{x}_0}^N f)(\mathbf{x} - \mathbf{x}_0).$$

*See Kemeny, Snell, Thompson, *Finite Mathematics*, Prentice-Hall, 1966, p. 109.

The function $d_{\mathbf{x}_0} f$ is exactly the same as the differential defined in Section 7 of Chapter 2. For completeness we can also define the 0th differential by

$$(d^0_{\mathbf{x}_0} f)(\mathbf{x}) = f(\mathbf{x}_0).$$

EXAMPLE 4. The second-degree Taylor expansion of $e^{x_1 + \cdots + x_n}$ about $\mathbf{x} = 0$ is

$$1 + \frac{1}{1!}\left(x_1 \frac{\partial}{\partial x_1} + \cdots + x_n \frac{\partial}{\partial x_n}\right)_0 f + \frac{1}{2!}\left(x_1 \frac{\partial}{\partial x_1} + \cdots + x_n \frac{\partial}{\partial x_n}\right)_0^2 f$$

$$= 1 + \frac{1}{1!}(x_1 + \cdots + x_n) + \frac{1}{2!}(x_1^2 + 2x_1 x_2 + \cdots + x_2^2 + \cdots + x_n^2).$$

According to the preceding paragraphs the Taylor expansion of a function f is defined in such a way that the coefficients of the polynomial can be computed in a routine manner from the derivatives of f. The Taylor expansion is important because it provides a polynomial approximation to f near $\mathbf{x}_0$ that exhibits in a simple way many of the characteristics of f near $\mathbf{x}_0$. Furthermore, as higher-degree terms are included in the expansion, the approximation gets better. Consider first the one-variable case. The expansion

$$f(x_0) + \frac{1}{1!} f'(x_0)(x - x_0) = f(x_0) + d_{x_0} f(x - x_0)$$

is the affine approximation to f provided by $d_{x_0} f$. In other words, as x approaches x_0,

$$f(x) - f(x_0) - f'(x_0)(x - x_0)$$

tends to zero faster than $x - x_0$.

Having found a first-degree approximation, we now ask for one of the second-degree. Indeed, the next theorem shows that the desired approximation is the second-degree Taylor expansion and that as x approaches x_0,

$$f(x) - f(x_0) - \frac{1}{1!} f'(x_0)(x - x_0) - \frac{1}{2!} f''(x_0)(x - x_0)^2$$

tends to zero faster than $(x - x_0)^2$. For a function of two variables, the first-degree Taylor expansion can be written

$$f(x_0, y_0) + \frac{1}{1!}\left(\frac{\partial f}{\partial x}(x_0, y_0)(x - x_0) + \frac{\partial f}{\partial y}(x_0, y_0)(y - y_0)\right)$$

$$= f(x_0, y_0) + (d_{\binom{x_0}{y_0}} f)\binom{x - x_0}{y - y_0}$$

and so is just the affine approximation to f provided by the differential. We shall see that to find a second-degree approximation of a similar kind we need to take the second-degree Taylor expansion. The complete statement follows.

3.2 Taylor's theorem. Let $\mathcal{R}^n \xrightarrow{f} \mathcal{R}$ have all derivatives of order N continuous in a neighborhood of $\mathbf{x}_0$. Let $T_N(\mathbf{x} - \mathbf{x}_0)$ be the Nth-degree Taylor expansion of f about $\mathbf{x}_0$. That is,

$$T_N(\mathbf{x} - \mathbf{x}_0) = f(\mathbf{x}_0) + (d_{\mathbf{x}_0} f)(\mathbf{x} - \mathbf{x}_0) + \dots + \frac{1}{N!}(d_{\mathbf{x}_0}^N f)(\mathbf{x} - \mathbf{x}_0).$$

Then

$$\lim_{\mathbf{x} \to \mathbf{x}_0} \frac{(f(\mathbf{x}) - T_N(\mathbf{x} - \mathbf{x}_0))}{|\mathbf{x} - \mathbf{x}_0|^N} = 0, \tag{4}$$

and T^N is the only Nth-degree polynomial having this property.

Proof. Let $\mathbf{y} = \mathbf{x} - \mathbf{x}_0$ and define

$$F(t) = f(\mathbf{x}_0 + t(\mathbf{x} - \mathbf{x}_0)) = f(\mathbf{x}_0 + t\mathbf{y}).$$

Then for $k = 0, 1, \dots, N$, we can apply the chain rule to get

$$F^{(k)}(t) = (d_{\mathbf{x}_0 + t\mathbf{y}}^k f)(\mathbf{y}). \tag{5}$$

To see this, notice that for $k = 0$ the formula is true by definition. Assuming it to hold for some $k < N$, we have

$$
\begin{aligned}
F^{(k+1)}(t) &= \frac{d}{dt}(d_{\mathbf{x}_0 + t\mathbf{y}}^k f)(\mathbf{y}) \\
&= \frac{d}{dt}\left(y_1 \frac{\partial}{\partial x_1} + \dots + y_n \frac{\partial}{\partial x_n}\right)_{\mathbf{x}_0 + t\mathbf{y}}^k f \\
&= d_{\mathbf{x}_0 + t\mathbf{y}}\left[\left(y_1 \frac{\partial}{\partial x_1} + \dots + y_n \frac{\partial}{\partial x_n}\right)^k f\right](\mathbf{y}) \\
&= \left(y_1 \frac{\partial}{\partial x_1} + \dots + y_n \frac{\partial}{\partial x_n}\right)_{\mathbf{x}_0 + t\mathbf{y}}^{k+1} f \\
&= (d_{\mathbf{x}_0 + t\mathbf{y}}^{k+1} f)(\mathbf{y}).
\end{aligned}
$$

This completes the proof of Equation (5) by induction. In particular,

$$F^{(k)}(0) = (d_{\mathbf{x}_0}^k f)(\mathbf{y}).$$

From Equation (1) we obtain

$$
\begin{aligned}
F(1) - F(0) - \frac{1}{1!}F'(0) &- \dots - \frac{1}{N!}F^{(N)}(0) \\
&= \frac{1}{(N-1)!}\int_0^1 (1 - t)^{N-1}[F^{(N)}(t) - F^{(N)}(0)]\,dt.
\end{aligned}
$$

In terms of f, this is

$$
\begin{aligned}
f(\mathbf{x}) - T_N(\mathbf{x} - \mathbf{x}_0) &= f(\mathbf{x}) - f(\mathbf{x}_0) - \frac{1}{1!}(d_{\mathbf{x}_0} f)(\mathbf{y}) - \dots - \frac{1}{N!}(d_{\mathbf{x}_0}^N f)(\mathbf{y}) \\
&= \frac{1}{(N-1)!}\int_0^1 (1 - t)^{N-1}[(d_{\mathbf{x}_0 + t\mathbf{y}}^N f)(\mathbf{y}) - (d_{\mathbf{x}_0}^N f)(\mathbf{y})]\,dt.
\end{aligned}
$$

We now estimate this difference.

$$|f(\mathbf{x}) - T_N(\mathbf{y})| \leq \frac{1}{(N-1)!} \max_{0 \leq t \leq 1} |(d^N_{\mathbf{x}_0 + t\mathbf{y}} f)(\mathbf{y}) - (d^N_{\mathbf{x}_0} f)(\mathbf{y})|$$

$$\leq \max_{0 \leq t \leq 1} \left| \left(y_1 \frac{\partial}{\partial x_1} + \dots + y_n \frac{\partial}{\partial x_n} \right)^N_{\mathbf{x}_0 + t\mathbf{y}} f \right.$$
$$\left. - \left(y_1 \frac{\partial}{\partial x_1} + \dots + y_n \frac{\partial}{\partial x_n} \right)^N_{\mathbf{x}_0} f \right|$$

$$= \max_{0 \leq t \leq 1} \left| \sum_{k_1 + \dots + k_n = N} \binom{N}{k_1 \ \dots \ k_n} y_1^{k_1} \dots y_n^{k_n} \right.$$
$$\left. \cdot \left(\frac{\partial^N f}{\partial x_1^{k_1} \dots \partial x_n^{k_n}} (\mathbf{x}_0 + t\mathbf{y}) - \frac{\partial^N f}{\partial x_1^{k_1} \dots \partial x_n^{k_n}} (\mathbf{x}_0) \right) \right|.$$

Then, since $|y_i| \leq |\mathbf{y}|$, we have

$$\frac{|y_1^{k_1} \dots y_n^{k_n}|}{|\mathbf{y}|^N} \leq 1,$$

and so

$$\frac{|f(\mathbf{x}) - T_N(\mathbf{y})|}{|\mathbf{y}|^N} \leq \sum_{k_1 + \dots + k_n = N} \binom{N}{k_1 \ \dots \ k_n} \cdot$$
$$\max_{0 \leq t \leq 1} \left| \frac{\partial^N f}{\partial x_1^{k_1} \dots \partial x_n^{k_n}} (\mathbf{x}_0 + t\mathbf{y}) - \frac{\partial^N f}{\partial x_1^{k_1} \dots \partial x_n^{k_n}} (\mathbf{x}_0) \right|. \qquad (6)$$

By assumption the derivatives of f through order N are continuous functions at $\mathbf{x}_0$. Then as $\mathbf{y}$ tends to zero, each term in the last sum tends to zero, which proves Equation (4). The inequality (6) shows that if f is a polynomial of degree N, then it equals its Nth-degree Taylor expansion. For then all the terms on the right are zero.

The proof that T_N is the only Nth-degree polynomial satisfying Equation (4) goes as follows. Let T_N and T'_N be two such polynomials. By (4),

$$\lim_{\mathbf{y} \to 0} \frac{T_N(\mathbf{y}) - T'_N(\mathbf{y})}{|\mathbf{y}|^N} = 0.$$

Suppose that $T_N - T'_N$ were not identically zero, and let

$$P_k(\mathbf{y}) + R(\mathbf{y}) = T_N(\mathbf{y}) - T'_N(\mathbf{y}),$$

where P_k is the polynomial consisting of the terms of lowest degree (say k) that actually occur in $T_N - T'_N$. Then, there is a vector $\mathbf{y}_0$ such that $P_k(\mathbf{y}_0) \neq 0$. On the other hand, since $k \leq N$,

$$0 = \lim_{t \to 0} \frac{T_N(t\mathbf{y}_0) - T'_N(t\mathbf{y}_0)}{|t\mathbf{y}_0|^k}$$
$$= \lim_{t \to 0} \frac{P_k(t\mathbf{y}_0) + R(t\mathbf{y}_0)}{|t\mathbf{y}_0|^k}$$
$$= \frac{P_k(\mathbf{y}_0)}{|\mathbf{y}_0|^k} + \lim_{t \to 0} \frac{R(t\mathbf{y}_0)}{|t|^k |\mathbf{y}_0|^k}.$$

However, because all the terms of R have degree greater than k, the last limit is zero. But then $P_k(\mathbf{y}_0) = 0$, which is a contradiction.

As we have remarked above, Equation (6) shows that a polynomial of degree N is equal to its Nth-degree Taylor expansion about an arbitrary point $\mathbf{x}_0$.

EXAMPLE 5. The polynomial $x^2y + x^3 + y^3$ can be written as a polynomial in $(x - 1)$ and $(y + 1)$ by computing its Taylor expansion about $(1, -1)$. The result is

$$x^2y + x^3 + y^3 = -1 + \frac{1}{1!}((x - 1) + 4(y + 1))$$

$$+ \frac{1}{2!}(4(x - 1)^2 + 4(x - 1)(y + 1) - 6(y + 1)^2)$$

$$+ \frac{1}{3!}(6(x - 1)^3 + 6(x - 1)^2(y + 1) + 6(y + 1)^3)$$

$$= -1 + (x - 1) + 4(y + 1) + 2(x - 1)^2$$
$$+ 2(x - 1)(y + 1) - 3(y + 1)^2 + (x - 1)^3$$
$$+ (x - 1)^2(y + 1) + (y + 1)^3.$$

EXAMPLE 6. The infinite series expansion $e^t = 1 + t + (1/2!)t^2 + \ldots$ is valid for all t. Letting $t = x + y$ we get

$$e^{x+y} = 1 + \frac{1}{1!}(x + y) + \frac{1}{2!}(x^2 + 2xy + y^2) + \ldots, \qquad \text{for all } x \text{ and } y.$$

It follows that

$$1 + \frac{1}{1!}(x + y) + \frac{1}{2!}(x^2 + 2xy + y^2)$$

is the 2nd degree Taylor expansion of e^{x+y}. The remainder, $(1/3!)(x + y)^3 + \ldots$, tends to zero when it is divided by $(\sqrt{x^2 + y^2})^2$ and (x, y) tends to $(0, 0)$. According to Taylor's theorem, there is only one polynomial of degree two having this property.

EXAMPLE 7. Let $f(x, y) = e^{xy} \sin(x + y)$. Since

$$e^{xy} = 1 + xy + \frac{1}{2!}x^2y^2 + R_1$$

and

$$\sin(x + y) = (x + y) - \frac{1}{3!}(x + y)^3 + R_2,$$

we can multiply the expansions together, putting into the remainder all terms of degree greater than three. The result is

$$f(x, y) = e^{xy} \sin(x + y) = (x + y) + x^2y + xy^2 - \frac{1}{3!}(x + y)^3 + R,$$

where $R/|(x, y)|^3$ tends to zero as (x, y) tends to $(0, 0)$. In other words, we have found the third-degree Taylor expansion of $e^{xy} \sin(x + y)$ about $(0, 0)$. In standard form the expansion looks like

$$f(x, y) = e^{xy} \sin(x + y) = \frac{1}{1!}(x + y)$$

$$+ \frac{1}{3!}(-x^3 + 3x^2y + 3xy^2 - y^3) + R.$$

We can conclude that

$$\frac{\partial^3 f}{\partial y^3}(0, 0) = \frac{\partial^3 f}{\partial x^3}(0, 0) = -1,$$

$$\frac{\partial^3 f}{\partial x \partial y^2}(0, 0) = \frac{\partial^3 f}{\partial x^2 \partial y}(0, 0) = 1.$$

EXAMPLE 8. The functions e^x and $\cos x$ have second-degree expansions about $x = 0$

$$e^x = 1 + x + \frac{x^2}{2} + R(x), \qquad \cos x = 1 - \frac{x^2}{2} + R'(x).$$

Then

$$e^{\cos x} = 1 + \left(1 - \frac{x^2}{2} + R'(x)\right) + \frac{1}{2}\left(1 - \frac{x^2}{2} + R'(x)\right)^2$$

$$+ R\left(1 - \frac{x^2}{2} + R'(x)\right).$$

Since $R(1 - x^2/2 + R'(x))$ does not even tend to zero as x tends to zero, we must proceed differently to find a Taylor expansion of $e^{\cos x}$. We have

$$e^{\cos x} = e(e^{-1+\cos x})$$

$$= e\left[1 + \left(-\frac{x^2}{2} + R'(x)\right) + \frac{1}{2}\left(-\frac{x^2}{2} + R'(x)\right)^2 + R\left(-\frac{x^2}{2} + R'(x)\right)\right]$$

$$= e\left(1 - \frac{x^2}{2}\right) + R''(x),$$

where $R''(x)/x^2$ tends to zero as x tends to zero. The coefficients can also be found by direct computation of the derivatives of $e^{\cos x}$.

EXAMPLE 9. Since $1/(1 + x^2) = 1 - x^2 + R(x)$,

$$\prod_{k=1}^{n} \frac{1}{1 + x_k^2} = \prod_{k=1}^{n}(1 - x_k^2 + R(x_k))$$

$$= 1 - (x_1^2 + x_2^2 + \ldots + x_n^2) + R'(x_1, \ldots, x_n),$$

where $R'/|(x_1, \ldots, x_n)|^2$ tends to zero as $(x_1, \ldots, x_n)$ tends to zero.

EXAMPLE 10. The Taylor expansion of $f(\mathbf{x}) = (x_1 + \ldots + x_n)^N$ about $\mathbf{x}_0 = 0$ is

$$(x_1 + \ldots + x_n)^N = \frac{1}{N!}\left(x_1\frac{\partial}{\partial x_1} + \ldots + x_n\frac{\partial}{\partial x_n}\right)_0^N f$$

$$= \frac{1}{N!}\sum_{k_1+\cdots+k_n=N}\binom{N}{k_1\ \ldots\ k_n}x_1^{k_1}\ldots x_n^{k_n}\frac{\partial^N f}{\partial x_1^{k_1}\ldots\partial x_n^{k_n}}$$

$$= \sum_{k_1+\cdots+k_n=N}\binom{N}{k_1\ \ldots\ k_n}x_1^{k_1}\ldots x_n^{k_n}.$$

Only the Nth-order differential is different from zero at $\mathbf{x}_0 = 0$. To compute the multinomial coefficient, differentiate both sides by $\partial^N/(\partial x_1^{k_1}\ldots\partial x_n^{k_n})$. Then, setting $\mathbf{x} = 0$, we get

$$N! = \binom{N}{k_1\ \ldots\ k_n}k_1!\ \ldots\ k_n!,$$

from which the formula of Example 3 follows.

EXERCISES

1. Find the third-degree Taylor expansion of $(u + v)^3$
   (a) about the point $(u_0, v_0) = (0, 0)$.
   (b) about the point $(u_0, v_0) = (1, 2)$.

2. Find the best second-degree approximation to the function $f(x, y) = xe^y$ near the point $(x_0, y_0) = (2, 0)$.
   [*Ans.* $2 + (x - 2) + 2y + y^2 + (x - 2)y$.]

3. Find the best second-degree approximation to the function $f(x, y) = x^{y+1}$ near the point $(x_0, y_0) = (2, 0)$.

4. Find the quadratic terms of the Taylor expansion of xe^{x+y} about $(0, 0)$
   (a) by computing derivatives.
   (b) by substitution.

5. Find the quadratic terms of the Taylor expansion of $e^{\sin (x+y)}$ about $(0, 0)$.

6. If $f(x, y) = (x^2 + y^2)e^{x^2+y^2}$, use a Taylor expansion of f to compute
   $$\frac{\partial^3 f}{\partial x^2 \partial y}(0, 0).$$
   [*Ans.* 0]

7. Compute the second-degree Taylor expansion of $\sqrt{1 + x^2 + y^2}$ about the point $(x_0, y_0) = (-1, 1)$.

8. Compute the second-degree Taylor expansion of
   (a) $f(x, y, z) = (x^2 + 2xy + y^2)e^z$, about $(x_0, y_0, z_0) = (1, 2, 0)$.
   (b) $g(x, y, z) = xy^2z^3$, about $(x_0, y_0, z_0) = (1, 2, -1)$.

9. Write the polynomial xy^2z^3 as a polynomial in $(x - 1), y$, and $z + 1$.

10. Compute the second-degree Taylor expansion of $\log_2 x$ at $x = 1$. Sketch the graph of the expansion near $x = 1$.

11. Compute the second-degree Taylor expansion of $\log \cos (x + y)$ at $(x_0, y_0) = (0, 0)$

   (a) by computing derivatives.
   (b) by substitution.

12. Compute the second-degree Taylor expansion of $\exp (-x_1^2 - x_2^2 - \ldots - x_n^2)$ about $(x_1, x_2, \ldots, x_n) = (0, 0 \ldots 0)$.

13. Prove that the Taylor expansion of degree N of a polynomial of degree K, $K \geq N$, consists of the terms of the polynomial that are of degree less than or equal to N.

14. Compute the differentials $d_{\mathbf{x}_0}^k f(\mathbf{y})$ for arbitrary $\mathbf{y}$.

   (a) $k = 2$, $\mathbf{x}_0 = (1, 2)$, $f(x, y) = x^3y + 3x^2 + 2xy^3$.
   [*Ans.* $18x^2 + 54xy + 24y^2$.]
   (b) $k = 1$, $\mathbf{x}_0 = (a, b, c)$, $f(x, y, z) = 1/(x + y + z + 1)$.
   (c) $k = 2$, $\mathbf{x}_0 = (0, 0, 0)$, $f(x, y, z) = 1/(x + y + z + 1)$.
   [*Ans.* $2(x + y + z)^2$.]
   (d) $k = 4$, $\mathbf{x}_0 = (0, 0, 0)$, $f(x, y, z) = x^3 + 3xy^2 + 4xy^3 + 6x^2y^3 + 7y^5$.
   [*Ans.* $96xy^3$.]

15. Find the second differential of $\sin (x_1 + x_2 + \ldots + x_n)$ at $(x_1, x_2, \ldots, x_n) = (0, 0, \ldots, 0)$.   [*Ans.* 0.]

4. APPLICATIONS OF TAYLOR EXPANSIONS TO MAXIMA AND MINIMA

The tangent $\mathcal{T}$ to the graph of a function $\mathcal{R}^n \xrightarrow{f} \mathcal{R}$ at a point $(\mathbf{x}_0, f(\mathbf{x}_0))$ is found by computing the first-degree Taylor expansion of f about $\mathbf{x}_0$. We now consider the question of whether or not the graph of f crosses $\mathcal{T}$ at $(\mathbf{x}_0, f(\mathbf{x}_0))$. The possibilities for a function of one variable are shown in Figure 13.

Consider first a very much simplified situation in which f is equal to its second-degree Taylor expansion. That is, assume that

$$f(\mathbf{x}) = f(\mathbf{x}_0) + (d_{\mathbf{x}_0} f)(\mathbf{x} - \mathbf{x}_0) + \tfrac{1}{2}(d_{\mathbf{x}_0}^2 f)(\mathbf{x} - \mathbf{x}_0).$$

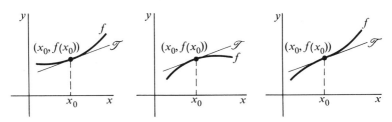

Figure 13

The first two terms of the expansion constitute the best affine approxima-
tion to f near $\mathbf{x}_0$, and the graph of $f(\mathbf{x}_0) + (d_{\mathbf{x}_0}f)(\mathbf{x} - \mathbf{x}_0)$ is the tangent
$\mathscr{T}$ to the graph of f at $\mathbf{p}_0 = (\mathbf{x}_0, f(\mathbf{x}_0))$. It is clear that if $(d_{\mathbf{x}_0}^2 f)(\mathbf{x} - \mathbf{x}_0)$ is
positive for all $\mathbf{x}$ in $\mathscr{R}^n$ except $\mathbf{x} = \mathbf{x}_0$, then

$$f(\mathbf{x}) > f(\mathbf{x}_0) + (d_{\mathbf{x}_0}f)(\mathbf{x} - \mathbf{x}_0), \qquad \text{for} \quad \mathbf{x} \neq \mathbf{x}_0,$$

which implies that the graph of f lies above the tangent $\mathscr{T}$. Similarly, if
$(d_{\mathbf{x}_0}^2 f)(\mathbf{x} - \mathbf{x}_0)$ is negative except for $\mathbf{x} = \mathbf{x}_0$, the graph of f lies below $\mathscr{T}$.
On the other hand, if $(d_{\mathbf{x}_0}^2 f)(\mathbf{x} - \mathbf{x}_0)$ changes sign at $\mathbf{x}_0$, then the graph of
f will cross $\mathscr{T}$ at $\mathbf{p}_0$.

To say that the quadratic polynomial $Q(\mathbf{x} - \mathbf{x}_0) = (d_{\mathbf{x}_0}^2 f)(\mathbf{x} - \mathbf{x}_0)$
changes sign at $\mathbf{x}_0$ means that there are points $\mathbf{x}_1$ and $\mathbf{x}_2$ arbitrarily close to
$\mathbf{x}_0$ such that

$$Q(\mathbf{x}_1 - \mathbf{x}_0) > 0 \quad \text{and} \quad Q(\mathbf{x}_2 - \mathbf{x}_0) < 0. \tag{1}$$

The phrase "arbitrarily close" is superfluous, because every homogeneous
quadratic polynomial Q has the property

$$Q(t\mathbf{x}) = t^2 Q(\mathbf{x}). \tag{2}$$

It follows that if (1) holds for two vectors $\mathbf{x}_1$ and $\mathbf{x}_2$, not necessarily close to
$\mathbf{x}_0$, then (1) also holds for $t(\mathbf{x}_1 - \mathbf{x}_0) + \mathbf{x}_0$ and $t(\mathbf{x}_2 - \mathbf{x}_0) + \mathbf{x}_0$, for any
$t \neq 0$. By choosing t small enough, we can bring the latter vectors as close
to $\mathbf{x}_0$ as we like.

EXAMPLE 1. The function

$$f(x, y) = 2x^2 - xy - 3y^2 - 3x + 7y$$

equals its second-degree Taylor expansion. It has one critical point at
$\mathbf{x}_0 = (1, 1)$, and the tangent plane $\mathscr{T}$ at $(1, 1, 2)$ is therefore horizontal.
The second differential is given by

$$(d_{\mathbf{x}_0}^2 f) \begin{pmatrix} x - 1 \\ y - 1 \end{pmatrix} = 4(x - 1)^2 - 2(x - 1)(y - 1) - 6(y - 1)^2.$$

Trying $\mathbf{x}_1 = (2, 1)$ and $\mathbf{x}_2 = (1, 2)$, we obtain

$$(d_{\mathbf{x}_0}^2 f)(\mathbf{x}_1 - \mathbf{x}_0) = 4 > 0,$$
$$(d_{\mathbf{x}_0}^2 f)(\mathbf{x}_2 - \mathbf{x}_0) = -6 < 0.$$

We conclude that the graph of f crosses the tangent plane $\mathscr{T}$ at $(1, 1, 2)$
and, consequently, that f has neither a local maximum nor minimum at $\mathbf{x}_0$.

The assumption that f equals its second-degree Taylor expansion is too
strong to be of much practical value. However, the next theorem shows
that under more general hypothesis, the sign of the second differential still
determines whether or not f crosses its tangent. The quadratic polynomial
$(d_{\mathbf{x}_0}^2 f)(\mathbf{x} - \mathbf{x}_0)$ is always zero at $\mathbf{x} = \mathbf{x}_0$. If it is positive except at that one

point, it is said to be **positive definite**, and if it is negative except at that one point then it is said to be **negative definite**.

4.1 Theorem. Let $\mathscr{R}^n \xrightarrow{f} \mathscr{R}$ have all its second partial derivatives continuous in a neighborhood of $\mathbf{x}_0$, and denote the tangent to the graph of f at $\mathbf{p}_0 = (\mathbf{x}_0, f(\mathbf{x}_0))$ by $\mathscr{T}$.

   (i) If $(d^2_{\mathbf{x}_0} f)(\mathbf{x} - \mathbf{x}_0)$ is positive definite, then f lies above $\mathscr{T}$ in some neighborhood of $\mathbf{x}_0$.

   (ii) If $(d^2_{\mathbf{x}_0} f)(\mathbf{x} - \mathbf{x}_0)$ is negative definite, then f lies below $\mathscr{T}$ in some neighborhood of $\mathbf{x}_0$.

   (iii) If $(d^2_{\mathbf{x}_0} f)(\mathbf{x} - \mathbf{x}_0)$ assumes both positive and negative values, then f crosses the tangent $\mathscr{T}$ at $\mathbf{p}_0$.

Notice that not all possible cases are covered by (i), (ii), and (iii). It may happen, for example, that the second differential is zero somewhere other than at $\mathbf{x}_0$, but that it still does not change sign.

Proof (of 4.1). By Taylor's theorem we have

$$f(\mathbf{x}) - f(\mathbf{x}_0) - (d_{\mathbf{x}_0} f)(\mathbf{x} - \mathbf{x}_0) = \tfrac{1}{2}(d^2_{\mathbf{x}_0} f)(\mathbf{x} - \mathbf{x}_0) + R, \qquad (3)$$

where

$$\lim_{\mathbf{x} \to \mathbf{x}_0} \frac{R}{|\mathbf{x} - \mathbf{x}_0|^2} = 0.$$

Under assumption (i), we must show that

$$\tfrac{1}{2}(d^2_{\mathbf{x}_0} f)(\mathbf{x} - \mathbf{x}_0) + R > 0$$

in some neighborhood of $\mathbf{x}_0$, excluding $\mathbf{x}_0$ itself. The homogeneity of the quadratic polynomial $d^2_{\mathbf{x}_0} f$ (see Equation (2)) implies that

$$\frac{(d^2_{\mathbf{x}_0} f)(\mathbf{x} - \mathbf{x}_0)}{|\mathbf{x} - \mathbf{x}_0|^2} = (d^2_{\mathbf{x}_0} f)\left(\frac{\mathbf{x} - \mathbf{x}_0}{|\mathbf{x} - \mathbf{x}_0|}\right).$$

Since $d^2_{\mathbf{x}_0} f$ is positive definite, its values for unit vectors are bounded away from zero by a constant $m > 0$. (See Exercise 14, Section 2). Now choose $\delta > 0$ so that, for $0 < |\mathbf{x} - \mathbf{x}_0| < \delta$,

$$\frac{|R|}{|\mathbf{x} - \mathbf{x}_0|^2} \leq \frac{m}{4}.$$

It follows that

$$\frac{1}{2}(d^2_{\mathbf{x}_0} f)(\mathbf{x} - \mathbf{x}_0) + R \geq \frac{m}{2}|\mathbf{x} - \mathbf{x}_0|^2 - \frac{m}{4}|\mathbf{x} - \mathbf{x}_0|^2 > 0$$

which, according to Equation (3), is what we wanted to show.

    The proof of (ii) is practically the same as the proof just given. To prove (iii), suppose that $(d^2_{\mathbf{x}_0} f)(\mathbf{x}_1 - \mathbf{x}_0) > 0$ and $(d^2_{\mathbf{x}_0} f)(\mathbf{x}_2 - \mathbf{x}_0) < 0$. Set

$$\mathbf{x}_i(t) = t(\mathbf{x}_i - \mathbf{x}_0) + \mathbf{x}_0, \qquad i = 1, 2, \quad -\infty < t < \infty.$$

Using the homogeneity property of the polynomial $d_{x_0}^2 f$, and also of the norm, we obtain, for any $t \neq 0$,

$$f(x_i(t)) - f(x_0) - (d_{x_0} f)(x_i(t) - x_0)$$
$$= t^2 \left[\frac{1}{2} (d_{x_0}^2 f)(x_i - x_0) + |x_i - x_0|^2 \frac{R}{|x_i(t) - x_0|^2} \right]. \quad (4)$$

Since

$$\lim_{t \to 0} \frac{R}{|x_i(t) - x_0|^2} = 0,$$

it follows that, for any nonzero t sufficiently small, the left-hand side of Equation (4) is positive if $i = 1$ and negative if $i = 2$. In other words, the graph of f lies both above and below the tangent $\mathcal{T}$ for some values of x arbitrarily close to x_0. This completes the proof.

EXAMPLE 2. The function

$$f(x, y) = (x^2 + y^2) e^{x^2 - y^2}$$

has its critical points at $(0, 0)$, $(0, 1)$, and $(0, -1)$. This implies that the tangents at these points are horizontal planes. The second-degree Taylor expansions at the three points are, respectively,

$$f(0, 0) + \frac{1}{2} (d_{(0,0)}^2 f)\binom{x}{y} = x^2 + y^2,$$

$$f(0, 1) + \frac{1}{2} (d_{(0,1)}^2 f)\binom{x}{y-1} = \frac{1}{e}[1 + 2x^2 - 2(y-1)^2],$$

$$f(0, -1) + \frac{1}{2} (d_{(0,-1)}^2 f)\binom{x}{y+1} = \frac{1}{e}[1 + 2x^2 - 2(y+1)^2].$$

Clearly, $d_{(0,0)}^2 f$ is positive definite, while $d_{(0,1)}^2 f$ and $d_{(0,-1)}^2 f$ assume both positive and negative values arbitrarily close to their respective critical points. We conclude that f has a local minimum value at $(0, 0)$ and neither a maximum nor a minimum at the points $(0, 1)$ and $(0, -1)$. The graph of f and the horizontal tangent planes at $(0, 0, 0)$ and $(0, 1, 1/e)$ are shown in Figure 14.

EXAMPLE 3. The function

$$f(x, y, z) = x \sin z + z \sin y$$

has a critical point at $x_0 = (-1, \pi/2, 0)$. The second differential at x_0 is

$$(d_{x_0}^2 f)\begin{pmatrix} x+1 \\ y - \dfrac{\pi}{2} \\ z \end{pmatrix} = 2z(x+1).$$

Since $d_{x_0}^2 f$ has both positive and negative values, the function f has neither a local maximum nor minimum at x_0.

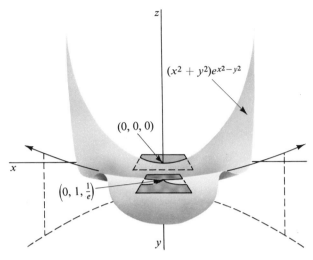

Figure 14

EXAMPLE 4. If $f(x) = x \sin^3 x$, the first four terms of the Taylor expansion at $x = 0$ are identically zero, while

$$(d_0^4 f)x = 24x^4.$$

The criteria of Theorem 4.1 do not cover this example. However, a similar proof would show that f behaves like its Taylor expansion in the matter of crossing its tangent. The conclusion is that $x \sin^3 x$ has a local minimum at $x = 0$.

For distinguishing among the critical points of a function those that are maximum points or minimum points, a detailed examination of the polynomial $(d_{\mathbf{x}_0}^2 f)(\mathbf{x} - \mathbf{x}_0)$ is not necessary. It is enough to know that this quadratic approximation is positive or negative definite. In addition to the criteria of Section 2, we list here for reference a simple test for quadratic polynomials in two or three variables. (See Section 2, Example 4 and Exercise 16.)

The polynomial

$$ax^2 + 2bxy + cy^2 = (x \quad y) \begin{pmatrix} a & b \\ b & c \end{pmatrix} \begin{pmatrix} x \\ y \end{pmatrix}$$

is positive definite if and only if

$$a > 0 \quad and \quad \begin{vmatrix} a & b \\ b & c \end{vmatrix} > 0$$

and is negative definite if and only if

$$a < 0 \quad and \quad \begin{vmatrix} a & b \\ b & c \end{vmatrix} > 0.$$

The character of the polynomial

$$ax^2 + by^2 + cz^2 + 2dyz + 2exz + 2fxy = (x \quad y \quad z) \begin{pmatrix} a & f & e \\ f & b & d \\ e & d & c \end{pmatrix} \begin{pmatrix} x \\ y \\ z \end{pmatrix}$$

depends on the sign of the three determinants

$$a, \qquad \begin{vmatrix} a & f \\ f & b \end{vmatrix}, \qquad \begin{vmatrix} a & f & e \\ f & b & d \\ e & d & c \end{vmatrix}.$$

The polynomial is positive definite if and only if all three determinants are positive, and is negative definite if and only if the middle one is positive and the other two are negative.

EXAMPLE 5. The function $g(x, y, z) = x^2 + y^2 + z^2 + xy$ has critical points only when

$$\begin{aligned} g_x &= 2x + y = 0, \\ g_y &= 2y + x = 0, \\ g_z &= 2z \qquad = 0, \end{aligned}$$

so the only critical point occurs at $(0, 0, 0)$. Since $d_x^2 g = g$, we can test g itself for positive definiteness. We have

$$a = 1, \qquad \begin{vmatrix} a & f \\ f & b \end{vmatrix} = \begin{vmatrix} 1 & \frac{1}{2} \\ \frac{1}{2} & 1 \end{vmatrix} = \tfrac{3}{4}, \qquad \begin{vmatrix} a & f & e \\ f & b & d \\ e & d & c \end{vmatrix} = \begin{vmatrix} 1 & \frac{1}{2} & 0 \\ \frac{1}{2} & 1 & 0 \\ 0 & 0 & 1 \end{vmatrix} = \tfrac{3}{4}.$$

Thus g is positive definite, and, as a result, g has minimum value 0 at $(0, 0, 0)$.

EXERCISES

1. Find all the critical points of the following functions:

(a) $(x + y)e^{-xy}$.   [*Ans.* $(\pm 1/\sqrt{2}, \pm 1/\sqrt{2})$.]
(b) $xy + xz$.   [*Ans.* $(0, y, -y)$, any y.]
(c) $(x^2 + y^2) \ln (x^2 + y^2)$.
(d) $\cos (x^2 + y^2 + z^2)$.
(e) $x^2 + y^2 + z^2$.

2. Compute the second-degree Taylor expansion of the function in Exercise 1(a) at each of its critical points.

3. Classify the critical points in 1(a), 1(b), and 1(e) as maximum, minimum, or neither.

4. In each of the following consider the tangent to the graph of the function at the point indicated. Decide whether the function lies above or below the tangent near the indicated point, or whether it crosses there.

(a) $x^2 \sin x$ at $x = 1$.   [*Ans.* Lies above.]

(b) $1/(x - y)$ at $(x, y) = (2, 1)$.

(c) $x^4 + y^4$ at $(0, 0)$.

(d) $e^{z+w} - x^2 - y^2$ at $(0, 0, 0, 0)$.   [*Ans.* Crosses.]

5. Locate all the critical points x_0 of each of the following functions and by looking at $d_{x_0}^2 f$ decide whether the function has a local maximum, or a local minimum, or neither, at x_0. If examination of the second differential fails to give any information, consider the next highest term of the Taylor expansion that does give information.

(a) $\sin x \cos x$.

(b) $x^2 y^2$.   [*Ans.* $x = 0$ or $y = 0$, min.]

(c) $x^2 + 4xy - y^2 - 8x - 6y$.

(d) $x^2 - xy - y^2 + 5y - 1$.   [*Ans.* $(1, 2)$, neither.]

(e) $x^2 + 2y^2 - x$.

(f) $x \sin y$.

(g) $x^4 + y^4$.   [*Ans.* $(0, 0)$, min.]

(h) $(x - y)^4$.

(i) $\exp(-x_1^2 - x_2^2 - \ldots - x_n^2)$.

5. FOURIER SERIES

The Nth degree Taylor expansion of a function f requires the existence of at least N derivatives at a point x_0. Furthermore, because the derivatives $f^{(k)}(x_0)$ that occur in the Taylor expansion are determined by the properties of f in a neighborhood of x_0, the expansion in general approximates f near x_0 only. Another approach to the problem of approximating a function is by using a **trigonometric polynomial**

$$s_N(x) = \frac{a_0}{2} + \sum_{k=1}^{N} (a_k \cos kx + b_k \sin kx). \tag{1}$$

Instead of using the values of the function f to be approximated near only a single point, the Fourier method is to compute the coefficients a_k and b_k by taking certain weighted averages of f over the interval on which it is defined. We shall assume at first that f is continuous on the interval $-\pi \leq x \leq \pi$, and define the **Fourier coefficients** of f by the formulas

5.1 $$a_k = \frac{1}{\pi} \int_{-\pi}^{\pi} \cos kx \, f(x) \, dx, \qquad b_k = \frac{1}{\pi} \int_{-\pi}^{\pi} \sin kx \, f(x) \, dx.$$

The results of Examples 1 and 2 below give some idea of how well this choice of coefficients works. (See also Theorem 5.3)

The trigonometric polynomial (1), with its coefficients determined by Formula 5.1, is called the Nth **Fourier approximation** to f on the interval $[-\pi, \pi]$. The polynomial is evidently a periodic function of period 2π. In order to see the nature of its approximation to f we shall compute some examples.

EXAMPLE 1. Let $f(x) = |x|$ for $-\pi \le x \le \pi$.
Then

$$a_k = \frac{1}{\pi} \int_{-\pi}^{\pi} |x| \cos kx \, dx, \qquad b_k = \frac{1}{\pi} \int_{-\pi}^{\pi} |x| \sin kx \, dx.$$

Clearly $|x| \sin kx$ has integral zero over $[-\pi, \pi]$, because the integrals over $[-\pi, 0]$ and $[0, \pi]$ are negatives of one another. Hence $b_k = 0$ for $k = 1, 2,$ .... On the other hand, the graph of $|x| \cos kx$ is symmetric about the y-axis, so for $k \ne 0$ we integrate by parts, getting

$$\begin{aligned}
a_k &= \frac{2}{\pi} \int_0^{\pi} x \cos kx \, dx \\
&= \frac{2}{\pi} \left[\frac{x \sin kx}{k} \right]_0^{\pi} - \frac{2}{\pi k} \int_0^{\pi} \sin kx \, dx \\
&= \left[\frac{2}{\pi k^2} \cos kx \right]_0^{\pi} = \frac{2}{\pi k^2}(\cos k\pi - 1) \\
&= \begin{cases} 0, & k = 2, 4, 6, \ldots, \\ -\dfrac{4}{\pi k^2}, & k = 1, 3, 5, \ldots. \end{cases}
\end{aligned}$$

When $k = 0$, we have

$$a_0 = \frac{2}{\pi} \int_0^{\pi} x \, dx = \pi.$$

To summarize,

$$a_0 = \pi, \qquad a_k = \begin{cases} 0, & k = 2, 4, 6, \ldots. \\ -\dfrac{4}{\pi k^2}, & k = 1, 3, 5, \ldots. \end{cases}$$

$$b_k = 0, \qquad k = 1, 2, 3, \ldots.$$

Hence, the Nth Fourier approximation is given for $N = 1, 3, 5, \ldots,$ by the trigonometric polynomial

$$s_N(x) = \frac{\pi}{2} - \frac{4}{\pi} \cos x - \frac{4}{\pi} \frac{\cos 3x}{3^2} - \cdots - \frac{4}{\pi} \frac{\cos Nx}{N^2}.$$

If N is even, we have $s_N(x) = s_{N-1}(x)$. Figure 15 shows how the graphs of s_0, s_1, and s_3 approximate that of $|x|$ on $[-\pi, \pi]$.

EXAMPLE 2. Let

$$g(x) = \begin{cases} 1, & 0 \le x \le \pi \\ -1, & -\pi \le x < 0. \end{cases}$$

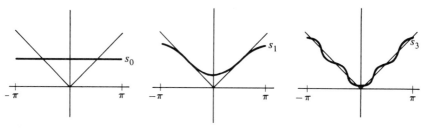

Figure 15

Then the Fourier coefficients of g are given by integration as

$$a_k = 0, \qquad k = 0, 1, 2, \ldots$$

$$b_k = \begin{cases} 0, & k = 2, 4, 6, \ldots \\ \dfrac{4}{\pi k}, & k = 1, 3, 5, \ldots \end{cases}$$

Hence, for N odd, the Nth Fourier approximation to g is given by

$$s_N(x) = \frac{4}{\pi} \sin x + \frac{4}{\pi} \frac{\sin 3x}{3} + \cdots + \frac{4}{\pi} \frac{\sin Nx}{N}.$$

The graphs of s_1, s_3, and s_5 are shown in Figure 16, together with that of $g(x)$.

If the function f to be approximated is defined not on the interval $[-\pi, \pi]$ but on $[-p, p]$, a suitable change in the computation of the approximation can be made as follows. With f defined on $[-p, p]$, we define

$$f_p(x) = f\left(\frac{px}{\pi}\right), \qquad -\pi \le x \le \pi.$$

Then we can compute the Fourier coefficients of f_p by Formula 5.1, and the resulting trigonometric polynomials s_N approximate f_p on $[-\pi, \pi]$. To approximate f on $[-p, p]$, we consider

$$s_N\left(\frac{\pi x}{p}\right) = \frac{a_0}{2} + \sum_{k=1}^{N} \left(a_k \cos \frac{k\pi x}{p} + b_k \sin \frac{k\pi x}{p}\right).$$

The coefficients a_k and b_k can be computed directly in terms of f by making a change of variable. We have

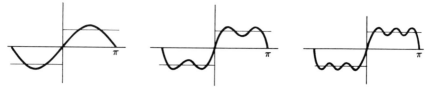

Figure 16

$$a_k = \frac{1}{\pi} \int_{-\pi}^{\pi} f_p(x) \cos kx \, dx = \frac{1}{\pi} \int_{-\pi}^{\pi} f\left(\frac{px}{\pi}\right) kx \, dx$$

$$= \frac{1}{p} \int_{-p}^{p} f(x) \cos\left(\frac{k\pi x}{p}\right) dx.$$

A similar computation holds for b_k, and we have

5.2 $\qquad a_k = \frac{1}{p} \int_{-p}^{p} f(x) \cos \frac{k\pi x}{p} \, dx, \qquad b_k = \frac{1}{p} \int_{-p}^{p} f(x) \sin \frac{k\pi x}{p} \, dx$

for the coefficients in the Fourier approximation

$$\frac{a_0}{2} + \sum_{k=1}^{N} \left(a_k \cos \frac{k\pi x}{p} + b_k \sin \frac{k\pi x}{p} \right)$$

to the function f defined on $[-p, p]$.

EXAMPLE 3. If

$$h(t) = \begin{cases} 1, & 0 \le t \le p \\ -1, & -p \le t \le 0, \end{cases}$$

then

$$a_k = 0, \qquad k = 0, 1, 2, \ldots,$$

$$b_k = \frac{2}{p} \int_{0}^{p} \sin \frac{k\pi x}{p} \, dx$$

$$= \frac{2}{\pi} \int_{0}^{\pi} \sin kx \, dx = \begin{cases} 0, & k = 2, 4, 6, \ldots, \\ \dfrac{4}{\pi k}, & k = 1, 3, 5, \ldots. \end{cases}$$

Hence, the Nth Fourier approximation to h is given, for odd N, by

$$s_N(x) = \frac{4}{\pi} \sin \frac{\pi x}{p} + \frac{4}{3\pi} \sin \frac{3\pi x}{p} + \ldots + \frac{4}{N\pi} \sin \frac{N\pi x}{p}, \qquad -p \le x \le p.$$

This result could have been got directly from that of Example 2 by simply changing scale.

EXAMPLE 4. As an application of the Fourier method we shall find an approximate solution to the partial differential equation

$$a^2 u_{xx} = u_t, \tag{2}$$

with boundary and initial conditions

$$u(0, t) = u(p, t) = 0, \qquad t \ge 0 \tag{3}$$

$$u(x, 0) = h(x), \qquad 0 \le x \le p. \tag{4}$$

The initial condition (4) specifies the value of u at each point of the interval $0 \le x \le p$, for $t = 0$, while the boundary conditions (3) fix the value of u to be 0 on the lines $x = 0$ and $x = p$ in the x, t-plane.

To find solutions of (2) together with (3) and (4), we observe that the equation with boundary conditions (3) is *linear*, which means that if u_1 and u_2 are functions of x and t satisfying (2) and (3), then $au_1 + bu_2$ is such a function for any constants a and b. The method to be applied consists in finding special solutions of (2) and (3) and then to form linear combinations of them to satisfy not only (2) and (3) but also the initial condition (4). We try to find solutions u of the special form

$$u(x, t) = G(x) H(t)$$

with boundary condition $G(0) = G(p) = 0$. If such exist, substitution into $a^2 u_{xx} = u_t$ gives

$$a^2 G''(x) H(t) = G(x) H'(t),$$

for $0 \le x \le p$, $0 < t$. Dividing through by $G(x) H(t)$ gives

$$a^2 \frac{G''(x)}{G(x)} = \frac{H'(t)}{H(t)}. \tag{5}$$

For this equation to be satisfied for varying x and t, both sides must be equal to a constant, which we denote by $-\lambda^2$. This procedure is called separation of variables.

Setting both sides of (5) equal to $-\lambda^2$ gives two equations:

$$a^2 G'' + \lambda^2 G = 0, \tag{6}$$

$$H' + \lambda^2 H = 0. \tag{7}$$

Equation (6) has solutions

$$G(x) = c_1 \cos\left(\frac{\lambda}{a}\right)x + c_2 \sin\left(\frac{\lambda}{a}\right)x.$$

But $G(0) = 0$ requires $c_1 = 0$, and $G(p) = 0$ then requires $c_2 \sin(\lambda/a)p = 0$. This condition can be achieved, without making $c_2 = 0$, only by choosing λ so that $(\lambda/a)p = k\pi$, where k is an integer. That is, we must take $\lambda = (ka\pi)/p$, with the result that G has the form

$$G(x) = c_2 \sin\left(\frac{k\pi}{p}\right)x, \qquad k = 1, 2, \ldots.$$

Equation (7) has solution

$$H(t) = e^{-\lambda^2 t},$$

which, because $\lambda^2 = (k^2 a^2 \pi^2)/p^2$, becomes

$$H(t) = e^{-k^2(a^2 \pi^2/p^2)t}.$$

The product solution $u(x, t)$ is thus given, except for a constant factor, by

$$u_k(x, t) = e^{-k^2(a^2 \pi^2/p^2)t} \sin\left(\frac{k\pi}{p}\right)x, \qquad k = 1, 2, \ldots,$$

and linear combinations

$$\sum_{k=1}^{N} b_k u_k(x, t)$$

look like

$$u(x, t) = \sum_{k=1}^{N} b_k e^{-k^2(a^2\pi^2/p^2)t} \sin\left(\frac{k\pi}{p}\right)x. \tag{8}$$

To satisfy the initial condition $u(x, 0) = h(x)$, we require

$$\sum_{h=1}^{N} b_k \sin\left(\frac{k\pi}{p}\right)x = h(x), \tag{9}$$

for some N. If $h(x)$ happens to be of this form, it follows that a solution to the problem is given by Equation (8).

The solution $u(x, t)$ found in the previous example has a graph of the general form shown in Figure 17. The partial differential equation, $a^2 u_{xx} = u_t$, that u satisfies, is called the 1-dimensional diffusion or heat equation, and it is, for example the differential equation satisfied by the temperature at a point x in a wire of length p at time t, insulated so that heat can enter or leave the wire only at the ends. The boundary conditions, $u(0, t) = u(p, t) = 0$, require that the temperature remain zero at the ends, and the initial condition $u(x, 0) = h(x)$ specifies the initial temperature at each point x of the wire between 0 and p. (See Problem 10 for the interpretation of the equation.)

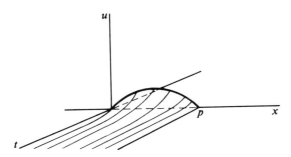

Figure 17

If the initial values given by the function h in the previous example happen not to be of the special form shown in Equation (9), then it is impossible to determine a finite sequence of coefficients b_k so that the solution to the initial value problem is given by Equation (8). In that case we try to find an *infinite* sequence of coefficients so that h is represented by the series

$$h(x) = \sum_{k=1}^{\infty} b_k \sin\left(\frac{k\pi}{p}\right)x,$$

and then to justify representing the solution to the problem in the form

$$u(x, t) = \sum_{k=1}^{\infty} b_k e^{-k^2(a^2\pi^2/p^2)t} \sin\left(\frac{k\pi}{p}\right)x. \tag{10}$$

Returning to the standard interval $[-\pi, \pi]$, we shall try to represent a function f defined there by its **Fourier series** in the form

$$f(x) = \frac{a_0}{2} + \sum_{k=1}^{\infty} (a_k \cos kx + b_k \sin kx),$$

where the numbers a_k and b_k are the Fourier coefficients of f, computed by Formula 5.1. Indeed, suppose that the graph of f is **piecewise smooth**. This means that the interval $[-\pi, \pi]$ can be broken into finitely many subintervals, with end-points $-\pi < x_1 < x_2 < \ldots < x_k < \pi$, such that f can be extended continuously from each open interval (x_k, x_{k+1}) to the closed interval $[x_k, x_{k+1}]$ so that f' is continuous on $[x_k, x_{k+1}]$. Then we can show that the Fourier series of f converges to $f(x)$ wherever f is continuous, and, at a possible discontinuity at x_k, will converge to the average value $(\frac{1}{2})[f(x_k-) + f(x_k+)]$. Here $f(x-)$ stands for the left-hand limit of f at x, and $f(x+)$ for the right-hand limit. The graph of a typical piecewise smooth function is shown in Figure 18, with the average value indicated by a dot at each jump.

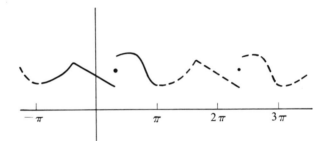

Figure 18

5.3 Theorem. Let f be piecewise smooth on $[-\pi, \pi]$. Then the Fourier series of f converges at every point x of the interval to $(\frac{1}{2})[f(x-) + f(x+)]$. In particular, if f is continuous at x, then the series converges to $f(x)$.

The proof is given in Section 4 of the Appendix.

EXAMPLE 5. Continuing with the problem of Example 4, we assume for simplicity that $p = \pi$, and recall that to solve the equation $a^2 u_{xx} = u_t$ with boundary condition $u(0, t) = u(\pi, t) = 0$, and initial condition $u(x, 0) = h(x)$, we want in general to be able to represent h by an infinite series of the form

$$h(x) = \sum_{k=1}^{\infty} b_k \sin kx. \tag{11}$$

Suppose, for example, that h is given on $[0, \pi]$ by

$$h(x) = \begin{cases} x, & 0 \le x \le \pi/2 \\ \pi - x, & \pi/2 \le x \le \pi. \end{cases}$$

The graph of h is shown in Figure 19.

To make Equation (11) represent the Fourier expansion of h on $[0, \pi]$, we extend h to the interval $[-\pi, \pi]$ in such a way that the cosine terms in the expansion of h will all be zero, leaving only the sine terms to be computed. We do this by extending the graph of h symmetrically about the origin, as shown in Figure 19. Then

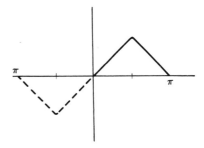

$$a_k = \frac{1}{\pi} \int_{-\pi}^{\pi} h(x) \cos kx \, dx = 0,$$

Figure 19

because $h(-x) \cos k(-x) = -h(x) \cos kx$, and so the integrals over $[-\pi, 0]$ and $[0, \pi]$ are negatives of one another. To compute b_k we use the fact that $h(-x) \sin k(-x) = h(x) \sin kx$, so that the graph of this function is symmetric about the y-axis. Then

$$b_k = \frac{1}{\pi} \int_{-\pi}^{\pi} h(x) \sin kx \, dx$$

$$= \frac{2}{\pi} \int_0^{\pi} h(x) \sin kx \, dx$$

$$= \frac{2}{\pi} \int_0^{\pi/2} x \sin kx \, dx + \frac{2}{\pi} \int_{\pi/2}^{\pi} (\pi - x) \sin kx \, dx$$

$$= \frac{4}{\pi k^2} \sin \left(\frac{k\pi}{2}\right).$$

Hence,

$$b_k = \begin{cases} 0, & k \text{ even} \\ \dfrac{4}{\pi k^2}, & k = 1, 5, 9, \ldots, \\ \dfrac{-4}{\pi k^2}, & k = 3, 7, 11, \ldots. \end{cases}$$

Theorem 5.3 then implies that

$$h(x) = \frac{4}{\pi} \left(\frac{\sin x}{1^2} - \frac{\sin 3x}{3^2} + \frac{\sin 5x}{5^2} - \frac{\sin 7x}{7^2} + - \cdots\right)$$

for each x in $[0, \pi]$. Finally, from Equation (10) of Example 4, we expect the solution to the equation $a^2 u_{xx} = u_t$ to be given by

$$u(x, t) = \frac{4}{\pi} \left(e^{-a^2 t} \sin x - \frac{1}{3^2} e^{-3^2 a^2 t} \sin 3x + \frac{1}{5^2} e^{-5^2 a^2 t} \sin 5x\right.$$

$$\left. - \frac{1}{7^2} e^{-7^2 a^2 t} \sin 7x + - \cdots\right)$$

Verification that $u(0, t) = u(\pi, t) = 0$ follows immediately from setting $x = 0$ and $x = \pi$. By setting $t = 0$ we get the representation of h by its Fourier series, which is guaranteed by Theorem 5.3. That $u(x, t)$ satisfies the equation $a^2 u_{xx} = u_t$ depends on term-by-term differentiation of the series for u. This will be justified in the next section, though the formal verification is left as Problem 9 at the end of this section.

EXERCISES

1. Compute the Fourier coefficients of each of the following functions. Sketch the graph of each function, together with the first three Fourier approximations $s_N(x)$ that differ from one another

(a) $f_1(x) = x, \ -\pi \leq x \leq \pi$ [*Ans.* $b_k = (2(-1)^{k+1})/k$.]

(b) $f_2(x) = \begin{cases} (-\pi - x), & -\pi \leq x \leq 0 \\ (\ \pi - x), & 0 < x \leq \pi \end{cases}$

(c) $f_3(x) = x^2, \ -\pi \leq x \leq \pi$

(d) $f_4(x) = x, \ -1 \leq x \leq 1$.

2. (a) With respect to the inner product $\langle f, g \rangle$ of two continuous functions defined by

$$\langle f, g \rangle = \frac{1}{\pi} \int_{-\pi}^{\pi} f(x)\, g(x)\, dx,$$

prove the orthogonality relations

$$\langle \cos nx, \cos mx \rangle = \begin{cases} 1, & m = n \neq 0 \\ 0, & m \neq n \end{cases}$$

$$\langle \sin nx, \sin mx \rangle = \begin{cases} 1, & m = n \neq 0 \\ 0, & m \neq n \end{cases}$$

$$\langle \sin nx, \cos mx \rangle = 0, \quad \text{all } n, m,$$

where n and m are integers.

(b) Use the result of part (a) to show that if

$$f(x) = \frac{c_0}{2} + \sum_{k=1}^{N} (c_k \cos kx + d_k \sin kx),$$

then the Fourier coefficients of f are given by

$$\langle f(x), \cos kx \rangle = c_k, \ k = 0, 1, 2, \ldots$$

and

$$\langle f(x), \sin kx \rangle = d_k, \ k = 1, 2, \ldots.$$

3. Prove that if s_N and t_N are the Nth Fourier approximations to f and g respectively, then $as_N + bt_N$ is the Nth Fourier approximation to $af + bg$, where a and b are constants.

4. (a) Let f be an odd function on $[-\pi, \pi]$ (i.e., $f(-x) = -f(x)$), and let g be an even function (i.e., $g(-x) = g(x)$). Let a_k, b_k and a'_k, b'_k be the Fourier coefficients of f and g respectively. Show that

$$a_k = 0, \qquad b_k = \frac{2}{\pi} \int_0^{\pi} f(x) \sin kx \, dx,$$

$$a'_k = \frac{2}{\pi} \int_0^{\pi} g(x) \cos kx \, dx, \qquad b'_k = 0.$$

5. Problem 4 shows that an even function has only cosine terms in its Fourier expansion, and an odd function has only sine terms. Thus, if a function f defined on $[0, \pi]$ is extended to be even on $[-\pi, \pi]$, the resulting function f_e will have only cosine terms in its expansion. Similarly, an odd extension of f to $[-\pi, \pi]$ gives a function f_o with only sine terms in its expansion. The restrictions of the even and odd expansions back to the interval $[0, \pi]$ are called the cosine and sine expansions of f respectively. Compute both: (a) the cosine, and (b) the sine expansion of $f(x) = x$ for $0 \le x \le \pi$. Compare the results with that of Problem 1(a).

6. (a) Prove the identity

$$\frac{1}{2} + \sum_{k=1}^{N} \cos ku = \frac{\sin (N + 1/2)u}{2 \sin (u/2)}.$$

   [*Hint.* Sum the identity $2 \sin (u/2) \cos ku = \sin (k + \tfrac{1}{2})u - \sin (k - \tfrac{1}{2})u$ for k from 1 to N.]

   (b) Is the sum on the left the Fourier expansion of the function on the right?

7. Let f be a complex-valued continuous function defined on $[-\pi, \pi]$, and define $c_k = \dfrac{1}{2\pi} \displaystyle\int_{-\pi}^{\pi} e^{ikx} f(x)\, dx$, $k = 0, \pm 1, \pm 2, \ldots$. Then $\displaystyle\sum_{k=-N}^{N} c_k e^{-ikx}$ is called the Nth complex Fourier approximation to f.

   (a) Show that if

   $$f(x) = \sum_{k=-N}^{N} d_k e^{-ikx},$$

   then the constants d_k are the complex Fourier coefficients of f.

   (b) Show that if f is real-valued, then

   $$2c_0 = a_0, \qquad 2c_k = a_k + ib_k,$$

   and

   $$2c_{-k} = a_k - ib_k \quad \text{for} \quad k = 1, 2, 3, \ldots.$$

8. Show that if $\lim_{k \to \infty} b_k = 0$, then

   $$\sum_{k=1}^{\infty} b_k e^{-k^2 t} \sin kx$$

   converges for all $t > 0$ and for all real x. Will a weaker assumption about the b_k suffice?

9. Verify that the series expansion for $u(x, t)$ given in Example 5 of the text is a formal solution of $a^2 u_{xx} = u_t$. Use term-by-term differentiation of the series. (The method is justified by Theorem 6.5 of the next section.)

10. Consider a wire of uniform density and length p, insulated everywhere but at the ends. Let x represent a point along the wire for $0 \le x \le p$, and let $u(x, t)$ be the temperature at x for time t. The heat entering a segment of the wire between points x_1 and x_2 has the following two alternative expressions, assuming $x_1 < x_2$:

(i)
$$-K\frac{\partial u}{\partial x}(x_1, t) + K\frac{\partial u}{\partial x}(x_2, t)$$

(ii)
$$c\int_{x_1}^{x_2}\frac{\partial u}{\partial t}(x, t)\, dt,$$

where K and c are certain positive constants depending on properties of the wire. Show that if u_{xx} and u_t are continuous, then u satisfies the heat equation: $a^2 u_{xx} = u_t$. [*Hint.* Express (i) as an integral of u_{xx} from x_1 to x_2.]

11. Use the method of separation of variables to solve the 1-dimensional heat equation $a^2 u_{xx} = u_t$, subject to each of the following boundary and initial conditions.

(a) $u(0, t) = u(p, t) = 0$, $u(x, 0) = \sin(\pi x/p)$.
(b) $u(0, t) = u(\pi, t) = 0$, $u(x, 0) = x(\pi - x)$.
(c) $u_x(0, t) = u_x(\pi, t) = 0$, $u(x, 0) = \sin x$.

12. Use the method of separation of variables to solve the 1-dimensional wave equation $a^2 u_{xx} = u_{tt}$, subject to each of the following boundary and initial conditions.

(a) $u(0, t) = u(\pi, t) = 0$, $u(x, 0) = \sin x$, $u_t(x, 0)=0$.
(b) $u(0, t) = u(\pi, t) = 0$, $u(x, 0) = \begin{cases} x, 0 \le x \le \pi/2 \\ \pi - x, \pi/2 \le x \le \pi \end{cases}$, $u_t(x, 0)=0$.
(c) $u(0, t) = u(\pi, t) = 0$, $u(x, 0) = 0$, for $0 \le x \le \pi$,
$$u_t(x, 0) = \begin{cases} 0, 0 \le x < \pi/2 \\ 1, \pi/2 \le x \le \pi. \end{cases}$$

13. The 2-dimensional heat equation is $a^2(u_{xx} + u_{yy}) = u_t$, and if u is independent of t, $u_t \equiv 0$. This results in the Laplace equation $u_{xx} + u_{yy} = 0$ for the temperature in a 2-dimensional steady-state heat flow problem. Using the method of separation of variables, solve the equation $u_{xx} + u_{yy} = 0$ in the rectangle $0 \le x \le \pi$, $0 \le y \le \pi$, subject to the boundary conditions $u(0, y) = u(\pi, y) = 0$, $u(x, 0) = 0$, $u(\pi, x) = \sin x$.

6. UNIFORM CONVERGENCE

Let $f_k(x)$, $k = 1, 2, 3, \ldots$, be a sequence of real-valued functions defined for all x in some set S. Then for each x, we consider the series $\sum_{k=1}^{\infty} f_k(x)$. If it converges for each x in S, we say that the series **converges pointwise** on S. Calling the limit $f(x)$ for each x in S, we write

$$f(x) = \sum_{k=1}^{\infty} f_k(x)$$
$$= \lim_{N \to \infty} \sum_{k=1}^{N} f_k(x).$$

Recall that this means that, for each $\mathbf{x}$ in S, there is a number $f(\mathbf{x})$ such that, given $\epsilon > 0$, there is an integer K sufficiently large that

$$\left| \sum_{k=1}^{N} f_k(\mathbf{x}) - f(\mathbf{x}) \right| < \epsilon,$$

whenever $N \geq K$.

EXAMPLE 1. The series $\sum_{k=0}^{\infty} x^k$ has as $(N + 1)$th partial sum the finite sum

$$\sum_{k=0}^{N} x_k = \begin{cases} \dfrac{1 - x^{N+1}}{1 - x}, & x \neq 1 \\ N + 1, & x = 1. \end{cases}$$

Then

$$\sum_{k=0}^{\infty} x^k = \lim_{N \to \infty} \sum_{k=0}^{N} x^k = \frac{1}{1 - x}, \qquad \text{for } -1 < x < 1.$$

For real values of x outside the interval $(-1, 1)$ the series fails to converge.

The trigonometric series $\sum_{k=1}^{\infty} (\sin kx)/k^2$ converges pointwise for all real x. The reason is that its terms can be compared with those of the convergent series $\sum_{k=1}^{\infty} 1/k^2$, by observing that

$$\left| \frac{\sin kx}{k^2} \right| \leq \frac{1}{k^2}, \qquad k = 1, 2, \ldots.$$

The result is that the given series even converges absolutely.

An infinite series $\sum_{k=1}^{\infty} f_k(\mathbf{x})$ that converges for each $\mathbf{x}$ in a set S to a number $f(\mathbf{x})$ defines a function f on S. However, in general, very little can be concluded about the properties of f from pointwise convergence alone. For this reason it is sometimes helpful to consider a stronger form of convergence on S. We say that $\sum_{k=1}^{\infty} f_k$ **converges uniformly** to a function f on a set S, if, given $\epsilon > 0$, there is an integer K such that for all $\mathbf{x}$ in S and for all $N \geq K$,

$$\left| \sum_{k=1}^{N} f_k(\mathbf{x}) - f(\mathbf{x}) \right| < \epsilon.$$

The definition just given should be compared carefully with that of pointwise convergence. Notice that uniform convergence implies pointwise convergence, but not conversely. Roughly speaking, uniform convergence of a series of functions defined on a set S means that the series converges with at least a certain minimum rate for all points in S. A pointwise convergent series may have points at which the convergence is arbitrarily slow. Figure 20

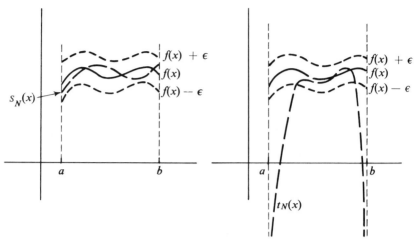

Figure 20

is a picture of uniform and nonuniform convergence to the same function f; $s_N(x)$ and $t_N(x)$ are Nth partial sums of two series.

To determine that a series converges uniformly we have the following:

6.1 Weierstrass test. Let $\sum_{k=1}^{\infty} f_k$ be a series of real-valued functions defined on a set S. If there is a constant series $\sum_{k=1}^{\infty} p_k$, such that

(i) $|f_k(\mathbf{x})| \leq p_k$ for all $\mathbf{x}$ in S and for $k = 1, 2, \ldots$,

(ii) $\sum_{k=1}^{\infty} p_k$ converges,

then $\sum_{k=1}^{\infty} f_k$ converges uniformly to a function f defined on S.

Proof. The comparison test for series shows that $\sum_{k=1}^{\infty} f_k(\mathbf{x})$ converges (even absolutely) for each $\mathbf{x}$ in S to a number that we shall write $f(\mathbf{x})$. Hence we can write

$$f(\mathbf{x}) - \sum_{k=1}^{N} f_k(\mathbf{x}) = \sum_{k=1}^{\infty} f_k(\mathbf{x}) - \sum_{k=1}^{N} f_k(\mathbf{x})$$

$$= \sum_{k=N+1}^{\infty} f_k(\mathbf{x}).$$

It follows that

$$\left| f(\mathbf{x}) - \sum_{k=1}^{N} f_k(\mathbf{x}) \right| \leq \sum_{k=N+1}^{\infty} |f_k(\mathbf{x})| \leq \sum_{k=N+1}^{\infty} p_k.$$

Since $\sum\limits_{1}^{\infty} p_k$ converges, we can, given $\epsilon > 0$, find a K such that $\sum\limits_{k=N+1}^{\infty} p_k < \epsilon$ if $N > K$. This completes the proof, because the number K depends only on ϵ and not on $\mathbf{x}$.

EXAMPLE 2. The trigonometric series $\sum\limits_{k=1}^{\infty} (\sin kx)/k^2$ converges uniformly for all real x, because

$$\left|\frac{\sin kx}{k^2}\right| \leq \frac{1}{k^2},$$

and $\sum\limits_{k=1}^{\infty} 1/k^2$ converges. However, the power series $\sum\limits_{k=0}^{\infty} x^k$, while it converges pointwise for $-1 < x < 1$, fails to converge uniformly on $(-1, 1)$. See Problem 6. The Weierstrass test can be applied on any closed subinterval $[-r, r]$ by observing that $|x^k| \leq r^k$ for x on $[-r, r]$ and that $\sum\limits_{k=0}^{\infty} r^k$ converges if $0 \leq r \leq 1$. Hence, the power series converges pointwise on $(-1, 1)$ and uniformly on $[-r, r]$ for any $r < 1$.

The next four theorems are about uniformly convergent series of functions. They all assert that certain limit operations can be interchanged with the summing of a series, provided that some series converges uniformly. If uniform convergence is replaced by pointwise convergence, then the resulting statements are false.

6.2 **Theorem.** Let $f_k(\mathbf{x})$ be a sequence of functions defined on a set S in $\mathscr{R}^n$ having $\mathbf{x}_0$ as a limit point, and such that the limit

$$\lim_{\mathbf{x}\to\mathbf{x}_0} f_k(\mathbf{x})$$

exists for $k = 1, 2, \ldots$. Then

$$\lim_{\mathbf{x}\to\mathbf{x}_0} \sum_{k=1}^{\infty} f_k(\mathbf{x}) = \sum_{k=1}^{\infty} [\lim_{\mathbf{x}\to\mathbf{x}_0} f_k(\mathbf{x})],$$

provided the series of numbers on the right converges, and the series on the left converges uniformly on S.

Proof. Let $\lim\limits_{\mathbf{x}\to\mathbf{x}_0} f_k(\mathbf{x}) = a_k$. Then, adding and subtracting $\sum\limits_{k=1}^{N} f_k(\mathbf{x})$ and $\sum\limits_{k=1}^{N} a_k$, we get

$$\left|\sum_{k=1}^{\infty} f_k(\mathbf{x}) - \sum_{k=1}^{\infty} a_k\right| \leq \left|\sum_{k=1}^{\infty} f_k(\mathbf{x}) - \sum_{k=1}^{N} f_k(\mathbf{x})\right| +$$
$$+ \left|\sum_{k=1}^{N} f_k(\mathbf{x}) - \sum_{k=1}^{N} a_k\right| + \left|\sum_{k=1}^{N} a_k - \sum_{k=1}^{\infty} a_k\right|. \tag{1}$$

Now let $\epsilon > 0$. Since $\sum_{k=1}^{\infty} f_k$ converges uniformly we can choose K such that $N > K$ implies

$$\left| \sum_{k=1}^{\infty} f_k(\mathbf{x}) - \sum_{k=1}^{N} f_k(\mathbf{x}) \right| < \frac{\epsilon}{3}, \qquad \text{for all } \mathbf{x} \text{ in } S.$$

Then choose an $N > K$ such that

$$\left| \sum_{k=1}^{N} a_k - \sum_{k=1}^{\infty} a_k \right| < \frac{\epsilon}{3}.$$

Finally, pick $\delta > 0$ so that $|\mathbf{x} - \mathbf{x}_0| < \delta$ implies by the relation $\lim\limits_{\mathbf{x} \to \mathbf{x}_0} \sum_{k=1}^{N} f_k(\mathbf{x}) = \sum_{k=1}^{N} a_k$, that

$$\left| \sum_{k=1}^{N} f_k(\mathbf{x}) - \sum_{k=1}^{N} a_k \right| < \frac{\epsilon}{3}.$$

Then for $\mathbf{x}$ satisfying $|\mathbf{x} - \mathbf{x}_0| < \delta$ the left hand side of (1) is less than ϵ.

6.3 Corollary. If $\sum_{k=1}^{\infty} f_k(\mathbf{x})$ is a uniformly convergent series of continuous functions f_k defined on a set S in $\mathscr{R}^n$, then the function f defined by

$$f(\mathbf{x}) = \sum_{k=1}^{\infty} f_k(\mathbf{x}) \text{ is continuous on } S.$$

In the next two theorems we restrict ourselves to functions of one variable, though by treating one variable at a time they can be applied to functions of several variables.

6.4 Theorem. If the series $\sum_{k=1}^{\infty} f_k$ converges uniformly on the interval $[a, b]$, and the functions f_k are continuous on $[a, b]$, then

$$\sum_{k=1}^{\infty} \int_a^b f_k(x)\,dx = \int_a^b \left[\sum_{k=1}^{\infty} f_k(x) \right] dx.$$

Proof. By Theorem 6.3 the function $\sum_{k=1}^{\infty} f_k(x)$ is continuous on $[a, b]$ and so is integrable there. We have

$$\int_a^b \left[\sum_{k=1}^{\infty} f_k(x) \right] dx - \sum_{k=1}^{N} \int_a^b f_k(x)\,dx = \int_a^b \sum_{k=N+1}^{\infty} f_k(x)\,dx. \qquad (2)$$

Let $\epsilon > 0$, and choose K so large that if $N > K$, then $\left| \sum_{k=N+1}^{\infty} f_k(x) \right| < \epsilon(b - a)^{-1}$, for all x in $[a, b]$. Then using the fact that, for continuous g,

$$\left| \int_a^b g(x)\,dx \right| \le (b - a) \max_{a \le x \le b} \left| g(x) \right|,$$

we have $\left| \int_a^b \sum_{k=N+1}^{\infty} f_k(x)\, dx \right| \leq (b-a)\cdot\epsilon\cdot(b-a)^{-1} = \epsilon,$ for $N > K.$

Thus the left side of Equation (2) is less than ϵ in absolute value for $N > K$, which was to be shown.

The interchange of differentiation with the summing of a series requires somewhat more in the way of hypotheses than did the previous theorem on integration.

6.5 Theorem. Let $\{f_k(x)\}_{k=1,2,\dots}$ be a sequence of continuously differentiable functions defined on an interval $[a, b]$. If $\sum_{k=1}^{\infty} f_k(x) = f(x)$ for all x in $[a, b]$ (pointwise convergence), and $\sum_{k=1}^{\infty} \dfrac{df_k}{dx}(x)$ converges uniformly on $[a, b]$, then f is continuously differentiable, and

$$\frac{d}{dx} \sum_{k=1}^{\infty} f_k(x) = \sum_{k=1}^{\infty} \frac{df_k}{dx}(x).$$

Proof. By the fundamental theorem of calculus,

$$\sum_{k=1}^{N} [f_k(x) - f_k(a)] = \sum_{k=1}^{N} \int_a^x f_k'(t)\, dt$$

$$= \int_a^x \left[\sum_{k=1}^{N} f_k'(t) \right] dt. \tag{3}$$

Letting N tend to infinity we get $\sum_{k=1}^{\infty} f_k(x) = f(x)$, so

$$f(x) - f(a) = \int_a^x \left[\sum_{k=1}^{\infty} f_k'(t) \right] dt,$$

where we have used pointwise convergence on the left side of Equation (3), and, on the right, have used uniform convergence, together with Theorem 6.4. Differentiation of both sides of the last equation gives

$$f'(x) = \sum_{k=1}^{\infty} f_k'(x),$$

which is the conclusion of the theorem.

EXAMPLE 3. Consider the trigonometric series

$$\sum_{k=1}^{\infty} \frac{\sin kx}{k^4}.$$

Clearly the series converges for all real x. Furthermore the series of derivatives of the terms of the given series is

$$\sum_{k=1}^{\infty} \frac{\cos kx}{k^3}.$$

This series converges uniformly for all x by the Weierstrass test, because

$$\left|\frac{\cos kx}{k^3}\right| \le \frac{1}{k^3},$$

and $\sum_1^\infty (1/k^3)$ converges. Hence, by Theorem 6.5,

$$\frac{d}{dx}\sum_{k=1}^\infty \frac{\sin kx}{k^4} = \sum_{k=1}^\infty \frac{\cos kx}{k^3}.$$

The same argument can be applied again to give

$$\frac{d^2}{dx^2}\sum_{k=1}^\infty \frac{\sin kx}{k^4} = -\sum_{k=1}^\infty \frac{\sin kx}{k^2}.$$

EXERCISES

1. Show that the series $\sum_{k=0}^\infty x^k$ converges uniformly for $-d \le x \le d$, if $0 < d < 1$.

2. (a) Show that the trigonometric series $\sum_{k=1}^\infty \frac{\cos kx}{k^2}$ converges uniformly for all real x.

   (b) Prove that the series of part (a) defines a continuous function for all real x.

3. (a) Show that if a trigonometric series

$$\frac{a_0}{2} + \sum_{k=1}^\infty a_k \cos kx + b_k \sin kx$$

   converges uniformly on $[-\pi, \pi]$, then it converges uniformly for *all* real x.

   (b) Prove that the uniformly convergent series of part (a) is necessarily the Fourier series of the function it represents. [*Hint.* Use Theorem 6.4]

4. (a) Show that if $|c_k| \le B$ for some fixed number B, then the series

$$u(x, t) = \sum_{k=1}^\infty c_k e^{-k^2 t} \sin kx$$

   is a solution of the differential equation

$$u_{xx} = u_t \text{ for } t > 0 \text{ and } x \text{ in } [0, \pi],$$

   satisfying $u(0, t) = u(\pi, t) = 0$. [*Hint.* Use Theorem 6.5.]

   (b) Show that if $u(x, t)$ in part (a) is defined for $t = 0$ by a uniformly convergent series, then $u(x, t)$ is continuous on the set S in $\mathcal{R}^2$ defined by $0 \le t, 0 \le x \le \pi$.

   (c) Show that the function $u(x, t)$ is infinitely often differentiable with respect to both x and t, for $t > 0$.

5. Show that if a trigonometric series of the form shown in problem 3(a) satisfies $|a_n| \le A/n^2$, $|b_n| \le B/n^2$ for $n = 1, 2, 3, \ldots$, and some constants A and B, then the trigonometric series is a Fourier series.

6. By considering the partial sums of the power series $\sum_{k=0}^{\infty} x^k$ for $-1 < x < 1$, show that the series fails to converge uniformly on $(-1, 1)$.

7. Show that $\sum_{k=0}^{\infty} (-1)^k (1 - x)x^k$ converges uniformly on $[0, 1]$, but that $\sum_{k=0}^{\infty} (1 - x)x^k$ only converges pointwise on $[0, 1]$.

8. (a) Assume that the series $\sum_{k=1}^{\infty} k^2 a_n$ and $\sum_{k=1}^{\infty} k^2 b_n$ both converge absolutely. Show that

$$w(x, t) = \sum_{k=1}^{\infty} \sin kx \, (a_k \cos kat + b_k \sin kat)$$

is a solution of the 1-dimensional wave equation $a^2 w_{xx} = w_{tt}$. [*Hint.* Use the Weierstrass test and Theorem 6.5.]

(b) Show that the solution $w(x, t)$ of part (a) satisfies the boundary conditions $w(0, t) = w(\pi, t) = 0$ for $t \ge 0$ and an initial condition $w(x, 0) = h(x)$, where h is twice continuously differentiable.

9. Show that with uniform convergence replaced by pointwise convergence, the statements of Theorems: (a) 6.3, (b) 6.4, and (c) 6.5 become false.

10. Can Theorems 6.4 and 6.5 be proved under the more general assumption that the functions involved are vector-valued, with values in $\mathcal{R}^n$? [*Hint.* See Problems 16 and 17 of Chapter 2, Section 3.]

7. ORTHOGONAL FUNCTIONS

Some of the properties of Fourier expansions are shared by a large class of similar expansions in which the functions $\sin kx$ and $\cos kx$ are replaced by some sequence $\{\varphi_k\}_{k=1, 2, \ldots}$ of functions, all of which are mutually orthogonal. The orthogonality is measured in terms of an inner product on a vector space of functions. For example, if f and g are elements in the space $\mathcal{C}[-\pi, \pi]$ of continuous functions on the interval $[-\pi, \pi]$, we can define an inner product of f and g by

$$\langle f, g \rangle = \int_{-\pi}^{\pi} f(x)g(x) \, dx. \tag{1}$$

It follows by direct computation (compare Problem 2 of Section 5) that if we set $\varphi_1(x) = 1/\sqrt{2\pi}$, $\varphi_{2n}(x) = (\cos nx)/\sqrt{\pi}$, and $\varphi_{2n+1}(x) = (\sin nx)/\sqrt{\pi}$, then

$$\langle \varphi_k, \varphi_l \rangle = \begin{cases} 1, & k = l \\ 0, & k \ne l. \end{cases}$$

The sequence $\{\varphi_k\}_{k=1,2,\ldots}$ is **orthonormal** with respect to the inner product given by Equation (1). The term "normal" comes from the fact the functions have been normalized by requiring $\|\varphi_k\| = \langle \varphi_k, \varphi_k \rangle^{1/2} = 1$. In the trigonometric case the normalization is achieved by dividing the sines and cosines by $\sqrt{\pi}$.

To see the importance of orthonormal sequences in general, we consider the following problem: Let $\langle f, g \rangle$ be an inner product on a vector space, and let $\{\varphi_k\}_{k=1,2,\ldots}$ be a sequence of elements, orthonormal with respect to the inner product. Using the norm defined by $\|f\| = \langle f, f \rangle^{1/2}$, we try to determine coefficients c_k, $k = 1, 2, \ldots, N$, such that

$$\left\| g - \sum_{k=1}^{N} c_k \varphi_k \right\|$$

is minimized for given g and N. The fact that the sequence φ_k is orthonormal makes the solution very simple. For, by adding and subtracting $\sum_{k=1}^{N} \langle g, \varphi_k \rangle^2$, we get

$$
\begin{aligned}
0 \le \left\| g - \sum_{k=1}^{N} c_k \varphi_k \right\|^2 &= \left\langle g - \sum_{k=1}^{N} c_k \varphi_k, g - \sum_{k=1}^{N} c_k \varphi_k \right\rangle \\
&= \|g\|^2 - 2 \sum_{k=1}^{N} c_k \langle g, \varphi_k \rangle + \sum_{k=1}^{N} c_k^2 \\
&= \|g\|^2 - \sum_{k=1}^{N} \langle g, \varphi_k \rangle^2 \qquad (2) \\
&\quad + \sum_{k=1}^{N} [\langle g, \varphi_k \rangle^2 - 2c_k \langle g, \varphi_k \rangle + c_k^2] \\
&= \|g\|^2 - \sum_{k=1}^{N} \langle g, \varphi_k \rangle^2 + \sum_{k=1}^{N} [\langle g, \varphi_k \rangle - c_k]^2.
\end{aligned}
$$

But the first two terms in the last expression are independent of the choice of the c_k's, and the last sum is then minimized by taking $c_k = \langle g, \varphi_k \rangle$. The numbers $\langle g, \varphi_k \rangle$ are called the **Fourier coefficients** of g with respect to the orthonormal sequence $\{\varphi_k\}$. Notice that the simplicity of the answer to the problem depends very much on the orthogonality of the φ_k's.

We can summarize what has just been proved as

7.1 Theorem. Let $\{\varphi_k\}_{k=1,2,\ldots}$ be an orthonormal sequence in a vector space with an inner product. Then, given an element g of the space, the distance

$$\left\| g - \sum_{k=1}^{N} c_k \varphi_k \right\|$$

is minimized for $N = 1, 2, \ldots$ by taking c_k to be the Fourier coefficient $\langle g, \varphi_k \rangle$.

The important thing about the conclusion of Theorem 7.1 is that the c_k's are uniquely determined, independently of N. In other words, if we wanted to improve the closeness of the approximation to g by increasing N, then Theorem 7.1 says that the c_k's already computed are to be left unchanged, and it is only necessary to compute additional coefficients $c_{N+1} = \langle g, \varphi_{N+1} \rangle$, etc.

As a by-product of the proof of Theorem 7.1 we have

7.2 Bessel's inequality.

$$\| g \|^2 \geq \sum_{k=1}^{\infty} \langle g, \varphi_k \rangle^2.$$

Proof. The inequality

$$0 \leq \| g \|^2 - \sum_{k=1}^{N} \langle g, \varphi_k \rangle^2 + \sum_{k=1}^{N} [\langle g, \varphi_k \rangle - c_k]^2$$

was established in the last step of Equation (2.) On taking $c_k = \langle g, \varphi_k \rangle$, the inequality becomes

$$0 \leq \| g \|^2 - \sum_{k=1}^{N} \langle g, \varphi_k \rangle^2.$$

Bessel's inequality follows by letting N tend to infinity.

EXAMPLE 1. The approximation of g by a sum $\sum_{k=1}^{N} c_k \varphi_k$ has been measured by a norm in Theorem 7.1. To see what this means for approximation by trigonometric polynomials, we use the inner product given by Equation (1) on the space $\mathscr{C}\,[-\pi, \pi]$ of continuous functions on $[-\pi, \pi]$. Given the orthonormal sequence $\varphi_1(x) = 1/\sqrt{2\pi}$, $\varphi_{2n}(x) = (\cos nx)/\sqrt{\pi}$, $\varphi_{2n+1}(x) = (\sin nx)/\sqrt{\pi}$, we try to minimize, for given g in $\mathscr{C}\,[-\pi, \pi]$, the norm

$$\| g - \sum_{k=1}^{2N+1} c_k \varphi_k \|.$$

We have seen that this is done by taking $c_k = \langle g, \varphi_k \rangle$. But, by the definition of the inner product,

$$\langle g, \varphi_k \rangle = \begin{cases} \int_{-\pi}^{\pi} \dfrac{1}{\sqrt{2\pi}} g(t)\, dt, & k = 1 \\[2ex] \int_{-\pi}^{\pi} g(t) \dfrac{\cos nt}{\sqrt{\pi}}\, dt, & k = 2n \\[2ex] \int_{-\pi}^{\pi} g(t) \dfrac{\sin nt}{\sqrt{\pi}}\, dt, & k = 2n + 1. \end{cases}$$

Hence, the terms $c_k \varphi_k$ become

$$\langle g, \varphi_1 \rangle \varphi_1(x) = \frac{1}{2\pi} \int_{-\pi}^{\pi} g(t)\, dt,$$

$$\langle g, \varphi_{2n} \rangle \varphi_{2n}(x) = \left[\frac{1}{\pi} \int_{-\pi}^{\pi} g(t) \cos nt\, dt \right] \cos nx,$$

$$\langle g, \varphi_{2n+1} \rangle \varphi_{2n+1}(x) = \left[\frac{1}{\pi} \int_{-\pi}^{\pi} g(t) \sin nt\, dt \right] \sin nx.$$

Then

$$\sum_{k=1}^{2N+1} c_k \varphi_k(x) = \frac{a_0}{2} + \sum_{n=1}^{N} (a_k \cos kx + b_k \sin kx),$$

where a_k and b_k are the trigonometric Fourier coefficients as defined in Section 5. The square of the norm to be minimized takes the form

$$\int_{-\pi}^{\pi} [g(x) - \frac{a_0}{2} - \sum_{k=1}^{N} (a_k \cos kx + b_k \sin kx)]^2 \, dx,$$

and Theorem 7.1 says that the minimum will be attained for any fixed N by taking a_k and b_k to be the Fourier coefficients of g.

The minimization of an integral of the form

$$\int_{a}^{b} [g(x) - \sum_{k=1}^{N} c_k \varphi_k(x)]^2 \, dx$$

is called a best **mean-square approximation** to g. In this sense we can say that the Fourier approximation provides the best mean-square approximation by a trigonometric polynomial.

In Section 5 we observed that the functions $\cos kx$ and $\sin kx$ are solutions of the differential equation $y'' = -k^2 y$. The result can be stated by saying that $\cos kx$ and $\sin kx$ are **eigenfunctions** of the differential operator $d^2/(dx^2)$, corresponding to the **eigenvalue** $-k^2$. More generally, let L be a linear transformation defined on some vector space, and having its range in the same space. We say that a *nonzero* vector f is an **eigenvector** of L, corresponding to the **eigenvalue** λ if $Lf = \lambda f$, for some number λ.

To see the connection between eigenvectors and orthogonal sets of functions, we need one more definition. Let $\mathscr{F}$ be a vector space with an inner product $\langle f, g \rangle$. Let L be a linear transformation from $\mathscr{F}$ into $\mathscr{F}$. Then L is **symmetric** with respect to the inner product if $\langle Lf, g \rangle = \langle f, Lg \rangle$, for all vectors f and g for which Lf and Lg are defined as elements of $\mathscr{F}$. A linear transformation with the same domain space and range space is sometimes called a **linear operator**.

EXAMPLE 2. Let $\langle f, g \rangle$ be the inner product defined by Equation (1) on $\mathscr{C}[-\pi, \pi]$. If we let $Lf = d^2 f/dx^2$, then it is clear that Lf is in $\mathscr{C}[-\pi, \pi]$ only for those f in $\mathscr{C}[-\pi, \pi]$ that happen to have continuous second derivatives. Thus, in order for L to be symmetric, we must have $\langle Lf, g \rangle = \langle f, Lg \rangle$ for all twice continuously differentiable f and g on $[-\pi, \pi]$. Equivalently, we must have, because of the definition of the inner product,

$$\int_{-\pi}^{\pi} f''(x)g(x) \, dx = \int_{-\pi}^{\pi} f(x)g''(x) \, dx.$$

Integration by parts twice shows that

$$\int_{-\pi}^{\pi} f''(x)g(x) \, dx = f'(\pi)g(\pi) - f'(-\pi)g(-\pi) - f(\pi)g'(\pi)$$

$$+ f(-\pi)g'(-\pi) + \int_{-\pi}^{\pi} f(x)g''(x) \, dx.$$

Hence to make L symmetric we restrict its domain to some subspace of $\mathscr{C}[-\pi, \pi]$ for which the nonintegrated terms will always add up to zero. This can be done in several ways. For example, we may restrict L to the subspace consisting of those functions h in $\mathscr{C}[-\pi, \pi]$ for which $h(\pi) = h(-\pi) = 0$, or to the subspace for which $h'(\pi) = h'(-\pi) = 0$. With either of these restrictions L becomes symmetric. Notice that a restriction of the required type is a boundary condition, in that it specifies the values of f at the end-points π and $-\pi$ of its domain of definition.

The connection between orthogonal functions and symmetric operators is as follows:

7.3 Theorem. Let L be a symmetric linear operator defined on a vector space $\mathscr{F}$ with an inner product. If f_1 and f_2 are eigenvectors of L corresponding to distinct eigenvalues λ_1 and λ_2, then f_1 and f_2 are orthogonal.

Proof. We assume that

$$Lf_1 = \lambda_1 f_1, \qquad Lf_2 = \lambda_2 f_2,$$

and prove that $\langle f_1, f_2 \rangle = 0$. We have

$$\langle Lf_1, f_2 \rangle = \langle \lambda_1 f_1, f_2 \rangle = \lambda_1 \langle f_1, f_2 \rangle,$$

and

$$\langle f_1, Lf_2 \rangle = \langle f_1, \lambda_2 f_2 \rangle = \lambda_2 \langle f_1, f_2 \rangle.$$

Because L is symmetric, $\langle Lf_1, f_2 \rangle = \langle f_1, Lf_2 \rangle$, so $\lambda_1 \langle f_1, f_2 \rangle = \lambda_2 \langle f_1, f_2 \rangle$, or $(\lambda_1 - \lambda_2)\langle f_1, f_2 \rangle = 0$. Since λ_1 and λ_2 are not equal, we must have $\langle f_1, f_2 \rangle = 0$.

We consider the **Sturm-Liouville** differential operator of the form

$$Lf = (pf')' + qf, \tag{4}$$

where p is a continuously differentiable function and q is assumed only continuous. (The operator d^2/dx^2 is a special case if we set $p(x) \equiv 1, q(x) \equiv 0$.) We want to see what boundary conditions should be imposed on the domain of L in order to make L symmetric with respect to the inner product

$$\langle f, g \rangle = \int_a^b f(x)\, g(x)\, dx.$$

The following formula simplifies the problem.

7.4 Lagrange formula. If L is given by $Lf = (pf')' + qf$ on an interval $[a, b]$, then

$$\langle f_1, Lf_2 \rangle - \langle Lf_1, f_2 \rangle = [p(f_1 f_2' - f_1' f_2)]_a^b.$$

Proof. Starting with the definition of L, we rearrange $f_1(Lf_2) - (Lf_1)f_2$ as follows:

$$f_1(Lf_2) - (Lf_1)f_2 = f_1[(pf'_2)' + qf_2] - f_2[(pf'_1)' + qf_1]$$
$$= f_1(pf'_2)' - f_2(pf'_1)'$$
$$= f_1[pf''_2 + p'f'_2] - f_2[pf''_1 + p'f'_1]$$
$$= p'[f_1f'_2 - f'_1f_2] + p[f_1f''_2 - f''_1f_2]$$
$$= [p(f_1f'_2 - f'_1f_2)]'.$$

Integration of both sides from a to b gives the Lagrange formula.

Formula 7.4 shows that any condition on the coefficient p, or on the space containing f_1 and f_2, which makes $[p(f_1f'_2 - f'_1f_2)]_a^b = 0$, will also make L symmetric.

EXAMPLE 3. The operator L defined by $Lf(x) = (1 - x^2)f''(x) - 2xf'(x)$, has the form shown in Equation (4) if we set $p(x) = (1 - x^2)$ and $q(x) \equiv 0$. We shall consider L to be operating on twice continuously differentiable functions defined on $[-1, 1]$. To make L symmetric, we need to ensure that the right-hand side of the Lagrange formula is always zero for $a = -1$, $b = 1$. But $p(x) = (1 - x^2)$, so $p(-1) = p(1) = 0$. Hence, L is symmetric on the space $\mathscr{C}[-1, 1]$ without further restriction, and its domain consists of all twice continuously differentiable functions in $\mathscr{C}[-1, 1]$.

The symmetric operator Lf defined in the previous example is usually associated with the differential equation

$$(1 - x^2)y'' - 2xy' + n(n + 1)y = 0. \tag{5}$$

This is called the **Legendre equation** of index n, and it is satisfied by the nth **Legendre polynomial**, defined by

7.5 $$P_n(x) = \frac{1}{2^n n!} \frac{d^n}{dx^n}(x^2 - 1)^n, \qquad n = 0, 1, 2, \ldots .$$

That P_n satisfies Equation (5) can be verified by repeated differentiation. See Problem 8. The significance of the fact that P_n satisfies the Legendre equation comes from writing the equation in the form $Ly = -n(n + 1)y$, where L is the symmetric operator $Ly = (1 - x^2)y'' - 2xy'$ on $\mathscr{C}[-1, 1]$. Then P_n can be looked at as an eigenfunction of L, corresponding to the eigenvalue $-n(n + 1)$. Hence, by Theorem 7.3, the Legendre polynomials are orthogonal. That is,

$$\int_{-1}^{1} P_n(x)P_m(x)\, dx = 0, \qquad n \neq m.$$

Furthermore, a fairly complicated calculation (see Problem 10) shows that

$$\int_{-1}^{1} P_n^2(x)\, dx = \frac{2}{2n + 1}, \qquad n = 0, 1, 2, \ldots .$$

Therefore, the normalized sequence $\left\{\sqrt{\dfrac{2n+1}{2}}P_n(x)\right\}$ $n = 0, 1, 2, \ldots$ is an orthonormal sequence in $\mathscr{C}[-1, 1]$.

The Nth **Fourier-Legendre approximation** to a function g in $\mathscr{C}[-1, 1]$ is the finite sum

$$\sum_{k=0}^{N} c_k P_k(x),$$

where

$$c_k = \frac{2k+1}{2} \int_{-1}^{1} g(x) P_k(x)\, dx. \tag{6}$$

Theorem 7.1 then implies that the best mean-square approximation to g by a linear combination of Legendre polynomials is given by the Fourier-Legendre approximation. In other words,

$$\int_{-1}^{1} [g(x) - \sum_{k=0}^{N} c_k P_k(x)]^2\, dx$$

is minimized by computing c_k by Equation (6).

EXERCISES

1. (a) Verify that

$$\langle f, g \rangle = \int_{a}^{b} f(x)\, g(x)\, dx$$

   defines an inner product on the space $\mathscr{C}[a, b]$ of continuous functions defined on $[a, b]$.

   (b) What condition is required of a continuous function w defined on $[a, b]$ in order that

$$\langle f, g \rangle = \int_{a}^{b} f(x)\, g(x)\, w(x)\, dx$$

   define an inner product?

2. Let $\{\varphi_k\}$ be an orthonormal sequence of functions in $\mathscr{C}[a, b]$, and let g be in $\mathscr{C}[a, b]$. Show that if the real-valued function

$$\Delta(c_1, \ldots, c_N) = \int_{a}^{b} \left[g(x) - \sum_{k=1}^{N} c_k \varphi_k(x) \right]^2 dx$$

   has a local minimum as a function of $(c_1, \ldots, c_N)$ then $c_k = \int_{a}^{b} g(x)\, \varphi_k(x)\, dx$. [*Hint.* Differentiate the formula for Δ under the integral sign. This is justified under the assumptions made here. (See Problem 7 of Chapter 4, Section 2.)]

3. Let $\{\varphi_k\}$ be an orthonormal sequence of functions in $\mathscr{C}[a, b]$ and let g be in $\mathscr{C}[a, b]$. Use Bessel's inequality to show the following:

   (a) $\displaystyle\sum_{k=1}^{\infty} \left[\int_{a}^{b} g(x)\, \varphi_k(x)\, dx \right]^2$ converges,

(b) If c_k is the kth Fourier coefficient of g with respect to $\{\varphi_k\}$, then $\lim_{k \to \infty} c_k = 0$.

(c) Find an example of a function whose trigonometric Fourier series has coefficients a_k and b_k such that $\sum_{k=1}^{\infty} (a_k^2 + b_k^2)$ converges, but such that $\sum_{k=1}^{\infty} a_k$ or $\sum_{k=1}^{\infty} b_k$ does not converge.

4. Let L be a linear transformation from a vector space $\mathscr{F}_1$ to an otherwise unrelated vector space $\mathscr{F}_2$. Can L have eigenvectors?

5. Find all eigenfunctions and corresponding eigenvalues of the differential operator d^2/dx^2 satisfying each of the following sets of boundary conditions. That is, solve $y'' = \lambda y$, subject to the boundary conditions.

   (a) $y(0) = y(\pi) = 0$
   (b) $y(0) = y(\pi) + y'(\pi) = 0$
   (c) $y(0) = y'(\pi) = 0$.

6. Let $\mathscr{C}[a, b]$ be the continuous real-valued functions defined on $[a, b]$, $\mathscr{C}'[a, b]$ the continuously differentiable functions on that interval, and $\mathscr{C}''[a, b]$ the twice continuously differentiable functions there.

   (a) Show that $\mathscr{C}[a, b]$, $\mathscr{C}'[a, b]$, and $\mathscr{C}''[a, b]$ are vector spaces, each contained in the preceding one.

   (b) Let $\mathscr{B}_{x_0}[a, b]$ be the set of functions f contained in $\mathscr{C}[a, b]$ and satisfying a condition of the form

   $$cf(x_0) + df'(x_0) = 0,$$

   where c and d are constants, not both zero. Show that $\mathscr{B}_{x_0}[a, b]$ is a vector subspace of $\mathscr{C}[a, b]$.

   (c) Show that $\mathscr{C}''[a, b] \cap \mathscr{B}_a[a, b] \cap \mathscr{B}_b[a, b]$ is a vector subspace of $\mathscr{C}[a, b]$.

7. Show that the differential operator d^2/dx^2 is symmetric with respect to the inner product

$$\langle f, g \rangle = \int_{-1}^{1} f(x) g(x) \, dx,$$

and with each of the following sets of boundary conditions.

   (a) $f(-1) = f(1) = 0$
   (b) $f'(1) = f'(-1) = 0$
   (c) $c_1 f(-1) + d_1 f'(-1) = c_2 f(1) + d_2 f'(1) = 0$,
   where $c_i^2 + d_i^2 > 0$.

8. Verify that the Legendre polynomial P_n defined by Formula 7.5 satisfies the Legendre equation: $(1 - x^2)y'' - 2xy' + n(n + 1)y = 0$. [*Hint.* Let $u = (x^2 - 1)^n$. Then $(x^2 - 1)u' = 2nxu$. Differentiate both sides $(n + 1)$ times with respect to x.]

9. Compute the Legendre polynomials P_0, P_1, and P_2.

10. (a) By using Formula 7.5 and repeated integration by parts, show that

$$\int_{-1}^{1} P_n^2(x)\, dx = \frac{(2n)!}{2^{2n}(n!)^2} \int_{-1}^{1} (1 - x^2)^n\, dx.$$

(b) Show that

$$\int_{-1}^{1} (1 - x^2)^n\, dx = 2 \int_{0}^{\pi/2} \sin^{2n+1} \theta\, d\theta.$$

(c) Show that

$$\int_{0}^{\pi/2} \sin^{2n+1} \theta\, d\theta = \frac{2 \cdot 4 \cdot 6 \cdot \ldots \cdot (2n)}{1 \cdot 3 \cdot 5 \cdot \ldots \cdot (2n + 1)}.$$

(d) Show that

$$\int_{-1}^{1} P_n^2(x)\, dx = \frac{2}{2n + 1}.$$

11. Prove that P_n, the nth Legendre polynomial, has n distinct roots in the interval $[-1, 1]$. [*Hint.* Use Formula 7.5 and Rolle's theorem.]

12. The 3-dimensional Laplace equation in spherical coordinates (r, φ, θ) has the form

$$\frac{\partial}{\partial r}\left(r^2 \frac{\partial u}{\partial r}\right) + \frac{1}{\sin \varphi} \frac{\partial}{\partial \varphi}\left(\sin \varphi \frac{\partial u}{\partial \varphi}\right) + \frac{1}{\sin^2 \varphi} \frac{\partial^2 u}{\partial \theta^2} = 0.$$

(a) Show that for solutions $u(r, \varphi, \theta) = v(r, \varphi)$ that are independent of θ, the equation has the form

$$r \frac{\partial^2}{\partial r^2}(rv) + \frac{1}{\sin \varphi} \frac{\partial}{\partial \varphi}\left(\sin \varphi \frac{\partial v}{\partial \varphi}\right) = 0.$$

(b) Show that the method of separation of variables applied to the equation of part (a) leads to the two ordinary differential equations

$$r^2 G'' + 2rG' = \lambda G,$$

$$\frac{1}{\sin \varphi} \frac{d}{d\varphi}\left(\sin \varphi \frac{dH}{d\varphi}\right) = -\lambda H.$$

(c) Show that the equation for $G(r)$ has solutions

$$r^{-(1/2) + \sqrt{\lambda + (1/4)}} \quad \text{and} \quad r^{-(1/2) - \sqrt{\lambda + (1/4)}}. \qquad [\textit{Hint.} \ \text{Let } r = e^t.]$$

(d) Show that the equation for H can be put in the form of the Legendre equation

$$(1 - x^2)H'' - 2xH' + \lambda H = 0.$$

[*Hint.* Let $x = \cos \varphi$.]

(e) By setting $\lambda = n(n + 1)$ find a sequence of solutions to the partial differential equation of part (a).

13. Show that in the case of the orthonormal sequence derived from the Legendre polynomials, the general expansion $\sum_{k=0}^{N} \langle g, \varphi_k \rangle \varphi_k$ reduces to $\sum_{k=0}^{N} c_k P_n(x)$, where c_k is given by Equation (6) of the text.

14. The orthonormal sequence $\{\sqrt{(2n + 1)/2}\, P_n(x)\}$ of normalized Legendre polynomials can be derived by applying the so called Gram-Schmidt orthogonalization process to the sequence $\{1, x, x^2, \ldots\}$. We use the inner product $\langle f, g \rangle = \int_{-1}^{1} f(x)\, g(x)\, dx$ defined on $\mathscr{C}[-1, 1]$. First determine φ_0 so that it lies in the 1-dimensional subspace spanned by the constant function 1, and so that $\langle \varphi_0, \varphi_0 \rangle = 1$. Then determine φ_1 so that it lies in the subspace spanned by 1 and x, and so that $\langle \varphi_0, \varphi_1 \rangle = 0$, $\langle \varphi_1, \varphi_1 \rangle = 1$. In general, determine φ_k so that it lies in the subspace spanned by $\{1, x, \ldots, x^k\}$, and so that $\langle \varphi_j, \varphi_k \rangle = 0$, $j = 0, 1, \ldots,$ $k - 1$, and $\langle \varphi_k, \varphi_k \rangle = 1$. Compute the polynomials φ_0, φ_1, and φ_2, and show that, up to sign, the sequence is the same as the sequence of normalized Legendre polynomials.

MULTIPLE INTEGRALS 4

1. ITERATED INTEGRALS

This chapter is devoted to the study of the integral of real-valued functions with domains in n-dimensional euclidean space. In the present section we introduce the iterated integral, based on the ordinary definite integral,

$$\int_a^b f(x)\, dx,$$

of a real-valued function of one real variable. We begin with $n = 2$, that is, with the iterated integral of functions $\mathscr{R}^2 \xrightarrow{f} \mathscr{R}$.

Suppose $f(x, y)$ is a function defined on a rectangle $a \leq x \leq b$, $c \leq y \leq d$. By

$$\int_c^d f(x, y)\, dy$$

is meant simply the definite integral of the function of one variable obtained by holding x fixed; for example

$$\int_0^2 x^3 y^2\, dy = \frac{x^3 y^3}{3}\Bigg]_{y=0}^{y=2} = \frac{8}{3} x^3.$$

295

As this example shows, if the integral exists, it depends on x. Thus, we may set

$$F(x) = \int_c^d f(x, y)\, dy$$

and form the **iterated integral**

$$\int_a^b F(x)\, dx = \int_a^b \left[\int_c^d f(x, y)\, dy \right] dx.$$

A common notational convention, which we shall adopt, is to omit the brackets and write the iterated integral as

$$\int_a^b dx \int_c^d f(x, y)\, dy.$$

This notation has the advantage of emphasizing which variable goes with which integral sign, namely, x with $\int_a^b$ and y with $\int_c^d$.

EXAMPLE 1. Consider $f(x, y) = x^2 + y$, defined on the rectangular region $0 \le x \le 1$, $1 \le y \le 2$.

$$\int_0^1 dx \int_1^2 (x^2 + y)\, dy = \int_0^1 \left[x^2 y + \frac{y^2}{2} \right]_{y=1}^{y=2} dx$$

$$= \int_0^1 \left[(2x^2 + 2) - \left(x^2 + \frac{1}{2} \right) \right] dx$$

$$= \int_0^1 \left(x^2 + \frac{3}{2} \right) dx = \frac{1}{3} + \frac{3}{2} = \frac{11}{6}.$$

To interpret this example geometrically, look at the surface defined by $z = x^2 + y$ shown in Figure 1. For each x in the interval between 0 and 1, the integral

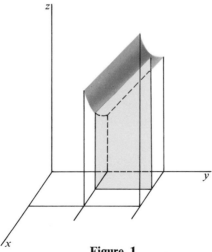

Figure 1

$$\int_1^2 (x^2 + y)\, dy = x^2 + \frac{3}{2}$$

is the area of the shaded cross section. It is natural to interpret the definite integral of an area-valued function as volume. Thus it is reasonable to regard the iterated integral

$$\int_0^1 dx \int_1^2 (x^2 + y)\, dy = \frac{11}{6}$$

as the volume of the 3-dimensional region lying below the surface and above the rectangle $0 \leq x \leq 1,\, 1 \leq y \leq 2$.

EXAMPLE 2. We can perform the integration in Example 1 in the opposite order.

$$\int_1^2 dy \int_0^1 (x^2 + y)\, dx = \int_1^2 \left[\frac{x^3}{3} + yx \right]_{x=0}^{x=1} dy$$

$$= \int_1^2 \left(\frac{1}{3} + y \right) dy = \frac{y}{3} + \frac{y^2}{2} \Big]_1^2$$

$$= \left(\frac{2}{3} + 2 \right) - \left(\frac{1}{3} + \frac{1}{2} \right) = \frac{11}{6}.$$

This time

$$\int_0^1 (x^2 + y)\, dx = \frac{1}{3} + y$$

is the area of a cross section parallel to the xz-plane. See Figure 2. The second integral again gives the volume of the 3-dimensional region lying below the surface $z = x^2 + y$ and above the rectangle $0 \leq x \leq 1,\, 1 \leq y \leq 2$. It is not surprising, therefore, that the two iterated integrals of Examples 1 and 2 are equal.

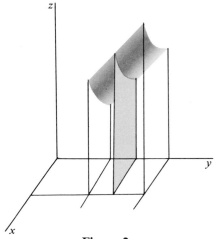

Figure 2

It is important to be able to integrate over subsets of the plane that are more general than rectangles. In such problems the limits in the first integration will depend on the remaining variable.

EXAMPLE 3. Consider the iterated integral

$$\int_0^1 dx \int_0^{1-x^2} (x+y)\, dy = \int_0^1 \left[xy + \frac{y^2}{2} \right]_0^{1-x^2} dx$$

$$= \int_0^1 \left(x(1-x^2) + \frac{(1-x^2)^2}{2} \right) dx$$

$$= \int_0^1 \left(x - x^3 + \frac{1 - 2x^2 + x^4}{2} \right) dx = \frac{31}{60}.$$

For each x between 0 and 1, the number y is between $y = 0$ and $y = 1 - x^2$. In other words the point (x, y) runs along the line segment joining $(x, 0)$ and $(x, 1 - x^2)$. As x varies between 0 and 1, this line segment sweeps out the shaded region B as shown in Figure 3. The integrand $f(x, y) = x + y$ has a graph (see Figure 4), and the iterated integral is the volume under the graph and above the region B.

Suppose we are given an iterated integral over a plane region B in which the integrand is the constant function f defined by $f(x, y) = 1$, for all (x, y) in B. The integral may then be interpreted either as the volume of the slab of unit thickness and with base B or simply as the area of B. For example,

$$\int_0^1 dx \int_0^{1-x^2} dy = \frac{2}{3}$$

is the area of the region B shown in Figure 3.

EXAMPLE 4. Let f be defined by $f(x, y) = x^2 y + xy^2$ over the region bounded by $y = |x|$, $y = 0$, $x = -1$, and $x = 1$. See Figure 5. The two iterated integrals over the region are

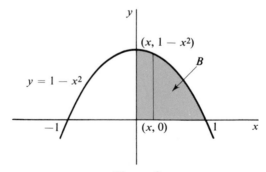

Figure 3

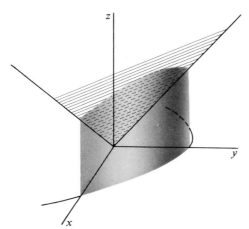

Figure 4

$$\int_{-1}^{1} dx \int_{0}^{|x|} (x^2 y + xy^2)\, dy$$

and

$$\int_{0}^{1} dy \left[\int_{-1}^{-y} (x^2 y + xy^2)\, dx + \int_{y}^{1} (x^2 y + xy^2)\, dx \right].$$

The second integral breaks into two pieces because for fixed y between 0 and 1 the integration with respect to x is carried out over two separate intervals. Computation of the integral is straightforward. We get

$$\int_{0}^{1} \left[\frac{x^3 y}{3} + \frac{x^2 y^2}{2} \right]_{-1}^{-y} + \left[\frac{x^3 y}{3} + \frac{x^2 y^2}{2} \right]_{y}^{1} dy = \int_{0}^{1} \frac{2}{3}(y - y^4)\, dy = \frac{1}{3} - \frac{2}{15} = \frac{1}{5}.$$

The iterated integral in the other order is

$$\int_{-1}^{1} \left[\frac{x^2 y^2}{2} + \frac{xy^3}{3} \right]_{0}^{|x|} dx = \int_{-1}^{1} \left(\frac{x^4}{2} + \frac{x|x|^3}{3} \right) dx$$

$$= \int_{-1}^{1} \frac{x^4}{2}\, dx + \int_{-1}^{1} \frac{x|x|^3}{3}\, dx.$$

The functions $x^4/2$ and $x|x|^3/3$ are even and odd, respectively. It follows that

$$\int_{-1}^{1} \frac{x^4}{2}\, dx + \int_{-1}^{1} \frac{x|x|^3}{3}\, dx = \int_{0}^{1} x^4\, dx = \frac{1}{5}.$$

The theorem which states that, under quite general hypotheses, the value of an iterated integral is independent of the order of integration will be proved in the next section. This will prove that

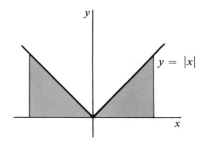

Figure 5

different orders of integration in computing volume must lead to the same result.

Iterated integrals for functions defined on subsets of dimension greater than two can also be computed by repeated 1-dimensional integration.

EXAMPLE 5.

$$\int_0^1 dx \int_{x^2}^x dy \int_x^{2x+y} (x + y + 2z)\, dz = \int_0^1 dx \int_{x^2}^x (4x^2 + 6xy + 2y^2)\, dy$$

$$= \int_0^1 \left(\frac{23}{3}x^3 - 4x^4 - 3x^5 - \frac{2x^6}{3}\right) dx$$

$$= \frac{23}{12} - \frac{4}{5} - \frac{1}{2} - \frac{2}{21}.$$

It is not possible to give a complete interpretation of this integral by drawing a picture. However, the region of integration B can be drawn and is shown in Figure 6. It is bounded on the top by the surface $z = 2x + y$ and on the bottom by $z = x$. On the sides it is bounded by the surfaces obtained by projecting the curves $y = x^2$ and $y = x$ parallel to the z-axis. With the same limits of integration the integral

$$\int_0^1 dx \int_{x^2}^x dy \int_x^{2x+y} dz$$

is the volume of B. For fixed x and y the first integral,

$$\int_x^{2x+y} dz,$$

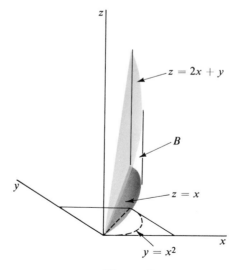

Figure 6

is the length of the vertical segment joining the point (x, y, x) to the point $(x, y, 2x + y)$. For fixed x, the integral

$$\int_{x^2}^{x} dy \int_{x}^{2x+y} dz$$

is the area of a cross section parallel to the yz-plane. Finally, the triply iterated integral is the volume.

EXAMPLE 6. The n-fold iterated integral

$$\int_{0}^{1} dx_1 \int_{0}^{x_1} dx_2 \ldots \int_{0}^{x_{n-1}} dx_n$$

can be thought of as the volume of the region in n-dimensional euclidean space defined by the inequalities

$$0 \le x_n \le x_{n-1} \le \ldots \le x_2 \le x_1 \le 1.$$

To get some idea of what this region is like, consider the cases $n = 1$, $n = 2$, and $n = 3$. For $n = 1$, the integral

$$\int_{0}^{1} dx_1 = 1$$

is simply the length of the unit interval $0 \le x_1 \le 1$. If $n = 2$, we have $0 \le x_2 \le x_1 \le 1$. The region of integration is the intersection of the regions $0 \le x_2$, $x_2 \le x_1$, and $x_1 \le 1$ shown in Figure 7. For $n = 3$, we have simultaneously $0 \le x_3$, $x_3 \le x_2$, $x_2 \le x_1$, and $x_1 \le 1$. See Figure 8. If we denote the n-fold integral by I_n, then $I_1 = 1$, $I_2 = \frac{1}{2}$, and $I_3 = \frac{1}{6}$. These numbers can be obtained either by direct computation or by observing that they are the length, area, and volume, respectively, of the regions of integration. Direct evaluation of I_n is straightforward:

$$I_n = \int_{0}^{1} dx_1 \int_{0}^{x_1} dx_2 \ldots \int_{0}^{x_{n-1}} dx_n$$

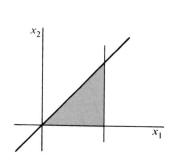

Figure 7

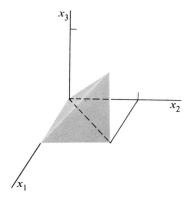

Figure 8

$$= \int_0^1 dx_1 \int_0^{x_1} dx_2 \ldots \int_0^{x_{n-2}} x_{n-1}\, dx_{n-1}$$

$$= \int_0^1 dx_1 \int_0^{x_1} dx_2 \ldots \int_0^{x_{n-3}} \frac{x_{n-2}^2}{2}\, dx_{n-2}$$

$$= \int_0^1 dx_1 \int_0^{x_1} dx_2 \ldots \int_0^{x_{n-4}} \frac{x_{n-3}^3}{3!}\, dx_{n-3}$$

$$= \ldots = \int_0^1 \frac{x_1^{n-1}}{(n-1)!}\, dx_1 = \frac{1}{n!}.$$

EXERCISES

Evaluate the following iterated integrals and sketch the region of integration for each.

1. $\displaystyle\int_{-1}^0 dx \int_1^2 (x^2 y^2 + xy^3)\, dy.$

2. $\displaystyle\int_0^2 dy \int_1^3 |x - 2| \sin y\, dx.$ [*Ans.* $1 - \cos 2$.]

3. $\displaystyle\int_1^0 dx \int_2^0 (x + y^2)\, dy.$

4. $\displaystyle\int_0^{\pi/2} dy \int_{-y}^y \sin x\, dx.$ [*Ans.* 0.]

5. $\displaystyle\int_{-2}^1 dy \int_0^{y^2} (x^2 + y)\, dx.$

6. $\displaystyle\int_{-1}^1 dx \int_0^{|x|} dy.$ [*Ans.* 1.]

7. $\displaystyle\int_0^1 dx \int_0^{\sqrt{1-x^2}} dy.$

8. $\displaystyle\int_1^{-1} dx \int_x^{2x} e^{x+y}\, dy.$

9. $\displaystyle\int_0^{\pi/2} dy \int_0^{\cos y} x \sin y\, dx.$

10. $\displaystyle\int_1^2 dx \int_{x^2}^{x^3} x\, dy.$ [*Ans.* 49/20.]

11. $\displaystyle\int_0^1 dz \int_0^z dy \int_0^y dx.$

12. $\displaystyle\int_0^2 dx \int_1^x dy \int_2^{x+y-1} y\, dz.$ [*Ans.* 2/3.]

13. $\displaystyle\int_1^2 dy \int_0^1 dx \int_x^y dz.$

14. $\displaystyle\int_{-1}^1 dx \int_0^{|x|} dy \int_0^1 (x + y + z)\, dz.$ [*Ans.* 5/6.]

15. $\int_0^\pi \sin x \, dx \int_0^1 dy \int_0^2 (x + y + z) \, dz.$

16. Evaluate the integral $\int_0^1 dx \int_{-x}^x dy \int_{-x-y}^{x+y} dz \int_{-z}^x dw.$

17. Sketch the subset B defined by $0 \le x \le 1$, $0 \le y \le x$, and write down the integral over B in each of the two possible orders of $f(x, y) = x \sin y$. Evaluate both integrals.

18. Sketch the region defined by $x \ge 0$, $x^2 + y^2 \le 2$, and $x^2 + y^2 \ge 1$. Write down the integral over the region in each of the two possible orders of $f(x, y) = x^2$. Evaluate both integrals.　　　　　　[*Ans.* $3\pi/8$.]

19. Consider two real-valued functions $c(x)$ and $d(x)$ of a real variable x. Suppose that for all x in the interval $a \le x \le b$, we have $c(x) \le d(x)$.

(a) Make a sketch of two such functions and of the subset B of the xy-plane consisting of all (x, y) such that $a \le x \le b$ and $c(x) \le y \le d(x)$.

(b) Express the area of B as an iterated integral.

(c) Set up the iterated integral of $f(x, y)$ over B.

20. Sketch the subset B of $\mathscr{R}^3$, defined by $0 \le x \le 1$, $0 \le y \le 1 + x$, and $0 \le z \le 2$. Write down the iterated integral with order of integration z, then y, and then x, of the function $f(x, y, z) = x^2 + z$ over the subset B. Compute the integral.　　　　　　[*Ans.* $25/6$.]

21. Sketch the region defined by $0 \le x \le 1$, $x^2 \le y \le \sqrt{x}$, and $1 \le z \le x + y$ and evaluate the iterated integral, in some order, of $f(x, y, z) = x + y + z$ over the region.

22. Let f be defined by $f(x, y, z) = 1$ on the hemisphere bounded by the plane $z = 0$ and the surface $z = \sqrt{1 - x^2 - y^2}$. Evaluate an iterated integral of f in some order over the region.　　　　　　[*Ans.* $2\pi/3$.]

23. Let f be defined by $f(x_1, \ldots, x_n) = x_1 x_2 \ldots x_n$ on the cube $0 \le x_1 \le 1$, $0 \le x_2 \le 1, \ldots, 0 \le x_n \le 1$. Evaluate

$$\int_0^1 dx_1 \int_0^1 dx_2 \ldots \int_0^1 x_1 x_2 \ldots x_n \, dx_n.$$

24. Show that if in the integral

$$\int_{a_1}^{b_1} dx_1 \int_{a_2}^{b_2} dx_2 \ldots \int_{a_n}^{b_n} f(x_1, \ldots, x_n) \, dx_n$$

the order of the limits of integration is interchanged on an even number of integral signs, then the value of the integral is unchanged. If the limits are interchanged on an odd number of integral signs, then the whole iterated integral changes sign.

25. Evaluate

$$\int_0^1 dx_1 \int_0^1 dx_2 \ldots \int_0^1 dx_{n-1} \int_0^{x_1} (x_1 + x_2) \, dx_n.$$

26. Prove that

$$\int_0^x dx_1 \int_0^{x_1} dx_2 \ldots \int_0^{x_{n-1}} f(x_n)\, dx_n = \frac{1}{(n-1)!} \int_0^x (x-t)^{n-1} f(t)\, dt.$$

2. MULTIPLE INTEGRALS

Multiple integrals are closely related to the iterated integrals of the preceding section, but they are not the same things. One-dimensional integrals are associated with the idea of area under a curve. Similarly, multiple integrals can be used to define volume.

We first consider some simple sets in $\mathscr{R}^n$. **A closed coordinate rectangle** is a subset of $\mathscr{R}^n$ consisting of all points $\mathbf{x} = (x_1, \ldots, x_n)$ that satisfy a set of inequalities

$$a_i \leq x_i \leq b_i, \qquad i = 1, \ldots, n. \tag{1}$$

If in Formula (1) some of the symbols "$\leq$" are replaced by "$<$", the resulting set is still called a **coordinate rectangle**. In particular, if all the inequalities are of the form $a_i < x_i < b_i$, the set is open and is called an **open coordinate rectangle**. A coordinate rectangle has its edges parallel to the coordinate axes. Throughout this section the word "rectangle" will be understood to mean "coordinate rectangle". Rectangles in $\mathscr{R}^2$ and $\mathscr{R}^3$ are illustrated in Figure 9. A rectangle in $\mathscr{R}$ is just an interval.

Let R be a rectangle (open, closed, or neither) defined by Formula (1) with replacement of any symbols "$\leq$" by "$<$" permitted. The **volume** or **content** of R, written $V(R)$, is defined by

$$V(R) = (b_1 - a_1)(b_2 - a_2) \ldots (b_n - a_n). \tag{2}$$

In the examples shown in Figure 9, $V(R_2) = (4-1)(1-(-1)) = 6$ and $V(R_3) = (3-1)(3-1)(2-1) = 4$. If, for some i in Formula (1), $a_i = b_i$,

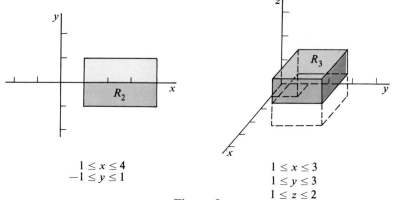

$$1 \leq x \leq 4$$
$$-1 \leq y \leq 1$$

$$1 \leq x \leq 3$$
$$1 \leq y \leq 3$$
$$1 \leq z \leq 2$$

Figure 9

then R is called **degenerate**, and $V(R) = 0$. For rectangles in $\mathscr{R}^2$, content is the same thing as area, and we often write $A(R)$ instead of $V(R)$ in recognition of this fact.

A subset B of $\mathscr{R}^n$ is called **bounded** if there is a real number k such that $|\mathbf{x}| < k$ for all $\mathbf{x}$ in B. A finite set of $(n-1)$-dimensional planes in $\mathscr{R}^n$ (lines in $\mathscr{R}^2$) parallel to the coordinate planes will be called a **grid**. As illustrated in Figure 10, a grid separates $\mathscr{R}^n$ into a finite number of closed, bounded rectangles $R_1, \ldots, R_r$ and a finite number of unbounded regions. A grid **covers** a subset B of $\mathscr{R}^n$ if B is contained in the union of the bounded rectangles $R_1, \ldots, R_r$. Obviously, a set can be covered by a grid if and only if the set is bounded. As a measure of the fineness of a grid, we take the maximum of the lengths of the edges of the rectangles $R_1, \ldots, R_r$. This number is called the **mesh** of the grid.

We now give the definition of multiple integral, also called the Riemann integral after Bernhard Riemann (1826–1866). Consider a function $\mathscr{R}^n \xrightarrow{f} \mathscr{R}$ and a set B such that

    (a) B is a bounded subset of the domain of f.

    (b) f is bounded on B.

Assertion (b) means that there exists a real number K such that $|f(\mathbf{x})| \leq K$, for all $\mathbf{x}$ in B. The multiple integral of f over B will be defined in terms of the function f_B, which is f altered to be zero outside B. That is,

$$f_B(\mathbf{x}) = \begin{cases} f(\mathbf{x}), & \text{if } \mathbf{x} \text{ is in } B. \\ 0, & \text{if } \mathbf{x} \text{ is not in } B. \end{cases}$$

Let G be a grid that covers B and has mesh equal to $m(G)$. In each of the bounded rectangles R_i formed by G, $i = 1, \ldots, r$, choose an arbitrary point $\mathbf{x}_i$. The sum

$$\sum_{i=1}^{r} f_B(\mathbf{x}_i) V(R_i)$$

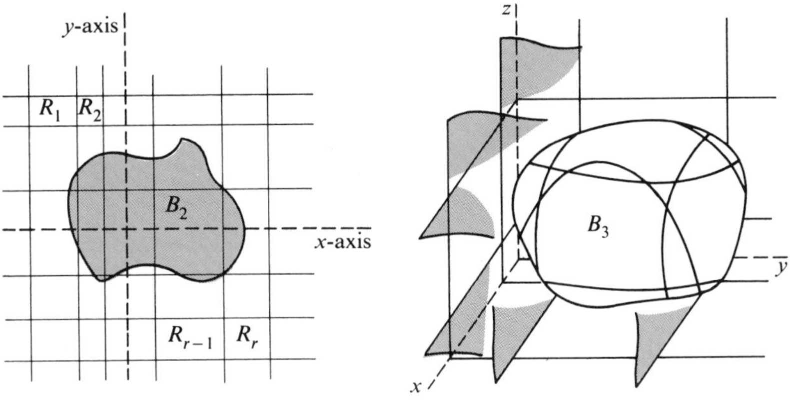

Figure 10

is called a **Riemann sum** for f over B. Its value, for given f and B, depends on G and $\mathbf{x}_1, \ldots, \mathbf{x}_r$. If no matter how we choose grids G with mesh $m(G)$ tending to zero, it happens that

$$\lim_{m(G)\to 0} \sum_{i=1}^{r} f_B(\mathbf{x}_i) V(R_i)$$

exists and is always the same number, then this limit is the **integral of f over B** and is denoted by $\int_B f\, dV$. If the integral exists, f is said to be **integrable** over B.

The limit that defines the multiple integral is something different from the limit of vector function defined in Chapter 2, Section 2, although the idea is similar. The defining equation

$$\lim_{m(G)\to 0} \sum_{i=1}^{r} f_B(\mathbf{x}_i) V(R_i) = \int_B f\, dV$$

means that, for any $\epsilon > 0$, there exists $\delta > 0$ such that if G is any grid that covers B and has mesh less than δ, and S is an arbitrary Riemann sum for f_B formed from G, then

$$\left| S - \int_B f\, dV \right| < \epsilon.$$

It should be emphasized that the integral is not defined for functions $\mathscr{R}^n \xrightarrow{f} \mathscr{R}$ and sets B unless the boundedness conditions (a) and (b) are satisfied. For without these conditions, some Riemann sums may not be defined.

If f is a real-valued function of one real variable, that is, if $n = 1$, and if B is an interval $a \leq x \leq b$, the Riemann integral of f over B is the familiar definite integral

$$\int_a^b f(x)\, dx.$$

Other common notations for the integral of $\mathscr{R}^n \xrightarrow{f} \mathscr{R}$ over B are

$$\int_B f\, dA \quad \text{and} \quad \int_B f(x, y)\, dx\, dy, \qquad \text{if} \quad n = 2,$$

$$\int_B f(x, y, z)\, dx\, dy\, dz, \qquad \text{if} \quad n = 3,$$

$$\int_B f\, dx_1 \ldots dx_n, \qquad \text{for arbitrary } n.$$

The definition of the integral by no means makes it apparent what functions can be integrated over what sets. The following theorem, the proof of which is given in the Appendix, describes a class of integrable functions large enough for many purposes.

2.1 Theorem. Let f be defined and bounded on a bounded set B in $\mathscr{R}^n$, and let the boundary of B be contained in finitely many smooth sets. If f is continuous on B except perhaps on finitely many smooth sets, then f is integrable over B. The integral $\int_B f\, dV$ is independent of the values of f on any smooth set.

By a **smooth set** in $\mathscr{R}^n$ is meant the image of a closed bounded set under a continuously differentiable function $\mathscr{R}^m \xrightarrow{\phi} \mathscr{R}^n$, $m < n$. Thus, if $n = 2$ and $m = 1$, we may get a smooth curve. A smooth set in $\mathscr{R}^1$ will be understood to be just a point. To say that the value of $\int_B f\, dV$ is independent of the values of f on such a set means that f can be assigned arbitrary values on the set without affecting the existence or the value of the integral.

EXAMPLE 1. Evaluate the multiple integral

$$\int_B (2x + y)\, dx\, dy,$$

where B is the rectangle $0 \leq x < 1$, $0 \leq y \leq 2$. The existence of the integral is ensured by Theorem 2.1. For this reason, any sequence of Riemann sums with mesh tending to zero may be used to evaluate it. For each $n = 1, 2, \ldots$, consider the grid G_n consisting of the lines $x = i/n$, $i = 0, \ldots, n$, and $y = j/n$, $j = 0, \ldots, 2n$. See Figure 11(b). The mesh of G_n is $1/n$, and the area of each of the rectangles R_{ij} is $1/n^2$. Setting

$$\mathbf{x}_{ij} = (x_i, y_j) = \left(\frac{i}{n}, \frac{j}{n}\right),$$

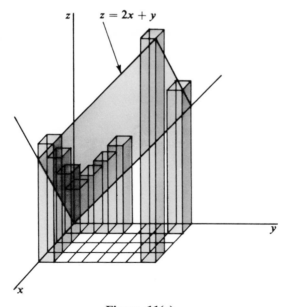

Figure 11(a)

we form the Riemann sum

$$\sum_{i=1}^{n} \sum_{j=1}^{2n} (2x_i + y_j) A(R_{ij}) = \sum_{i=1}^{n} \sum_{j=1}^{2n} \left(\frac{2i}{n} + \frac{j}{n} \right) \frac{1}{n^2}$$

$$= \frac{1}{n^3} \left(4n \sum_{i=1}^{n} i + n \sum_{j=1}^{2n} j \right)$$

$$= \frac{1}{n^2} \left(4 \frac{n^2 + n}{2} + \frac{4n^2 + 2n}{2} \right)$$

$$= \frac{4n^2 + 3n}{n^2} = 4 + \frac{3}{n}.$$

Hence,

$$\int_B (2x + y)\, dx\, dy = \lim_{n \to \infty} \left(4 + \frac{3}{n} \right) = 4.$$

A direct evaluation of a multiple integral will be very arduous for most functions we wish to integrate. Fortunately, in many instances the multiple integral can be easily evaluated by repeated application of ordinary 1-dimensional integration instead of by finding the limits of Riemann sums. The pertinent theorem, which we prove at the end of this section, is the following.

2.2 Theorem. Let B be a subset of $\mathcal{R}^n$ such that the iterated integral

$$\int dx_1 \int dx_2 \ldots \int f\, dx_n$$

exists over B. If, in addition, the multiple integral

$$\int_B f\, dV$$

exists, then the two integrals are equal.

Since the argument used to prove Theorem 2.2 applies equally well to any order of iterated integration, we have as an immediate corollary

2.3 Theorem. If $\int_B f\, dV$ exists, and iterated integrals exist for some orders of integration, then all of these integrals are equal.

EXAMPLE 2. Evaluate $\int_B (2x + y)\, dx\, dy$, where B is the rectangle $0 \le x \le 1$, $0 \le y \le 2$. This is the same integral that occurs in Example 1. Theorem 2.2 is applicable, and we obtain

$$\int_B (2x + y)\, dx\, dy = \int_0^1 dx \int_0^2 (2x + y)\, dy$$

$$= \int_0^1 (4x + 2)\, dx$$

$$= 2x^2 + 2x \,]_0^1 = 4.$$

EXAMPLE 3. Let R be the 3-dimensional rectangle defined by $-1 \leq x \leq 2$, $0 \leq y \leq 1$, $1 \leq z \leq 2$, and shown in Figure 12. Consider $f(x, y, z) = xyz$. Then

$$\int_R f \, dV = \int_R xyz \, dx \, dy \, dz$$

$$= \int_{-1}^{2} dx \int_0^1 dy \int_1^2 xyz \, dz = \int_{-1}^2 x \, dx \int_0^1 y \, dy \int_1^2 z \, dz$$

$$= (\tfrac{3}{2})(\tfrac{1}{2})(\tfrac{3}{2}) = \tfrac{9}{8}.$$

EXAMPLE 4. Let $f(x, y, z) = xyz$, and let the subset B of $\mathscr{R}^3$ be defined by $x^2 + y^2 + z^2 \leq 4$, $y \geq 0$, $z \geq 0$. B is the interior and boundary of one quarter of the spherical ball of radius 2 with center at the origin, shown in Figure 13. The integral $\int_B f \, dV$ equals the triple iterated integral of the function $f(x, y, z) = xyz$ over B. For fixed x and y, the variable z runs from 0 to $\sqrt{4 - x^2 - y^2}$, which are the limits of the first integration with respect to z. The result of this integration is a function of x and y that next must be integrated over the 2-dimensional subset obtained by projecting B on the xy-plane, that is, over the region $x^2 + y^2 \leq 4$, $y \geq 0$. For fixed x, the variable y runs from 0 to $\sqrt{4 - x^2}$; hence, these are the limits on the integration with respect to y. Finally, x runs from -2 to 2, so we conclude that

$$\int_B f \, dV = \int_{-2}^2 dx \int_0^{\sqrt{4-x^2}} dy \int_0^{\sqrt{4-x^2-y^2}} xyz \, dz.$$

Then

$$\int_B f \, dV = \frac{1}{2} \int_{-2}^2 x \, dx \int_0^{\sqrt{4-x^2}} y(4 - x^2 - y^2) \, dy$$

$$= \frac{1}{2} \int_{-2}^2 x \left(2(4 - x^2) - \frac{x^2}{2}(4 - x^2) - \frac{(4 - x^2)^2}{4} \right) dx.$$

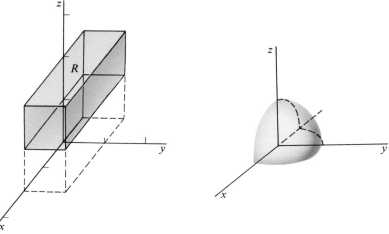

Figure 12   Figure 13

The last integrand is an odd function, and for that reason the integral has value zero.

If the constant function 1 is integrable over a subset B of $\mathcal{R}^n$, the **content**, or **volume**, of B is denoted by $V(B)$ and defined by

$$V(B) = \int_B 1 \, dV = \int_B dV.$$

For sets B in $\mathcal{R}^2$, we write $A(B)$, for area, instead of $V(B)$. It follows from the last part of Theorem 2.1 that the content of a continuously differentiable k-dimensional $(k < n)$ curve or surface S is zero, for

$$V(S) = \int_S dV = 0.$$

For some sets B, the integral $\int_B dV$ does not exist. If this happens, the content of B is not defined (see Exercise 21). Notice that for rectangles R, $V(R)$ has been defined twice: first as the product of the lengths of mutually perpendicular edges and second as an integral. That the two definitions agree follows immediately from Theorems 2.1 and 2.2.

EXAMPLE 5. Let B be the region in $\mathcal{R}^2$ under the curve $y = f(x)$ from $x = a$ to $x = b$, where f is a nonnegative function. Assuming the existence of the following integrals, we obtain, using the iterated integral theorem (Theorem 2.2),

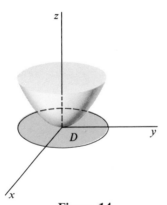

Figure 14

$$A(B) = \int_B dA = \int_a^b dx \int_0^{f(x)} dy = \int_a^b f(x) \, dx.$$

Hence, the above definition of content is consistent with the usual one for the area under the graph of a nonnegative integrable function of one variable. If f is integrable over B and also nonnegative on B, we could similarly show that the volume under the graph of f and above the set B is the double integral $\int_B f \, dA$.

EXAMPLE 6. The volume above the disc D defined by $x^2 + y^2 \le 1$ and under the graph of $f(x, y) = x^2 + y^2$ (see Figure 14) is equal to

$$\int_D (x^2 + y^2) \, dx \, dy = \int_{-1}^1 dx \int_{-\sqrt{1-x^2}}^{\sqrt{1-x^2}} (x^2 + y^2) \, dy$$

$$= 2 \int_{-1}^1 \left(x^2 \sqrt{1 - x^2} + \frac{1}{3}(1 - x^2)\sqrt{1 - x^2} \right) dx$$

$$= \frac{4}{3} \int_0^1 (\sqrt{1 - x^2} + 2x^2\sqrt{1 - x^2})\, dx$$

$$= \frac{4}{3}\left(\frac{\pi}{4} + \frac{\pi}{8}\right) = \frac{\pi}{2}.$$

EXAMPLE 7. Find the volume of the region B in $\mathscr{R}^3$ bounded by the four planes $x = 0$, $y = 0$, $z = 0$, and $x + y + z = 1$, shown in Figure 15.

$$V(B) = \int_B dV = \int_0^1 dx \int_0^{1-x} dy \int_0^{1-x-y} dz = \frac{1}{6}.$$

The volume of the region B can be computed directly as a double integral. The projection of B on the xy-plane is the triangle D bounded by the lines $x = 0$, $y = 0$, $x + y = 1$. The set B itself can be described as the region under the graph of the function $f(x, y) = 1 - x - y$ and above D. Hence, according to the remark at the end of Example 5,

$$V(B) = \int_D f\, dA = \int_0^1 dx \int_0^{1-x} (1 - x - y)\, dy = \frac{1}{6}.$$

Notice that what we have called the content of a subset of $\mathscr{R}^n$ is more properly called its **n-dimensional content**. For example, the square defined by the inequalities $0 \le x \le 2$, $0 \le y \le 2$ in $\mathscr{R}^2$ has 2-dimensional content 4, whereas the square defined in $\mathscr{R}^3$ by $0 \le x \le 2$, $0 \le y \le 2$, $z = 0$, and which looks the same, has 3-dimensional content 0. Thus the content of a set depends on the dimension of the containing Euclidean space with respect to which it is being measured, as well as on the shape of the set itself. Having already indicated that 2-dimensional content is called area, we remark that 1-dimensional content is length.

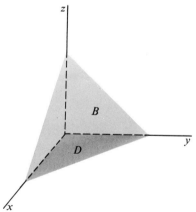

Some characteristic properties of the Riemann integral are summarized in the following four theorems.

Figure 15

2.4 Theorem. Linearity. If f and g are integrable over B and a and b are any two real numbers, then $af + bg$ is integrable over B and

$$\int_B (af + bg)\, dV = a \int_B f\, dV + b \int_B g\, dV.$$

2.5 Theorem. Positivity. If f is nonnegative and integrable over B, then

$$\int_B f\, dV \ge 0.$$

2.6 Theorem. If R is a rectangle, then $\int_R dV = V(R)$ (where the content $V(R)$ is defined by Equation (2)).

2.7 Theorem. If B is a subset of a bounded set C, then $\int_B f \, dV$ exists if and only if $\int_C f_B \, dV$ exists. Whenever both integrals exist, they are equal.

Proof of 2.4. Let $\epsilon > 0$ be given, and choose $\delta > 0$ so that if S_1 and S_2 are two Riemann sums for f_B and g_B respectively, and whose grids have mesh less than δ, then

$$|a| \left| S_1 - \int_B f \, dV \right| < \frac{\epsilon}{2} \quad \text{and} \quad |b| \left| S_2 - \int_B g \, dV \right| < \frac{\epsilon}{2}.$$

Let S be any Riemann sum for $(af + bg)_B$ whose grid has mesh less than δ. Then

$$S = \sum_i (af + bg)_B (\mathbf{x}_i) V(R_i)$$
$$= a \sum_i f_B(\mathbf{x}_i) V(R_i) + b \sum_i g_B(\mathbf{x}_i) V(R_i)$$
$$= aS_1 + bS_2.$$

Hence,

$$\left| S - a \int_B f \, dV - b \int_B g \, dV \right|$$
$$= \left| aS_1 - a \int_B f \, dV + bS_2 - b \int_B g \, dV \right|$$
$$\leq |a| \left| S_1 - \int_B f \, dV \right| + |b| \left| S_2 - \int_B g \, dV \right|$$
$$< \frac{\epsilon}{2} + \frac{\epsilon}{2} = \epsilon.$$

Thus

$$\lim_{m(G) \to 0} \sum_i (af + bg)_B(\mathbf{x}_i) V(R_i) = a \int_B f \, dV + b \int_B g \, dV,$$

and the proof is complete.

Proof of 2.5. Since all the Riemann sums are nonnegative, the limit must also be nonnegative.

Proof of 2.6. This follows immediately from Theorems 2.1 and 2.2.

Proof of 2.7. The existence and the value of the integral $\int_B f \, dV$ depend only on the function f_B. Similarly, $\int_C f_B \, dV$ is defined by using $(f_B)_C$, which is equal to f_B.

Many of the important properties of the integral can be derived directly from the preceding four theorems, without reference to the original definition. The next two theorems are given as examples.

2.8 Theorem. If f and g are integrable over B and $f \leq g$ on B, then

$$\int_B f \, dV \leq \int_B g \, dV.$$

Proof. The function $g - f$ is nonnegative and, by Theorem 2.4, is integrable over B. Hence, by Theorems 2.4 and 2.5,

$$0 \leq \int_B (g - f) \, dV = \int_B g \, dV - \int_B f \, dV,$$

from which the conclusion follows.

The second theorem establishes an analogue for the equation

$$\int_a^c f(x) dx = \int_a^b f(x) \, dx + \int_b^c f(x) \, dx$$

that holds for functions of one variable.

2.9 Theorem. If f is integrable over each of two disjoint sets B_1 and B_2, then f is integrable over their union and

$$\int_{B_1 \cup B_2} f \, dV = \int_{B_1} f \, dV + \int_{B_2} f \, dV.$$

Proof. By Theorem 2.7,

$$\int_{B_1} f \, dV + \int_{B_2} f \, dV = \int_{B_1 \cup B_2} f_{B_1} \, dV + \int_{B_1 \cup B_2} f_{B_2} \, dV.$$

Since B_1 and B_2 are disjoint, $f_{B_1 \cup B_2} = f_{B_1} + f_{B_2}$. Hence, by Theorem 2.4, $f_{B_1 \cup B_2}$ is integrable over $B_1 \cup B_2$, and

$$\int_{B_1 \cup B_2} f_{B_1} \, dV + \int_{B_1 \cup B_2} f_{B_2} \, dV = \int_{B_1 \cup B_2} f_{B_1 \cup B_2} \, dV.$$

Finally, by Theorem 2.7 again, f is integrable over $B_1 \cup B_2$ and

$$\int_{B_1 \cup B_2} f_{B_1 \cup B_2} \, dV = \int_{B_1 \cup B_2} f \, dV.$$

This completes the proof.

The next theorem will show that for functions f and regions B for which $\int_B f \, dV$ exists, the value of the integral is completely determined by the properties stated in the four Theorems 2.4–2.7.

2.10 Theorem. Suppose I is a function that assigns to certain bounded functions $\mathscr{R}^n \xrightarrow{f} \mathscr{R}$, and bounded sets B a real number $I_B f$, and which satisfies the conditions:

(a) If $I_B f$ and $I_B g$ are defined and a and b are real numbers, then $I_B(af + bg)$ is defined and

$$I_B(af + bg) = aI_B f + bI_B g.$$

(b) If f is nonnegative and $I_B f$ is defined, then $I_B f \geq 0$.

(c) If R is a rectangle, then $I_R 1 = V(R)$ (as defined by Equation (2)).

(d) If B is contained in a bounded set C, then $I_B f$ is defined if and only if $I_C f_B$ is defined. Whenever both exist, they are equal.

Then, if $I_B f$ and $\int_B f \, dV$ both exist, they are equal.

Proof. Suppose $\int_B f \, dV < I_B f$. Set

$$\epsilon = I_B f - \int_B f \, dV,$$

and choose $\delta > 0$ so that if S is any Riemann sum for f_B whose grid has mesh less than δ, then

$$\left| \int_B f \, dV - S \right| < \frac{\epsilon}{2}.$$

Let G be an arbitrary grid that covers B and has mesh less than δ, and denote the closed bounded rectangles formed by G by $R_1, \ldots, R_r$. Set

$$C = R_1 \cup \ldots \cup R_r,$$

$$\bar{f}_i = \text{least upper bound of } f_B \text{ in } R_i.$$

Consider the function g defined by

$$g = \sum_{i=1}^{r} \bar{f}_i \, \chi_{R_i}.$$

The function χ_{R_i} is the characteristic function of R_i. It is defined by

$$\chi_{R_i}(\mathbf{x}) = \begin{cases} 1, & \text{if } \mathbf{x} \text{ is in } R_i. \\ 0, & \text{otherwise.} \end{cases}$$

It follows immediately from (c), (d), and (a) that $I_C g$ is defined and that

$$I_C g = \sum_{i=1}^{r} \bar{f}_i V(R_i).$$

The definition of least upper bound implies that there exists a Riemann sum for f_B on the grid G that is arbitrarily close to $I_C g$. Hence,

$$\left| \int_B f \, dV - I_C g \right| \leq \frac{\epsilon}{2},$$

and so, by the definition of ϵ,

$$I_C g < I_B f. \tag{4}$$

By (d), $I_B f = I_C f_B$. Moreover the function g has been constructed so that $f_B \leq g$. It follows from (b) (as extended in Theorem 2.8) that

$$I_B f = I_C f_B \leq I_C g. \tag{5}$$

The inequalities (4) and (5) are contradictory, so that we conclude

$$\int_B f \, dV \geq I_B f.$$

By an entirely analogous argument using the notion of greatest lower bound instead of least upper bound, we can obtain

$$\int_B f \, dV \leq I_B f,$$

and this completes the proof.

For an application of Theorem 2.10, take the functions $\mathscr{R}^2 \xrightarrow{f} \mathscr{R}$ and sets B for which the iterated integral $\int dx \int f \, dy$ over B is defined. Let

$$I_B f = \int_{(over\ B)} dx \int f \, dy.$$

Verification of the conditions of Theorem 2.10 is straightforward and reduces to a knowledge of the corresponding properties of the definite integral for functions of one variable. For example, for integration over intervals,

$$\int_\alpha^\beta (af + bg) \, dx = a \int_\alpha^\beta f \, dx + b \int_\alpha^\beta g \, dx.$$

$$\int_\alpha^\beta f \, dx \geq 0 \qquad\qquad \text{if } f \geq 0.$$

$$\int_\alpha^\beta dx = \beta - \alpha.$$

$$\int_\gamma^\delta f \, dx = \int_\alpha^\beta f_{[\gamma,\delta]} \, dx \qquad \text{if } \alpha \leq \gamma \leq \delta \leq \beta \text{ and } [\gamma, \delta] \text{ is the interval } \gamma \leq x \leq \delta.$$

It follows immediately from Theorem 2.10 that if both the iterated integral and the double integral of f exist over B, then they are equal. This proves Theorem 2.2 for two variables. The general case is no harder.

A second application of Theorem 2.10 has to do with the Lebesgue integral, named after Henri Lebesgue (1875–1941). The Lebesgue integral is a generalization of the Riemann integral in that it is defined for a larger class of functions f and sets B. The Lebesgue integral also has the characteristic properties of Theorem 2.10. It follows that if a function has both Riemann and Lebesgue integrals, the two integrals are equal.

EXERCISES

1. Make a drawing of the set B and compute $\int_B f \, dA$, where

(a) $f(x, y) = x^2 + 3y^2$ and B is the disc $x^2 + y^2 \leq 1$.   [Ans. π.]

(b) $f(x, y) = 1/(x + y)$ and B is the region bounded by the lines $y = x$, $x = 1$, $x = 2$, $y = 0$.   [Ans. log 2.]

(c) $f(x, y) = x \sin xy$ and B is the rectangle $0 \leq x \leq \pi$, $0 \leq y \leq 1$.   [Ans. π.]

(d) $f(x, y) = x^2 - y^2$ and B consists of all (x, y) such that $0 \leq x \leq 1$ and $x^2 - y^2 \geq 0$.   [Ans. $\frac{1}{3}$.]

2. Using the definition of the double integral as a limit of Riemann sums, compute $\int_B f(x, y)\, dx\, dy$, where

(a) $f(x, y) = x + 4y$ and B is the rectangle $0 \le x \le 2, 0 \le y \le 1$.
[Ans. 6.]

(b) $f(x, y) = 3x^2 + 2y$ and B is the rectangle $0 \le x \le 2, 0 \le y \le 1$.
[Ans. 10.]

The following formulas will be useful in doing this problem:

$$\sum_{i=1}^{n} i = \frac{n(n + 1)}{2},$$

$$\sum_{i=1}^{n} i^2 = \frac{n(n + 1)(2n + 1)}{6},$$

$$\sum_{i=1}^{n} i^3 = \left(\sum_{i=1}^{n} i \right)^2.$$

3. Find the volume under the graph of f and above the set B, where

(a) $f(x, y) = x + y^2$ and B is the rectangle with corners $(1, 1)$, $(1, 3)$, $(2, 3)$, and $(2, 1)$.   [Ans. $\frac{35}{3}$.]

(b) $f(x, y) = x + y + 2$ and B is the region bounded by the curves $y^2 = x$ and $x = 2$.   [Ans. $\frac{128}{15}\sqrt{2}$.]

(c) $f(x, y) = |x + y|$ and B is the disc $x^2 + y^2 \le 1$.   [Ans. $4\sqrt{2}/3$.]

4. Find by integration the area of the subset of $\mathscr{R}^2$ bounded by the curve $x^2 - 2x + 4y^2 - 8y + 1 = 0$.   [Ans. 2π.]

5. Find an approximate value for each integral in Problem 1 by computing a Riemann sum with an appropriately fine grid.

6. Consider the rectangles

$$B_1 \quad \text{defined by} \quad 0 < x \le 1, 0 \le y < 1$$
$$B_2 \quad \text{defined by} \quad 1 \le x \le 2, -1 \le y \le 1$$

and the function

$$f(x, y) = \begin{cases} 2x - y, & \text{if} \quad x < 1. \\ x^2 + y, & \text{if} \quad x \ge 1. \end{cases}$$

Compute $\int_{B_1 \cup B_2} f(x, y)\, dx\, dy$.   [Ans. $\frac{31}{6}$.]

7. (a) Prove the **Leibnitz rule** for differentiating an integral with respect to a parameter: If $g_y(x, y)$ is continuous on a rectangle $a \le x \le b$, $c \le y \le d$, then

$$\frac{d}{dy} \int_a^b g(t, y)\, dt = \int_a^b g_y(t, y)\, dt.$$

[*Hint.* Interchange the order of integration in $\int_c^y dy \int_a^b g_y(t, y)\, dt$, and then differentiate both sides with respect to y.]

(b) Use part (a) and the chain rule to show that if g_y is continuous, and h_1 and h_2 are differentiable, then

$$\frac{d}{dy} \int_{h_1(y)}^{h_2(y)} g(t, y)\, dt$$

$$= \int_{h_1(y)}^{h_2(y)} g_y(t, y)\, dt + h_2'(y)g(h_2(y), y) - h_1'(y)g(h_1(y), y).$$

8. Prove Theorem 6.1 of Chapter 2: If f_x, f_y, and f_{xy} are continuous on an open set, then $f_{xy} = f_{yx}$. [*Hint.* Apply the Leibnitz rule of Problem 7(a) to the equation

$$f(x, y) - f(a, y) = \int_a^x f_x(t, y)\, dt,$$

and then differentiate both sides with respect to x.]

9. Given that $f(x, y, z) = xyz$ and that

$$\int_B f(x, y, z)\, dx\, dy\, dz = \int_0^2 dx \int_0^x dy \int_0^{x+y} xyz\, dz,$$

sketch the region B and evaluate the integral.   [*Ans.* $\frac{68}{9}$.]

10. Compute the multiple integral of $f(x, y, z, w) = xyzw$ over the 4-dimensional rectangle

$$0 \le x \le 1, \quad -1 \le y \le 2, \quad 1 \le z \le 2, \quad 2 \le w \le 3.$$

                                                 [*Ans.* $\frac{45}{16}$.]

11. Sketch the region B in $\mathscr{R}^3$ bounded by the surface $z = 4 - 4x^2 - y^2$ and the xy-plane. Set up the volume of B as a triple integral and also as a double integral. Compute the volume.   [*Ans.* 4π.]

12. Write an expression for the volume of the ball $x^2 + y^2 + z^2 \le a^2$,

  (a) as a triple integral.
  (b) as a double integral.

13. Sketch in $\mathscr{R}^3$ the two cylindrical solids defined by $x^2 + z^2 \le 1$ and $y^2 + z^2 \le 1$ respectively. Find the volume of their intersection.

                                                 [*Ans.* $\frac{16}{3}$.]

14. The 4-dimensional ball B of radius 1 and with center at the origin is the subset of $\mathscr{R}^4$ defined by $x_1^2 + x_2^2 + x_3^2 + x_4^2 \le 1$. Set up an expression for the volume $V(B)$ as a four-fold iterated integral.

15. Use Theorem 2.8 to show that if f and $|f|$ are integrable over B then $|\int_B f\, dV| \le \int_B |f|\, dV$.

16. Let $\mathscr{R}^n \xrightarrow{f} \mathscr{R}^m$ be defined on a set B in $\mathscr{R}^n$. We define

$$\int_B f\, dV = \left(\int_B f_1\, dV, \ldots, \int_B f_m\, dV \right),$$

provided that the integrals of the coordinate functions $f_1, \ldots, f_m$ of f all exist.

  (a) Show that if $\mathscr{R}^n \xrightarrow{f} \mathscr{R}^m$ and $\mathscr{R}^n \xrightarrow{g} \mathscr{R}^m$ are both integrable over B, then

$$\int_B (af + bg)\, dV = a \int_B f\, dV + b \int_B g\, dV,$$

where a and b are constants.

(b) If $\mathbf{k}$ is a fixed vector in $\mathcal{R}^m$, and $\mathcal{R}^n \xrightarrow{f} \mathcal{R}^m$ is integrable over B, show that

$$\int_B \mathbf{k} \cdot f\, dV = \mathbf{k} \cdot \int_B f\, dV.$$

(c) Show that if $\mathcal{R}^n \xrightarrow{f} \mathcal{R}^m$ and $\mathcal{R}^n \xrightarrow{|f|} \mathcal{R}$ are integrable over B, then $|\int_B f\, dV| \le \int_B |f|\, dV$. [*Hint*: By the Cauchy-Schwarz inequality $f(\mathbf{x}) \cdot \int_B f\, dV \le |f(\mathbf{x})| \, |\int_B f\, dV|$, for all $\mathbf{x}$ in B. Integrate with respect to $\mathbf{x}$ and apply the result of part (b).]

17. Use the result of Problem 16(c) to show that if $\mathcal{R}^n \xrightarrow{f} \mathcal{R}^m$ is continuous on a set B, and $\mathbf{x}_0$ is interior to B, then

$$\lim_{r \to 0} \frac{1}{V(B_r)} \int_{B_r} f\, dV = f(\mathbf{x}_0),$$

where B_r is a ball of radius r centered at $\mathbf{x}_0$.

18. Let R be a region in $\mathcal{R}^n$ having a finite volume. The vector

$$\mathbf{z}_0 = \frac{1}{V(R)} \int_R \mathbf{x}\, dV$$

is called the **centroid** of R, and the real number

$$I(\mathbf{z}) = \int_R |\mathbf{x} - \mathbf{z}|^2\, dV_{\mathbf{x}}$$

is called the **moment of inertia** of R about $\mathbf{z}$.

(a) Show that the centroid of a ball is its center.

(b) Show that $I(\mathbf{z})$ is minimized by taking $\mathbf{z}$ to be the centroid of R. [*Hint.* Show that

$$I(\mathbf{z}) = I(0) - V(R)|\mathbf{z}_0|^2 + V(R)|\mathbf{z} - \mathbf{z}_0|^2.]$$

19. Prove the analogue for multiple integrals of Theorem 6.4 of Chapter 3: If R has finite volume, and the series $\sum_{k=1}^{\infty} f_k$ of continuous functions converges to f uniformly on R, then

$$\sum_{k=1}^{\infty} \int_R f_k\, dV = \int_R \left[\sum_{k=1}^{\infty} f_k \right] dV.$$

20. A function $\mathcal{R}^n \xrightarrow{p} \mathcal{R}$, integrable over a region R in $\mathcal{R}^n$ is called a **probability density** on R if

(i) $p(\mathbf{x}) \ge 0$ for all $\mathbf{x}$ in R.

(ii) $\int_R p\, dV = 1.$

If E is an experiment with possible outcomes in $\mathcal{R}^n$ distributed according to the density p, then the **probability** that the outcome lies in a set B in $\mathcal{R}^n$ is defined by

$$Pr\,[E \text{ in } B] = \int_B p\, dV.$$

(a) For what constant k is the function $\mathscr{R}^2 \xrightarrow{p} \mathscr{R}$,

$$p(x, y) = \begin{cases} k(1 - x^2 - y^2), & x^2 + y^2 \leq 1 \\ 0, & x^2 + y^2 > 1, \end{cases}$$

a probability density? 　　　　　　　　　　　　　　　　[*Ans.* $k = 2/\pi$.]

(b) If the outcomes of E are distributed according to the density of part (a), find the probability that E has an x-coordinate bigger than $\frac{1}{2}$.

21. Let B be the subset of $\mathscr{R}^2$ consisting of all points (x, y) such that $0 \leq y \leq 1$, and x is rational, $0 \leq x \leq 1$. What is the area of B?

22. On the rectangle $0 \leq x \leq 1$ and $0 \leq y \leq 1$, let $f(x, y) = 1$, if x is rational, and $f(x, y) = 2y$, if x is irrational. Show that

$$\int_0^1 dx \int_0^1 f(x, y)\, dy = 1,$$

but that f is not Riemann integrable over the rectangle.

23. Prove that

$$\int_0^1 dy \int_1^\infty (e^{-xy} - 2e^{-2xy})\, dx \neq \int_1^\infty dx \int_0^1 (e^{-xy} - 2e^{-2xy})\, dy.$$

3. CHANGE OF VARIABLE IN MULTIPLE INTEGRALS

The change-of-variable formula for 1-dimensional integrals is

$$\int_{\phi(a)}^{\phi(b)} f(x)\, dx = \int_a^b f(\phi(u))\phi'(u)\, du. \tag{1}$$

For example, taking $\phi(u) = \sin u$, we obtain

$$\int_0^1 \sqrt{1 - x^2}\, dx = \int_0^{\pi/2} \cos^2 u\, du = \frac{\pi}{4}.$$

In this section Equation (1) will be extended to dimensions higher than one. In n-dimensional space a change of variable is effected by a function $\mathscr{R}^n \xrightarrow{T} \mathscr{R}^n$. In what follows it will usually be more convenient to consider the domain space and range space of T as distinct. We therefore regard T as a transformation from one copy of $\mathscr{R}^n$, which we label $\mathscr{U}^n$, to another copy, which we continue to label $\mathscr{R}^n$, writing typically $T(\mathbf{u}) = \mathbf{x}$ where $\mathbf{u}$ is in $\mathscr{U}^n$ and $\mathbf{x}$ is in $\mathscr{R}^n$. The statement of the n-dimensional change-of-variable theorem follows.

3.1 Theorem. Let $\mathscr{U}^n \xrightarrow{T} \mathscr{R}^n$ be a continuously differentiable transformation. Let R be a set in $\mathscr{U}^n$ having a boundary consisting of finitely many smooth sets. Suppose that R and its boundary are contained in the interior of the domain of T and that

(a) T is one-one on R.

(b) $\det T'$, the Jacobian determinant of T, is different from zero on R.

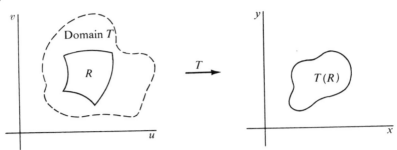

Figure 16

Then, if the function f is bounded and continuous on $T(R)$ (the image of R under T), we have

$$\int_{T(R)} f \, dV = \int_R (f \circ T) |\det T'| \, dV.$$

Either (a) or (b) is allowed to fail on a set of zero content.

The proof is in the Appendix. Before showing why the formula works, we give some examples of its application. Notice that the factor ϕ' that occurs in Equation (1) has been replaced in higher dimensions by the absolute value of the Jacobian determinant of T. Aside from the computation of $\det T'$, the application of the transformation formula is a matter of finding the geometric relationship between the subset R and its image $T(R)$ for various transformations T.

EXAMPLE 1. The integral $\int_P (x + y) \, dx \, dy$, in which P is the parallelogram shown in Figure 17, can be transformed into an integral over a rectangle. This is done by means of the transformation

$$\begin{pmatrix} x \\ y \end{pmatrix} = T \begin{pmatrix} u \\ v \end{pmatrix} = \begin{pmatrix} u + v \\ v \end{pmatrix}$$

The Jacobian determinant of T is

$$\det T' = \begin{vmatrix} 1 & 1 \\ 0 & 1 \end{vmatrix} = 1.$$

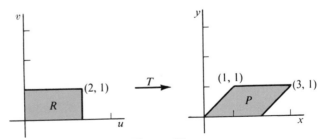

Figure 17

By the change-of-variable theorem,

$$\int_P (x+y)\, dx\, dy = \int_R [(u+v)+v]1\, du\, dv$$
$$= \int_0^2 du \int_0^1 (u+2v)\, dv = 4.$$

The transformation T is clearly one-one, because it is a linear transformation with nonzero determinant. Notice that the region of integration in the given integral is in the range of the transformation rather than in its domain.

EXAMPLE 2. The transformation

$$\begin{pmatrix} x \\ y \end{pmatrix} = \begin{pmatrix} u \cos v \\ u \sin v \end{pmatrix}$$

makes correspond the regions shown in Figure 18. The Jacobian is

$$\det T' = \begin{vmatrix} \cos v & -u \sin v \\ \sin v & u \cos v \end{vmatrix} = u.$$

The transformation is one-one between R and $T(R)$. This can be seen geometrically because of the interpretation of v and u as angle and radius respectively, or directly from the relations

$$u = \sqrt{x^2 + y^2}, \qquad \cos v = \frac{x}{\sqrt{x^2 + y^2}},$$

together with the fact that $\cos v$ is one-one for $0 \le v \le \pi/2$. Given the integral of $x^2 + y^2$ over $T(R)$, we can transform as follows:

$$\int_{T(R)} (x^2 + y^2)\, dA = \int_R u^2\, u\, dA = \int_1^2 u^3\, du \int_0^{\pi/2} dv = \frac{15\pi}{8}.$$

EXAMPLE 3. Let B be the subset of 3-dimensional space $\mathscr{R}^3$ defined by the inequalities

$$x^2 + y^2 + z^2 \le 1, \qquad \begin{cases} x \ge 0. \\ y \ge 0. \\ z \ge 0. \end{cases}$$

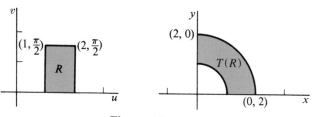

Figure 18

To transform the integral $\int_B (x^2 + y^2)\,dx\,dy\,dz$, we can define T by

$$\begin{pmatrix} x \\ y \\ z \end{pmatrix} = T\begin{pmatrix} u \\ v \\ w \end{pmatrix} = \begin{pmatrix} u \sin v \cos w \\ u \sin v \sin w \\ u \cos v \end{pmatrix}$$

Restricting (u, v, w) to the rectangle R defined by

$$\begin{cases} 0 \le u \le 1, \\ 0 \le v \le \pi/2, \\ 0 \le w \le \pi/2, \end{cases}$$

we get $T(R) = B$. The corresponding regions are shown in Figure 19. Since

$$u = \sqrt{x^2 + y^2 + z^2},$$

$$\cos v = \frac{z}{\sqrt{x^2 + y^2 + z^2}},$$

$$\cos w = \frac{x}{\sqrt{x^2 + y^2}},$$

we conclude that the transformation T is one-one from R to B except on the boundary planes $u = 0$ and $v = 0$. The Jacobian determinant is

$$\det T' = \begin{vmatrix} \sin v \cos w & u \cos v \cos w & -u \sin v \sin w \\ \sin v \sin w & u \cos v \sin w & u \sin v \cos w \\ \cos v & -u \sin v & 0 \end{vmatrix}$$

$$= u^2 \sin v.$$

The transformed integral is

$$\int_B (x^2 + y^2)\,dx\,dy\,dz = \int_R (u^2 \sin^2 v \cos^2 w + u^2 \sin^2 v \sin^2 w)\,u^2 \sin v\,du\,dv\,dw$$

$$= \int_0^1 u^4\,du \int_0^{\pi/2} \sin^3 v\,dv \int_0^{\pi/2} dw$$

$$= \frac{1}{5} \cdot \frac{2}{3} \cdot \frac{\pi}{2} = \frac{\pi}{15}.$$

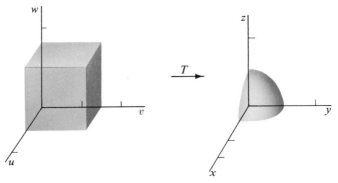

Figure 19

Notice that values of u and v appear in the transformed integral for which the Jacobian $u^2 \sin v$ is zero, that is, for $u = 0$ and $v = 0$. We have already remarked that the transformation fails to be one-one for points satisfying these conditions. However, the set of points on which this failure occurs has zero content, so the change-of-variable theorem still applies. Of course, the value of neither integral is affected by including or excluding these points.

EXAMPLE 4. Let a function $\mathcal{U}^2 \xrightarrow{\ T\ } \mathcal{R}^2$ be defined by

$$\begin{pmatrix} x \\ y \end{pmatrix} = T\begin{pmatrix} u \\ v \end{pmatrix} = \begin{pmatrix} u^2 - v \\ u + v^2 \end{pmatrix}$$

The unit square R_{uv} defined by the inequalities $0 \le u \le 1$, $0 \le v \le 1$ is carried by T onto the subset R_{xy} shown in Figure 20. Corresponding pieces of the boundaries are indicated in the picture. The image of each of the four line segments that comprise the boundary of R_{uv} is computed as follows:

(a) If $u = 0$ and $0 \le v \le 1$, then $x = -v$ and $y = v^2$. That is, $y = x^2$ and $-1 \le x \le 0$.

(b) If $v = 0$ and $0 \le u \le 1$, then $x = u^2$ and $y = u$. That is, $x = y^2$ and $0 \le y \le 1$.

(c) If $u = 1$ and $0 \le v \le 1$, then $x = 1 - v$ and $y = 1 + v^2$. That is, $y - 1 = (x - 1)^2$ and $0 \le x \le 1$.

(d) If $v = 1$ and $0 \le u \le 1$, then $x = u^2 - 1$ and $y = u + 1$. That is, $(y - 1)^2 = x + 1$ and $1 \le y \le 2$.

It is not hard to verify that T is one-one on R_{uv}. For suppose

$$T\begin{pmatrix} u_1 \\ v_1 \end{pmatrix} = T\begin{pmatrix} u_2 \\ v_2 \end{pmatrix}$$

Then

$$u_1^2 - v_1 = u_2^2 - v_2,$$
$$u_1 + v_1^2 = u_2 + v_2^2.$$

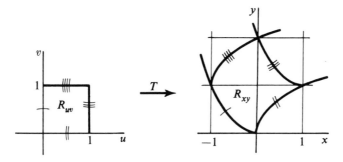

Figure 20

Obviously, if $u_1 = u_2$, then $v_1 = v_2$. Suppose $u_1 < u_2$. This implies

$$0 < u_2^2 - u_1^2 = v_2 - v_1,$$
$$0 < u_2 - u_1 = v_1^2 - v_2^2.$$

Hence, $v_1 < v_2$ whereas $v_2^2 < v_1^2$. This is impossible if both v_1 and v_2 are non-negative; so the one-oneness of T on R_{uv} is established. The Jacobian determinant of T is

$$\det T' = \begin{vmatrix} 2u & -1 \\ 1 & 2v \end{vmatrix} = 4uv + 1,$$

and we therefore have as an application of the change-of-variable theorem

$$\int_{R_{xy}} x \, dx \, dy = \int_{R_{uv}} (u^2 - v)(4uv + 1) \, du \, dv$$
$$= \int_0^1 dv \int_0^1 (4u^3 v - 4uv^2 + u^2 - v) \, du$$
$$= \int_0^1 \left(-2v^2 + \frac{1}{3} \right) dv = -\frac{1}{3}.$$

To understand why the change-of-variable formula works for a continuously differentiable vector function T, we need to know what effect T has on volume. We use the affine approximation to T that replaces $T(\mathbf{u})$ near $\mathbf{u}_0$ by $T(\mathbf{u}_0) + T'(\mathbf{u}_0)(\mathbf{u} - \mathbf{u}_0)$. The way in which T alters volume will be reflected in the way in which $d_{\mathbf{u}_0} T$ alters volume. In fact, translation of a subset by the vector $T(\mathbf{u}_0)$ leaves its volume unchanged, and the differential $d_{\mathbf{u}_0} T$, being a linear transformation, changes volume in a particularly simple way. Indeed, under a linear transformation volumes get multiplied by a constant factor, and the factor of proportionality is just the absolute value of the determinant of the transformation. For suppose T is taken to be a linear transformation, and f is the constant function 1, that is, $f(\mathbf{u}) = 1$ for all $\mathbf{u}$ in $\mathscr{U}^n$. The change-of-variable theorem (Theorem 3.1) then implies

3.2 Theorem. If T is a linear transformation from $\mathscr{R}^n$ to $\mathscr{R}^n$ having matrix A, then T multiplies volumes by the factor $|\det A|$.

Proof. By the change of variable theorem, setting $J = \det T'$, we get

$$V(T(R)) = \int_{T(R)} dV = \int_R |J| \, dV = |J| \, V(R).$$

The last step is valid because for a linear transformation with matrix A, the Jacobian determinant is a constant $\det A$. Then $|J| = |\det A|$, which can be taken outside the integral.

EXAMPLE 5. The transformation from $\mathscr{U}$ to $\mathscr{R}$ given by $x = 3u$ is linear. It is therefore its own differential (see Chapter 2, Section 7, Exercise 9) and has Jacobian determinant $J = 3$. It is clear from Figure 21 that lengths get multiplied by 3 under this transformation.

EXAMPLE 6. The transformation T from $\mathscr{U}^2$ to $\mathscr{R}^2$ given by

$$T\begin{pmatrix} u \\ v \end{pmatrix} = \begin{pmatrix} u^2 \\ u + v \end{pmatrix}$$

has as its differential at $\mathbf{u}_0 = \begin{pmatrix} u_0 \\ v_0 \end{pmatrix} = \begin{pmatrix} 1 \\ 1 \end{pmatrix}$

the linear transformation

$$(d_{\mathbf{u}_0} T)\begin{pmatrix} u \\ v \end{pmatrix} = \begin{pmatrix} 2u_0 & 0 \\ 1 & 1 \end{pmatrix}\begin{pmatrix} u \\ v \end{pmatrix} = \begin{pmatrix} 2 & 0 \\ 1 & 1 \end{pmatrix}\begin{pmatrix} u \\ v \end{pmatrix}$$

Near

$$\mathbf{u}_0 = \begin{pmatrix} 1 \\ 1 \end{pmatrix}$$

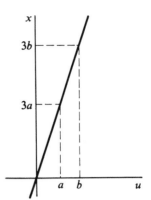

Figure 21

the function T is approximated by the affine transformation

$$A\begin{pmatrix} u \\ v \end{pmatrix} = T\begin{pmatrix} 1 \\ 1 \end{pmatrix} + T'(\mathbf{u}_0)\begin{pmatrix} u - 1 \\ v - 1 \end{pmatrix} = \begin{pmatrix} 1 \\ 2 \end{pmatrix} + \begin{pmatrix} 2 & 0 \\ 1 & 1 \end{pmatrix}\begin{pmatrix} u - 1 \\ v - 1 \end{pmatrix} = \begin{pmatrix} 2u - 1 \\ u + v \end{pmatrix}$$

The square R in the uv-plane in Figure 22 is carried by T onto the curved figure on the right. The affine approximation A carries R onto the parallelogram outlined with dashes. Notice that the area of the parallelogram is roughly equal to that of the curved figure. The exact area of the parallelogram is easily computed to be $\frac{1}{2}$, twice the area of R. The important point is that the affine approximation to T doubles the area of the square, while T itself approximately doubles that area. The magnification factor, 2, is given by the Jacobian determinant of T at $\mathbf{u}_0 = \begin{pmatrix} 1 \\ 1 \end{pmatrix}$. In fact

$$\det T' = \begin{vmatrix} 2 & 0 \\ 1 & 1 \end{vmatrix} = 2.$$

To find the exact area of the image $T(R)$, we use the change-of-variable

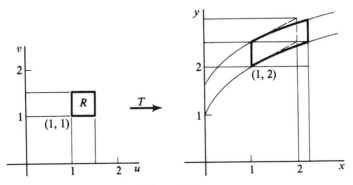

Figure 22

theorem. Since u is positive on R, the transformation T is one-one there. The inverse function is given explicitly by

$$T^{-1}\begin{pmatrix} x \\ y \end{pmatrix} = \begin{pmatrix} \sqrt{x} \\ y - \sqrt{x} \end{pmatrix},$$

so T is one-one. Moreover, the Jacobian determinant $J = 2u$ is positive on R. Hence,

$$A(T(R)) = \int_{T(R)} dA = \int_R |J|\, dA$$
$$= \int_1^{3/2} dv \int_1^{3/2} 2u\, du = \frac{1}{2} u^2 \Big]_1^{3/2} = \frac{5}{8}.$$

To understand the change-of-variable theorem itself, let T be a continuously differentiable transformation and consider the corresponding regions R and $T(R)$. A 2-dimensional example is illustrated in Figure 23. Decompose R into regions R_i by means of coordinate lines. Denoting approximate equality by the symbol $\approx$, we have

$$\int_{T(R)} f\, dV = \sum_i \int_{T(R_i)} f\, dV \approx \sum_i f_i V(T(R_i)), \tag{3}$$

where the number f_i is a value assumed by the function f in $T(R_i)$. We assume that $f_i V(T(R_i))$ is a reasonable approximation to $\int_{T(R_i)} f\, dV$. Next, approximate $V(T(R_i))$ by $|J_i|\, V(R_i)$, where J_i is a value assumed by the Jacobian determinant of T in R_i. Thus we are led to the approximation

$$\sum_i f_i V(T(R_i)) \approx \sum_i f_i |J_i|\, V(R_i). \tag{4}$$

But the number f_i is equally well a value of $f \circ T$ in R_i, which we can write $(f \circ T)_i$, getting from Formulas (3) and (4)

$$\int_{T(R)} f\, dV \approx \sum_i (f \circ T)_i |J_i|\, V(R_i).$$

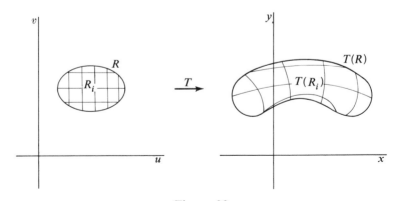

Figure 23

Finally, the last sum can be used to approximate $\int_R (f \circ T)|J| \, dV$. To make this argument precise is difficult, so the proof given in the Appendix follows other lines.

The above discussion shows that the Jacobian determinant can be interpreted as an approximate local magnification factor for volume. A one-one continuously differentiable transformation, looked at as a co-ordinate change, leads to another slightly different interpretation of J.

EXAMPLE 7. Polar coordinate curves in $\mathscr{R}^2$ bound regions like S in Figure 24. Since the Jacobian determinant of the polar coordinate transformation

$$\begin{pmatrix} x \\ y \end{pmatrix} = \begin{pmatrix} r \cos \theta \\ r \sin \theta \end{pmatrix} = T\begin{pmatrix} r \\ \theta \end{pmatrix}$$

is

$$J = \begin{vmatrix} \cos \theta & -r \sin \theta \\ \sin \theta & r \cos \theta \end{vmatrix} = r,$$

we expect an approximation to the shaded area $S = T(R)$ in the xy-plane to be $r_0 \, \Delta r \, \Delta \theta$. Computation of the exact area of S, using the change-of-variable theorem, gives

$$\int_S dA = \int_R r \, dA = \int_{r_0}^{r_0 + \Delta r} r \, dr \int_{\theta_0}^{\theta_0 + \Delta \theta} d\theta$$

$$= (\tfrac{1}{2}(r_0 + \Delta r)^2 - \tfrac{1}{2}r_0^2) \, \Delta \theta$$

$$= r_0 \, \Delta r \, \Delta \theta + \tfrac{1}{2}(\Delta r)^2 \, \Delta \theta$$

$$\approx r_0 \, \Delta r \, \Delta \theta \qquad \text{(for small } \Delta r, \Delta \theta).$$

Thus the significance of J in this case is that $J \, \Delta r \, \Delta \theta$ is an approximation to the area of a polar coordinate "rectangle," or region bounded by polar coordinate curves, with Δr and $\Delta \theta$ as the difference between pairs of values of r and θ.

The expression $r \, \Delta r \, \Delta \theta$ is called the **area element** in polar coordinates. More generally, if J is the Jacobian determinant of a coordinate change, then $|J| \, \Delta V$ is called its **volume element**.

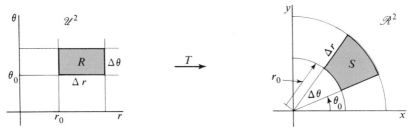

Figure 24

EXAMPLE 8. Spherical coordinates are introduced in $\mathscr{R}^3$ by means of the transformation

$$\begin{pmatrix} x \\ y \\ z \end{pmatrix} = \begin{pmatrix} r \sin \phi \cos \theta \\ r \sin \phi \sin \theta \\ r \cos \phi \end{pmatrix}.$$

Except for a notational change, the same transformation is considered in Example 3. The Jacobian determinant is $J = r^2 \sin \phi$. This suggests the approximation $r^2 \sin \phi \, \Delta r \, \Delta \phi \, \Delta \theta$ for the volume of the spherical coordinate "cube" C shown in Figure 25. The spherical ball with center at the origin and radius 1 is defined in $\mathscr{R}^3$ by $x^2 + y^2 + z^2 \leq 1$ and is denoted below by B_{xyz}. With respect to polar coordinates, the same ball is defined by the inequalities

$$0 \leq r \leq 1, \qquad 0 \leq \phi \leq \pi, \qquad 0 \leq \theta \leq 2\pi,$$

and is denoted below by $B_{r\phi\theta}$. Using the change-of-variable theorem, we compute the volume of the ball to be

$$V(B_{xyz}) = \int_{B_{xyz}} dx \, dy \, dz = \int_{B_{r\phi\theta}} r^2 \sin \phi \, dr \, d\phi \, d\theta$$

$$= \int_0^1 r^2 \, dr \int_0^\pi \sin \phi \, d\phi \int_0^{2\pi} d\theta$$

$$= \frac{1}{3}(1 + 1) 2\pi = \frac{4\pi}{3}.$$

Notice (as in Example 3) that both conditions (a) and (b) of Theorem 3.1 fail to hold on $B_{r\phi\theta}$. However, except on a subset of $B_{r\phi\theta}$ having zero volume, the Jacobian $J = r^2 \sin \phi$ is positive and the coordinate transformation is one-one. The change-of-variable formula is therefore applicable.

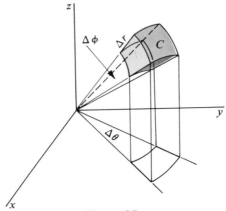

Figure 25

EXERCISES

1. Let

$$\begin{pmatrix} x \\ y \end{pmatrix} = T\begin{pmatrix} u \\ v \end{pmatrix} = \begin{pmatrix} u^2 - v^2 \\ 2uv \end{pmatrix}.$$

(a) Sketch the image under T of the square in $\mathcal{U}^2$ with vertices at $(1, 1)$, $(1, \frac{3}{2})$, $(\frac{3}{2}, 1)$, $(\frac{3}{2}, \frac{3}{2})$.

(b) Sketch the image under $T'\begin{pmatrix} 1 \\ 1 \end{pmatrix}$ of the square in part (a).

(c) Sketch the translate of the image found in part (b) by the vector

$$T\begin{pmatrix} 1 \\ 1 \end{pmatrix} - T'\begin{pmatrix} 1 \\ 1 \end{pmatrix}\begin{pmatrix} 1 \\ 1 \end{pmatrix}.$$

Verify that this is the image of the square under the affine approximation to T at $\begin{pmatrix} 1 \\ 1 \end{pmatrix}$.

(d) Find the area of the region sketched in (c). [*Ans.* 2.]

(e) Find the area of the region sketched in (a). [*Ans.* $\frac{19}{6}$.]

2. Let

$$\begin{pmatrix} x \\ y \end{pmatrix} = T\begin{pmatrix} u \\ v \end{pmatrix} = \begin{pmatrix} u \cos v \\ u \sin v \end{pmatrix}.$$

(a) Sketch the image under T of the square S with vertices at $(0, 0)$, $(0, \pi/2)$, $(\pi/2, 0)$, and $(\pi/2, \pi/2)$.

(b) Sketch the image under $T'\begin{pmatrix} \pi/2 \\ 0 \end{pmatrix}$ of the square S. What is the area of the image?

(c) Sketch the image of S under the affine approximation to T at $(\pi/4, \pi/4)$. What is the area of the image?

(d) What is the area of the region sketched in (a)?

3. Let

$$T\begin{pmatrix} u \\ v \end{pmatrix} = \begin{pmatrix} u \cos v \\ u \sin v \end{pmatrix}.$$

Show that $T'\begin{pmatrix} u \\ v \end{pmatrix}$ transforms a rectangle of area A into a region having area uA.

4. Compute the area of the image of the rectangle in the uv-plane with vertices at $(0, 0)$, $(0, 1)$, $(2, 0)$, and $(2, 1)$ under the transformation

$$\begin{pmatrix} x \\ y \end{pmatrix} = \begin{pmatrix} 2 & 3 \\ 2 & 1 \end{pmatrix}\begin{pmatrix} u \\ v \end{pmatrix}.$$ [*Ans.* 8.]

5. Consider the transformation T defined by

$$\begin{pmatrix} x \\ y \end{pmatrix} = T\begin{pmatrix} u \\ v \end{pmatrix} = \begin{pmatrix} u^2 - v^2 \\ 2uv \end{pmatrix}.$$

Let R_{uv} be the quarter of the unit disc lying in the first quadrant, i.e., $u^2 + v^2 \le 1$, $u \ge 0$, $v \ge 0$.

(a) Sketch the image region $R_{xy} = T(R_{uv})$.

(b) Compute $\displaystyle\int_{R_{xy}} \frac{dx\,dy}{\sqrt{x^2 + y^2}}$.   [*Ans.* π.]

6. Let the transformation from the uv-plane to the xy-plane be defined by $x = u + v$, $y = u^2 - v$. Let R_{uv} be the region bounded by (1) u-axis, (2) v-axis, (3) the line $u + v = 2$.

(a) Find and sketch the image region R_{xy}.

(b) Compute the integral

$$\int_{R_{xy}} \frac{dx\,dy}{\sqrt{1 + 4x + 4y}}.$$ [*Ans.* 2.]

7. Let a transformation of the uv-plane to the xy-plane be given by

$$x = u, \qquad y = v(1 + u^2)$$

and let R_{uv} be the rectangular region given by $0 \le u \le 3$ and $0 \le v \le 2$.

(a) Find and sketch the image region R_{xy}.

(b) Find $\dfrac{\partial(x, y)}{\partial(u, v)}$.

(c) Transform $\int_{R_{xy}} x\,dx\,dy$ to an integral over R_{uv} and compute either one of them.   [*Ans.* $\frac{99}{2}$.]

8. The transformation $u = x^2 - y^2$, $v = 2xy$ maps the region D (see sketch) onto a region R in the uv-plane, and is one-one on D.

(a) Find R.

(b) Compute $\int_R 1\,du\,dv$ by integrating directly over R, then by using the transformation formulas to integrate over D.   [*Ans.* $\frac{128}{3}$.]

(c) Compute $\int_R v\,du\,dv$ both directly and by using the change-of-variable theorem.   [*Ans.* 128.]

9. Let a transformation from the xy-plane to the uv-plane be given by

$$u = x$$
$$v = y(1 + 2x).$$

(a) What happens to horizontal lines in the xy-plane?

(b) If D is the rectangular region

$$0 \le x \le 3$$
$$1 \le y \le 3,$$

find the image region R of D.

(c) Find

$$\int_R du\, dv, \qquad \int_R v\, dv\, du, \qquad \text{and} \int_R u\, dv\, du$$

by direct integration, then by reducing them to integrals over D.

[*Ans.* 24, 228, 45.]

10. Compute the area bounded by the polar coordinate curves $\theta = 0$, $\theta = \pi/4$, and $r = \theta^2$. [*Ans.* $\pi^5/2^{10} \cdot 10$.]

11. Find the area bounded by the lemniscate $(x^2 + y^2)^2 = 2a^2(x^2 - y^2)$ by changing to polar coordinates. [*Ans.* $2a^2$.]

12. Compute the volume of the ellipsoid

$$\frac{x^2}{a^2} + \frac{y^2}{b^2} + \frac{z^2}{b^2} \le 1.$$

[Use the transformation $(x, y, z) = (au, bv, cw)$ to transform the sphere $u^2 + v^2 + w^2 \le 1$ onto the ellipsoid. Assume the volume of the sphere to be known.]

13. Evaluate the integral of $f(x, y, z) = a$ over the hemisphere $x^2 + y^2 + z^2 \le 1$, $x \ge 0$ by changing to spherical coordinates. [*Ans.* $\frac{2}{3}\pi a$.]

14. (a) Compute the Jacobian of the cylindrical coordinate transformation

$$\begin{pmatrix} x \\ y \\ z \end{pmatrix} = \begin{pmatrix} r\cos\theta \\ r\sin\theta \\ z \end{pmatrix}.$$

(b) Use cylindrical coordinates to compute

$$\int_{x^2+y^2\le 1,\, 0\le z\le 1.} x^2\, dx\, dy\, dz.$$

15. Prove that the transformation

$$x_1 = u_1$$
$$x_2 = u_1 + u_2$$
$$x_3 = u_1 + u_2 + u_3$$
$$\cdot$$
$$\cdot$$
$$\cdot$$
$$x_n = u_1 + u_2 + \ldots + u_n$$

leaves volumes of corresponding regions unchanged.

16. Cutting a solid of revolution R into thin cylindrical shells, with axis the same as the axis of revolution, leads intuitively to the following formula for the volume of the solid:

$$\int 2\pi\, r\, h(r)\, dr.$$

Here $h(r)$ is the thickness of the solid at a distance r from its axis, measured along a line parallel to the axis. Show that introducing cylindrical coordinates in the integral $\int_R dx\, dy\, dz$ leads to the same formula.

17. (a) Let a ball B of radius a have density ρ at each of its points equal to the distance of the point from a fixed diameter. Find the total mass of the ball.

[*Hint*. Compute the integral $\int_B \rho \, dV$ by using spherical coordinates.]

(b) Let a cylinder of height h and radius a have a density ρ equal at each point to the distance of the point from the axis of the cylinder. Find the total mass of the cylinder.

4. IMPROPER INTEGRALS

The definition of the integral can be extended to functions that are unbounded and not necessarily zero outside some bounded set. We shall first consider some examples.

EXAMPLE 1. The function $f(x, y) = 1/x^2 y^2$, defined for $x \geq 1$ and $y \geq 1$, has the graph shown in Figure 26. If B is the set of points (x, y) for which $x \geq 1$ and $y \geq 1$, it is natural to define $\int_B f \, dA$ in such a way that it can be called the volume under the graph of f. We can approximate this volume by computing the volume lying above bounded subrectangles of B. To be specific, let B_N be the rectangle with corners at $(1, 1)$ and (N, N) and with edges parallel to the edges of B. For $N > 1$ we have

$$\int_{B_N} f \, dA = \int_1^N dx \int_1^N \frac{1}{x^2 y^2} \, dy$$

$$= \left(\int_1^N \frac{dx}{x^2} \right)^2 = \left(1 - \frac{1}{N} \right)^2 .$$

As N tends to infinity, the rectangles B_N eventually cover every point of B, and the regions above the B_N fill out the region under the graph of f. Then, by definition,

$$\int_B f \, dA = \lim_{N \to \infty} \int_{B_N} f \, dA = 1.$$

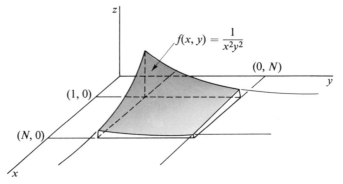

Figure 26

EXAMPLE 2. Let B be the disc $x^2 + y^2 \leq 1$ in $\mathcal{R}^2$, and suppose

$$f(x, y) = -\log (x^2 + y^2), \qquad 0 < x^2 + y^2 \leq 1.$$

The graph of f is shown in Figure 27. Since f is unbounded near $(0, 0)$, we cut out from B a disc centered at $(0, 0)$ and with radius ϵ. Call the part of B that is left B_ϵ. We have, using polar coordinates,

$$\begin{aligned}
\int_{B_\epsilon} -\log (x^2 + y^2)\, dx\, dy &= \int_0^{2\pi} d\theta \int_\epsilon^1 -(\log r^2) r\, dr \\
&= -2\pi[r^2 \log r - \tfrac{1}{2}r^2]_\epsilon^1 \\
&= \pi + 2\pi\epsilon^2 \log \epsilon - \pi\epsilon^2.
\end{aligned}$$

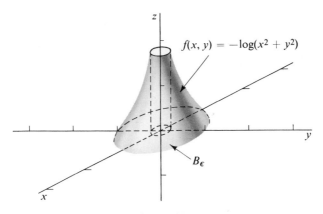

$$f(x, y) = -\log(x^2 + y^2)$$

B_ϵ

Figure 27

Since $\lim_{\epsilon \to 0} (2\pi\epsilon^2 \log \epsilon - \pi\epsilon^2) = 0$, we get, by definition,

$$\int_B -\log (x^2 + y^2)\, dx\, dy = \lim_{\epsilon \to 0} \int_{B_\epsilon} -\log (x^2 + y^2)\, dx\, dy = \pi.$$

In the previous example the function $-\log (x^2 + y^2)$ becomes unbounded in the disc $x^2 + y^2 \leq 1$ only at the point $(0, 0)$. It is of course important to find all such points in attempting to integrate an unbounded function. In general we define an **infinite discontinuity point** for a function f to be a point $\mathbf{x}$ such that in any neighborhood of $\mathbf{x}$, $|f|$ assumes arbitrarily large values.

EXAMPLE 3. Consider the function $g(x, y, z) = (x^2 + y^2 + z^2 - 1)^{-1/2}$ for (x, y, z) satisfying $1 < x^2 + y^2 + z^2 \leq 2$. The domain of g is the region between the concentric spheres shown in Figure 28. Every point of the sphere $x^2 + y^2 + z^2 = 1$ is an infinite discontinuity point for g. In order to define the integral of g, we approximate its domain by shells B_ϵ determined by $1 + \epsilon \leq x^2 + y^2 + z^2 \leq 2$. These shells have the property of filling out the entire domain of g as ϵ tends to zero, although none of them

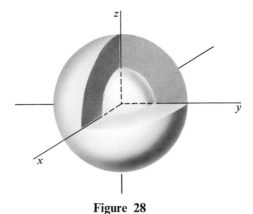

Figure 28

contains an infinite discontinuity point. Introducing spherical coordinates, we obtain

$$\int_{B_\epsilon} (x^2 + y^2 + z^2 - 1)^{-1/2} \, dx \, dy \, dz$$

$$= \int_{1+\epsilon}^{2} dr \int_{0}^{2\pi} d\theta \int_{0}^{\pi} (r^2 - 1)^{-1/2} r^2 \sin \phi \, d\phi$$

$$= 4\pi \int_{1+\epsilon}^{2} (r^2 - 1)^{-1/2} r^2 \, dr$$

$$= 4\pi \left[\frac{1}{2} r \sqrt{r^2 - 1} + \frac{1}{2} \log (r + \sqrt{r^2 - 1}) \right]_{1+\epsilon}^{2}.$$

It follows immediately that

$$\lim_{\epsilon \to 0} \int_{B_\epsilon} (x^2 + y^2 + z^2 - 1)^{1/2} \, dx \, dy \, dz = 4\pi \sqrt{3} + 2\pi \log (2 + \sqrt{3}).$$

Before collecting the ideas illustrated above into a general definition, we make two requirements about the integrand f and the set B over which it is to be integrated.

  (a) Let D be the set of points of B at which f is not continuous. The part of D lying in an arbitrary bounded rectangle is to be contained in finitely many smooth sets.
  (b) The part of B lying in an arbitrary bounded rectangle is to have a boundary consisting of finitely many smooth sets.

Both conditions are satisfied in the three examples considered so far, and we shall assume that they hold throughout the rest of the section.

In the examples we have seen that the integral $\int_B f \, dV$ can sometimes be defined when either f or B is unbounded. The extended definition of the integral will be made in such a way that both phenomena can occur at once. We proceed as follows: An increasing family $\{B_N\}$ of subsets of B will be said to **converge to** B if every bounded subset of B on which f is bounded is contained in some one of the sets B_N. Notice that this notion of convergence depends not only on B but also on f. The index N can be chosen in any convenient way; it may, for example, tend to ∞ continuously or through integer values, or it may tend to some finite number. Throughout the rest of this section we shall assume that in any increasing family $\{B_N\}$ converging to B, each of the sets B_N satisfies condition (b).

The **integral of f over B** is by definition

$$\lim_N \int_{B_N} f\, dV = \int_B f\, dV,$$

provided that the limit is finite and is the same for every increasing family of bounded sets B_N converging to B. It is assumed that the B_N are chosen so that the ordinary Riemann integrals $\int_{B_N} f\, dV$ (as defined in Section 2) exist. The integral thus obtained is called the **improper Riemann integral** when it is necessary to distinguish it from the Riemann integral of a bounded function over a bounded set.

Although the requirement that the value of the integral be independent of the converging family of sets used to define it is a natural one, we shall see later that it is sometimes interesting to disregard it. Nevertheless, the next theorem shows that for positive functions the limit of $\int_{B_N} f\, dV$ is always independent of family of sets.

4.1 Theorem. Let f be nonnegative on B and suppose that

$$\lim_N \int_{B_N} f\, dV$$

is finite for some particular increasing family of sets B_N converging to B. Then $\int_B f\, dV$ is defined and has the same value,

$$\lim_N \int_{C_N} f\, dV,$$

for every other family $\{C_N\}$ converging to B.

Proof. Since f is bounded on each B_N, we have for each N an index K such that

$$B_N \subset C_K.$$

Similarly there is an index M depending on K such that

$$C_K \subset B_M.$$

Then, because f is nonnegative

$$\int_{B_N} f\, dV \le \int_{C_K} f\, dV \le \int_{B_M} f\, dV.$$

In addition

$$\int_{C_N} f\, dV \le \lim_N \int_{B_N} f\, dV$$

for all N. Because $\int_{C_N} f \, dV$ increases and is bounded above,

$$\lim_N \int_{C_N} f \, dV$$

exists. The double inequality shows that

$$\lim_N \int_{B_N} f \, dV = \lim_N \int_{C_N} f \, dV.$$

This completes the proof.

EXAMPLE 4. Let f be defined on the infinite strip S in $\mathscr{R}^2$, shown in Figure 29, by $f(x, y) = y^{-1/2} e^{-x}$. Clearly f has an infinite discontinuity at every point of the positive x-axis. We define R_N to be the rectangle in S bounded by the lines $x = N$ and $y = 1/N$, for $N > 1$. As N tends to infinity, R_N will converge to S. We have

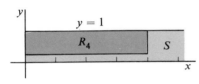

Figure 29

$$\int_{R_N} f \, dA = \int_0^N dx \int_{1/N}^1 y^{-1/2} e^{-x} \, dy$$

$$= \left(\int_0^N e^{-x} \, dx \right) \left(\int_{1/N}^1 y^{-1/2} \, dy \right)$$

$$= (1 - e^{-N}) \left(2 - \frac{2}{\sqrt{N}} \right).$$

Then

$$\int_S y^{-1/2} e^{-x} \, dx \, dy = \lim_{N \to \infty} (1 - e^{-N}) \left(2 - \frac{2}{\sqrt{N}} \right) = 2.$$

EXAMPLE 5. The integral of $1/x^a$ over the positive x-axis, denoted by $\int_0^\infty x^{-a} \, dx$, fails to exist for any a. Consider, for $N > 0$,

$$\int_{1/N}^N x^{-a} \, dx = \begin{cases} \dfrac{N^{1-a} - 1/N^{1-a}}{1 - a}, & a \neq 1. \\ 2 \log N, & a = 1. \end{cases}$$

As N tends to infinity, we get infinity for a limit in every case. However, it is easy to verify that

$$\int_1^\infty x^{-a} \, dx = \frac{1}{a - 1}, \qquad \text{for } a > 1,$$

and

$$\int_0^1 x^{-a} \, dx = \frac{1}{1 - a}, \qquad \text{for } a < 1.$$

The integral

$$\int_{-1}^1 \frac{1}{x} \, dx$$

fails to exist if we require that its value be independent of the limit process
by which it is computed. Indeed, if we integrate first over the intervals
$[-1, -\delta]$ and $[\epsilon, 1]$ with $0 < \delta < 1$ and $0 < \epsilon < 1$, we get

$$\int_{-1}^{-\delta} \frac{1}{x}\, dx + \int_{\epsilon}^{1} \frac{1}{x}\, dx = \log|x|\Big]_{-1}^{-\delta} + \log x\Big]_{\epsilon}^{1}$$

$$= \log \frac{\delta}{\epsilon}.$$

As ϵ and δ tend to zero, $\log(\delta/\epsilon)$ can be made to tend to any given number.
In particular, though, if we keep $\epsilon = \delta$, the limit is zero. For functions f
having certain symmetries, it is sometimes significant to compute $\int_B f\, dV$
by a limit involving rather special sets B_N, even though some other family
of sets may yield a different limit. When this is done and a limit is obtained,
we speak of finding a **principal value** (p.v.) of the integral, and we write
p.v. $\int_B f\, dV$ for the result. For the integral in the last part of Example 5 we
would then write p.v. $\int_{-1}^{1} (1/x)\, dx = 0$.

EXAMPLE 6. Let (r, θ) be polar coordinates in $\mathscr{R}^2$, and set $f(r, \theta)$
$= (\sin\theta)/r^2$ over the disc D of radius 1 centered at the origin. Clearly f has
an infinite discontinuity at the origin because, for instance, along the line
$\theta = \pi/2$, f tends to ∞ and along the line $\theta = 3\pi/2$, f tends to $-\infty$. (See
Figure 30 for the graph of f.) However, $\int_D f\, dA$ fails to exist in the ordinary
improper integral sense because the limit obtained from a sequence of
regions in D will depend on the way in which the positive and negative

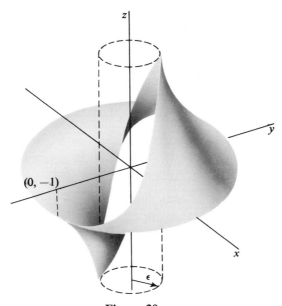

Figure 30

values of f are balanced. A principal value of the integral can be determined by taking a limit over a family of annular regions. Let D_ϵ be the annulus $\epsilon \leq r \leq 1$. Then

$$\text{p.v.} \int_D f \, dV = \lim_{\epsilon \to 0} \int_{D_\epsilon} \frac{\sin \theta}{r^2} r \, dr \, d\theta$$

$$= \lim_{\epsilon \to 0} \int_0^{2\pi} \sin \theta \, d\theta \int_\epsilon^1 \frac{dr}{r} = 0.$$

The next theorem is a convenient test for the existence of an improper integral.

4.2 Theorem. Let f and g have the same infinite discontinuity points. If $|f| \leq g$ and $\int_B g \, dV$ exists, then so does $\int_B f \, dV$.

Proof. Let $\{B_N\}$ be an increasing family of sets converging to B. Since $f + |f| \leq 2|f| \leq 2g$, we have

$$\int_{B_N} (f + |f|) \, dV \leq 2 \int_{B_N} g \, dV \leq 2 \int_B g \, dV.$$

Then, because $f + |f| \geq 0$, $\int_{B_N} (f + |f|) \, dV$ increases as B_N increases, and we have

$$\lim_N \int_{B_N} (f + |f|) \, dV = l_1 \leq 2 \int_B g \, dV.$$

Similarly,

$$\lim_N \int_{B_N} |f| \, dV = l_2 \leq \int_B g \, dV.$$

Finally,

$$\lim_N \int_{B_N} f \, dV = \lim_N \left(\int_{B_N} (f + |f|) \, dV - \int_{B_N} |f| \, dV \right)$$

$$= \lim_N \int_{B_N} (f + |f|) \, dV - \lim_N \int_{B_N} |f| \, dV = l_1 - l_2.$$

Since the family B_N is arbitrary, $\int_B f \, dV$ is defined.

EXAMPLE 7. Let B be the disc $x^2 + y^2 \leq 1$ in $\mathscr{R}^2$, and let f be defined by

$$f(x, y) = \begin{cases} (x^2 + y^2)^{-1/2}, & \text{for } x \geq 0 \text{ and } x^2 + y^2 > 0. \\ (x^2 + y^2)^{1/2}, & \text{for } x < 0. \end{cases}$$

Since $\int_B (x^2 + y^2)^{-1/2} \, dx \, dy$ exists, and $|f(x, y)| \leq (x^2 + y^2)^{-1/2}$ for $0 < x^2 + y^2 \leq 1$, it follows from Theorem 4.2 that $\int_B f \, dx \, dy$ exists. The computation of the integral of f is left as an exercise.

Figure 31

EXAMPLE 8. Let $j(x) = (-1)^{n-1}/n$ for $n - 1 \leq x < n$ and $n = 1, 2, 3,$ .... The graph of j is shown in Figure 31 as far out as $x = 4$. Then,

$$\lim_{n\to\infty} \int_0^n j(x)\, dx = \sum_{n=1}^\infty \frac{(-1)^{n-1}}{n} = \log 2,$$

and we can write

$$\int_0^\infty j(x)\, dx = \log 2,$$

if it is understood that the passage to the limit has been carried out in this special way. This example shares with the principal value examples the property that the value assigned to the integral depends on having taken a limit over some particular sequence of regions. Such an integral is called **conditionally convergent**. For another example see Exercise 8.

EXERCISES

1. In each part determine whether the integral is defined or not. If it is defined compute its value.

(a) $\displaystyle\int_0^\infty \frac{dx}{x^2+1}$.   [*Ans.* $\pi/2$.]

(b) $\displaystyle\int_{-\infty}^\infty \frac{dx}{x^2-1}$.

(c) $\displaystyle\int_0^1 \frac{dx}{\sqrt{1-x^2}}$.

(d) $\displaystyle\int_{x^2+y^2\le 1} \frac{dx\, dy}{\sqrt{x^2+y^2}}$.

(e) $\displaystyle\int_R \frac{(x-y)\, dx\, dy}{x^2+y^2}$, where R is the rectangle max $(|x|,|y|)\le 1$.

(f) $\displaystyle\int_{x^2+y^2+z^2\ge 1} \frac{dx\, dy\, dz}{(x^2+y^2+z^2)^2}$.

(g) $\displaystyle\int_{x^2+y^2+z^2\ge 1} \frac{dx\, dy\, dz}{xyz}$.

(h) $\displaystyle\int_C e^{-x-y-z}\, dx\, dy\, dz$, where C is the infinite column
$$\max (|x|,|y|)\le 1, \qquad z\ge 0.$$

2. Prove that

(a) $\qquad\qquad \Gamma(n) = \displaystyle\int_0^\infty e^{-x}x^{n-1}\, dx = (n-1)!$

for $n > 1$ an integer.

(b) Express $\displaystyle\int_T e^{-x}(x-y)^{-1/2}\, dx\, dy$ in terms of Γ, where T is the region $x\ge 0$, $y\ge x$.

3. Let B be the ball $|\mathbf{x}|\le 1$ in $\mathscr{R}^n$. For what values of a does $\displaystyle\int_B \frac{dV}{|\mathbf{x}|^a}$ exist?

4. Compute: (a) p.v. $\displaystyle\int_{-\infty}^\infty \frac{x\, dx}{x^2+1}$,   (b) p.v. $\displaystyle\int_{-1}^1 \frac{x\, dx}{2x-1}$.

5. Compute the values of the function $g(y) = \displaystyle\int_{-1}^1 \frac{x\, dx}{x-y}$, taking a principal value of the integral when necessary.

6. Compute the integral of the function f in Example 7 in the text, and compute $\int_B (x^2 + y^2)^{-1/2} \, dx \, dy$.   [*Ans.* $\frac{4}{3}\pi$, 2π.]

7. Show that the integral of the function j in Example 8 of the text depends on the sequence of sets used to compute the limit. [*Suggestion.* Take each B_N to be a disconnected set of intervals.]

8. Let $f(x, y) = \sin (x^2 + y^2)$ over the quadrant Q defined by $x \geq 0$, $y \geq 0$. Show that $\int_Q f \, dA$ converges conditionally. (*Suggestion.* To get a limit, integrate over increasing squares. Then integrate over quarter discs.)

9. In what sense does each of the following integrals exist? The possibilities are ordinary Riemann integral, improper integral, conditionally convergent integral, or none of these.

(a) $\int_\pi^\infty \frac{\sin x}{x^2} \, dx$.   (b) $\int_0^\infty \frac{\sin x}{x} \, dx$.

(c) $\int_0^\infty \sin x \, dx$.   (d) $\int_0^1 \sin \frac{1}{x} \, dx$.

10. The integral $\int_0^\infty f(x) \, dx$ is said to be **Abel summable** to the value k if

$$\lim_{\epsilon \to 0+} \int_0^\infty e^{-\epsilon x} f(x) \, dx = k.$$

Find the Abel value of (a) $\int_0^\infty \sin x \, dx$,   (b) $\int_0^\infty \cos x \, dx$.

11. (a) Compute $\int_{\mathscr{R}^2} e^{-x^2 - y^2} \, dx \, dy$. (Use polar coordinates.)

(b) Use the result of part (a) to compute $\int_{-\infty}^\infty e^{-x^2} \, dx$.

(c) Compute $\int_{\mathscr{R}^n} \exp(-x_1^2 - \ldots - x_n^2) \, dV$.

12. (a) Show that the area bounded by the graph of $y = 1/x$, the x-axis, and the line $x = 1$ is infinite.

(b) Compute the volume swept out by rotating the region described in (a) about the x-axis.

13. Let f be positive and unbounded on an unbounded set B in $\mathscr{R}^2$. Consider the region C between the graph of f and B, and show that if

$$\int_B f \, dA \quad \text{and} \quad \int_C dV$$

both exist, then they are equal.

14. Show that if $\int_B |f| \, dV$ exists, then so does $\int_B f \, dV$. Without conditions (a) and (b) this is false. For example, let B be the unit interval $0 \leq x \leq 1$ and f the function

$$f(x) = \begin{cases} 1, & \text{if } x \text{ is rational.} \\ -1, & \text{if } x \text{ is irrational.} \end{cases}$$

15. Show that if the ordinary Riemann integral $\int_B f \, dV$ exists, then it exists as an improper integral (given conditions (a) and (b)) and the two integrals are equal.

16. A nonnegative function $\mathscr{R}^n \xrightarrow{p} \mathscr{R}$, integrable over a region R in $\mathscr{R}^n$ is called a probability density if $\int_R p \, dV = 1$. The **mean** of p is defined to be the vector

$$M[p] = \int_R \mathbf{x} p(\mathbf{x}) \, dV,$$

and the **variance** of p is the real number

$$\sigma^2[p] = \int_R |\mathbf{x} - M[p]|^2 p(\mathbf{x}) \, dV.$$

Show that each of the following functions is a probability density, and compute its mean and variance if they exist.

(a) $p(x, y) = (1/2\pi)e^{-(x^2+y^2)/2}$ [*Hint*. Use polar coordinates.]
(b) $p(x) = 1/\pi(1 + x^2)$.

VECTOR FIELD THEORY 5

1. GREEN'S THEOREM

The fundamental theorem of calculus says that if f' is continuous for $a \leq t \leq b$, then

$$\int_a^b f'(t)\, dt = f(b) - f(a).$$ (1)

In Section 10 of Chapter 2 the theorem has been extended to line integrals of a gradient ∇f by the equation

$$\int_\mathbf{a}^\mathbf{b} \nabla f(\mathbf{x}) \cdot d\mathbf{x} = f(\mathbf{b}) - f(\mathbf{a}).$$ (2)

The main theorems of the present chapter are also variations on the idea that an integral of some kind of derivative of a function can be evaluated by using the values of the function itself on a set of lower dimension. We begin with the version known as Green's theorem.

Let D be a plane region whose boundary is a single curve γ, parametrized by a function g in such a way that as t increases from a to b, $g(t)$ traces γ once in the counterclockwise direction. An example is shown in Figure 1.

If F_1 and F_2 are real-valued functions defined on D, including its boundary, then Green's theorem says that

$$\int_D \left(\frac{\partial F_2}{\partial x_1} - \frac{\partial F_1}{\partial x_2} \right) dx_1\, dx_2 = \int_\gamma F_1\, dx_1 + F_2\, dx_2, \tag{3}$$

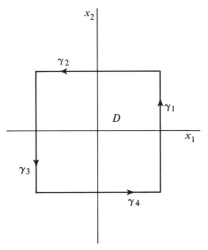

Figure 1

under appropriate smoothness conditions. The requirement that γ be traced counterclockwise is the analog of the fact that in Equations (1) and (2), the differences on the right have to be taken in the proper order. The analogy of Equation (3) with Equations (1) and (2) can be further strengthened if we think of the integrand $(\partial F_1/\partial x_2) - (\partial F_1/\partial x_2)$ as a kind of derivative of the vector field $F = (F_1, F_2)$. Section 8 contains a justification of this viewpoint.

EXAMPLE 1. Suppose D is the square defined by $-1 \leq x_1 \leq 1$, $-1 \leq x_2 \leq 1$, and let F_1 and F_2 be defined on D by $F_1(x_1, x_2) = -x_2 e^{x_1}$, and $F_2(x_1, x_2) = x_1 e^{x_2}$. Then

$$\frac{\partial F_2}{\partial x_1}(x_1, x_2) - \frac{\partial F_1}{\partial x_2}(x_1, x_2) = e^{x_2} + e^{x_1},$$

so

$$\int_D \left(\frac{\partial F_2}{\partial x_1} - \frac{\partial F_1}{\partial x_2} \right) dx_1\, dx_2 = \int_{-1}^1 dx_1 \int_{-1}^1 (e^{x_2} + e^{x_1})\, dx_2$$

$$= 4\left(e - \frac{1}{e} \right).$$

The boundary curve γ can be parametrized in four pieces γ_i, $i = 1, 2, 3, 4$, by

$$\binom{x_1}{x_2} = \begin{cases} \binom{1}{t} \\ \binom{-t}{1} \\ \binom{-1}{-t} \\ \binom{t}{-1} \end{cases}, \quad -1 \leq t \leq 1.$$

Notice that the traversal of γ is counterclockwise, as is shown in Figure 1. On the first side of the square we have

$$\int_{\gamma_1} F_1 dx_1 + F_2 dx_2 = \int_{\gamma_1} - x_2 e^{x_1} dx_1 + x_1 e^{x_2} dx_2$$

$$= \int_{-1}^{1} \left[(-te) \frac{dx_1}{dt} + e^t \frac{dx_2}{dt} \right] dt$$

$$= \int_{-1}^{1} e^t \, dt = e - \frac{1}{e}.$$

Similarly, the integrals over the other three sides are also equal to $(e - 1/e)$, so

$$\int_{\gamma} F_1 \, dx_1 + F_2 \, dx_2 = 4 \left(e - \frac{1}{e} \right).$$

Equation (3) is thus verified for this particular example.

In the computation of a line integral, a given parametrization can always be replaced by an equivalent one, for which the line integral will have the same value. In the previous example the boundary curve γ was given what appears to be the simplest parametrization, though any equivalent one would do. The question becomes more important if the boundary is presented without any parametrization, but merely as a set. It may be necessary to choose a parametrization, and if Green's theorem is to be applied, we shall see that this must be done so that the boundary is traced just once, and in the proper direction.

The importance of the clockwise *versus* counterclockwise traversal of the boundary becomes apparent when we observe that, for any line integral, a reversal of the direction of the path changes the sign of the integral. Thus, if γ is parametrized by $g(t)$ for $a \leq t \leq b$, we can denote by γ^- the curve parametrized by $g^-(t) = g(a + b - t)$ for $a \leq t \leq b$. It is clear that γ^- is the same set as γ, but is traced in the opposite direction, that is, from $g(b)$ to $g(a)$ instead of the other way around. Then, since $g^{-\prime}(t) = -g'(a + b - t)$, we have

$$\int_{\gamma^-} F \cdot dx = - \int_a^b F(g(a + b - t)) \cdot g'(a + b - t) dt.$$

Changing variable by $t = a + b - u$ gives

$$\int_{\gamma^-} F \cdot dx = - \int_a^b F(g(u)) \cdot g'(u) \, du$$

$$= - \int_{\gamma} F \cdot dx$$

This proves the important formula

1.1 $$\int_{\gamma^-} F \cdot dx = - \int_{\gamma} F \cdot dx.$$

Green's theorem can be proved most easily for regions D such that γ, the boundary of D, is crossed at most twice by a line parallel to a coordinate axis. Such a region is called **simple**. Thus, a coordinate line intersects the boundary of a simple region either in a line segment or else in at most two points. In fact, using Equation 1.1, we can extend the theorem to finite unions of simple regions. A few such are shown in Figure 2, where only D_1 is simple. In D_2 the boundary is shown traced not always counterclockwise, but rather with the region always to the left as a point traces the curve. For bounded regions with a single boundary curve, the two descriptions of the orientation of the boundary amount to the same thing.

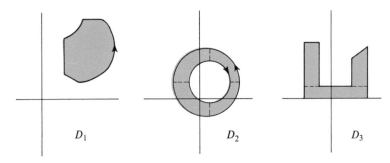

D_1 D_2 D_3

Figure 2

1.2 **Green's theorem.** Let D be a bounded plane region which is a finite union of simple regions, each with a boundary consisting of a piecewise smooth curve. Let F_1 and F_2 be continuously differentiable real-valued functions defined on D together with γ, the boundary of D. Then

$$\int_D \left(\frac{\partial F_2}{\partial x_1} - \frac{\partial F_1}{\partial x_2} \right) dx_1\, dx_2 = \int_\gamma F_1\, dx_1 + F_2\, dx_2,$$

where γ is parametrized so that it is traced once with D on the left.

Proof. Consider first the case in which D is a simple region, with boundary γ parametrized by

$$\begin{pmatrix} x_1 \\ x_2 \end{pmatrix} = \begin{pmatrix} g_1(t) \\ g_2(t) \end{pmatrix}, \qquad a \le t \le b.$$

Since

$$\int_\gamma F_1\, dx_1 + F_2\, dx_2 = \int_\gamma F_1\, dx_1 + \int_\gamma F_2\, dx_2,$$

we can work with each of the terms on the right separately. We have

$$\int_\gamma F_1(x_1, x_2)\, dx_1 = \int_a^b F_1(g_1(t), g_2(t)) g_1'(t)\, dt.$$

The curve γ consists of the graphs of two functions $u(x_1)$ and $v(x_1)$, perhaps together with one or two vertical segments, as shown in Figure 3.

On a vertical segment, g_1 is constant, so $g_1' = 0$ there. On the remaining parts of γ we apply the change of variable $x_1 = g_1(t)$ so that, on the top curve, $g_2(t) = u(x_1)$, while on the bottom, $g_2(t) = v(x_1)$. It follows that

$$\int_\gamma F_1(x_1, x_2)\, dx_1 = \int_\beta^\alpha F_1(x_1, u(x_1))\, dx_1 + \int_\alpha^\beta F_1(x_1, v(x_1))\, dx_1,$$

where the integration from β to α occurs because the graph of u is traced from right to left. Reversing the limits in the first integral, we get

$$\int_\gamma F_1(x_1, x_2)\, dx = \int_\alpha^\beta [-F_1(x_1, u(x_1)) + F_1(x_1, v(x_1))]\, dx_1$$

$$= \int_\alpha^\beta \left[-\int_{v(x_1)}^{u(x_1)} \frac{\partial F_1}{\partial x_2}(x_1, x_2)\, dx_2 \right] dx_1$$

$$= \int_D -\frac{\partial F_1}{\partial x_2}\, dx_1\, dx_2.$$

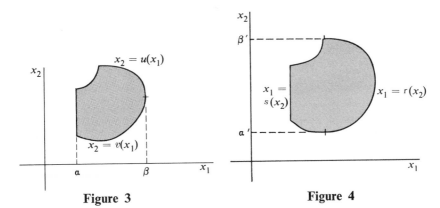

Figure 3   **Figure 4**

A similar proof, referred to Figure 4, shows that

$$\int_\gamma F_2(x_1, x_2)\, dx_2 = \int_D \frac{\partial F_2}{\partial x_1}\, dx_1\, dx_2.$$

Combining this equation with the previous ones gives Green's theorem for the special class of simple regions.

We extend the theorem to a finite union, $D = D_1 \cup \ldots \cup D_K$, of simple regions each with a piecewise smooth boundary curve γ_k, $k = 1, \ldots, K$. Applying Green's theorem to each simple region D_k we get

$$\int_{D_k} \left(\frac{\partial F_2}{\partial x_1} - \frac{\partial F_1}{\partial x_2} \right) dx_1\, dx_2 = \int_{\gamma_k} F_1\, dx_1 + F_2\, dx_2$$

The sum of integrals over D_k is an integral over D, so

$$\int_D \left(\frac{\partial F_2}{\partial x_1} - \frac{\partial F_1}{\partial x_2} \right) dx_1\, dx_2 = \int_{\gamma_1} F_1\, dx_1 + F_2\, dx_2 + \ldots + \int_{\gamma_K} F_1\, dx_1 + F_2\, dx_2.$$

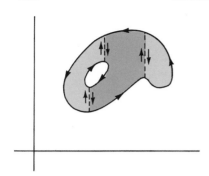

Figure 5

Now the boundary of D consists of pieces taken from several of the curves γ_k. In addition there may be parts of curves γ_k that are not a part of γ but which act as common boundary to two simple regions. The effect is illustrated in Figure 5.

A piece δ of common boundary will be traced in one direction or the opposite, depending on which simple region it is associated with. But for a line integral we always have, by Equation 1.1,

$$\int_\delta F_1 \, dx_1 + F_2 \, dx_2 + \int_{\delta^-} F_1 \, dx_1 + F_2 \, dx_2 = 0.$$

Thus, while the parts of the curves γ_k that make up γ contribute to $\int_\gamma F_1 \, dx_1 + F_2 \, dx_2$, the other parts cancel, leaving

$$\int_D \left(\frac{\partial F_2}{\partial x_1} - \frac{\partial F_1}{\partial x_2}\right) dx_1 \, dx_2 = \int_\gamma F_1 \, dx_1 + F_2 \, dx_2.$$

This completes the proof of Green's theorem.

The last part of the proof just given extends Green's theorem from simple regions to ones like those shown in Figure 6. The extension has an important consequence for line integrals $\int F_1 \, dx_1 + F_2 \, dx_2$ over two curves γ and δ, whenever the functions F_1 and F_2 are continously differentiable in the region D between γ and δ as well as on the boundary curves. In Figure 6(a) the curves are traced in the same direction (counterclockwise in the figure) and in Figure 6(b) the curves go from one point to another in the same direction. If it happens that the equation

$$\frac{\partial F_2}{\partial x_1} - \frac{\partial F_1}{\partial x_2} = 0 \tag{4}$$

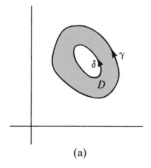

(a)

(b)

Figure 6

holds throughout D, then we can conclude that

$$\int_\gamma F_1 \, dx_1 + F_2 \, dx_2 = \int_\delta F_1 \, dx_1 + F_2 \, dx_2.$$

The principle is illustrated in the next two examples.

EXAMPLE 2. Let F_1 and F_2 be defined by

$$F_1(x_1, x_2) = \frac{-x_2}{x_1^2 + x_2^2}, \qquad F_2(x_1, x_2) = \frac{x_1}{x_1^2 + x_2^2},$$

for $(x_1, x_2) \neq (0, 0)$. Direct computation shows that these functions satisfy Equation (4). If γ is the ellipse defined by

$$\begin{pmatrix} x_1 \\ x_2 \end{pmatrix} = \begin{pmatrix} 2 \cos t \\ 3 \sin t \end{pmatrix}, \qquad 0 \le t \le 2\pi,$$

then the line integral $\int_\gamma F_1 \, dx_1 + F_2 \, dx_2$ would be troublesome to compute directly, even using tables. However, we can apply Green's theorem to the region D between γ and the circle c of radius 1 about the origin, parametrized by $(x_1, x_2) = (\cos t, \sin t)$, $0 \le t \le 2\pi$. Because Equation (4) is satisfied, Green's theorem yields

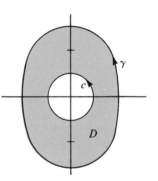

Figure 7

$$\int_{\gamma \cup c^-} F_1 \, dx_1 + F_2 \, dx_2 = 0,$$

where c^- is c traced clockwise, so that D is on its left. The last equation can be written, by Equation 1.1,

$$\int_\gamma F_1 \, dx_1 + F_2 \, dx_2 = \int_c F_1 \, dx_1 + F_2 \, dx_2.$$

But on c we have $x_1^2 + x_2^2 = 1$ so

$$\int_\gamma F_1 \, dx_1 + F_2 \, dx_2 = \int_c -x_2 \, dx_1 + x_1 \, dx_2$$

$$= \int_0^{2\pi} (\sin^2 t + \cos^2 t) \, dt = 2\pi.$$

It is important to observe that Green's theorem could not have been applied directly to the entire interior of the ellipse because $(\partial F_2 / \partial x_1)$ and $(\partial F_1 / \partial x_2)$ fail to exist at the origin.

EXAMPLE 3. The curve γ_1 given by $g(t) = (t, t^2)$, $0 \le t \le 1$, is shown in Figure 8. Suppose that $F(x_1, x_2) = (F_1(x_1, x_2), F_2(x_1, x_2))$ is a continuously differentiable vector field for $x_1^2 + x_2^2 < 4$ and satisfies Equation (4) there.

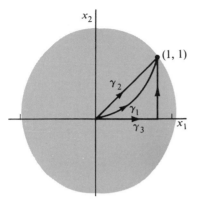

Figure 8

The line integral of F over γ_1 could perhaps be computed directly in the form

$$\int_{\gamma_1} F \cdot dx = \int_0^1 [F_1(t,t^2) + F_2(t,t^2)(2t)]\,dt.$$

However there are other possibilities. For example, the curve γ_2 can be parametrized by $g_2(t) = (t, t)$, $0 \le t \le 1$. Since we can apply Green's theorem to the region between γ_1 and γ_2, the fact that

$$\int_D \left(\frac{\partial F_2}{\partial x_1} - \frac{\partial F_1}{\partial x_2}\right) dx_1\, dx_2 = 0$$

would imply

$$\int_{\gamma_1} F \cdot dx + \int_{\gamma_2^-} F \cdot dx = 0,$$

where γ_2^- is given by $g_2^-(t) = (1 - t, 1 - t)$ for $0 \le t \le 1$. Then the line integrals over γ_1 and γ_2 are equal by Equation 1.1, and the latter integral can be written

$$\int_{\gamma_2} F \cdot dx = \int_0^1 [F_1(t, t) + F_2(t, t)]\,dt.$$

Another alternative would be to replace γ_1 by γ_3, where γ_3 is parametrized in two pieces by

$$g_3(t) = \begin{cases} \begin{pmatrix} t \\ 0 \end{pmatrix} \\[6pt] \begin{pmatrix} 1 \\ t \end{pmatrix} \end{cases}, \qquad 0 \le t \le 1.$$

Thus

$$\int_{\gamma_3} F \cdot dx = \int_0^1 F_1(t, 0)\, dt + \int_0^1 F_2(1, t)\, dt.$$

This may be easier to compute than either of the integrals over γ_1 and γ_2, although all three are equal.

Line integrals around a *closed* path, sometimes called a **circuit**, are of sufficient importance that they are often distinguished from other integrals by using an integral sign like $\oint$. In the plane this notation has the special advantage that $\oint$ and $\ointclockwise$ can be used to indicate a counterclockwise or clockwise traversal of the path.

EXAMPLE 4. Green's theorem has two distinct but closely related physical interpretations. We assume D to be a region in $\mathscr{R}^2$ whose boundary is a single counterclockwise oriented curve γ. If γ has a smooth parametrization $g(t)$

$= (g_1(t), g_2(t))$, $a \le t \le b$, and has a nonzero tangent at each point, we can form the unit tangent and normal vectors

$$\mathbf{t}(t) = \frac{g'(t)}{|g'(t)|} = \left(\frac{g_1'(t)}{|g'(t)|}, \frac{g_2'(t)}{|g'(t)|} \right)$$

and

$$\mathbf{n}(t) = \left(\frac{g_2'(t)}{|g'(t)|}, \frac{-g_1'(t)}{|g'(t)|} \right).$$

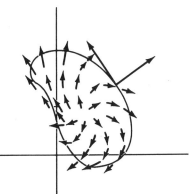

An example is shown in Figure 9. If $F = (F_1, F_2)$ is a continuously differentiable vector field defined on a region containing D and γ, then the line integral in Green's theorem can be written in the form

Figure 9

$$\oint_\gamma F_1 \, dx_1 + F_2 \, dx_2 = \int_a^b F(g(t)) \cdot \mathbf{t}(t) |g'(t)| \, dt$$

$$= \oint_\gamma F \cdot \mathbf{t} \, ds$$

We define a real-valued function, curl F, called the **curl** of F by

$$\text{curl } F(\mathbf{x}) = \frac{\partial F_2}{\partial x_1}(\mathbf{x}) - \frac{\partial F_1}{\partial x_2}(\mathbf{x}).$$

Green's theorem then becomes

$$\int_D \text{curl } F \, dA = \oint_\gamma F \cdot \mathbf{t} ds,$$

sometimes called Stokes's theorem. Now interpret F as a force field in the plane. The line integral represents the work $W(\gamma)$ done in moving a particle around γ in the counterclockwise direction under the influence of F. Stokes's theorem says that $W(\gamma)$ is equal to the integral of the curl of F over D. In particular, if curl F is identically zero in D, then $W(\gamma) = 0$ for every smooth circuit γ contained in D, whether γ is oriented counterclockwise or not. For this conclusion to hold, it is of course necessary that curl F be defined throughout the inside of every circuit in D to which Stokes's theorem is applied. Conversely, it is possible to show that if $W(\gamma) = 0$ for every smooth circuit, then curl F is identically zero.

F can also be interpreted as the velocity field of a fluid flow in D. That is, the vector field F at each point of D represents the speed and direction of the flow at that point. In this case the line integral in Stokes's theorem is called the **circulation** of F around γ, and Stokes's theorem says that the circulation of F along γ is the integral of the curl of F over D. Thus to say that curl F is identically zero in D is to say that the circulation is zero around every smooth closed curve with its interior contained in D. A field F for which curl F is zero is called **irrotational** for this reason.

Now using the unit normal $\mathbf{n}(t)$, we can rewrite Green's theorem in another way. Instead of applying the fundamental Equation (3) to the field $F = (F_1, F_2)$, we apply it to the related pair of functions $(-F_2, F_1)$. Thus the line integral becomes

$$\oint_\gamma -F_2\, dx_1 + F_1\, dx_2 = \int_a^b F(g(t)) \cdot \mathbf{n}(t) |g'(t)|\, dt$$

$$= \oint_\gamma F \cdot \mathbf{n} ds.$$

On the other hand the area integral over D becomes

$$\int_D \left(\frac{\partial F_1}{\partial x_1} + \frac{\partial F_2}{\partial x_2}\right) dx_1\, dx_2.$$

We define a real-valued function div F, called the **divergence** of F, by

$$\text{div } F(\mathbf{x}) = \frac{\partial F_1}{\partial x_1}(\mathbf{x}) + \frac{\partial F_2}{\partial x_2}(\mathbf{x}),$$

and so Green's theorem can be written

$$\int_D \text{div } F\, dA = \oint_\gamma F \cdot \mathbf{n} ds,$$

which in this form is called Gauss's theorem.

Using the fluid flow interpretation, in which F represents a velocity field, the line integral in Gauss's theorem is the integral of the outward normal coordinate of F over γ. Hence, this integral is called the total flow, or **flux** of F across γ in the outward direction. Gauss's theorem shows that the flux, $\Phi(\gamma)$, across γ is equal to the integral of the divergence of F over the region bounded by γ. Thus div $F(\mathbf{x})$ measures the rate of change of the density of the fluid at the point $\mathbf{x}$. If div $F(\mathbf{x})$ is predominantly positive in D, then $\Phi(\gamma)$, the outward flow, will be positive, and a negative $\Phi(\gamma)$ indicates that more fluid is going into D than is going out. If div F is identically zero, then F is said to represent an **incompressible** flow.

EXERCISES

1. Use Green's theorem to compute the value of the line integral $\int_\gamma x_2\, dx_1 + x_1^2\, dx_2$, where γ is each of the following closed paths.

   (a) The circle given by $g(t) = (\cos t, \sin t)$, $0 \le t \le 2\pi$.
   (b) The square with corners at $(\pm 1, \pm 1)$, traced counterclockwise.
   (c) The square with corners at $(0, 0)$, $(1, 0)$, $(1, 1)$, and $(0, 1)$, traced counterclockwise.

2. Using some one of the paths γ_1, γ_2, or γ_3 in Example 3 of the text, compute the line integral $\int_{\gamma_k} x_2\, dx_1 + x_1\, dx_2$.

3. Let γ be the curve parametrized by $g(t) = (2 \cos t, 3 \sin t)$, $0 \le t \le 2\pi$. Compute $\int_\gamma (2x_1 + x_2)\, dx_1 + (x_1 + 3x_2)\, dx_2$.

4. Evaluate the following line integrals by whatever method seems simplest.

(a) $\int_\gamma e^x \cos y \, dx + e^x \sin y \, dy$, where γ is the triangle with vertices $(0, 0)$, $(1, 0)$, $(1, \pi/2)$, traced counterclockwise.

(b) Use the same integrand as in part (a), but change the path to the square with corners at $(0, 0)$, $(1, 0)$, $(1, 1)$, and $(0, 1)$ traced counterclockwise.

(c) $\int_c (x^2 - y^2) \, dx + (x^2 + y^2) \, dy$, where c is the circle of radius 1 centered at $(0, 0)$ and traced *clockwise*.

5. Show that if D is a simple region bounded by a piecewise smooth curve γ, then the area of D is given by

$$A(D) = \tfrac{1}{2} \oint_\gamma (-y \, dx + x \, dy).$$

6. Let f be a real-valued function with continuous second order derivatives in an open set D in $\mathscr{R}^2$. Let F be the vector field defined in D by $F(\mathbf{x}) = \nabla f(\mathbf{x})$, the gradient of f. Show that if $F(\mathbf{x}) = (F_1(\mathbf{x}), F_2(\mathbf{x}))$, then the equation $(\partial F_2/\partial x_1) - (\partial F_1/\partial x_2) = 0$ is satisfied in D.

7. Let $f(x_1, x_2) = \arctan(x_2/x_1)$, for $x_1 > 0$. Let the vector field $\nabla f(x_1, x_2)$ have coordinate functions $F_1(x_1, x_2)$ and $F_2(x_1, x_2)$. Show that F_1 and F_2 can be extended in a natural way to all $(x_1, x_2) \neq (0, 0)$. Let γ be a smooth curve parametrized to run from the point $(1, 0)$ to a fixed point (x_1, x_2), but on the way winding k times counterclockwise around the origin. Compute the line integral

$$\int_\gamma \nabla f \cdot d\mathbf{x},$$

(a) for $k = 0$; (b) for $k = 1$; (c) for k an arbitrary positive integer. (d) What interpretation can be given the line integral if k is a negative integer?

8. Let F be a continuously differentiable vector field defined everywhere but at two points $\mathbf{x}_1$ and $\mathbf{x}_2$ in $\mathscr{R}^2$, and satisfying $(\partial F_2/\partial x_1) - (\partial F_1/\partial x_2) = 0$. Let c_1 and c_2 be counterclockwise-oriented circles centered at $\mathbf{x}_1$ and $\mathbf{x}_2$, and with radii less than $|\mathbf{x}_1 - \mathbf{x}_2|$. Suppose

$$\int_{c_k} F \cdot d\mathbf{x} = I_k, \qquad k = 1, 2.$$

Show that if γ is any closed smooth path that avoids $\mathbf{x}_1$ and $\mathbf{x}_2$, then

$$\int_\gamma F \cdot d\mathbf{x} = n_1 I_1 + n_2 I_2,$$

for some integers n_1 and n_2.

9. (a) Consider a particle moving in a plane vertical to the surface of the earth and subject to the gravitational field $G(x, y) = (0, mg)$, where m is the mass of the particle and g is the acceleration of gravity. Show that as the particle moves in the plane, the amount of work done is independent of the path between two points and depends only on the initial and final points. In particular, the work done in moving along a closed path is zero.

(b) Replace the field G by a field $F = (F_1, F_2)$ satisfying $(\partial F_2/\partial x_1)$ $= (\partial F_1/\partial x_2)$ throughout the plane. Show that the same conclusions hold.

10. (a) Let $\mathscr{R} \xrightarrow{g} \mathscr{R}^2$ trace a simple closed curve γ in the counterclockwise direction. Show that, if a unit tangent vector to γ is given by $\mathbf{t}(t) = g'(t)/\|g'(t)\|$, then the *outward* pointing unit normal to γ at $g(t)$ is given by $\mathbf{n}(t) = (g_2'(t)/\|g'(t)\|, -g_1'(t)/\|g'(t)\|)$, where g_1 and g_2 are the coordinate functions of g.

(b) Show that Green's theorem can be written in the form

$$\int_D \left(\frac{\partial F_2}{\partial x_1} - \frac{\partial F_1}{\partial x_2} \right) dx_1 \, dx_2 = \int_\gamma F \cdot \mathbf{t} \, ds,$$

where $F = (F_1, F_2)$, and ds denotes integration with respect to arc-length.

(c) Show that Green's theorem can also be written in the form

$$\int_D \left(\frac{\partial F_1}{\partial x_1} + \frac{\partial F_2}{\partial x_2} \right) dx_1 \, dx_2 = \int_\gamma F \cdot \mathbf{n} \, ds.$$

[*Hint.* In the previous formula, replace F_2 by F_1 and F_1 by $-F_2$.]

11. Assume that the vector field $F = (F_1, F_2)$ in Problem 10(c) is a gradient field, that is, $F = \nabla f$ for some real-valued f. Show that Green's theorem can be written in the form

$$\int_D \Delta f \, dA = \int_\gamma \nabla f \cdot \mathbf{n} \, ds,$$

where $\Delta f = (\partial^2 f/\partial x_1^2) + (\partial^2 f/\partial x_2^2)$, the Laplacian of f.

12. (a) Show that if f is a continuous real-valued function defined in an open set D of $\mathscr{R}^2$, and $\int_M f \, dA = 0$ for every circular disc M in D, then f is identically zero in D. [*Hint.* Show that if $f(\mathbf{x}_0) \neq 0$ for some $\mathbf{x}_0$ in D, then there is a disc M centered at $\mathbf{x}_0$ such that $|f(\mathbf{x})| \geq \delta$ for some $\delta > 0$, and all $\mathbf{x}$ in M.]

(b) Use part (a) and Stokes's theorem to show that if curl F is continuous in an open set D, and the circulation of F is zero around every smooth circuit in D, then F is irrotational in D, that is, curl F is identically zero in D.

(c) Use part (a) and Gauss's theorem to show that if div F is continuous in D and $\Phi(\gamma) = 0$ for every smooth circuit γ in D, then F is incompressible.

13. The equations curl $F = 0$ and div $F = 0$ occur in complex variable theory in a slightly different form as the Cauchy-Riemann equations. Show that if $u(x, y)$ and $v(x, y)$ are the real and imaginary parts respectively of the following complex valued functions, then the vector field $F(x, y) = (v(x, y), u(x, y))$ is irrotational and incompressible.

(a) $(x + iy)^2$
(b) e^{x+iy}
(c) $(\frac{1}{2}) \log (x^2 + y^2) + i \arctan y/x, \ x > 0.$

2. CONSERVATIVE VECTOR FIELDS

The examples of the previous section show that, under certain conditions, it is possible to alter the path of integration in a line integral in the plane without affecting the value of the integral. Not all line integrals have this property, but those that do are particularly important, not only for the computational reasons already illustrated, but also because of their relation to the gradient. In fact, we have the following theorem, valid in $\mathscr{R}^n$, which is a converse to Theorem 9.5 of Chapter 2.

2.1 Theorem. Let F be a continuous vector field defined in a polygonally connected open subset D of $\mathscr{R}^n$. If the line integral

$$\int_\gamma F \cdot d\mathbf{x}$$

is independent of the piecewise smooth path γ from $\mathbf{x}_0$ to $\mathbf{x}$ in D, then the real-valued function defined by

$$f(\mathbf{x}) = \int_{\mathbf{x}_0}^{\mathbf{x}} F \cdot d\mathbf{x}$$

is continuously differentiable and satisfies the vector equation $\nabla f = F$ throughout D.

Proof. We have to show that, for each $\mathbf{x}$ in D, $\nabla f(\mathbf{x}) = F(\mathbf{x})$. Since $\mathbf{x}$ is an interior point of D, there is a ball of radius δ centered at $\mathbf{x}$ and contained in D. This implies that, for any unit vector $\mathbf{u}$ and for all real numbers t satisfying $|t| < \delta$, the vectors $\mathbf{x} + t\mathbf{u}$ are contained in D. Since the line integral is independent of the path, we choose an arbitrary piecewise smooth path from $\mathbf{x}_0$ to $\mathbf{x}$, lying in D, and extend it by a linear segment to the vectors $\mathbf{x} + t\mathbf{u}, |t| < \delta$, as shown in Figure 10. To show that f is continuously differentiable we observe that

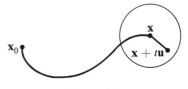

Figure 10

$$f(\mathbf{x} + t\mathbf{u}) - f(\mathbf{x}) = \int_{\mathbf{x}_0}^{\mathbf{x}+t\mathbf{u}} F \cdot d\mathbf{x} - \int_{\mathbf{x}_0}^{\mathbf{x}} F \cdot d\mathbf{x}$$

$$= \int_{\mathbf{x}}^{\mathbf{x}+t\mathbf{u}} F \cdot d\mathbf{x}$$

$$= \int_0^t F(\mathbf{x} + v\mathbf{u}) \cdot \mathbf{u} \, dv.$$

Then taking $\mathbf{u} = \mathbf{e}_j$, the jth natural basis vector in $\mathscr{R}^n$, we get

$$\frac{\partial f}{\partial x_j}(\mathbf{x}) = \lim_{t \to 0} \frac{f(\mathbf{x} + t\mathbf{e}_j) - f(\mathbf{x})}{t}$$

$$= \lim_{t \to 0} \frac{1}{t} \int_0^t F(\mathbf{x} + v\mathbf{e}_j) \cdot \mathbf{e}_j \, dv$$

$$= \frac{d}{dt} \int_0^t F(\mathbf{x} + v\mathbf{e}_j) \cdot \mathbf{e}_j dv \Big|_{t=0}$$

$$= F(\mathbf{x}) \cdot \mathbf{e}_j = F_j(\mathbf{x}),$$

where F_j is the jth coordinate function of F. Since F was assumed continuous, so are the partial derivatives $\partial f/\partial x_j$, and so f is continuously differentiable on D. Finally, the equations $(\partial f/\partial x_j)(\mathbf{x}) = F_j(\mathbf{x})$, $j = 1$, $\ldots, n$, and $\mathbf{x}$ in D, mean that $\nabla f = F$ in D.

A vector field F for which there is a real-valued function f such that $F = \nabla f$ is called a **conservative**, or **gradient**, **field**. In that case f is called the **potential** of F. The motivation for this terminology is discussed in the next example.

EXAMPLE 1. Suppose that a continuous force field F, defined in a region D of $\mathscr{R}^3$, is such that the work done in moving a particle from one point to another under the influence of the field is independent of the path taken between the two points. Thus, if $\mathbf{x}_1$ and $\mathbf{x}_2$ are two points in the field and $W(\mathbf{x}_1, \mathbf{x}_2)$ represents the work done in going from $\mathbf{x}_1$ to $\mathbf{x}_2$, we can write

$$W(\mathbf{x}_1, \mathbf{x}_2) = \int_{\mathbf{x}_1}^{\mathbf{x}_2} F \cdot d\mathbf{x}.$$

If the particle follows a particular path given by $g(t)$, then the velocity and acceleration vectors are $\mathbf{v}(t) = g'(t)$, $\mathbf{a}(t) = g''(t)$, and we have $F(g(t)) = m\mathbf{a}(t)$, where m is the mass of the particle. Hence,

$$W(\mathbf{x}_1, \mathbf{x}_2) = \int_{t_1}^{t_2} m\mathbf{a}(t) \cdot \mathbf{v}(t) \, dt,$$

if $g(t_i) = \mathbf{x}_i$. But since $\mathbf{a}(t) = \mathbf{v}'(t)$, and $(d/dt)v^2(t) = 2\mathbf{v}(t) \cdot \mathbf{v}'(t)$, we have

$$W(\mathbf{x}_1, \mathbf{x}_2) = \frac{m}{2} \int_{t_1}^{t_2} \frac{d}{dt} [v^2(t)] \, dt,$$

$$= \frac{m}{2} (v^2(t_2) - v^2(t_1)). \tag{1}$$

The function $k(t) = (m/2)v^2(t)$ is called the **kinetic energy** of the particle at time t.

On the other hand, if we fix a point $\mathbf{x}_0$ in D, then by Theorem 2.1, the equation

$$u(\mathbf{x}) = -\int_{\mathbf{x}_0}^{\mathbf{x}} F \cdot d\mathbf{x}$$

defines a continuously differentiable function u in D. Using the independence of path to integrate from $\mathbf{x}_1$ to $\mathbf{x}_2$ via $\mathbf{x}_0$, we get

$$W(\mathbf{x}_1, \mathbf{x}_2) = \int_{\mathbf{x}_1}^{\mathbf{x}_2} F \cdot d\mathbf{x}$$

$$= \int_{\mathbf{x}_0}^{\mathbf{x}_2} F \cdot d\mathbf{x} - \int_{\mathbf{x}_0}^{\mathbf{x}_1} F \cdot d\mathbf{x} \qquad (2)$$

$$= -u(\mathbf{x}_2) + u(\mathbf{x}_1).$$

Comparison of Equations (1) and (2) shows that

$$u(\mathbf{x}_2) + \frac{m}{2} v^2(t_2) = u(\mathbf{x}_1) + \frac{m}{2} v^2(t_1).$$

In other words, along the path traced by $g(t)$, the sum $u(g(t)) + k(t)$ is a constant, independent of t, called the total energy of the path. For this reason, the function $u(\mathbf{x})$, which is a function of position in D, is called the **potential energy** of the field F. Notice that there is an arbitrary choice made in defining the potential in that the point $\mathbf{x}_0$ was picked to have zero potential. The choice of some other point $\mathbf{x}_0$ would change the function u at most by an additive constant equal to $W(\mathbf{x}_0, \mathbf{x}_1)$. It is the constant total energy which is "conserved" and which gives rise to the term "conservative field".

For a vector field F defined in a region D of $\mathscr{R}^n$, independence of path in the line integral $\int_\gamma F \cdot d\mathbf{x}$ has been defined to mean that

2.2. $$\int_{\gamma[\mathbf{x}_1, \mathbf{x}_2]} F \cdot d\mathbf{x} = \int_{\delta[\mathbf{x}_1, \mathbf{x}_2]} F \cdot d\mathbf{x}$$

where $\gamma[\mathbf{x}_1, \mathbf{x}_2]$ and $\delta[\mathbf{x}_1, \mathbf{x}_2]$ are any two piecewise smooth curves in D, both with initial point $\mathbf{x}_1$ and terminal point $\mathbf{x}_2$. An alternative formulation of the independence property is that

2.3. $$\oint_\gamma F \cdot d\mathbf{x} = 0$$

for every piecewise smooth closed curve γ lying in D. The equivalence of the two properties follows from the observations that $\gamma[\mathbf{x}_1, \mathbf{x}_2]$ followed by $\delta[\mathbf{x}_1, \mathbf{x}_2]$ in reverse direction is a closed path, and that a closed path can be separated at points $\mathbf{x}_1$ and $\mathbf{x}_2$ into different paths joining $\mathbf{x}_1$ and $\mathbf{x}_2$. The details of the proof have already been illustrated in Section 1 and will be left as an exercise.

We can summarize what we have proved about gradient fields in Theorem 9.5 of Chapter 2, Theorem 2.1 of the present section, and in the previous remark, as

2.4. **Theorem.** Let F be a continuous vector field defined in a polygonally connected open set D of $\mathscr{R}^n$. Then the following are equivalent:
   (a) F is the gradient of a function f, continuously differentiable in D.
   (b) the line integral of F over a path from $\mathbf{x}_1$ to $\mathbf{x}_2$ is independent of the piecewise smooth curve γ from $\mathbf{x}_1$ to $\mathbf{x}_2$, and so can be written

$$\int_{\mathbf{x}_1}^{\mathbf{x}_2} F \cdot d\mathbf{x}.$$

(c) $$\oint F \cdot d\mathbf{x} = 0$$

for every piecewise smooth close curve lying in D.

A more intrinsic criterion for deciding whether a continuous vector field is a gradient field or not arises as follows: Suppose first that $\mathscr{R}^2 \xrightarrow{F} \mathscr{R}^2$ is continuous on an open set D, and that F is a gradient field, that is, there is a real-valued function f defined on D such that $\nabla f = F$. In terms of coordinate functions F_1 and F_2 of F, this means

$$\frac{\partial f}{\partial x_1} = F_1 \quad \text{and} \quad \frac{\partial f}{\partial x_2} = F_2.$$

If F itself is continuously differentiable, we can form the second partials,

$$\frac{\partial^2 f}{\partial x_2 \partial x_1} = \frac{\partial F_1}{\partial x_2} \quad \text{and} \quad \frac{\partial^2 f}{\partial x_1 \partial x_2} = \frac{\partial F_2}{\partial x_1},$$

and conclude from their equality that

$$\frac{\partial F_1}{\partial x_2} = \frac{\partial F_2}{\partial x_1} \tag{3}$$

throughout D. By the definition of curl F, Equation 3 can be written curl $F = 0$. The equation can also be expressed another way: We consider the more general field $\mathscr{R}^n \xrightarrow{F} \mathscr{R}^n$, which we assume continuously differentiable in an open subset D of $\mathscr{R}^n$. If F is a gradient field, there is an f such that $\nabla f = F$, or, in terms of coordinate functions

$$\frac{\partial f}{\partial x_j} = F_j, \quad j = 1, \ldots, n.$$

Differentiating with respect to x_i, we get

$$\frac{\partial F_j}{\partial x_i} = \frac{\partial^2 f}{\partial x_i \partial x_j} = \frac{\partial^2 f}{\partial x_j \partial x_i} = \frac{\partial F_i}{\partial x_j}. \tag{4}$$

But the functions $\partial F_i/\partial x_j$ are the entries in the n-by-n Jacobian matrix of $\mathscr{R}^n \xrightarrow{F} \mathscr{R}^n$, and Equation (4) expresses the fact that this matrix is symmetric. Hence

2.5 Theorem. If $\mathscr{R}^n \xrightarrow{F} \mathscr{R}^n$ is a continuously differentiable gradient field, then F', the Jacobian matrix of F, is symmetric.

EXAMPLE 2. The converse of Theorem 2.5 is false, as we see by looking at the example in $\mathscr{R}^2$,

$$F(x, y) = \left(\frac{-y}{x^2 + y^2}, \frac{x}{x^2 + y^2} \right),$$

defined for all $(x, y) \neq (0, 0)$. It is easy to check that $\partial F_1/\partial y = \partial F_2/\partial x$. But there is no continuously differentiable f such that $\nabla f = F$. The reason is that, for $x > 0$, the function $f(x, y) = \arctan(y/x)$ satisfies $\nabla f = F$, but this f cannot be extended to be a single-valued solution of the equation in the entire plane with the origin deleted.

Example 2 shows that the nature of the region D on which F is defined is significant in determining whether F is a gradient field. By making a special assumption about D we can obtain a partial converse to Theorem 2.5.

2.6 Theorem. Let R be an open coordinate rectangle in $\mathscr{R}^n$, and let F be a continuously differentiable vector field on R. If $F'(x)$, the Jacobian matrix of F, is symmetric on R, then F is a gradient field.

Proof. Pick a fixed point x_0 in R and let x be any other point of R. We consider paths from x_0 to x, each consisting of a sequence of line segments parallel to the axes and such that each coordinate variable varies on at most one such segment. Three-dimensional examples are shown in Figure 11. The reason for looking at such paths is to be able to approach x from any coordinate direction for the purpose of taking partial derivatives at x. Choose one of these paths, call it γ_x, and define a real-valued function f by

$$f(x) = \int_{\gamma_x} F \cdot dx. \tag{5}$$

While the particular path γ_x is only one of several of the same type, we shall see that any of the other possible choices would lead to the same value for $f(x)$. The reason is that any one of these paths can be altered step by step into any one of the others by changes, each of which leaves the value of the integral (5) unaltered. Each path can be described by a sequence of coordinate directions, only one of which is allowed to vary at a time. (For example, the dotted path in Figure 11 corresponds to x_1, x_2, x_3, and the solid one to x_2, x_3, x_1.) Clearly, chang-

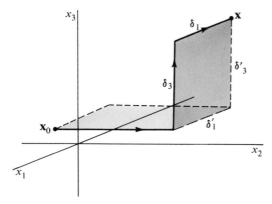

Figure 11

ing one such sequence into another can be accomplished by successively interchanging adjacent variables in pairs until the desired order is reached. But each interchange replaces a pair of segments (δ_i, δ_j) by another pair (δ_i', δ_j') lying in the same 2-dimensional plane. To see that the replacement leaves the value of the integral invariant, we form the circuit δ consisting of the segments δ_i and δ_j, followed by δ_i' and δ_j' in the reverse of their original directions. On these segments, x_i and x_j are the only variables that vary, so the circuit integral can be written

$$\oint_\delta F \cdot dx = \oint_\delta F_i \, dx_j + F_j \, dx_j.$$

We apply Green's theorem to the 2-dimensional rectangle R_δ bounded by δ, and get

$$\oint_\delta F \cdot dx = \int_{R_\delta} \left(\frac{\partial F_j}{\partial x_i} - \frac{\partial F_i}{\partial x_j} \right) dx_i \, dx_j = 0,$$

since by the symmetry assumption, $\partial F_j/\partial x_i - \partial F_i/\partial x_j = 0$ in R. Thus

$$\oint_\delta F \cdot dx = \int_{(\delta_i, \delta_j)} F \cdot dx - \int_{(\delta_j', \delta_i')} F \cdot dx = 0,$$

and so the change of path leaves the value of the integral invariant.

Once it has been established that x can be approached along a path of integration that varies only in an arbitrary coordinate, say the kth, we have, as in the proof of Theorem 2.1, the equation $\partial f/\partial x_k(x) = F_k(x)$, for all k. Thus $\nabla f(x) = F(x)$ for all x in R.

EXAMPLE 3. Applying Theorem 2.4 to the field

$$F(x, y) = \left(\frac{-y}{x^2 + y^2}, \frac{x}{x^2 + y^2} \right), (x, y) \neq (0, 0),$$

of Example 2, we conclude that F, when restricted to any coordinate rectangle not containing the origin, is a gradient field. This is true, for example, in any of the four half-planes bounded by a coordinate axis. A potential function f for the half-plane $x > 0$, can be computed by the line integral

$$f(x, y) = \int_{(1,0)}^{(x, y)} \frac{-y \, dx}{x^2 + y^2} + \frac{x \, dy}{x^2 + y^2},$$

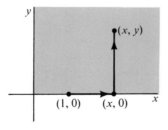

Figure 12

where the path of integration is any piecewise smooth curve from $(1, 0)$ to (x, y). A polygonal path from $(1, 0)$ to $(x, 0)$ and from $(x, 0)$ to (x, y) is particularly simple. On the first segment the entire integral is zero, because y is identically zero, and on the second segment, with x constant, the integral reduces to

$$\int_0^y \frac{x \, dy}{x^2 + y^2} = \arctan\left(\frac{y}{x} \right).$$

The most general potential of F in the right half-plane differs from this one by at most a constant (Why?), so the general solution there of $\nabla f = F$ is

$$f(x, y) = \arctan \frac{y}{x} + c.$$

Compare the method of solution described in Problem 11 of Chapter 2, Section 9.

EXERCISES

1. Consider the approximation to the earth's gravitational field acting on a particle of mass 1 represented by the vector field $F(x, y, z) = (0, 0, -g)$.

   (a) Find for F the potential function $u(x, y, z)$ that is zero when $(x, y, z) = (0, 0, 0)$.

   (b) If a particle of mass 1 has at $(0, 0, 0)$ a velocity vector (v_1, v_2, v_3) with $v_3 > 0$, and no force but F acts on the particle, find the path of the particle.

   (c) Verify that the sum of potential and kinetic energy remains constant for the path of part (b).

2. (a) Show that if F and G are gradient fields defined on the same domain D, then $F + G$ and cF are gradient fields, where c is a constant.

   (b) Let $\mathscr{V}$ be the vector space of gradient fields defined on a domain D. Show that $\mathscr{V}$ has infinite dimension.

3. Use Theorem 2.4 or 2.6 to decide whether the following vector fields are gradient fields.

   (a) $F(x, y) = (x - y, x + y)$, for (x, y) in $\mathscr{R}^2$.

   (b) $G(x, y, z) = (y, z, x)$, for (x, y, z) in $\mathscr{R}^3$.

   (c) $H(x, y) = \left(\frac{-y}{x^2 + y^2}, \frac{x}{x^2 + y^2}\right)$, $(x, y) \neq (0, 0)$.

4. Use Theorem 2.5 to show that the vector fields in Problems 3(a) and 3(b) are not gradient fields in any open subset of $\mathscr{R}^2$ or $\mathscr{R}^3$, respectively.

5. Show that the vector field of problem 3(c) is a gradient field in the region $y > 0$ of $\mathscr{R}^2$ and find an explicit representation for its potential.

6. Consider the vector field defined in $\mathscr{R}^3$, with the z-axis deleted, by

$$F(x, y, z) = \left(\frac{-y}{x^2 + y^2}, \frac{x}{x^2 + y^2}, 0\right).$$

   Is F a gradient field?

7. Find a potential for each of the following fields.

   (a) $F(x, y, z) = (2xy, x^2 + z^2, 2yz)$.

   (b) $G(x, y) = (y \cos xy, x \cos xy)$.

   (c) $L(x_1, x_2) = \left(\frac{x_1}{x_1^2 + x_2^2}, \frac{x_2}{x_1^2 + x_2^2}\right)$, with $(x_1, x_2) \neq (0, 0)$.

8. Consider the vector field F which is the gradient of the Newtonian potential $f(\mathbf{x}) = -|\mathbf{x}|^{-1}$ for nonzero $\mathbf{x}$ in $\mathscr{R}^3$. Find the work done in moving a particle from $(1, 1, 1)$ to $(-2, -2, -2)$ along a smooth curve lying in the domain of F.

9. Give a detailed proof of the equivalence of Relations 2.2 and 2.3 of the text.

10. In $\mathscr{R}^n$, how many paths can there be from $\mathbf{x}_0$ to $\mathbf{x}$ of the special kind described in the proof of Theorem 2.6?

3. SURFACE INTEGRALS

In Chapter 2, Section 5, we have defined integrals both of a real-valued function and of a vector field over a smooth curve. Defining an integral over a surface S leads to a different geometric situation, having, however, a close analogy with the line integral. To begin, we assume that S is parametrized by a continuously differentiable function $\mathscr{R}^2 \xrightarrow{g} \mathscr{R}^3$. We shall write g in the form

$$g(u, v) = \begin{pmatrix} g_1(u, v) \\ g_2(u, v) \\ g_3(u, v) \end{pmatrix}, \tag{1}$$

with $\mathbf{u} = (u, v)$ in some set D in $\mathscr{R}^2$, which we assume bounded by a piecewise smooth curve. We further assume that at each point $g(u, v)$ of S the tangent vectors defined by the vector partial derivatives

$$\frac{\partial g}{\partial u}(u, v), \qquad \frac{\partial g}{\partial v}(u, v)$$

determine a two-dimensional tangent plane to S; in other words, that the two tangents are linearly independent. If S satisfies all the above conditions, we shall refer to it as a **piece of smooth surface**.

On a smooth curve, the choice of a parametrization going from one end-point to the other establishes an orientation for the curve. Analogously, on a piece of smooth surface, a one-to-one parametrization determines a unique normal vector

$$\frac{\partial g}{\partial u}(u, v) \times \frac{\partial g}{\partial v}(u, v) \tag{2}$$

at $g(u, v)$. See Figure 13.

We recall that the length of the cross product of two vectors $\mathbf{a}$ and $\mathbf{b}$ is the area of the parallelogram spanned by $\mathbf{a}$ and $\mathbf{b}$. In particular,

$$\left| \frac{\partial g}{\partial u}(u, v) \times \frac{\partial g}{\partial v}(u, v) \right|$$

represents the area of the tangent parallelogram shown in Figure 13(b). If we think of constructing such parallelograms at the points $g(u_k, v_k)$ cor-

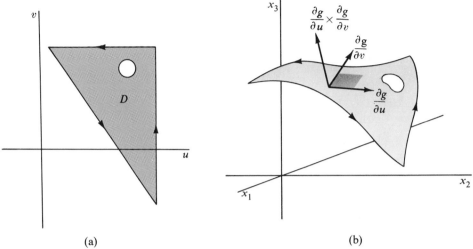

(a)   (b)

Figure 13

responding to the corner points (u_k, v_k) of a grid over D, then it is natural to define the **area** of S by

$$3.1 \qquad \sigma(S) = \int_D \left| \frac{\partial g}{\partial u}(u, v) \times \frac{\partial g}{\partial v}(u, v) \right| du\, dv.$$

We assume that g is one-to-one. The integral over D exists because g was assumed continuously differentiable on D. Similarly, if p is a continuous real-valued function defined on S, we define the integral of p over S by

$$3.2 \qquad \int_S p\, d\sigma = \int_D p(g(u, v)) \left| \frac{\partial g}{\partial u}(u, v) \times \frac{\partial g}{\partial v}(u, v) \right| du\, dv.$$

This definition is the analogue of that for a real-valued function over a smooth curve given by Equation (2) of Chapter 2, Section 5.

EXAMPLE 1. Let S be parametrized by

$$g(u, v) = \begin{pmatrix} u \\ v \\ u^2 + v^2 \end{pmatrix},$$

for

$$1 \leq u^2 + v^2 \leq 4,$$

so that S is actually the graph of $x^2 + y^2$ for $1 \leq x^2 + y^2 \leq 4$. The surface is shown in Figure 14. Then

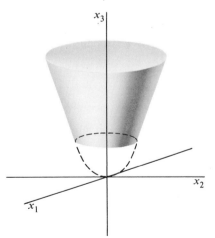

Figure 14

$$\frac{\partial g}{\partial u}(u, v) = \begin{pmatrix} 1 \\ 0 \\ 2u \end{pmatrix}, \qquad \frac{\partial g}{\partial v}(u, v) = \begin{pmatrix} 0 \\ 1 \\ 2v \end{pmatrix}.$$

We have

$$\frac{\partial g}{\partial u}(u, v) \times \frac{\partial g}{\partial v}(u, v) = \left(\begin{vmatrix} 0 & 1 \\ 2u & 2v \end{vmatrix}, \begin{vmatrix} 2u & 2v \\ 1 & 0 \end{vmatrix}, \begin{vmatrix} 1 & 0 \\ 0 & 1 \end{vmatrix} \right).$$

Hence

$$\sigma(S) = \int_{1 \le u^2 + v^2 \le 4} \sqrt{4u^2 + 4v^2 + 1} \, du \, dv$$

$$= \int_0^{2\pi} d\theta \int_1^2 \sqrt{4r^2 + 1} \, r \, dr = \frac{\pi}{6} [17^{3/2} - 5^{3/2}].$$

If S is given a nonuniform density equal at each point to the distance of that point from the axis of symmetry of S, then the density can be represented by the function $p(x, y, z) = \sqrt{x^2 + y^2}$. At a point $g(u, v)$ of S the density will be $p(g(u, v)) = \sqrt{u^2 + v^2}$. We can interpret the integral of p over S to be the total mass of the weighted surface, and we have

$$\int_S p \, d\sigma = \int_{1 \le u^2 + v^2 \le 4} \sqrt{u^2 + v^2} \sqrt{4u^2 + 4v^2 + 1} \, du \, dv$$

$$= \int_0^{2\pi} d\theta \int_1^2 r^2 \sqrt{4r^2 + 1} \, dr.$$

The main purpose of this section is the definition of the integral of a continuous vector field $\mathscr{R}^3 \xrightarrow{F} \mathscr{R}^3$ over a surface S. Continuing with the assumption that S is a piece of smooth surface represented by the function of Equation (1), we compare the normal vector $\partial g/\partial u \times \partial g/\partial v$ with the vector field F at a point $g(u, v)$ of S. These are shown in Figure 15 at one point. If $\mathbf{n}$ is a *unit* normal to S at $g(u, v)$, then the dot product $F \cdot \mathbf{n}$ at $g(u, v)$ is the coordinate of F in the direction of $\mathbf{n}$. But since

$$\mathbf{n} = \frac{\dfrac{\partial g}{\partial u} \times \dfrac{\partial g}{\partial v}}{\left| \dfrac{\partial g}{\partial u} \times \dfrac{\partial g}{\partial v} \right|},$$

it follows that

$$F(g(u, v)) \cdot \left(\frac{\partial g}{\partial u}(u, v) \times \frac{\partial g}{\partial v}(u, v) \right)$$

is equal to the coordinate of $F(g(u, v))$ in the direction of $\mathbf{n}$, multiplied by the area of the tangent parallelogram spanned by $\partial g/\partial u$ and $\partial g/\partial v$ at $g(u, v)$. We define the **surface integral** of F over S by

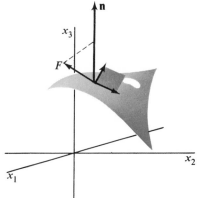

Figure 15

3.3 $$\int_D F(g(u, v)) \cdot \left(\frac{\partial g}{\partial u}(u, v) \times \frac{\partial g}{\partial v}(u, v)\right)du \, dv,$$

and denote it by $\int_S F \cdot dS$ or $\int_S F \cdot \mathbf{n} \, d\sigma$.

It is easy to check that the coordinates of the normal vector are given by Jacobian determinants as

$$\frac{\partial g}{\partial u} \times \frac{\partial g}{\partial v} = \left(\frac{\partial(x_2, x_3)}{\partial(u, v)}, \frac{\partial(x_3, x_1)}{\partial(u, v)}, \frac{\partial(x_1, x_2)}{\partial(u, v)}\right),$$

where x_1, x_2, and x_3 represent the coordinate functions of g. If the vector field F has coordinate functions F_1, F_2, F_3, then the surface integral is often written

$$\int_S F \cdot dS = \int_D F_1 \frac{\partial(x_2, x_3)}{\partial(u, v)} + F_2 \frac{\partial(x_3, x_1)}{\partial(u, v)} + F_3 \frac{\partial(x_1, x_2)}{\partial(u, v)} \, du \, dv$$

$$= \int_D F_1 \, dx_2 \, dx_3 + F_2 \, dx_3 \, dx_1 + F_3 \, dx_1 \, dx_2.$$

This last abbreviation is a particularly convenient one, and its significance is discussed in Section 7.

EXAMPLE 2. Suppose that a continuous vector field $\mathscr{R}^3 \xrightarrow{F} \mathscr{R}^3$ describes the speed and direction of a fluid flow at each point of a region R in which it is defined. We shall define, using a surface integral, the flux, or rate of flow per unit of area and time across a piece of smooth surface S lying in R. If S is perfectly flat and F is a constant field, then the flux is equal to $F_\mathbf{n}\sigma(S)$, where $F_\mathbf{n}$ is the coordinate of F in the direction of a unit normal to S. Thus, in this case, the flux is equal to the volume of a tube of fluid illustrated in Figure 16. Because $F_\mathbf{n} = F \cdot \mathbf{n}$, we get the formula

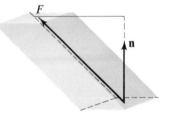

Figure 16

$$\Phi = F \cdot \mathbf{n}\sigma(S)$$

for the flux.

If S is a piece of smooth surface in R, we partition S along coordinate curves of the form $u = $ const. and $v = $ const. and assume that, within each part of S so formed, the field F is constant. Approximating S by tangent parallelograms spanned by vectors

$$\Delta u \frac{\partial g}{\partial u} \quad \text{and} \quad \Delta v \frac{\partial g}{\partial v}$$

leads to the picture shown in Figure 17. The approximate flux across a typical subdivision S_k of S will have the form

$$\Phi_k = F(g(\mathbf{u}_k)) \cdot \mathbf{n}_k \sigma(S_k)$$

$$= F(g(\mathbf{u}_k)) \cdot \left(\frac{\partial g}{\partial u}(\mathbf{u}_k) \times \frac{\partial g}{\partial v}(\mathbf{u}_k)\right) \Delta u \, \Delta v.$$

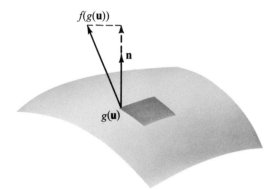

Figure 17

The sum

$$\sum_{k=1}^{N} \Phi_k = \sum_{k=1}^{N} F(g(\mathbf{u}_k)) \cdot \left(\frac{\partial g}{\partial u}(\mathbf{u}_k) \times \frac{\partial g}{\partial v}(\mathbf{u}_k)\right)\Delta u \, \Delta v$$

becomes a better approximation to what we would like to call the flux across S as the subdivision of S is refined by making finer the corresponding grid G in the parameter domain D. On the other hand, if F is continuous on S and g is continuously differentiable on D, then

$$\lim_{m(G) \to 0} \sum_{k=1}^{N} \Phi_k = \int_D F(g(\mathbf{u})) \cdot \left(\frac{\partial g}{\partial u}(\mathbf{u}) \times \frac{\partial g}{\partial v}(\mathbf{u})\right) d\sigma$$

$$= \int_D F \cdot dS,$$

which is the previously defined integral of F over S. Consequently, we define the **flux** of F across S by

$$\Phi = \int_S F \cdot dS.$$

We remark that the sign of Φ would change if S were reparametrized so that the normal vector determined by the parametrization pointed in the opposite direction.

EXAMPLE 3. Let a fluid flow outward from the origin in $\mathcal{R}^3$ be given by

$$F(x_1, x_2, x_3) = \left(\frac{x_1}{x_1^2 + x_2^2 + x_3^2}, \frac{x_2}{x_1^2 + x_2^2 + x_3^2}, \frac{x_3}{x_1^2 + x_2^2 + x_3^2}\right).$$

The flux of F across a sphere S_a centered at the origin and of radius a takes the form

$$\int_{S_a} F \cdot dS = \int_{S_a} \frac{x_1 \, dx_2 \, dx_3 + x_2 \, dx_3 \, dx_1 + x_3 \, dx_1 \, dx_2}{x_1^2 + x_2^2 + x_3^2}.$$

However, on S_a, the denominator is constantly equal to a^2, so the surface integral takes the simpler form

$$\frac{1}{a^2} \int_{S_a} x_1 \, dx_2 \, dx_3 + x_2 \, dx_3 \, dx_1 + x_3 \, dx_1, \, dx_2.$$

We can represent S_a parametrically by

$$\begin{pmatrix} x_1 \\ x_2 \\ x_3 \end{pmatrix} = \begin{pmatrix} a \sin \varphi \cos \theta \\ a \sin \varphi \sin \theta \\ a \cos \varphi \end{pmatrix}, \qquad \begin{array}{l} 0 \le \varphi \le \pi \\ 0 \le \theta \le 2\pi. \end{array}$$

so that

$$\frac{\partial(x_2, x_3)}{\partial(\varphi, \theta)} = a^2 \sin^2 \varphi \cos \theta$$

$$\frac{\partial(x_3, x_1)}{\partial(\varphi, \theta)} = a^2 \sin^2 \varphi \sin \theta$$

$$\frac{\partial(x_1, x_2)}{\partial(\varphi, \theta)} = a^2 \sin \varphi \cos \varphi.$$

These are the coordinates of a normal vector pointing out from the sphere. Then

$$\int_{S_a} F \cdot dS = a \int_0^{2\pi} d\theta \int_0^\pi \sin^3 \varphi \cos^2 \theta + \sin^3 \varphi \sin^2 \theta + \sin \varphi \cos^2 \varphi \, d\varphi$$

$$= a \int_0^{2\pi} d\theta \int_0^\pi \sin \varphi \, d\varphi = 4\pi a.$$

For the purpose of computing a line integral over a piecewise smooth curve, it is natural to orient the smooth pieces of the curve so that the terminal point of one piece is the same as the initial point of the one that follows it. To integrate a vector field over a piecewise smooth surface we need a notion of orientation for pieces of smooth surface S. If $\mathcal{R}^2 \xrightarrow{g} \mathcal{R}^3$ represents S parametrically with g defined on D, then Figure 13 shows how D and S may be related. The edge of S, corresponding under g to the boundary of D, we shall call the **border** of S. As a point **u** moves around the piecewise smooth boundary of D in the *counterclockwise* direction, its image $g(\mathbf{u})$ traces the border of S with what we shall call its **positive orientation**. A further geometric picture of the positive orientation can be had by observing that as the normal vector $\partial g/\partial u \times \partial g/\partial v$ runs around the border in the positive direction, the surface S remains on its left.

A **piecewise smooth surface** is of course a finite union of pieces of smooth surface that are joined along common border curves. A piecewise smooth surface is **orientable** if, when the border curves of its pieces are positively oriented, borders common to two pieces are traced in opposite directions. If one of the two curves is reversed, their parametrizations must be equivalent.

Figure 18

The surfaces pictured in Figure 18 are assumed to be representable as piecewise smooth surfaces, and the first two are orientable. However, the joining together of two rectangular strips, one of them with a twist, gives a Möbius strip, which is the standard example of a nonorientable surface.

We define the integral of a continuous vector field over a piecewise smooth surface to be the sum of the integrals over each of its smooth pieces. Thus if $S = S_1 \cup S_2$,

$$\int_S F \cdot dS = \int_{S_1} F \cdot dS + \int_{S_2} F \cdot dS.$$

This definition holds even if S is not orientable, but in practice it is of little interest to integrate a vector field over a nonorientable surface. On the other hand, the integral of a real-valued function over a surface can be computed without regard to orientation. The reason is that in Formulas 3.1 and 3.2 the so-called element of surface area,

$$d\sigma = \left| \frac{\partial g}{\partial u} \times \frac{\partial g}{\partial v} \right| du\, dv,$$

does not change when the orientation is reversed by interchanging the roles of u and v. But in Formula 3.3, the vector surface element,

$$dS = \left(\frac{\partial g}{\partial u} \times \frac{\partial g}{dv} \right) du\, dv,$$

does change sign when u and v are interchanged. We observe that the surface element dS can also be written in the form

$$dS = \mathbf{n}\, d\sigma,$$

where $\mathbf{n}$ is the unit normal to the surface given by

$$\mathbf{n} = \frac{\dfrac{\partial g}{\partial u} \times \dfrac{\partial g}{\partial v}}{\left| \dfrac{\partial g}{\partial u} \times \dfrac{\partial g}{\partial v} \right|}.$$

EXERCISES

1. (a) Find the area of the spiral ramp represented by

$$g(u, v) = \begin{pmatrix} u \cos v \\ u \sin v \\ v \end{pmatrix}, \qquad 0 \le u \le 1, \qquad 0 \le v \le 3\pi.$$

$$\left[Ans. \ \frac{3\pi}{2}(\sqrt{2} + \log(1 + \sqrt{2})). \right]$$

(b) Let the surface of part (a) have a density per unit of area at each point equal to the distance of that point from the central axis of the surface. Find the total mass of the weighted surface.

2. Compute $\int_S F \cdot dS$, where

(a) $F(x, y, z) = (x, y, z)$ and S is given by

$$g(u, v) = \begin{pmatrix} u - v \\ u + v \\ uv \end{pmatrix}, \qquad \begin{matrix} 0 \le u \le 1, \\ 0 \le v \le 2. \end{matrix}$$

(b) $F(x, y, z) = (x^2, 0, 0)$ and S is given by

$$g(u, v) = \begin{pmatrix} u \cos v \\ u \sin v \\ v \end{pmatrix}. \qquad \begin{matrix} 0 \le u \le 1 \\ 0 \le v \le 2\pi. \end{matrix}$$

3. Find the total mass of a spherical film having density at each point equal to the linear distance of the point from a single fixed point on the sphere.

4. Let $\mathbf{x} = g(u, v)$, for (u, v) in D, and $\mathbf{x} = h(s, t)$, for (s, t) in B, be parametrizations for the same piece of smooth surface S in $\mathscr{R}^3$. If there is a one-to-one transformation T, continuously differentiable both ways between D and B, such that the Jacobian determinant of T is positive, and such that $g(u, v) = h(T(u, v))$ for (u, v) in D, then g and h are called **equivalent** parametrizations of S.

(a) Show that equivalent parametrizations assign the same surface area to S. [*Hint.* Use the change-of-variable theorem.]

(b) Show that equivalent parametrizations assign the same value to the surface integral of a vector field over S.

5. Let the temperature at a point (x, y, z) of a region R be given by a continuously differentiable function $T(x, y, z)$. Then the vector field ∇T is called the **temperature gradient,** and under certain physical assumptions, $\nabla T(x, y, z)$ is proportional to the direction and rate of flow of heat per unit of area at (x, y, z).

(a) If $T(x, y, z) = x^2 + y^2$ for $x^2 + y^2 \le 4$, find the total rate of flow of heat across the cylindrical surface $x^2 + y^2 = 1, 0 \le z \le 1$.

(b) Give an example of a continuously differentiable vector field that cannot be a temperature gradient.

6. The Newtonian potential function $(x^2 + y^2 + z^2)^{-1/2}$ has as its gradient the attractive force field F of a charged particle at the origin acting on an oppositely charged particle at (x, y, z). The flux of the field across a piece of smooth surface is defined to be the surface integral of F over S. Show that the flux of F across a sphere of radius a centered at the origin is independent of a.

7. (a) If $\mathscr{R}^2 \xrightarrow{f} \mathscr{R}$ is continuously differentiable on a set D bounded by a piecewise smooth curve, show that the area of the graph of f is
$$\sigma(S) = \int_D \sqrt{1 + (f_x)^2 + (f_y)^2}\, dx\, dy.$$
(b) Find the area of the graph of $f(x, y) = x^2 + y$ for $0 \le x \le 1$, $0 \le y \le 1$. $\qquad$ [*Ans.* $\sqrt{3/2} + \frac{1}{2}\log(\sqrt{2} + \sqrt{3})$.]

8. Show that if $\mathscr{R}^3 \xrightarrow{G} \mathscr{R}$ is continuously differentiable and implicitly determines a piece of smooth surface S on which $\partial G/\partial z \ne 0$, and which lies over a region D of the x, y-plane, then
$$\sigma(S) = \int_D \sqrt{\left(\frac{\partial G}{\partial x}\right)^2 + \left(\frac{\partial G}{\partial y}\right)^2 + \left(\frac{\partial G}{\partial z}\right)^2}\, \left|\frac{\partial G}{\partial z}\right|^{-1} dx\, dy.$$
Assume that just one point of S lies over each point of D.

9. Prove that the border of a piece of smooth surface is a piecewise smooth curve.

10. For each of the following sets find a parametrization as a piecewise smooth orientable surface with outward pointing normal.
(a) The cylindrical can with bottom and no top given by $x^2 + y^2 = 1$, $0 \le z \le 1$ and $x^2 + y^2 \le 1$, $z = 0$.
(b) The funnel given by $x^2 + y^2 - z^2 = 0$, $1 \le z \le 4$ and $x^2 + y^2 = 1$, $0 \le z \le 1$.
(c) The trough given by $y - z = 0$, $0 \le x \le 1$, $0 \le z \le 1$ and $y + z = 0$, $0 \le x \le 1$, $0 \le z \le 1$.

11. Let F be the vector field in $\mathscr{R}^3$ given by $F(x, y, z) = (x, y, 2z - x - y)$. Find the integral of F over the oriented surfaces of Problem 10.

12. Let F be a continuous fluid flow field and let M be a piecewise smooth Möbius strip lying in the domain of F. Is it possible to define the flux of F across M?

13. Parametrize the set of Problem 10(a) so that it is unoriented, with normals pointing out on the bottom and in on the sides. Compute the integral of $F(x, y, z) = (x, y, 2z - x - y)$ over the unoriented surface.

14. Prove that if F and G are continuous vector fields on a piece of smooth surface S, then
$$\int_S (aF + bG) \cdot dS = a \int_S F \cdot dS + b \int_S G \cdot dS,$$
where a and b are constants.

15. (a) Let F be a continuous vector field on a piece of smooth surface S. Show that

$$\left| \int_S F \cdot dS \right| \leq M\sigma(S),$$

where M is the maximum of $|F(\mathbf{x})|$ for $\mathbf{x}$ on S. [*Hint.* Write $\int F \cdot dS$ in the form $\int F \cdot \mathbf{n} \, d\sigma$.]

(b) Use part (a) to show that if S contracts to a point $\mathbf{x}_0$ in such a way that $\sigma(S)$ tends to zero, then $(1/\sigma(S)) \int_S F \cdot dS$ tends to $F(\mathbf{x}_0) \cdot \mathbf{n}_0$ where $\mathbf{n}_0$ is a unit normal to S at $\mathbf{x}_0$.

16. Let f be a real-valued continuously differentiable function of one variable, nonnegative for $a \leq x \leq b$. The graph of f, rotated around the x-axis, generates a surface of revolution in $\mathcal{R}^3$.

(a) Find a parametric representation for S in terms of f.

(b) Prove that $\sigma(S) = 2\pi \int_a^b f(x)\sqrt{1 + (f'(x))^2} \, dx$.

17. The **solid angle** determined by one nappe of a solid cone $\mathscr{C}$ in $\mathcal{R}^3$, with vertex at the origin, is defined to be the area of the intersection of $\mathscr{C}$ with the unit sphere $|\mathbf{x}| = 1$. See Figure 19.

(a) Show that a suitable reduction of the above definition leads to the usual definition of the angle between two lines.

(b) Compute the solid angle determined by the cone $x^2 + y^2 \leq 2z^2$, $0 \leq z$.
[*Ans.* $2\pi(1 - 3^{-1/2})$.]

Figure 19

4. STOKES'S THEOREM

An important extension of Green's theorem can be made as follows: instead of considering a plane region D bounded by a curve, we can think of lifting such a region, together with its boundary curve, into a 2-dimensional surface S in $\mathcal{R}^3$. Then S will have as its border a space curve γ corresponding to the boundary of D. The lifting is made precise by defining on D and its piecewise smooth boundary a function $\mathcal{R}^2 \xrightarrow{g} \mathcal{R}^3$ having S as the image of D. A typical picture is shown in Figure 20. The region D has its boundary ori-

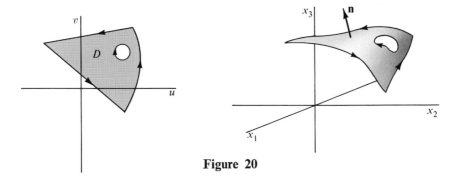

Figure 20

ented counterclockwise, and γ, the border curve of S, inherits what we have called the positive orientation with respect to S. If we parametrize the boundary of D by $\mathcal{R} \xrightarrow{h} \mathcal{R}^2$, for $a \le t \le b$, then the composition $g(h(t))$ will describe the border of S. We shall denote the positively oriented border of S by ∂S.

We can now relate the line integral of a vector field F around ∂S to the surface integral of an associated vector field over S. We assume that $\mathcal{R}^3 \xrightarrow{F} \mathcal{R}^3$ is a continuously differentiable vector field whose domain contains S. Then the vector field **curl F** is defined by

$$\operatorname{curl} F(\mathbf{x}) = \left(\frac{\partial F_3}{\partial x_2}(\mathbf{x}) - \frac{\partial F_2}{\partial x_3}(\mathbf{x}), \ \frac{\partial F_1}{\partial x_3}(\mathbf{x}) - \frac{\partial F_3}{\partial x_1}(\mathbf{x}), \ \frac{\partial F_2}{\partial x_1}(\mathbf{x}) - \frac{\partial F_1}{\partial x_2}(\mathbf{x}) \right),$$

where F_1, F_2, and F_3 are the coordinate functions of F. If the domain of F is an open set, then the domain of curl F is the same set. The vector field curl F has been chosen so that if S is a piece of sufficiently smooth surface, then it will turn out that

$$\int_S \operatorname{curl} F \cdot dS = \oint_{\partial S} F \cdot \mathbf{dx}. \tag{1}$$

Notice that if F were essentially a 2-dimensional vector field, with F_3 identically zero and F_1 and F_2 independent of x_3, then only the third coordinate function of curl F would be different from zero, and Equation (1) would reduce to Green's formula.

EXAMPLE 1. Let S be the spiral surface parametrized by

$$\begin{pmatrix} x_1 \\ x_2 \\ x_3 \end{pmatrix} = \begin{pmatrix} u \cos v \\ u \sin v \\ v \end{pmatrix}, \quad \text{for} \quad 0 \le u \le 1, \quad 0 \le v \le \frac{\pi}{2}.$$

Then the border of S consists of three line segments and a spiral curve shown in Figure 21 together with the domain D of the parametrization. Restricting the parametrization of S to the boundary of D gives the following parametrizations of the smooth pieces of the border of S:

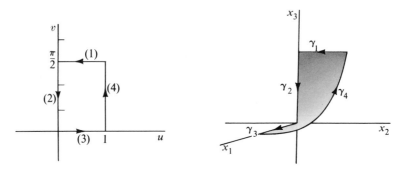

Figure 21

$$\gamma_1 : \begin{pmatrix} x_1 \\ x_2 \\ x_3 \end{pmatrix} = \begin{pmatrix} 0 \\ 1-t \\ \pi/2 \end{pmatrix}, \quad 0 \leq t \leq 1 \qquad \gamma_2 : \begin{pmatrix} x_1 \\ x_2 \\ x_3 \end{pmatrix} = \begin{pmatrix} 0 \\ 0 \\ (\pi/2) - t \end{pmatrix}, \quad 0 \leq t \leq \frac{\pi}{2}$$

$$\gamma_3 : \begin{pmatrix} x_1 \\ x_2 \\ x_3 \end{pmatrix} = \begin{pmatrix} t \\ 0 \\ 0 \end{pmatrix}, \quad 0 \leq t \leq 1 \qquad \gamma_4 : \begin{pmatrix} x_1 \\ x_2 \\ x_3 \end{pmatrix} = \begin{pmatrix} \cos t \\ \sin t \\ t \end{pmatrix}, \quad 0 \leq t \leq \frac{\pi}{2}.$$

Now let F be the vector field $F(x_1, x_2, x_3) = (x_3, x_1, x_2)$. The line integrals of F over the γ_i are all of the form

$$\int_{\gamma_i} x_3 \, dx_1 + x_1 \, dx_2 + x_2 \, dx_3.$$

It is easy to see that the integrals over γ_1, γ_2, and γ_3 are all zero, while over γ_4 we get

$$\int_{\gamma_4} F \cdot d\mathbf{x} = \int_0^{\pi/2} (\cos^2 t + \sin t - t \sin t) \, dt$$

$$= \frac{\pi}{4}.$$

On the other hand curl $F(x_1, x_2, x_3) = (1, 1, 1)$; so the integral of curl F over S is

$$\int_S \text{curl } F \cdot dS = \int_D \left(\frac{\partial(x_2, x_3)}{\partial(u, v)} + \frac{\partial(x_3, x_1)}{\partial(u, v)} + \frac{\partial(x_1, x_2)}{\partial(u, v)} \right) du \, dv$$

$$= \int_0^1 du \int_0^{\pi/2} (\sin v - \cos v + u) \, dv = \frac{\pi}{4}.$$

This verifies Equation (1) for our special example.

The proof that we give of Stokes's theorem depends on an application of Green's theorem to the region D on which the parametrization of S is defined. For this reason we need to assume enough about D to make Green's theorem hold on it. Also, if $\mathscr{R}^2 \xrightarrow{g} \mathscr{R}^3$ is the parametrization of S, we shall want the second order partial derivatives of g to be continuous, that is, g should be twice continuously differentiable on D. These conditions can be relaxed, but to do so makes the proof much more difficult.

4.1 Stokes's theorem. Let S be a piece of smooth surface in $\mathscr{R}^3$, parametrized by a twice continuously differentiable function g. Assume that D, the parameter domain of g, is a finite union of simple regions bounded by a piecewise smooth curve. If F is a continuously differentiable vector field defined on S, then

$$\int_S \text{curl } F \cdot dS = \oint_{\partial S} F \cdot d\mathbf{x},$$

where ∂S is the positively oriented border of S.

Proof. Let F_1, F_2, F_3 be coordinate functions of F. We shall prove that

$$\oint_{\partial S} F_1\, dx_1 = \int_S -\frac{\partial F_1}{\partial x_2}\, dx_1\, dx_2 + \frac{\partial F_1}{\partial x_3}\, dx_3\, dx_1. \tag{2}$$

The proofs that

$$\oint_{\partial S} F_2\, dx_2 = \int_S -\frac{\partial F_2}{\partial x_3}\, dx_2\, dx_3 + \frac{\partial F_2}{dx_1}\, dx_1\, dx_2$$

and

$$\oint_{\partial S} F_3\, dx_3 = \int_S -\frac{\partial F_3}{\partial x_1}\, dx_3\, dx_1 + \frac{\partial F_3}{dx_2}\, dx_2\, dx_3$$

are similar, and addition of the three equations gives Stokes's formula. To prove the top equation, suppose that $h(t) = (u(t), v(t))$ is a counter-clockwise-oriented parametrization of δ, the boundary of D. Then $g(h(t))$ is a piecewise smooth parametrization of the border of S, which by definition is then positively oriented. Writing g_1, g_2, g_3 for the coordinate functions of g, we have

$$\oint_{\partial S} F_1\, dx_1 = \int F_1(g(u,v)) \frac{d}{dt} g_1(u,v)\, dt$$

$$= \int F_1(g(u,v)) \left[\frac{\partial g_1}{\partial u}(u,v) \frac{du}{dt} + \frac{\partial g_1}{\partial v}(u,v) \frac{dv}{dt} \right] dt$$

$$= \oint_\delta F_1 \circ g \frac{\partial g_1}{\partial u}\, du + F_1 \circ g \frac{\partial g_1}{\partial v}\, dv.$$

This last integral is a line integral around the region D in $\mathscr{R}^2$, and we can apply Green's theorem to it, getting

$$\oint_{\partial S} F_1\, dx_1 = \int_D \left[\frac{\partial}{\partial u}\left(F_1 \circ g \frac{\partial g_1}{\partial v} \right) - \frac{\partial}{\partial v}\left(F_1 \circ g \frac{\partial g_1}{\partial u} \right) \right] du\, dv. \tag{3}$$

The fact that g is twice continuously differentiable ensures that the integral over D will exist. The same fact enables us to interchange the order of partial differentiation in a computation which shows that

$$\frac{\partial}{\partial u}\left(F_1 \circ g \frac{\partial g_1}{\partial v} \right) - \frac{\partial}{\partial v}\left(F_1 \circ g \frac{\partial g_1}{\partial u} \right) = -\frac{\partial F_1}{\partial x_2} \frac{\partial(g_1, g_2)}{\partial(u,v)} + \frac{\partial F_1}{\partial x_3} \frac{\partial(g_3, g_1)}{\partial(u,v)}. \tag{4}$$

Substitution of this identity into Equation (3) gives Equation (2), thus completing the proof.

Using Stokes's theorem we can derive an interpretation for the vector field curl F that gives some information about F itself. Let $\mathbf{x}_0$ be a point of an open set on which F is continuously differentiable. Let $\mathbf{n}_0$ be an arbitrary unit vector pointing away from $\mathbf{x}_0$, and construct a disk S_r of radius r centered at $\mathbf{x}_0$ and perpendicular to $\mathbf{n}_0$. This is shown in Figure 22. Applying Stokes's theorem to F on the surface S_r and its border γ_r gives

$$\oint_{\gamma_r} F \cdot d\mathbf{x} = \int_{S_r} \text{curl } F \cdot dS.$$

The value of the line integral is called the **circulation** of F around γ_r, and it measures the strength of the field tangential to γ_r. Thus, for small r, the circulation around γ_r is a measure of the tendency of the field near $\mathbf{x}_0$ to rotate around the axis determined by $\mathbf{n}_0$. On the other hand, the surface integral is, for small enough r, nearly equal to the dot product curl $F(\mathbf{x}_0)\cdot\mathbf{n}_0$, multiplied by the area of S_r. See Problem 15 of the previous section. It follows that the circulation around γ_r will tend to be larger if $\mathbf{n}_0$ points in the same direction as curl $F(\mathbf{x}_0)$. Thus we can think of curl $F(\mathbf{x}_0)$ as determining the axis about which the circulation of F is greatest near $\mathbf{x}_0$. Similarly, $|\text{curl } F(\mathbf{x}_0)|$ measures the magnitude of the circulation around this axis near $\mathbf{x}_0$.

The extension of Stokes's theorem to piecewise smooth orientable surfaces is very simple, though a little care is needed in defining the border of such a surface. Figure 23 illustrates the method. The surfaces S_1 and S_2 have their borders joined so as to produce a piecewise smooth positively oriented surface which we denote by $S_1 \cup S_2$. Recall that the surface integral of a vector field F over $S_1 \cup S_2$ has already been defined by

$$\int_{S_1 \cup S_2} F \cdot dS = \int_{S_1} F \cdot dS + \int_{S_2} F \cdot dS.$$

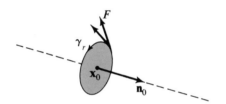

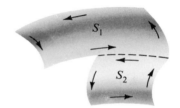

Figure 22   **Figure 23**

The piece of common border curve, indicated by a broken line in Figure 23, will be traced in opposite directions depending on whether the parametrization induced by S_1 or by S_2 is used. Hence, the respective line integrals of F over the common border will have opposite sign, and when the line integrals over ∂S_1 and ∂S_2 are added, the integrals over the common part will cancel, leaving a line integral over the rest of the borders of S_1 and S_2. It is this remaining part that we call the positively oriented border of $S_1 \cup S_2$, and denote by $\partial(S_1 \cup S_2)$. (Thus in general $\partial(S_1 \cup S_2) \neq \partial S_1 \cup \partial S_2$.) With this understanding we write Stokes's theorem in the form

$$\int_S \text{curl } F \cdot dS = \oint_{\partial S} F \cdot d\mathbf{x},$$

for a piecewise smooth surface S.

EXAMPLE 2. A sphere can be considered as a piecewise smooth surface on which all of the border curves cancel one another. In fact if we parametrize a sphere S_a in $\mathscr{R}^3$ by

$$g(u, v) = \begin{pmatrix} a \sin v \cos u \\ a \sin v \sin u \\ a \cos v \end{pmatrix}, \qquad \begin{matrix} 0 \le u \le 2\pi \\ 0 \le v \le \pi, \end{matrix}$$

then the positively oriented "border" of the sphere consists of the half-circle shown in Figure 24 traced once in each direction. Thus the half-circle corresponds to the segments $u = 0$ and $u = 2\pi$ in the parameter domain. (What happens to the segments $v = 0$ and $v = \pi$?) The result is that a line integral over ∂S_a will be zero, and Stokes's theorem applied to a vector field F on S_a gives

$$\int_{S_a} \operatorname{curl} F \cdot dS = 0.$$

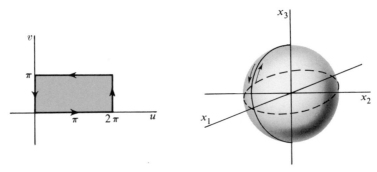

Figure 24

A surface like that in the previous example, in which the border is effectively nonexistent for the purpose of line integration over ∂S, is called a **closed surface**.

Stokes's theorem gives interesting information about gradient fields, that is, fields F such that $F = \nabla f$, or, using an alternative notation, $F = \operatorname{grad} f$. If we assume that F is the continuously differentiable gradient field of f, we can form the vector field $\operatorname{curl} F$. Since $F = (\partial f/\partial x_1, \partial f/\partial x_2, \partial f/\partial x_3)$, we get immediately from the definition of $\operatorname{curl} F$ and the equality of mixed partials that

4.2 $\operatorname{curl} (\operatorname{grad} f)(\mathbf{x}) = 0,$

for all $\mathbf{x}$ in the domain of f. We have already met the condition $\operatorname{curl} F = 0$ in Theorems 2.5 and 2.6, where, for the 3-dimensional case that we consider here, it was stated in terms of the Jacobian matrix

$$F' = \begin{pmatrix} \dfrac{\partial F_1}{\partial x_1} & \dfrac{\partial F_2}{\partial x_1} & \dfrac{\partial F_3}{\partial x_1} \\[2mm] \dfrac{\partial F_1}{\partial x_2} & \dfrac{\partial F_2}{\partial x_2} & \dfrac{\partial F_3}{\partial x_2} \\[2mm] \dfrac{\partial F_1}{\partial x_3} & \dfrac{\partial F_2}{\partial x_3} & \dfrac{\partial F_3}{\partial x_3} \end{pmatrix}.$$

It is clear that the symmetry of F' about its main diagonal is equivalent to curl $F = 0$. Theorem 2.5 says in particular that if F is a gradient field, then curl F is identically zero. Theorem 2.6 gives only a partial converse, to the effect that if curl F is identically zero, then there is some rectangle in which F equals a gradient field. This is sometimes paraphrased by saying that F is *locally* a gradient field. And Example 2 of Section 2 shows that the strict converse is false. Using Stokes's theorem, we can prove another partial converse, in which the local condition is replaced by a different kind of restriction on the domain of the given field.

For this purpose we shall define a **simply-connected** open set B in $\mathscr{R}^n$. Roughly, a set B is simply-connected if every closed curve γ in B can be contracted to a point in such a way as to stay within B during the contraction. As γ contracts to a point, it sweeps out a surface S lying in B, and γ is the border of S. The region between two spheres shown in Figure 25(a) is simply-connected. However, the open ball with a hole punched through it is not simply-connected, because any surface whose border encircles the hole must lie at least partly outside B. In $\mathscr{R}^2$, the typical simply-connected region is the inside of a closed curve, while the outside of such a curve is not simply-connected. In Figure 26(a), the curve γ is the border of the surface consisting of the part of the plane lying inside γ. However, the presence of the hole in Figure 26(b) prevents a similar construction. More precisely, we shall say

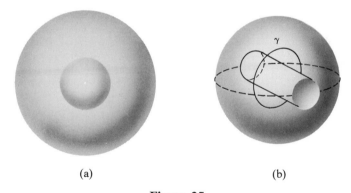

(a) (b)

Figure 25

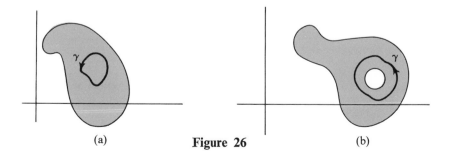

(a) **Figure 26** (b)

that an open set is simply-connected if every piecewise smooth closed curve γ lying in B is the border of some piecewise smooth orientable surface S lying in B, and with parameter domain a disc in $\mathscr{R}^2$. We assume for applications that S is parametrized by twice continuously differentiable functions. All the differentiability conditions assumed above are usually relaxed to just continuity, but, since we shall have no use for the latter definition, we shall not introduce a special term for the one involving differentiability.

Now we can prove the following:

4.3 Theorem. Let F be a continuously differentiable vector field defined on an open set B in $\mathscr{R}^2$ or $\mathscr{R}^3$. If

(i) B is simply-connected, and
(ii) curl F is identically zero in B,

then F is a gradient field in B, that is, there is a real-valued function f such that $F = \nabla f$.

Proof. By Theorem 2.4 it is enough to show that $\oint_\gamma F \cdot d\mathbf{x} = 0$ for every piecewise smooth curve γ lying in B. Because B is simply-connected, there is a piecewise smooth surface S of which γ is the border and to which we can apply Stokes's theorem in either 2 or 3 dimensions. Thus

$$\oint_{\partial S} F \cdot d\mathbf{x} = \int_S \text{curl } F \cdot dS = 0.$$

EXERCISES

1. Compute curl F if

    (a) $F(x_1, x_2, x_3) = (x_2 - x_3^2, x_3 - x_1^2, x_1 - x_2^3)$.
    (b) $F(x, y, z) = (x, 2y, 3z)$.

2. Verify by computing both integrals that Stokes's theorem holds for the vector field $F(x_1, x_2, x_3) = (x_1, x_2, x_3)$ on a hemisphere centered at the origin in $\mathscr{R}^3$.

3. (a) Verify that if $F(x_1, x_2, x_3)$ is independent of x_3 and the third coordinate function of F is identically zero, then Stokes's formula, applied to a planar surface in the x_1, x_2-plane, is the same as Green's formula.
    (b) Consider the function $\mathscr{R}^2 \xrightarrow{g} \mathscr{R}^3$ defined by

$$g(u, v) = \begin{pmatrix} u \cos v \\ u \sin v \\ 0 \end{pmatrix}, \qquad \begin{array}{l} 1 \le u \le 2 \\ 0 \le v \le 4\pi \end{array}$$

If S is the image in $\mathscr{R}^3$ of g, give a precise description of the border of S.
    (c) If F is a continuously differentiable vector field on S of the type described in part (a), use Stokes's theorem to compute the integral of F over the positively oriented border of S.

4. Show that the Stokes formula can be written in the form

$$\int_S \operatorname{curl} F \cdot \mathbf{n} \, d\sigma = \oint_{\partial S} F \cdot \mathbf{t} \, ds,$$

where $\mathbf{n}$ is a unit normal to S and $\mathbf{t}$ is a unit tangent to ∂S.

5. Use the result of Problem 15 of the previous section and Stokes's theorem to prove that if F is a continuously differentiable vector field at $\mathbf{x}_0$, then

$$\lim_{r \to 0} \frac{1}{A(D_r)} \oint_c F \cdot \mathbf{t} \, ds = \operatorname{curl} F(\mathbf{x}_0) \cdot \mathbf{n}_0,$$

where D_r is a disc of radius r centered at $\mathbf{x}_0$, and $\mathbf{n}_0$ is a unit normal to the disk, and c is the boundary of D_r.

6. Prove that if F is a continuously differentiable vector field such that, at each point $\mathbf{x}$ of a piece of smooth surface S, the vector $\operatorname{curl} F(\mathbf{x})$ is tangent to S, then the integral of F around the border of S is zero.

7. Let F be a differentiable vector field defined in an open subset B of $\mathscr{R}^3$. Use the decomposition of a square matrix A into symmetric and skew-symmetric parts given by $A = \frac{1}{2}(A + A^t) + \frac{1}{2}(A - A^t)$, to show that for all $\mathbf{y}$ in $\mathscr{R}^3$

$$F'(\mathbf{x})\mathbf{y} = S(\mathbf{x})\mathbf{y} + \tfrac{1}{2} \operatorname{curl} F(\mathbf{x}) \times \mathbf{y},$$

where $S(\mathbf{x})$ is a symmetric matrix.

8. Let F be the gradient field of the Newtonian potential $f(x, y, z) = (x^2 + y^2 + z^2)^{-1/2}$. Show that near each point of the domain of F the circulation of F is zero.

9. Carry out the computation of the identity in Equation (4) of the proof of Stokes's theorem.

10. Consider the cylindrical can C of radius 1 having an unspecified smooth border and an orientation as shown in Figure 27. Let $F(x_1, x_2, x_3) = (2x_2^2, x_1^2, 3x_3^2)$. What is the value of the line integral of F over the border of C?

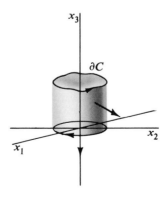

Figure 27

11. Compute the integral of curl F, where $F(x_1, x_2, x_3) = (x_2^3, -x_1^3, x_3^3)$, over the hemisphere $x_1^2 + x_2^2 + x_3^2 = 1$, $x_3 \geq 0$, by considering an integral over the disc that makes the hemisphere closed.

12. Show that the open subset of $\mathscr{R}^2$ consisting of $\mathscr{R}^2$ with the origin deleted, is not simply-connected by finding a vector field F for which curl F is identically zero, but such that F is not a gradient field. [*Hint.* See Problem 7 of Section 1.]

13. The open set in $\mathscr{R}^2$ consisting of $\mathscr{R}^2$ with two points $\mathbf{x}_1$ and $\mathbf{x}_2$ deleted is not simply-connected. However, show that if F is any continuously differentiable vector field in such a region such that curl $F = 0$ there, then the integral of F over the smooth curve shown in Figure 28 is equal to zero.

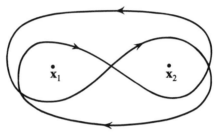

Figure 28

14. In the open subset B of $\mathscr{R}^3$ consisting of $\mathscr{R}^3$ with the origin deleted, show that a circle centered at the origin is the border of a piecewise smooth surface lying in B.

5. GAUSS'S THEOREM

The Gauss theorem has many applications, some of which are discussed in Section 6. Like Stokes's theorem, it can be looked at as an extension of Green's theorem. We begin with a region R in $\mathscr{R}^3$ having as boundary a piecewise smooth surface S. Each piece of S will be parametrized by a continuously differentiable function $\mathscr{R}^2 \xrightarrow{g} \mathscr{R}^3$ such that the normal vector $\partial g/\partial u \times \partial g/\partial v$ points away from R at each point of S. The boundary surface S is then said to have **positive orientation**, and we denote the positively oriented boundary of R by ∂R. To state the theorem, we consider a vector field F, continuously differentiable on R and its boundary. We define the **divergence** of F to be the real-valued function div F defined on R by

$$\text{div } F(\mathbf{x}) = \frac{\partial F_1}{\partial x_1}(\mathbf{x}) + \frac{\partial F_2}{\partial x_2}(\mathbf{x}) + \frac{\partial F_3}{\partial x_3}(\mathbf{x}),$$

where F_1, F_2, F_3 are the coordinate functions of F. Then the Gauss (or divergence) formula is

$$\int_R \text{div } F \, dV = \int_{\partial R} F \cdot dS.$$

The Gauss formula is like Stokes's formula, Green's formula, and the formula

$$\int_a^b \operatorname{grad} f \cdot d\mathbf{x} = f(\mathbf{b}) - f(\mathbf{a}),$$

in that it relates an integral of some kind of derivative of a function to the behavior of that function on a boundary. In each case the orientation of the boundary is important. For example, if we apply Gauss's theorem to the region R in $\mathscr{R}^3$ given by $1 \leq |\mathbf{x}| \leq 2$, then the oriented boundary, ∂R, must be such that its normal vectors on the outer sphere point away from the origin, and on the inner sphere point toward it, as shown in Figure 29. We shall say that ∂R is **positively oriented** with respect to R if the normal vectors given by the parametrization of ∂R point away from R.

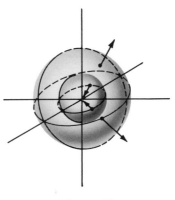

We shall prove Gauss's theorem for the case in which R is a finite union of simple regions, where a **simple region** in $\mathscr{R}^3$ is one whose boundary is crossed by a line parallel to a coordinate axis at most twice. The region between two spheres, shown in Figure 29, is a union of eight simple regions, one in each octant.

Figure 29

5.1 Gauss's theorem. Let R be a finite union of simple regions in $\mathscr{R}^3$, having a positively oriented piecewise smooth boundary ∂R. If F is a continuously differentiable vector field on R and ∂R, then

$$\int_R \operatorname{div} F \, dV = \int_{\partial R} F \cdot dS.$$

Proof. In terms of coordinate functions of F, Gauss's formula reads

$$\int_R \left(\frac{\partial F_1}{\partial x_1} + \frac{\partial F_2}{\partial x_2} + \frac{\partial F_3}{\partial x_3} \right) dx_1 \, dx_2 \, dx_3$$
$$= \int_{\partial R} F_1 \, dx_2 \, dx_3 + F_2 \, dx_3 \, dx_1 + F_3 \, dx_1 \, dx_2.$$

We assume first that R is a simple region, and prove only the equation

$$\int_R \frac{\partial F_2}{\partial x_2} \, dx_1 \, dx_2 \, dx_3 = \int_{\partial R} F_2 \, dx_3 \, dx_1,$$

the proofs for the terms containing F_1 and F_3 being similar. Addition of the resulting equation will then prove the theorem for simple regions. Because R is simple, ∂R consists of the graphs of two functions, $s(x_1, x_3)$

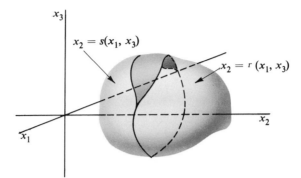

Figure 30

and $r(x_1, x_3)$, perhaps together with pieces parallel to the x_2-axis as shown in Figure 30. Let

$$g(u, v) = \begin{pmatrix} g_1(u, v) \\ g_2(u, v) \\ g_3(u, v) \end{pmatrix}, \qquad (u, v) \quad \text{in} \quad D,$$

be a parametrization for ∂R that orients it positively. Then, by the definition of the surface integral,

$$\int_{\partial R} F_2 \, dx_3 \, dx_1 = \int_D F_2(g_1, g_2, g_3) \frac{\partial(g_3, g_1)}{\partial(u, v)} \, du \, dv, \tag{1}$$

and, on the sections of ∂R that are parallel to the x_2-axis, the normal vector to ∂R is perpendicular to the x_2-axis. Hence $\partial(g_3, g_1)/\partial(u, v)$, the third coordinate of the normal, is equal to zero, thus eliminating the part of the integral that is not on the graph of r or s. We now apply the change of variable theorem to the two remaining parts of the integral in Equation (1). The appropriate transformations are

$$\begin{pmatrix} x_3 \\ x_1 \end{pmatrix} = \begin{pmatrix} g_3(u, v) \\ g_1(u, v) \end{pmatrix},$$

with (u, v) in either D_r or D_s, where D_r and D_s are the parts of D corresponding to the graphs of r and s. The Jacobian determinant $\partial(g_3, g_1)/\partial(u, v)$ is positive on the graph of r and negative on the graph of s, because it represents the x_2-coordinate of the outward normal. On D_r we have $g_2(u, v) = r(x_1, x_3)$, while on D_s, $g_2(u, v) = s(x_1, x_3)$. Using these facts, we get from the change of variable theorem and Equation (1),

$$\int_{\partial R} F_2 \, dx_3 \, dx_1 = \int_{R_2} F_2(x_1, s(x_1, x_3), x_3)(-1) \, dx_1 \, dx_3$$

$$+ \int_{R_2} F_2(x_1, r(x_1, x_3), x_3) \, dx_1 \, dx_3,$$

where R_2 is the plane region got by projecting R on the x_1, x_3-plane.

These last integrals are not surface integrals, but rather integrals over a set. Then, by the fundamental theorem of calculus,

$$\int_{\partial R} F_2 \, dx_3 \, dx_1 = \int_{R_2} \left[\int_{s(x_1, x_3)}^{r(x_1, x_3)} \frac{\partial F_2}{\partial x_2}(x_1, x_2, x_3) \, dx_2 \right] dx_1 \, dx_3$$

$$= \int_R \frac{\partial F_2}{\partial x_2} \, dx_1 \, dx_2 \, dx_3.$$

Similar arguments involving F_1 and F_3 complete the proof for simple regions, since the addition of the three resulting equations gives

$$\int_{\partial R} F_1 \, dx_2 \, dx_3 + F_2 \, dx_3 \, dx_1 + F_3 \, dx_1 \, dx_2$$

$$= \int_R \left(\frac{\partial F_1}{\partial x_1} + \frac{\partial F_2}{\partial x_2} + \frac{\partial F_3}{\partial x_3} \right) dx_1 \, dx_2 \, dx_3,$$

and this is the Gauss formula in coordinate form.

The extension of Gauss's theorem to a finite union R of simple regions is essentially the same as the analogous extension of Green's theorem. In the present case, when two simple regions have a common boundary surface, the respective outward normals will be negatives of one another. The corresponding surface integrals are then negatives of one another, and so cancel out. The remaining surface integrals extend over the surface ∂R.

EXAMPLE 1. Problem 6 of Section 3 consists in showing that the flux of the gradient field F of the potential function $f(x, y, z) = (x^2 + y^2 + z^2)^{-1/2}$ across a sphere of radius a, centered at the origin, is independent of a. Using Gauss's theorem we can prove something more general, and with a minimum of calculation. Thus, let S_1 and S_2 be any two piecewise smooth closed surfaces, one contained in the other, both containing the origin, and bounding a region R between them; for example, R might be the region between two spheres. A routine calculation of the gradient shows that $F(x, y, z) = (x^2 + y^2 + z^2)^{-3/2}(-x, -y, -z)$, and then that the divergence of this field is zero, i.e., div $F = 0$ everywhere except at the origin. In particular, div $F = 0$ throughout R. Applying Gauss's theorem to R gives

$$\int_{\partial R} F \cdot dS = \int_R \operatorname{div} F \, dV = 0.$$

But ∂R consists of S_1 with inward pointing normal and S_2 with outward pointing normal; so, with the understanding that S_1^- stands for the inner surface with reversed normal, we get

$$\int_{\partial R} F \cdot dS = -\int_{S_1^-} F \cdot dS + \int_{S_2} F \cdot dS = 0.$$

Thus the integrals over the outward oriented surfaces are equal. To find the actual value, it is enough to compute it for one surface, say a sphere. The result is -4π.

The divergence of a vector field F at a point $\mathbf{x}$ can be interpreted as a measure of the tendency of the field to radiate outward from $\mathbf{x}$, hence the term "divergence". To see this, consider a ball B_r of radius r, centered at an interior point $\mathbf{x}_0$ of the set on which F is continuously differentiable. Dividing both sides of Gauss's formula by $V(B_r)$ gives

$$\frac{1}{V(B_r)} \int_{B_r} \operatorname{div} F \, dV = \frac{1}{V(B_r)} \int_{\partial B_r} F \cdot \mathbf{n} \, d\sigma,$$

where $\mathbf{n}$ is the outward unit normal. As r tends to zero, the left side tends to $\operatorname{div} F(\mathbf{x}_0)$. See Problem 17 of Chapter 4, Section 2. On the right side, the integral is the average rate of flow per unit of volume across the sphere of radius r centered at $\mathbf{x}_0$. Hence the limit as r tends to zero is, by definition, the rate per unit of volume of flow outward from $\mathbf{x}_0$. Because of its connection with the interpretation of divergence, Gauss's theorem is often called the divergence theorem.

EXERCISES

1. Compute the divergence of the following vector fields:
   (a) $F(x_1, x_2, x_3) = (x_1^2, x_2^2, x_3^2)$.
   (b) $F(x, y, z) = (\sin xy, 0, 0)$.
   (c) $F(x_1, x_2, x_3) = (x_2, x_3, x_1)$.

2. Prove the following identities for any twice continuously differentiable vector field F or real-valued function f.
   (a) $\operatorname{div} (\operatorname{curl} F)(\mathbf{x}) = 0$.
   (b) $\operatorname{curl} (\operatorname{grad} f)(\mathbf{x}) = 0$.

3. (a) Show that for $f(x, y, z) = (x^2 + y^2 + z^2)^{-1/2}$ the equation $\operatorname{div} (\operatorname{grad} f)(\mathbf{x}) = 0$ holds for all $\mathbf{x} \neq 0$.
   (b) Show by example that
      $$\operatorname{div} (\operatorname{grad} f)(\mathbf{x}) \neq 0$$
      may hold for some twice continuously differentiable function f.
   (c) If the operator Δ is defined by
      $$\Delta f = \operatorname{div} (\operatorname{grad} f),$$
      find a formula for Δf in terms of partial derivatives of f. (A function f such that $\Delta f(\mathbf{x}) = 0$ for all $\mathbf{x}$ in the domain of f is called **harmonic**, and Δ is called the Laplace operator.)

4. The trace of a square matrix is defined as the sum of the elements on its main diagonal. If $\mathscr{R}^n \xrightarrow{F} \mathscr{R}^n$ is a differentiable vector field, we define $\operatorname{div} F$ to be the real-valued function given by
   $$\operatorname{div} F(\mathbf{x}) = \operatorname{tr} F'(\mathbf{x}),$$
   where $\operatorname{tr} A$ stands for the trace of A. Show that in the 2- and 3-dimensional cases this definition agrees with those previously given.

5. Use Gauss's theorem to compute

$$\int_S F \cdot dS$$

over the sphere of radius 1 centered at the origin in $\mathcal{R}^3$, and with outward pointing normal, where F is

(a) $F(x_1, x_2, x_3) = (x_1^2, x_2^2, x_3^2)$.
(b) $F(x, y, z) = (xz^2, 0, z^3)$.

6. Show that for a region R to which Gauss's theorem applies, the volume of R is given by

$$V(R) = \frac{1}{3} \int_{\partial R} x_1 \, dx_2 \, dx_3 + x_2 \, dx_3 \, dx_1 + x_3 \, dx_1 \, dx_2.$$

7. (a) Use Gauss's theorem to prove that if F is a continuously differentiable vector field with zero divergence in a region R, then the integral of F over ∂R is zero.

(b) Write an intuitive argument, based on the interpretation of the divergence, for the assertion in part (a).

8. Let S be the ellipsoid

$$\frac{x^2}{a^2} + \frac{y^2}{b^2} + \frac{z^2}{c^2} = 1,$$

and let $D(x, y, z)$ be the distance from the origin to the tangent plane to S at (x, y, z).

(a) Show that if $F(x, y, z) = (x/a^2, y/b^2, z/c^2)$, then $F \cdot \mathbf{n} = D^{-1}$, where $\mathbf{n}$ is the outward unit normal to S at (x, y, z).

(b) Show that $\int_S D^{-1} \, d\sigma = \frac{4\pi}{3} \left(\frac{bc}{a} + \frac{ca}{b} + \frac{ab}{c} \right).$

9. A vector field $\mathcal{R}^3 \xrightarrow{F} \mathcal{R}^3$ defined in a region R is called **irrotational** if curl $F(\mathbf{x}) = 0$ for all $\mathbf{x}$ in R, and **incompressible** if div $F(\mathbf{x}) = 0$ for all $\mathbf{x}$ in R. Assume F continuously differentiable.

(a) Show that if F is irrotational, then the circulation of F is zero around every sufficiently small circular path in R.

(b) Show that if F is incompressible, then the flux of F is zero across every sufficiently small sphere with its interior in R.

6. THE OPERATORS ∇, $\nabla \times$, AND $\nabla \cdot$

To facilitate the application of the Gauss and Stokes theorems it is helpful to extend the use of the symbol ∇, called "del", that is used in denoting the gradient field of a real-valued function. In terms of the natural basis $\mathbf{e}_1, \mathbf{e}_2, \mathbf{e}_3$ for $\mathcal{R}^3$, we recall that

$$\nabla f = \frac{\partial f}{\partial x_1} \mathbf{e}_1 + \frac{\partial f}{\partial x_2} \mathbf{e}_2 + \frac{\partial f}{\partial x_3} \mathbf{e}_3. \tag{1}$$

This equation defines ∇ as an operator from real-valued differentiable functions $\mathscr{R}^3 \xrightarrow{f} \mathscr{R}$, to vector fields $\mathscr{R}^3 \xrightarrow{F} \mathscr{R}^3$. If we write

$$\nabla = \frac{\partial}{\partial x_1}\mathbf{e}_1 + \frac{\partial}{\partial x_2}\mathbf{e}_2 + \frac{\partial}{\partial x_3}\mathbf{e}_3, \tag{2}$$

then Equation (1) follows by application of both sides of Equation (2) to f.

The formalism described above makes the following definitions natural. If F is a differentiable vector field given by

$$F(\mathbf{x}) = F_1(\mathbf{x})\mathbf{e}_1 + F_2(\mathbf{x})\mathbf{e}_2 + F_3(\mathbf{x})\mathbf{e}_3,$$

then the operator $\nabla \times$ is defined by taking the formal cross product of ∇ and F to get

$$\nabla \times F = \begin{vmatrix} \frac{\partial}{\partial x_2} & \frac{\partial}{\partial x_3} \\ F_2 & F_3 \end{vmatrix}\mathbf{e}_1 + \begin{vmatrix} \frac{\partial}{\partial x_3} & \frac{\partial}{\partial x_1} \\ F_3 & F_1 \end{vmatrix}\mathbf{e}_2 + \begin{vmatrix} \frac{\partial}{\partial x_1} & \frac{\partial}{\partial x_2} \\ F_1 & F_2 \end{vmatrix}\mathbf{e}_3$$

$$= \left(\frac{\partial F_3}{\partial x_2} - \frac{\partial F_2}{\partial x_3}\right)\mathbf{e}_1 + \left(\frac{\partial F_1}{\partial x_3} - \frac{\partial F_3}{\partial x_1}\right)\mathbf{e}_2 + \left(\frac{\partial F_2}{\partial x_1} - \frac{\partial F_1}{\partial x_2}\right)\mathbf{e}_3.$$

Thus $\nabla \times F$ is the vector field that we have called the curl of F and written curl F. Similarly, for a differentiable vector field F, we define the operator $\nabla \cdot$ by taking the formal dot product of ∇ and F to get

$$\nabla \cdot F = \frac{\partial F_1}{\partial x_1} + \frac{\partial F_2}{\partial x_2} + \frac{\partial F_3}{\partial x_3}. \tag{3}$$

This real-valued function we have called the divergence of F, and have written div F. The meaning of the notation just introduced is easy to remember if Equation (2) is kept in mind.

Using the ∇-notation, Stokes's formula becomes

6.1
$$\int_S (\nabla \times F) \cdot \mathbf{n}d\sigma = \oint_{\partial S} F \cdot \mathbf{t}\,ds,$$

and Gauss's formula becomes

6.2
$$\int_R \nabla \cdot F\,dV = \int_{\partial R} F \cdot \mathbf{n}\,d\sigma.$$

To exploit these formulas fully we need some identities involving ∇. In the formulas below, f and g are real-valued differentiable functions, F and G are differentiable vector fields, and a and b are constants.

$$\nabla (af + bg) = a\nabla f + b\nabla g \tag{4}$$

$$\nabla (fg) = f\nabla g + g\nabla f \tag{5}$$

$$\nabla \times (aF + bG) = a\nabla \times F + b\nabla \times G \tag{6}$$

$$\nabla \times (fF) = f\nabla \times F + \nabla f \times F \tag{7}$$

$$\nabla \cdot (aF + bG) = a\nabla \cdot F + b\nabla \cdot G \tag{8}$$

$$\nabla \cdot (fF) = f\nabla \cdot F + \nabla f \cdot F \tag{9}$$

$$\nabla \cdot (F \times G) = (\nabla \times F) \cdot G - F \cdot (\nabla \times G). \tag{10}$$

Each of these formulas is an immediate consequence of the coordinate definitions of the operators. Using the same kind of proof establishes that if f and F are twice differentiable, then

$$\nabla \cdot (\nabla \times F) = 0, \tag{11}$$

$$\nabla \times (\nabla f) = 0, \tag{12}$$

$$\nabla \cdot \nabla f = \nabla^2 f, \tag{13}$$

where $\nabla^2 f$ is the Laplacian of f, defined by

$$\nabla^2 f = \frac{\partial^2 f}{\partial x_1^2} + \frac{\partial^2 f}{\partial x_2^2} + \frac{\partial x^2 f}{\partial x_3^2}.$$

(Equations (11), (12), and (13) are the same as those in Problems 2 and 3 of the previous section, where the alternative symbol Δ was used for the Laplace operator.)

The formulas given above can be used to derive many special cases of the Gauss and Stokes theorems. A particularly important kind arises if the vector field F is assumed to be a gradient ∇f, or a multiple $f\nabla g$. If we set $F = \nabla f$ in Formula 6.2, the result is

$$\int_R \nabla \cdot \nabla f \, dV = \int_{\partial R} \nabla f \cdot \mathbf{n} \, d\sigma. \tag{14}$$

But by Equation (13), $\nabla \cdot \nabla f = \nabla^2 f$, and by Equation 9.1 of Chapter 2, $\nabla f \cdot \mathbf{n} = (\partial/\partial \mathbf{n})f$. Thus we have

$$\int_R \nabla^2 f \, dV = \int_S \frac{\partial f}{\partial \mathbf{n}} \, d\sigma. \tag{15}$$

If we replace F in Formula 6.2 by $f\nabla g$, instead of by ∇f, we have from Equation (9)

$$\nabla \cdot (f\nabla g) = f\nabla \cdot \nabla g + \nabla f \cdot \nabla g,$$

and so Gauss's formula yields

6.3 $$\int_R f\nabla^2 g \, dV + \int_R \nabla f \cdot \nabla g \, dV = \int_S f \frac{\partial g}{\partial \mathbf{n}} \, d\sigma.$$

This is called **Green's first identity**. Because of the symmetry in the middle term, interchange of f and g and subtraction of the corresponding terms gives **Green's second identity**.

6.4 $$\int_R (f\nabla^2 g - g\nabla^2 f) \, dV = \int_S \left(f\frac{\partial g}{\partial \mathbf{n}} - g\frac{\partial f}{\partial \mathbf{n}} \right) d\sigma.$$

EXAMPLE 1. Let R be a polygonally-connected region in $\mathscr{R}^3$ with a piecewise smooth boundary surface S. If h is a real-valued function defined in R, we consider a **Poisson equation**

$$\nabla^2 u = h,$$

subject to a preassigned boundary condition, $u(\mathbf{x}) = \varphi(\mathbf{x})$ for $\mathbf{x}$ on S. We suppose that there is at least one solution $u(\mathbf{x})$ defined in R and satisfying the boundary condition. We can show, using Green's first identity, that such a solution must be unique: let us suppose that there were two solutions u_1 and u_2; then the function u defined by $u(\mathbf{x}) = u_1(\mathbf{x}) - u_2(\mathbf{x})$ would satisfy the **Laplace equation** $\nabla^2 u = 0$ in R, together with the boundary condition $u(\mathbf{x}) = 0$ on S. Setting $f = g = u$ in Formula 6.3 gives

$$\int_R u \, \nabla^2 u \, dV + \int_R |\nabla u|^2 \, dV = \int_S u \, \frac{\partial u}{\partial \mathbf{n}} \, d\sigma.$$

But the first and last terms are zero, because $\nabla^2 u = 0$ in R and $u = 0$ on S. It follows from $\int_R |\nabla u|^2 \, dV = 0$ that $\nabla u = 0$ identically on R and S. Hence u must be a constant in the polygonally-connected region R. Finally, u must in fact be identically zero, because $u(\mathbf{x}) = 0$ for $\mathbf{x}$ on S. We remark that the Laplace equation is the special case of the Poisson equation obtained by taking h identically zero, and so we have proved a uniqueness theorem for the Laplace equation also.

EXAMPLE 2. As an application of Green's second identity we consider the following problem: Let D be a differential operator acting on functions f defined in a region R in $\mathscr{R}^3$ having a piecewise smooth boundary S. If we let $\mathscr{F}$ be the vector space of continuous functions defined on R together with S, we can define an inner product on $\mathscr{F}$ by

$$\langle f, g \rangle = \int_R fg \, dV.$$

It is easy to check that the integral is indeed an inner product. With respect to the inner product it is often important to know when the operator D is **symmetric** in the sense that

$$\langle Df, g \rangle = \langle f, Dg \rangle,$$

whenever Df and Dg are defined and continuous. See Exercise 17 of Chapter 3, Section 2 for the analogue for finite dimensional spaces. In general, to solve such a problem it is necessary to impose appropriate boundary conditions on the functions f in $\mathscr{F}$. Thus we can show that the Laplace operator ∇^2 is a symmetric operator acting on the subspace $\mathscr{F}_0$ of $\mathscr{F}$ consisting of continuous functions f that satisfy a fixed boundary condition of the form

$$a_1 f(\mathbf{x}) + a_2 \frac{\partial f}{\partial \mathbf{n}}(\mathbf{x}) = 0. \tag{16}$$

In Equation (16), a_1 and a_2 are constants, not both zero, and $\partial/\partial \mathbf{n}$ denotes differentiation with respect to the outward unit normal on S.

We suppose that f and g are two functions satisfying Equation (16) such that $\nabla^2 f$ and $\nabla^2 g$ are continuous. Then Formula 6.4, Green's second identity, shows that $\langle \nabla^2 f, g \rangle = \langle f, \nabla^2 g \rangle$, if and only if

$$\int_S \left(f \frac{\partial f}{\partial \mathbf{n}} - g \frac{\partial f}{\partial \mathbf{n}} \right) d\sigma = 0. \tag{17}$$

Since f and g both satisfy Equation (16), we have

$$g\, a_1 f + g\, a_2 \frac{\partial f}{\partial \mathbf{n}} = 0,$$

$$f\, a_1 g + f\, a_2 \frac{\partial g}{\partial \mathbf{n}} = 0,$$

and subtraction of one from the other gives

$$a_2 \left[g(\mathbf{x}) \frac{\partial f}{\partial \mathbf{n}}(\mathbf{x}) - f(\mathbf{x}) \frac{\partial g}{\partial \mathbf{n}}(\mathbf{x}) \right] = 0, \qquad \text{for all } \mathbf{x} \text{ on } S.$$

If $a_2 \neq 0$, this implies $g(\partial f/\partial \mathbf{n}) - f(\partial g/\partial \mathbf{n}) = 0$ identically on S, so Equation (17) is satisfied. If, on the other hand, $a_2 = 0$, then a_1 is not zero, and the boundary condition implies that both f and g are identically zero on S. But then Equation (17) is still satisfied. Thus we have shown that ∇^2 is symmetric on $\mathscr{F}_0$. Notice that $\nabla^2 f$ is not defined for all f in $\mathscr{F}_0$, but only for sufficiently differentiable f.

From Formula 6.2 we can derive some equations for vector-valued integrals. For the definition and properties of the integral, see Problem 16 of Chapter 4, Section 2. Let $\mathbf{k}$ be an arbitrary constant vector and let $F(\mathbf{x}) = f(\mathbf{x})\mathbf{k}$, where f is real-valued and continuously differentiable on a region R. Then, because $\nabla \cdot f\mathbf{k} = \nabla f \cdot \mathbf{k}$, Formula 6.2 becomes

$$\int_R \nabla f \cdot \mathbf{k} \, dV = \int_{\partial R} f\mathbf{k} \cdot \mathbf{n} \, d\sigma.$$

Since $\mathbf{k}$ is constant,

$$\mathbf{k} \cdot \int_R \nabla f \, dV = \mathbf{k} \cdot \int_{\partial R} f\mathbf{n} \, d\sigma,$$

and, from the fact that $\mathbf{k}$ is arbitrary, we conclude that

$$\int_R \nabla f \, dV = \int_{\partial R} f\mathbf{n} \, d\sigma. \tag{18}$$

Similarly, replacing F in Formula 6.2 by $\mathbf{k} \times F$, where $\mathbf{k}$ is a constant vector, we can show that

$$\int_R \nabla \times F \, dV = \int_{\partial R} \mathbf{n} \times F \, d\sigma. \tag{19}$$

The proof is left as an exercise.

As a final application of the ideas of this section we shall prove an analogue to Theorem 2.6. In the 3-dimensional case, that theorem says roughly that if $\nabla \times F$ is identically zero in some region B, then F is a gradient field *locally*, i.e., in some rectangle R contained in B. The following theorem says roughly that if $\nabla \cdot F$ is identically zero in some region B, then, locally, F is the curl of a vector field, i.e., $F = \nabla \times G$ for some G.

6.5 Theorem. Let B be a ball in $\mathscr{R}^3$, and F be a continuously differentiable vector field in B. If $\nabla \cdot F(\mathbf{x}) = 0$ for every $\mathbf{x}$ in B, then there is a vector field G such that $\nabla \times G = F$ throughout B.

Proof. We can assume that $\mathbf{x}_0$, the center of the ball, is the origin, for otherwise we could consider the vector field $F(\mathbf{x} + \mathbf{x}_0)$ on a ball centered at zero. Now, for every $\mathbf{x}$ in B, we define G by the vector-valued integral

$$G(\mathbf{x}) = \int_0^1 [F(t\mathbf{x}) \times (t\mathbf{x})]\, dt.$$

To complete the proof, all we have to do is verify that $\nabla \times G = F$. We shall leave the computation as an exercise, noting however that the equation

$$\nabla \times G(\mathbf{x}) = \int_0^1 \nabla \times [F(t\mathbf{x}) \times (t\mathbf{x})]\, dt \tag{20}$$

is valid because of the Leibnitz rule for differentiation of an integral. See Problem 7(a), Chapter 4, Section 2.

EXERCISES

1. Verify the identities (4) through (10) of the text.

2. If $F = (F_1, F_2, F_3)$ is a vector field, define the operator $F \cdot \nabla$ to be

$$F_1 \frac{\partial}{\partial x_1} + F_2 \frac{\partial}{\partial x_2} + F_3 \frac{\partial}{\partial x_3}.$$

(a) If $F(\mathbf{x}) = \mathbf{x}$, compute $(\mathbf{x} \cdot \nabla)G(\mathbf{x})$, where $G(x_1, x_2, x_3) = (x_1^2, x_1 x_2, x_3)$.
(b) Show that in general $(\nabla \cdot F)G \neq (F \cdot \nabla)G$.
(c) If $\mathbf{k}$ is a constant vector, show that

$$\nabla \times (\mathbf{k} \times F) = \mathbf{k}(\nabla \cdot F) - (\mathbf{k} \cdot \nabla)F,$$

where F is a differentiable vector field.
(d) Use part (c) to show that if F and G are differentiable, then

$$\nabla \times (F \times G) = F(\nabla \cdot G) - (F \cdot \nabla)G - G(\nabla \cdot F) + (G \cdot \nabla)F.$$

3. Prove that if $\mathbf{k}$ is a constant vector, then

$$\nabla \times \frac{\mathbf{k} \times \mathbf{x}}{|\mathbf{x}|} = \frac{\mathbf{k}}{|\mathbf{x}|} + \frac{\mathbf{k} \cdot \mathbf{x}}{|\mathbf{x}|^3}\mathbf{x}.$$

4. Prove that

(a) $\nabla \left(\dfrac{1}{|\mathbf{x}|} \right) = \dfrac{-\mathbf{x}}{|\mathbf{x}|^3}$, $\mathbf{x} \neq 0$.

(b) $\nabla^2 \left(\dfrac{1}{|\mathbf{x}|} \right) = 0$, $\mathbf{x} \neq 0$.

5. If $T(\mathbf{x})$ is the steady-state temperature at a point $\mathbf{x}$ of an open set R in $\mathscr{R}^3$, then the flux of the temperature gradient across any smooth closed surface in R is zero. Use this fact and Equation (15) to show that a steady-state temperature function that is twice continuously differentiable is harmonic, i.e., $\nabla^2 T \equiv 0$. [*Hint.* Suppose $\nabla^2 T(\mathbf{x}_0) > 0$. Show that $\nabla^2 T(\mathbf{x}) > 0$ in some ball centered at $\mathbf{x}_0$.]

6. The boundary condition (16) of Example 2 may be generalized to

$$\phi_1(\mathbf{x})f(\mathbf{x}) + \phi_2(\mathbf{x})\frac{\partial f}{\partial \mathbf{n}}(\mathbf{x}) = 0,$$

where ϕ_1 and ϕ_2 are continuous functions satisfying $\phi_1^2(\mathbf{x}) + \phi_2^2(\mathbf{x}) > 0$. Show that ∇^2, the Laplace operator, is still symmetric with this more general condition.

7. The calculation required in the proof of Theorem 6.5 consists of the following steps.

(a) If $G(\mathbf{x}) = \int_0^1 [F(t\mathbf{x}) \times (t\mathbf{x})]\, dt$, then show that $\nabla \times G(\mathbf{x}) = \int_0^1 \nabla \times [F(t\mathbf{x}) \times (t\mathbf{x})]\, dt$. [*Hint.* Apply the Leibnitz rule of Problem 7(a), Chapter 4, Section 2.]

(b) Show that $\nabla \times [F(t\mathbf{x}) \times (t\mathbf{x})] = 2tF(t\mathbf{x}) + t^2(d/dt)F(t\mathbf{x})$ by using the identity of Problem 2(d).

(c) Show that $\nabla \times G(\mathbf{x}) = F(\mathbf{x})$.

8. A vector field $\mathscr{R}^3 \xrightarrow{F} \mathscr{R}^3$ defined in a region R is called **solenoidal** if, in some neighborhood B of every point of R, the field F can be represented as the curl of another field G_B. The field F is called **incompressible** if the divergence of F is zero at every point of R. Show that a continuously differentiable field is solenoidal if and only if it is incompressible. See Problem 9 of the previous section for the interpretation of incompressibility.

9. Consider the newtonian potential function $N(\mathbf{x}) = |\mathbf{x}|^{-1}$ and its associated gradient field $\nabla N(\mathbf{x})$. (See Problem 4.) Show that $N(\mathbf{x})$ can be interpreted as the work done in moving a particle from ∞ to $\mathbf{x}$ along some smooth path through the field ∇N.

10. Let R be a bounded region in $\mathscr{R}^3$ and let $p(\mathbf{x})$ be the density of material at the point $\mathbf{x}$ in R. Then the integral

$$N_p(\mathbf{x}) = \int_R \frac{p(\mathbf{y})}{|\mathbf{x} - \mathbf{y}|}\, dV_y$$

is called the **newtonian potential** of the material distributed with density p throughout R.

(a) Show that if p is continuous on an open set R with a smooth boundary, then, for $\mathbf{x}$ *not* in R,

$$\nabla^2 N_p = 0.$$

That is, show that for $\mathbf{x}$ not in R, $N_p(\mathbf{x})$ is harmonic.

(b) Show that under the above assumptions on p and R, the integral $N_p(\mathbf{x})$ exists as an improper integral when $\mathbf{x}$ is in R.

7. DIFFERENTIAL FORMS

Having defined the line integral in Chapter 2, we observed that it could be abbreviated

$$\int_\gamma F_1\, dx_1 + F_2\, dx_2 + F_3\, dx_3$$

in the 3-dimensional case. Our purpose here is to show that the integrand $F_1\, dx_1 + F_2\, dx_2 + F_3\, dx_3$ has an interpretation which leads to another way of looking at the line integral. From there we can go naturally to a definition of surface integral.

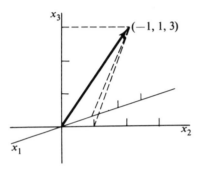

Figure 31

We shall denote by dx_k the function that assigns to a vector $\mathbf{a}$ in $\mathscr{R}^n$ its kth coordinate. Thus if $\mathbf{a} = (a_1, \ldots, a_k, \ldots, a_n)$ is in $\mathscr{R}^n$, then $dx_k(\mathbf{a}) = a_k$. In particular, if $\mathbf{a} = (-1, 1, 3)$, then $dx_1(\mathbf{a}) = -1$, $dx_2(\mathbf{a}) = 1$, and $dx_3(\mathbf{a}) = 3$. Geometrically, $dx_k(\mathbf{a})$ is the length, with appropriate sign, of the projection of $\mathbf{a}$ on the kth coordinate axis, as shown in Figure 31. Linear combinations of the functions dx_k with constant coefficients produce new functions

$$c_1\, dx_1 + \ldots + c_n\, dx_n.$$

Going one step further, if $F_1, \ldots, F_n$ are real-valued functions defined in a region D of $\mathscr{R}^n$, we can form for each $\mathbf{x}$ in D the linear combination

$$\omega_\mathbf{x} = F_1(\mathbf{x})\, dx_1 + \ldots + F_n(\mathbf{x})\, dx_n, \tag{1}$$

where $\omega_\mathbf{x}$ acts on vectors $\mathbf{a}$ in $\mathscr{R}^n$ by

$$\omega_\mathbf{x}(\mathbf{a}) = F_1(\mathbf{x})\, dx_1(\mathbf{a}) + \ldots + F_n(\mathbf{x})\, dx_n(\mathbf{a}). \tag{2}$$

For example, if in $\mathscr{R}^2$ we have $\omega_{(x,y)} = x^2\, dx + y^2\, dy$, then $\omega_{(x,y)}(a, b) = ax^2 + by^2$, and $\omega_{(-1,3)}(a, b) = a + 9b$. A function $\omega_\mathbf{x}$ as defined by Formula (2) is called a **differential 1-form**, or, briefly, a **1-form**.

EXAMPLE 1. Let $\mathscr{R}^3 \xrightarrow{f} \mathscr{R}$ be a differentiable function in a region D of $\mathscr{R}^3$. Then $d_\mathbf{x} f$, the differential of f at $\mathbf{x}$, is a 1-form in D; for $d_\mathbf{x} f$ acting on $\mathbf{a}$ can be written, if $\mathbf{a} = (a_1, a_2, a_3)$,

$$\begin{aligned} d_\mathbf{x} f(\mathbf{a}) &= \frac{\partial f}{\partial x_1}(\mathbf{x}) a_1 + \frac{\partial f}{\partial x_2}(\mathbf{x}) a_2 + \frac{\partial f}{\partial x_3}(\mathbf{x}) a_3 \\ &= \frac{\partial f}{\partial x_1}(\mathbf{x})\, dx_1(\mathbf{a}) + \frac{\partial f}{\partial x_2}(\mathbf{x})\, dx_2(\mathbf{a}) + \frac{\partial f}{\partial x_3}(\mathbf{x})\, dx_3(\mathbf{a}). \end{aligned}$$

Thus the coefficient functions $F_k(\mathbf{x})$ in Formula (1) have the form $F_k(\mathbf{x}) = (\partial f/\partial x_k)(\mathbf{x})$. However, not every 1-form is the differential of a function. To see this, recall that, for sufficiently differentiable f, we have $\partial^2 f/(\partial x_2 \partial x_1) = \partial^2 f/(\partial x_1 \partial x_2)$, but that $\partial F_1/\partial x_2 \neq \partial F_2/\partial x_1$, unless F_1 and F_2 are specially related, as they are by the requirement that $\nabla f = F$ for some F.

EXAMPLE 2. If $\omega_{\mathbf{x}}$ is a 1-form defined in a region D of $\mathscr{R}^3$, and γ is a differentiable curve lying in D and given by $\mathscr{R} \xrightarrow{g} \mathscr{R}^3$ for $a \leq t \leq b$, we can at each point $\mathbf{x} = g(t)$ of γ apply the linear function $\omega_{g(t)}$ to the tangent vector $g'(t)$ at $\mathbf{x}$. The result is a real number which we can express as

$$\omega_{g(t)}(g'(t)) = F_1(g(t))\, dx_1(g'(t)) + F_2(g(t))\, dx_2(g'(t)) + F_3(g(t))\, dx_3(g'(t))$$
$$= F_1(g(t))g_1'(t) + F_2(g(t))g_2'(t) + F_3(g(t))g_3'(t)$$
$$= F(g(t)) \cdot g'(t).$$

If we write

$$\int_a^b \omega_{g(t)}(g'(t))\, dt = \int_a^b F(g(t)) \cdot g'(t)\, dt,$$

we see that the right-hand integral is the line integral of the field F over γ.

The previous example leads us to the natural definition of the integral of a 1-form over a smooth curve γ. If $\omega_{\mathbf{x}}$ is defined by Formula (1) in a region D of $\mathscr{R}^n$, and γ, lying in D, is parametrized by $\mathscr{R} \xrightarrow{g} \mathscr{R}^n$ for $a \leq t \leq b$, we can do either of two things. We can use the coefficient functions $F_1, \ldots, F_n$ of $\omega_{\mathbf{x}}$ to form a vector field F in D and define

$$\int_\gamma \omega_{\mathbf{x}} = \int_a^b F(g(t)) \cdot g'(t)\, dt,$$

or we can form a partition P of the interval $a \leq t \leq b$ at points $a = t_0 < t_1 < \ldots < t_K = b$ and define

$$\int_\gamma \omega_{\mathbf{x}} = \lim_{m(P) \to 0} \sum_{k=1}^K \omega_{g(t_k)}(g'(t_k))(t_k - t_{k-1}).$$

It is clear that the two formulas give the same definition of $\int_\gamma \omega_{\mathbf{x}}$, the *integral of the 1-form* $\omega_{\mathbf{x}}$ *over* γ.

Next we define a product of 1-forms which is different from ordinary pointwise multiplication of functions. We first define the product of the basic 1-forms dx_1, dx_2, dx_3 in $\mathscr{R}^3$. The product $dx_1 \wedge dx_2$ is defined so that it is a function on ordered pairs of vectors in $\mathscr{R}^3$. Geometrically, $dx_1 \wedge dx_2\,(\mathbf{a}, \mathbf{b})$ will be the area of the parallelogram spanned by the projections of $\mathbf{a}$ and $\mathbf{b}$ into the x_1, x_2-plane. The sign of the area is determined so that if the projections of $\mathbf{a}$ and $\mathbf{b}$ have the same orientation as the positive x_1 and x_2 axes, then the area is positive; it is negative when these orientations are opposite. Such a projection is shown in Figure 32. Thus, if $\mathbf{a} = (a_1, a_2, a_3)$ and $\mathbf{b} = (b_1, b_2, b_3)$, then

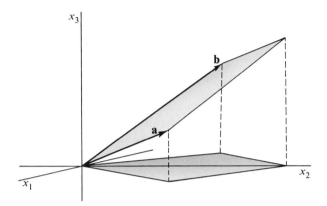

Figure 32

$$dx_1 \wedge dx_2(\mathbf{a}, \mathbf{b}) = \det \begin{pmatrix} a_1 & b_1 \\ a_2 & b_2 \end{pmatrix} = a_1 b_2 - a_2 b_1,$$

and the determinant automatically gives the area the correct sign. We can use the basic 1-forms dx_1 and dx_2 to write the last equation as

$$dx_1 \wedge dx_2(\mathbf{a}, \mathbf{b}) = \det \begin{pmatrix} dx_1(\mathbf{a}) & dx_1(\mathbf{b}) \\ dx_2(\mathbf{a}) & dx_2(\mathbf{b}) \end{pmatrix}.$$

The definitions of all possible products of dx_1, dx_2, and dx_3 in either order can thus all be written in one formula:

$$dx_i \wedge dx_j(\mathbf{a}, \mathbf{b}) = \det \begin{pmatrix} dx_i(\mathbf{a}) & dx_i(\mathbf{b}) \\ dx_j(\mathbf{a}) & dx_j(\mathbf{b}) \end{pmatrix}, \tag{3}$$

with a similar geometric interpretation for each one. For example, we have

$$dx_2 \wedge dx_3(\mathbf{a}, \mathbf{b}) = \det \begin{pmatrix} a_2 & b_2 \\ a_3 & b_3 \end{pmatrix},$$

which is the signed area of the projection of the $\mathbf{a}, \mathbf{b}$-parallelogram on the x_2, x_3-plane.

As a consequence of Equation (3) and the properties of determinants, the following relations hold:

7.1
$$dx_i \wedge dx_j = -dx_j \wedge dx_i,$$

7.2
$$dx_i \wedge dx_i = 0.$$

The first equation holds because the interchange of adjacent rows of a determinant changes its sign, the second because a determinant with two equal rows is zero. Similarly, we have, on interchanging columns,

7.3
$$dx_i \wedge dx_j(\mathbf{b}, \mathbf{a}) = -dx_i \wedge dx_j(\mathbf{a}, \mathbf{b}).$$

If we now ask for the most general linear combination of the functions $dx_i \wedge dx_j$, it is clear from 7.1 and 7.2 that it can be written in the form

$$c_1\, dx_2 \wedge dx_3 + c_2\, dx_3 \wedge dx_1 + c_3\, dx_1 \wedge dx_2.$$

Furthermore, if $F = (F_1, F_2, F_3)$ is a vector field in a region D of $\mathscr{R}^3$, we can define for each $\mathbf{x}$ in D the function

$$\tau_{\mathbf{x}} = F_1(\mathbf{x})\, dx_2 \wedge dx_3 + F_2(\mathbf{x})\, dx_3 \wedge dx_1 + F_3(\mathbf{x})\, dx_1 \wedge dx_2$$

of ordered pairs $(\mathbf{a}, \mathbf{b})$ of vectors in $\mathscr{R}^3$. The function $\tau_{\mathbf{x}}$ is called a **differential 2-form** or **2-form**.

EXAMPLE 3. The 2-form

$$\tau = 2\, dx_2 \wedge dx_3 + dx_3 \wedge dx_1 + 5\, dx_1 \wedge dx_2$$

is the same function at every point of $\mathscr{R}^3$, because its coefficients are constant. (We have written τ instead of $\tau_{\mathbf{x}}$, and we shall do this whenever explicit mention of the variable $\mathbf{x}$ is not needed.) Letting $\mathbf{a} = (1, 2, 3)$ and $\mathbf{b} = (0, 1, 1)$, we have

$$\tau(\mathbf{a}, \mathbf{b}) = 2 \det \begin{pmatrix} 2 & 1 \\ 3 & 1 \end{pmatrix} + \det \begin{pmatrix} 3 & 1 \\ 1 & 0 \end{pmatrix} + 5 \det \begin{pmatrix} 1 & 0 \\ 2 & 1 \end{pmatrix} = 2.$$

We recall, and it is easy to verify directly, that the vector $\mathbf{a} \times \mathbf{b}$ with coordinates

$$\det \begin{pmatrix} 2 & 1 \\ 3 & 1 \end{pmatrix}, \qquad \det \begin{pmatrix} 3 & 1 \\ 1 & 0 \end{pmatrix}, \qquad \det \begin{pmatrix} 1 & 0 \\ 2 & 1 \end{pmatrix}$$

is perpendicular to $(1, 2, 3)$ and to $(0, 1, 1)$, and that its length is equal to the area of the parallelogram $\mathscr{P}$ spanned by $\mathbf{a}$ and $\mathbf{b}$. Thus $\tau(\mathbf{a}, \mathbf{b}) = (2, 1, 5) \cdot (\mathbf{a} \times \mathbf{b})$, and is thus the coordinate of $(2, 1, 5)$ in the direction perpendicular to $\mathscr{P}$, multiplied by the area of $\mathscr{P}$. If we interpret $(2, 1, 5)$ as the constant velocity vector of a fluid flow in space, $\tau(\mathbf{a}, \mathbf{b})$ will be the total flow across $\mathscr{P}$ in 1 unit of time. Such a flow is shown in Figure 33. For a flow F of constant speed and direction across a flat surface S, the **flux** is defined to be the normal coordinate F_n of F, times the area of S, and so is equal to $(F \cdot \mathbf{n})\sigma(S)$.

We can summarize what has just been done by pointing out that we have defined a multiplication, called the **exterior product** of basic 1-forms dx_1, dx_2, etc. The resulting products written $dx_i \wedge dx_j$ are *basic* 2-forms in that

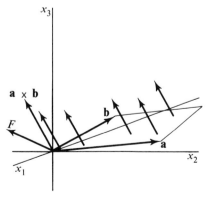

Figure 33

every 2-form is a linear combination of them. In $\mathscr{R}^2$ there is only one basic 2-form, $dx_1 \wedge dx_2$, while in $\mathscr{R}^3$ there are three of them. (How many in $\mathscr{R}^1$?) From here we can proceed to define the exterior product of any two 1-forms to be the 2-form got by multiplying the 1-forms as if they were polynomials in the variables dx_1, dx_2, etc., and then using the rules 7.1 and 7.2 to simplify. In practice, the wedges are often omitted from the notation.

EXAMPLE 4. To save writing subscripts, we shall denote basic 1-forms by dx, dy, dz, even though the latter notation is less convenient for formulating the general definition. We have

$$(x\,dx + y^2\,dy) \wedge (dx + x\,dy)$$
$$= x\,dx \wedge dx + y^2\,dy \wedge dx + x^2\,dx \wedge dy + xy^2\,dy \wedge dy$$
$$= 0 - y^2\,dx \wedge dy + x^2\,dx \wedge dy + 0$$
$$= (x^2 - y^2)\,dx \wedge dy.$$

In three variables we have the example

$$(dx + dy + dz) \wedge (x\,dx + z\,dy)$$
$$= x\,dx \wedge dx + x\,dy \wedge dx + x\,dz \wedge dx$$
$$+ z\,dx \wedge dy + z\,dy \wedge dy + z\,dz \wedge dy$$
$$= -z\,dy \wedge dz + x\,dz \wedge dx + (z - x)\,dx \wedge dy.$$

Three-forms arise in attempting to define the product of a 2-form and a 1-form. The meaning of the basic 3-form $dx_1 \wedge dx_2 \wedge dx_3$ is that of a signed volume function. Thus if $\mathbf{a} = (a_1, a_2, a_3)$, $\mathbf{b} = (b_1, b_2, b_3)$, and $\mathbf{c} = (c_1, c_2, c_3)$, we define

$$dx_1 \wedge dx_2 \wedge dx_3(\mathbf{a}, \mathbf{b}, \mathbf{c}) = \det \begin{pmatrix} a_1 & b_1 & c_1 \\ a_2 & b_2 & c_2 \\ a_3 & b_3 & c_3 \end{pmatrix},$$

which is the 3-dimensional oriented volume of the parallelepiped spanned by the vectors $\mathbf{a}$, $\mathbf{b}$, and $\mathbf{c}$. Higher dimensional forms are defined in Exercise 11.

A differential form of unspecified dimension will be called a p-form and denoted ω^p, σ^p, etc. As we did with the 1-form, we shall define the integral of a p-form in $\mathscr{R}^n$ over the image S of a set in $\mathscr{R}^p$ under a continuously differentiable function g. To simplify the discussion, we suppose that $\mathscr{R}^p \xrightarrow{g} \mathscr{R}^n$ is differentiable on a closed bounded rectangle R in $\mathscr{R}^p$. If ω^p is a p-form with coefficient functions defined on the image $S = \partial R$ in $\mathscr{R}^n$, we can apply ω^p at a point $g(\mathbf{u})$ to the derived vectors $(\partial g/\partial u_k)(\mathbf{u})$ for $k = 1, \ldots, p$. The result looks like

$$\omega^p_{g(\mathbf{u})}\left(\frac{\partial g}{\partial u_1}(\mathbf{u}), \ldots, \frac{\partial g}{\partial u_p}(\mathbf{u})\right). \tag{4}$$

Furthermore, if G is a grid over R with corner points $\mathbf{u}_1, \ldots, \mathbf{u}_N$, and rectangles $R_1, \ldots, R_N$, we can form the sum

$$\sum_{k=1}^{N} \omega_{g(\mathbf{u}_k)}^p \left(\frac{\partial g}{\partial u_1}(\mathbf{u}_k), \ldots, \frac{\partial g}{\partial u_p}(\mathbf{u}_k) \right) V(R_k),$$

where $V(R_k)$ is the p-dimensional volume of R_k. We define the integral of ω^p over S by

$$\int_S \omega^p = \lim_{m(G) \to 0} \sum_{k=1}^{N} \omega_{g(\mathbf{u}_k)}^p \left(\frac{\partial g}{\partial u_1}(\mathbf{u}_k), \ldots, \frac{\partial g}{\partial u_p}(\mathbf{u}_k) \right) V(R_k),$$

provided the limit exists in the Riemann sum sense. If g is continuously differentiable, and ω^p has continuous coefficient functions, then the function of $\mathbf{u}$ given by Formula (4) will be continuous on R, and $\int_S \omega^p$ will exist and be equal to the Riemann integral of that function. Thus

$$\int_S \omega^p = \int_R \omega_g^p \left(\frac{\partial g}{\partial u_1}, \ldots, \frac{\partial g}{\partial u_p} \right) dV.$$

EXAMPLE 5. If

$$\omega_\mathbf{x}^2 = F_1(\mathbf{x})\, dx_2 \wedge dx_3 + F_2(\mathbf{x})\, dx_3 \wedge dx_1 + F_3(\mathbf{x})\, dx_1 \wedge dx_2$$

has continuous coefficients in $\mathscr{R}^3$, and $\mathscr{R}^2 \xrightarrow{g} \mathscr{R}^3$ is continuously differentiable on R, with coefficient functions g_1, g_2, g_3, then

$$\omega_g^2 \left(\frac{\partial g}{\partial u_1}, \frac{\partial g}{\partial u_2} \right) = F_1 \circ g\, \frac{\partial(g_2, g_3)}{\partial(u_1, u_2)} + F_2 \circ g\, \frac{\partial(g_3, g_1)}{\partial(u_1, u_2)} + F_3 \circ g\, \frac{\partial(g_1, g_2)}{\partial(u_1, u_2)}.$$

Hence, in this case,

$$\int_S \omega^p = \int_S F_1\, dx_2 \wedge dx_3 + F_2\, dx_3 \wedge dx_1 + F_3\, dx_1 \wedge dx_2$$

$$= \int_R \left[F_1 \circ g\, \frac{\partial(g_2, g_3)}{\partial(u_1, u_2)} + F_2 \circ g\, \frac{\partial(g_3, g_1)}{\partial(u_1, u_2)} + F_3 \circ g\, \frac{\partial(g_1, g_2)}{\partial(u_1, u_2)} \right] du_1\, du_2.$$

Except for smoothness conditions on S, assumed here for convenience, this is the same as the definition of the surface integral given in Section 3.

EXERCISES

1. Find the value of each of the following differential forms acting on the indicated vector or ordered set of vectors.

   (a) $dx_1 + 2dx_2$; $(1, 1)$.
   (b) $3dx - dy + dz$; $(1, -1, 0)$.
   (c) $dx_2 + dx_3$; $(1, 3, -5)$.
   (d) $dx_1 + 2dx_2 + \ldots + n\, dx_n$; $(1, -1, 1, -1, \ldots)$.
   (e) $2dx_1 \wedge dx_2$; $((1, 1), (1, -1))$.
   (f) $dy \wedge dy + 2dx \wedge dz$; $((1, 2, 1), (-1, 2, 3))$.
   (g) $dx \wedge dy \wedge dz$; $((1, 1, 1), (1, 2, 1), (2, 1, 2))$.
   (h) $dx_1 \wedge dx_2$; $((-2, -3, 0), (2, 0, 2))$.

2. Multiply out and simplify the following products.

(a) $(dx_1 + dx_2) \wedge (dx_1 - dx_2)$.

(b) $(2dx + 3dy - 2dz) \wedge dx$.

(c) $(dx + dy) \wedge (dx + dy)$.

(d) $(x^2 dx + z^2 dz) \wedge (dx - 2dy)$.

(e) $(\sin z\, dx + \cos x\, dy) \wedge (dx + dz)$.

3. Compute $\int_\gamma y\, dx + x\, dy$, where γ is given by $g(t) = (\cos t, \sin t)$, $0 \le t \le \pi/2$.

4. Compute $\int_\gamma x_1\, dx_1 + x_2\, dx_2 + x_3\, dx_3$, where γ is given by

(a) $g(t) = (-t, t^2, t)$ for $-1 \le t \le 1$,

(b) $h(t) = (t, t, t)$ for $0 \le t \le 1$,

(c) $k(t) = (t^2, t^2, t^2)$ for $-1 \le t \le 1$.

5. Compute $\int_\gamma \omega$ where $\omega = x_1\, dx_1 + x_2^2\, dx_2 + \ldots + x_n^n\, dx_n$ and γ is given by $g(t) = (t, t, t, \ldots)$ for $0 \le t \le 1$.

6. Let ω and $\bar{\omega}$ be 1-forms defined in a region D of $\mathscr{R}^n$ and let f and g be real-valued functions defined in D.

(a) Show that $f\omega + g\bar{\omega}$ defines a 1-form in D.

(b) Show that if ω, ν, and μ are 1-forms in D, then

$$(f\omega + g\nu) \wedge \mu = f\omega \wedge \mu + g\nu \wedge \mu.$$

7. Prove that if ω and $\bar{\omega}$ are 1-forms and if γ_1 and γ_2 are curves over which ω and $\bar{\omega}$ are integrable, then

$$\int_{\gamma_1} (a\omega + b\bar{\omega}) = a\int_{\gamma_1} \omega + b\int_{\gamma_1} \bar{\omega},$$

where a and b are constant and

$$\int_{\gamma_1 \cup \gamma_2} \omega = \int_{\gamma_1} \omega + \int_{\gamma_2} \omega.$$

8. Let f be a continuously differentiable real-valued function defined on a region D of $\mathscr{R}^n$, and let γ be a continuously differentiable curve lying in D with parametrization $\mathscr{R} \xrightarrow{g} \mathscr{R}^n$, for $a \le t \le b$. Show that if $g(a) = \mathbf{a}$ and $g(b) = \mathbf{b}$, then

$$\int_\gamma d_\mathbf{x} f = f(\mathbf{b}) - f(\mathbf{a}).$$

9. (a) Prove that if $\omega_\mathbf{x}$ is a 1-form in a region D of $\mathscr{R}^n$, then for each fixed $\mathbf{x}_0$ in D, $\omega_{\mathbf{x}_0}$ is a real-valued linear function on all of $\mathscr{R}^n$.

(b) Prove the converse to part (a), namely, that if $\omega_{\mathbf{x}_0}$ is a real-valued linear function defined on all of $\mathscr{R}^n$, then $\omega_{\mathbf{x}_0}(\mathbf{a}) = \sum_{k=1}^{n} c_k(\mathbf{x}_0)\, dx_k(\mathbf{a})$, for all $\mathbf{a}$ in $\mathscr{R}^n$, where the $c_k(\mathbf{x}_0)$ are real numbers.

10. (a) Let τ be a real-valued function of pairs $(\mathbf{a}, \mathbf{b})$ of vectors in $\mathscr{R}^3$ such that $\tau(\mathbf{a}, \mathbf{b}) = -\tau(\mathbf{b}, \mathbf{a})$ and such that τ is linear in $\mathbf{a}$ and in $\mathbf{b}$. Show that there is a vector $\mathbf{c}_\tau$ in $\mathscr{R}^3$ such that $\tau(\mathbf{a}, \mathbf{b}) = \det(\mathbf{a}, \mathbf{b}, \mathbf{c}_\tau)$ for all $\mathbf{a}, \mathbf{b}$ in $\mathscr{R}^3$. [*Hint.* Show first that the result holds if $\mathbf{a}$ and $\mathbf{b}$ are in a basis for $\mathscr{R}^3$.]

(b) Use part (a) to show that if $\tau(\mathbf{a}, \mathbf{b}) = -\tau(\mathbf{b}, \mathbf{a})$, and τ is bilinear, then τ is a 2-form in $\mathscr{R}^3$.

11. For an ordered p-tuple $(\mathbf{a}_1, \mathbf{a}_2, \ldots, \mathbf{a}_p)$ of vectors in $\mathscr{R}^n$ where $p \geq 1$, define

$$dx_{k_1} \wedge dx_{k_2} \wedge \ldots dx_{k_p}(\mathbf{a}_1, \ldots, \mathbf{a}_p) = \det(dx_{k_i}(\mathbf{a}_j))_{\substack{i=1,\ldots,p \\ j=1,\ldots,p}}$$

This equation defines the basic p-forms in $\mathscr{R}^n$, of which the general p-forms are linear combinations.

(a) Compute $dx_2 \wedge dx_3 \wedge dx_4 + 2\,dx_1 \wedge dx_2 \wedge dx_4$ $((1, -1, 0, 2),$ $(-1, 1, 1, 1), (0, 1, 2, 0))$.

(b) Prove that the interchange of adjacent factors in a basic p-form changes the sign of the form.

(c) Prove that a basic p-form with a repeated factor is zero.

(d) Prove that the general p-form can be written

$$\omega^p = \sum_{i_1 < \ldots < i_p} f_{i_1, \ldots, i_p}\, dx_{i_1} \wedge \ldots \wedge dx_{i_p},$$

where $1 \leq i_k \leq n$ for $k = 1, \ldots, p$.

(e) Prove that if $p > n$, ω^p is identically zero.

(f) Prove that there are $\binom{n}{p}$ terms in the p-form of part (d).

12. If ω^p and ω^q are p- and q-forms in $\mathscr{R}^n$ with

$$\omega^p = \sum_{i_1 < \ldots < i_p} f_{i_1, \ldots, i_p}\, dx_{i_1} \wedge \ldots \wedge dx_{i_p}$$

and

$$\omega^q = \sum_{j_1 < \ldots < j_q} g_{j_1, \ldots, j_q}\, dx_{j_1} \wedge \ldots \wedge dx_{j_q},$$

define their exterior product $\omega^p \wedge \omega^q$ by

$$\omega^p \wedge \omega^q = \sum f_{i_1 \ldots i_p} g_{j_1 \ldots j_q}\, dx_{i_1} \wedge \ldots \wedge dx_{i_p} \wedge dx_{j_1} \wedge \ldots \wedge dx_{j_q}.$$

(a) Prove that if $\omega^p \wedge \omega^q$ is reduced to standard form by using Equations 7.1 and 7.2, then it has $\binom{n}{p+q}$ terms.

(b) Prove that $\omega^p \wedge \omega^q = (-1)^{pq}\,\omega^q \wedge \omega^p$.

13. Show that the definition of the integral of a p-form agrees with that given for a 1-form when $p = 1$.

14. Compute $\int_S \omega^2$ if $\omega^2 = dx \wedge dy + dx \wedge dz$, and S is the image of $0 \leq u \leq 1$, $0 \leq v \leq \pi/2$ under $g(u, v) = (u \cos v, u \sin v, v)$.

15. (a) If ω^3 is the 3-form $f\,dx_1 \wedge dx_2 \wedge dx_3$ in $\mathscr{R}^3$, and $\mathscr{R}^3 \overset{g}{\longrightarrow} \mathscr{R}^3$ is differentiable, show that

$$\omega_g^3\left(\frac{\partial g}{\partial u_1}, \frac{\partial g}{\partial u_2}, \frac{\partial g}{\partial u_3}\right) = f \circ g\, \frac{\partial(g_1, g_2, g_3)}{\partial(u_1, u_2, u_3)}.$$

(b) Compute the integral $\int_S dx \wedge dy \wedge dz$, where S is the image of $0 \leq u \leq 1$, $0 \leq v \leq 1$, $0 \leq w \leq 1$ under $g(u, v, w) = (u^2, v^2, w^2)$.

8. THE EXTERIOR DERIVATIVE

The fundamental theorem of calculus states that if $(d/dx)f$ is continuous on $[a, b]$, then

$$\int_a^b \frac{df}{dx}\, dx = f(b) - f(a). \tag{1}$$

The Stokes and Gauss formulas,

$$\int_S \operatorname{curl} F \cdot dS = \int_{\partial S} F \cdot \mathbf{t}\, ds, \tag{2}$$

$$\int_R \operatorname{div} F\, dV = \int_{\partial R} F \cdot \mathbf{n}\, d\sigma, \tag{3}$$

are similar in that they express the integral of a kind of derivative of a function in terms of the function itself on a set of lower dimension. Using differential forms, we shall define exterior differentiation, which unifies the above formulas.

The operation of **exterior differentiation** is defined inductively on differential forms as follows: Let f be a real-valued differentiable function on $\mathcal{R}^n$. Then, by definition,

$$df = \frac{\partial f}{\partial x_1}\, dx_1 + \ldots + \frac{\partial f}{\partial x_n}\, dx_n.$$

Thus the exterior derivative of f is the particular 1-form that at each point of the domain of f is equal to what we have earlier called the differential of f. To continue, if

$$\omega^1 = f_1\, dx_1 + \ldots + f_n\, dx_n$$

is a 1-form with differentiable coefficients, then in terms of the 1-forms $df_1, \ldots, df_n$, we define

$$d\omega^1 = (df_1) \wedge dx_1 + \ldots + (df_n) \wedge dx_n.$$

Thus $d\omega^1$ is a 2-form. In general, if ω^p is a p-form, then $d\omega^p$ is the $(p + 1)$-form got by replacing each coefficient function of ω^p by the 1-form that is its exterior derivative. To keep the terminology consistent, we may refer to a real-valued function as a 0-form.

EXAMPLE 1. If $f(x_1, x_2) = x_1^2 + x_2^3$, then df is given by

$$d(x_1^2 + x_2^3) = 2x_1\, dx_1 + 3x_2^2\, dx_2.$$

If $\omega^1_{(x_1, x_2)} = x_1 x_2\, dx_1 + (x_1^2 + x_2^2)\, dx_2$, then $d\omega^1$ is given by

$$d(x_1 x_2\, dx_1 + (x_1^2 + x_2^2)\, dx_2)$$
$$= (x_2\, dx_1 + x_1\, dx_2) \wedge dx_1 + (2x_1\, dx_1 + 2x_2\, dx_2) \wedge dx_2$$
$$= x_1\, dx_1 \wedge dx_2$$

If $\omega^2_{(x,y,z)} = xz\, dx \wedge dy + y^2z\, dx \wedge dz$, then $d\omega^2$ is given by

$$d(xz\, dx \wedge dy + y^2z\, dx \wedge dz)$$
$$= (z\, dx + x\, dz) \wedge dx \wedge dy + (2yz\, dy + y^2\, dz) \wedge dx \wedge dz$$
$$= (x - 2yz)\, dx \wedge dy \wedge dz.$$

Using the exterior derivative we can state the general Stokes formula in the form

8.1
$$\int_B d\omega^p = \int_{\partial B} \omega^p,$$

where B is $(p + 1)$-dimensional and ∂B is its p-dimensional boundary. We shall interpret the formula in several specific cases.

If ω^1 is a 1-form in $\mathscr{R}^2$, then we can write ω in the form

$$\omega^1 = F_1\, dx_1 + F_2\, dx_2,$$

and then

$$d\omega^1 = \left(\frac{\partial F_1}{\partial x_1}\, dx_1 + \frac{\partial F_1}{\partial x_2}\, dx_2\right) \wedge dx_1 + \left(\frac{\partial F_2}{\partial x_1}\, dx_1 + \frac{\partial F_2}{\partial x_2}\, dx_2\right) \wedge dx_2$$
$$= \left(\frac{\partial F_2}{\partial x_1} - \frac{\partial F_1}{\partial x_2}\right) dx_1 \wedge dx_2. \tag{4}$$

Substitution of $d\omega^1$ and ω^1 into Equation 8.1 gives

$$\int_B \left(\frac{\partial F_2}{\partial x_1} - \frac{\partial F_1}{\partial x_2}\right) dx_1 \wedge dx_2 = \int_{\partial B} F_1\, dx_1 + F_2\, dx_2. \tag{5}$$

This is almost Green's formula of Section 1, if B is a suitable set in $\mathscr{R}^2$, and ∂B stands for its counterclockwise-oriented boundary curve. However, the left-hand integral in Equation 5 has been defined as an integral over a parametrized set in the previous section, whereas the corresponding integral of Green's formula,

$$\int_D \left(\frac{\partial F_2}{\partial x_1} - \frac{\partial F_2}{\partial x_2}\right) dx_1\, dx_2 = \oint_\gamma F_1\, dx_1 + F_2\, dx_2,$$

is an integral over a set without a parametrization. The difference between the two is such that the parametrized set B may be covered more than once by its parametrization, while the integral over the set D covers each part of the set only once. See Exercise 9.

If ω^1 is a 1-form in $\mathscr{R}^3$ given by

$$\omega^1 = F_1\, dx_1 + F_2\, dx_2 + F_3\, dx_3,$$

then a straightforward calculation like that in Equation 4 yields

$$d\omega^1 = \left(\frac{\partial F_3}{\partial x_2} - \frac{\partial F_2}{\partial x_3}\right) dx_2 \wedge dx_3$$
$$+ \left(\frac{\partial F_1}{\partial x_3} - \frac{\partial F_3}{\partial x_1}\right) dx_3 \wedge dx_1 + \left(\frac{\partial F_2}{\partial x_1} - \frac{\partial F_1}{\partial x_2}\right) dx_1 \wedge dx_2. \tag{6}$$

Thus the 2-form $d\omega^1$ has as coefficient functions the coordinates of the vector field curl F where $F = (F_1, F_2, F_3)$. It is immediate that the general Stokes formula becomes precisely the Stokes formula of Section 4 if we make B and ∂B stand for a piece of smooth surface S and its positively oriented border ∂S.

The Gauss formula of Section 5 comes from considering a 2-form

$$\omega^2 = F_1 \, dx_2 \wedge dx_3 + F_2 \, dx_3 \wedge dx_1 + F_3 \, dx_1 \wedge dx_2.$$

A short computation shows that

$$d\omega^2 = \left(\frac{\partial F_1}{\partial x_1} + \frac{\partial F_2}{\partial x_2} + \frac{\partial F_3}{\partial x_3} \right) dx_1 \wedge dx_2 \wedge dx_3. \tag{7}$$

This 3-form has as coefficient the divergence of the field $F = (F_1, F_2, F_3)$, and substitution into the general Stokes formula gives the Gauss, or divergence, formula of Section 5, except that, as with Green's formula, the volume integral of Gauss's formula is not identical with the integral of a 3-form. See Exercise 10.

The correspondence between a vector field $F = (F_1, F_2, F_3)$ in $\mathscr{R}^3$, and a differential form with coefficient functions F_1, F_2, F_3, has been described in Equations (6) and (7), and can be summarized as follows:

$$\text{if} \quad \omega^2 \longleftrightarrow F, \quad \text{then} \quad d\omega^2 \longleftrightarrow \text{div } F,$$

$$\text{if} \quad \omega^1 \longleftrightarrow F, \quad \text{then} \quad d\omega^1 \longleftrightarrow \text{curl } F.$$

Finally, if $\omega^0 \longleftrightarrow f$, then $d\omega^0 \longleftrightarrow \text{grad } f$, where f is real-valued.

EXERCISES

1. Compute $d\omega$, where ω is
   (a) $(x_1^2 + x_2^2) \, dx_1 - x_2 \, dx_2$
   (b) $\sin x_1 \, dx_3$
   (c) $x_1 \, dx_1 \wedge dx_2 + x_2 \, dx_2 \wedge dx_3$
   (d) $yz \, dx + zx \, dy + xy \, dz$
   (e) $x_1 \, dx_1 \wedge dx_2 \wedge dx_3$.

2. (a) If $\mathscr{R}^2 \xrightarrow{f_1} \mathscr{R}$ and $\mathscr{R}^2 \xrightarrow{f_2} \mathscr{R}$ are differentiable functions with the same domain, show that

$$df_1 \wedge df_2 = \frac{\partial(f_1, f_2)}{\partial(x_1, x_2)} \, dx_1 \wedge dx_2.$$

   (b) Generalize part (a) to the case of three functions from $\mathscr{R}^3$ to $\mathscr{R}$.

3. Show that if ω^p and ω^q are p- and q-forms respectively, with differentiable coefficients, then

$$d(\omega^p \wedge \omega^q) = d\omega^p \wedge \omega^q + (-1)^p \omega^p \wedge (d\omega^q),$$

   (a) for ω^p and ω^q defined in $\mathscr{R}^2$.
   (b) for ω^p and ω^q defined in $\mathscr{R}^n$.

4. If ω^0 is a 0-form in $\mathscr{R}^n$ with coefficients that are twice continuously differentiable, show that $d(d\omega^0) = 0$.

5. (a) Let ω^1 be a 1-form in $\mathscr{R}^3$ with twice continuously differentiable coefficients. Show that $d(d\omega^1) = 0$.

    (b) Use the correspondence between a vector field $F = (F_1, F_2, F_3)$ and the 1-form with coefficients F_1, F_2, F_3, to show that the result of part (a) is equivalent to the relation div (curl F) = 0.

    (c) Show that $d(d\omega^0) = 0$ is equivalent to curl (grad f) = 0.

6. (a) Find an example of a 1-form ω^1 such that there is no 0-form ω^0 for which $d\omega^0 = \omega^1$.

    (b) Show similarly that if ω^2 is a 2-form, there may not exist a 1-form ω^1 such that $d\omega^1 = \omega^2$.

    (c) Interpret parts (a) and (b) in terms of gradient and curl.

7. Prove that if ω^p is a p-form with twice continuously differentiable coefficients, then $d(d\omega^p) = 0$.

8. (a) Let $F = (F_1, \ldots, F_n)$ be a vector field in $\mathscr{R}^n$, and consider the 1-form $\omega^1 = F_1 \, dx_1 + \ldots + F_n \, dx_n$. Show that the condition $d\omega^1 = 0$ is equivalent to the requirement that the Jacobian matrix F' be symmetric.

    (b) Show that if ω^1 is a 1-form with continuously differentiable coefficients in a rectangle R in $\mathscr{R}^n$, then $d\omega^1 = 0$ in R implies that there is a function $\mathscr{R}^n \xrightarrow{f} \mathscr{R}$ such that $df = \omega^1$. [*Hint.* Use Theorem 2.6.]

9. In the general Stokes formula, Equation 8.1, let B be a disk in $\mathscr{R}^2$ parametrized by $(x_1, x_2) = (u \cos v, \ u \sin v)$, $0 \le u \le 1$, $0 \le v \le 4\pi$. Notice that the disk is covered twice by this parametrization. What is the correct parametrization of ∂B to make 8.1 hold for this example? Take ω^p to be a 1-form with continuously differentiable coefficients.

10. In the general Stokes formula, Equation 8.1, let ω^p be a 2-form with continuously differentiable coefficients in the ball $|\mathbf{x}| \le 1$ of $\mathscr{R}^3$. Show that it is possible to parametrize the ball B in such a way that the corresponding parametrization of ∂B has an inward pointing normal. Explain the apparent contradiction to the requirement in the Gauss theorem of Section 5 that ∂B have an outward-pointing normal.

APPENDIX

1. INTRODUCTION

The fundamental theorems of analysis are derived from the algebraic properties and also from the limit properties of $\mathscr{R}^n$. In this book we have taken as assumptions two basic limit properties. The first and more fundamental concerns the notion of *supremum* and *infimum*. The *supremum* and *infimum* of a set S of real numbers are often called its *least upper bound* and its *greatest lower bound* respectively. These latter terms suggest that the *supremum* is the smallest number greater than or equal to all numbers in S, and that the *infimum* is the largest number less than or equal to all numbers in S. A more formal definition follows.

The **supremum** of a set S of real numbers is a number s with the properties (a) if x is in S, then $x \leq s$; (b) if y is a number such that $x \leq y$ for all x in S, then $s \leq y$. The definition of the **infimum** of S is obtained by reversing the inequalities in the above two conditions. For many sets, the supremum is the same as the maximum element and the infimum is the same as the minimum element. On the other hand, the open interval $0 < x < 1$ has infimum and supremum equal 0 and 1, respectively, but the interval has neither a minimum nor maximum element. It can be proved from the definition of the real numbers that *every bounded subset of the real numbers has an infimum and a supremum.*

The second limit property is itself a consequence of the first. *If the function $\mathscr{R}^n \xrightarrow{f} \mathscr{R}$ is continuous and K is a closed bounded subset of the domain of f, then there exists a point $\mathbf{x}_0$ in K such that*

$$f(\mathbf{x}) \leq f(\mathbf{x}_0), \qquad \text{for all } \mathbf{x} \text{ in } K.$$

This theorem is frequently paraphrased by saying that a continuous function on a closed bounded set attains its maximum. The two functions f and g defined by

$$f(x) = \frac{1}{x}, \qquad\qquad 0 < x \leq 1,$$

$$g(x) = \begin{cases} 1, & 0 \leq x \leq 1, \\ \dfrac{1}{x-1}, & 1 < x \leq 2, \end{cases}$$

illustrate the necessity of the two hypotheses of the theorem. Neither of these functions attains a maximum value on its domain. The trouble is that although f is continuous, its domain is not closed. On the other hand, the domain of g is closed and bounded, but g is not continuous.

Replacement of f by $-f$ shows that *a continuous function on a closed bounded set attains its minimum.*

Our application of the next theorem will be restricted to real-valued functions, but the proof is no different for vector-valued functions.

1.1 **Theorem.** If f is a continuous function defined on a closed bounded set C, then f is uniformly continuous on C. That is, given any $\epsilon > 0$, there is a $\delta > 0$ such that whenever $|\mathbf{x} - \mathbf{y}| < \delta$, then $|f(\mathbf{x}) - f(\mathbf{y})| < \epsilon$.

Proof. Let $\epsilon > 0$ be given. For each $\mathbf{x}$ in C, let $\Delta_\epsilon(\mathbf{x})$ be the set of real numbers d, $0 < d \leq 1$, such that for $\mathbf{y}$ and $\mathbf{z}$ in C, $|f(\mathbf{y}) - f(\mathbf{z})| < \epsilon$ whenever $|\mathbf{y} - \mathbf{x}| < d$ and $|\mathbf{z} - \mathbf{x}| < d$. Since

$$|f(\mathbf{y}) - f(\mathbf{z})| \leq |f(\mathbf{y}) - f(\mathbf{x})| + |f(\mathbf{x}) - f(\mathbf{z})|,$$

the continuity of f at $\mathbf{x}$ implies that $\Delta_\epsilon(\mathbf{x})$ is not empty. Define

$$\delta_\epsilon(\mathbf{x}) = \textit{supremum of } \Delta_\epsilon(\mathbf{x}).$$

We shall first prove that δ_ϵ is a continuous function of $\mathbf{x}$ on C. Fix $\mathbf{x}$ and let $\mathbf{x}'$ be such that $|\mathbf{x} - \mathbf{x}'| < \frac{1}{2}\delta_\epsilon(\mathbf{x})$. Then the ball of radius $\delta_0 = \delta_\epsilon(\mathbf{x}) - |\mathbf{x} - \mathbf{x}'|$ about $\mathbf{x}'$ is contained in the ball of radius $\delta_\epsilon(\mathbf{x})$ about $\mathbf{x}$. This implies, by the definition of δ_ϵ, that $\delta_0 \leq \delta_\epsilon(\mathbf{x}')$, or that

$$\delta_\epsilon(\mathbf{x}) - \delta_\epsilon(\mathbf{x}') \leq |\mathbf{x} - \mathbf{x}'|.$$

Notice that the last inequality depends only on having $|\mathbf{x} - \mathbf{x}'| < \delta_\epsilon(\mathbf{x})$.

However, by the stronger inequality $|\mathbf{x} - \mathbf{x}'| < \frac{1}{2}\delta_\epsilon(\mathbf{x})$, the ball of radius $\delta_\epsilon(\mathbf{x}')$ about $\mathbf{x}'$ contains $\mathbf{x}$. Therefore the role of $\mathbf{x}$ can be interchanged with that of $\mathbf{x}'$ to give

$$\delta_\epsilon(\mathbf{x}') - \delta_\epsilon(\mathbf{x}) \leq |\mathbf{x} - \mathbf{x}'|.$$

Putting this together with the previously obtained inequality, we get

$$|\delta_\epsilon(\mathbf{x}) - \delta_\epsilon(\mathbf{x}')| \leq |\mathbf{x} - \mathbf{x}'|,$$

from which follows the continuity of δ_ϵ at $\mathbf{x}$.

Let δ be the minimum value of the continuous function δ_ϵ on the closed bounded set C. Since δ_ϵ is positive, δ is also positive. It follows from the definitions of $\Delta_\epsilon(\mathbf{x})$ and of *supremum* that, for each $\mathbf{x}$ in C, the number $\delta_\epsilon(\mathbf{x})$ is a member of the set $\Delta_\epsilon(\mathbf{x})$. Finally, therefore, suppose that $|\mathbf{x} - \mathbf{y}| < \delta$. Then

$$|\mathbf{x} - \mathbf{y}| < \delta \leq \delta_\epsilon(\mathbf{x}),$$

and so

$$|f(\mathbf{x}) - f(\mathbf{y})| < \epsilon.$$

This completes the proof.

2. EQUIVALENCE OF NORMS

Basic to calculus are the **limit definitions**: limit point, limit, continuity, interior point, open set, boundary, closed set, and differentiability. Each of these has been given directly or indirectly in terms of the euclidean norm on $\mathscr{R}^n$, with respect to which the distance between two points $\mathbf{x} = (x_1, \ldots, x_n)$ and $\mathbf{y} = (y_1, \ldots, y_n)$ is the number

$$|\mathbf{x} - \mathbf{y}| = [(x_1 - y_1)^2 + \ldots + (x_n - y_n)^2]^{1/2}.$$

The same definitions can be made in an arbitrary vector space provided a norm is given. We recall that a norm on $\mathscr{V}$ is a real-valued function $\|\ \ \|$ with domain equal to $\mathscr{V}$ and with the three properties

2.1 Positivity: $\|\mathbf{x}\| > 0$, except that $\|0\| = 0$.

2.2 Homogeneity: $\|a\mathbf{x}\| = |a|\|\mathbf{x}\|$.

2.3 Triangle inequality: $\|\mathbf{x} + \mathbf{y}\| \leq \|\mathbf{x}\| + \|\mathbf{y}\|$.

The purpose of this section is to prove that in a finite-dimensional vector space the limit definitions are independent of the choice of norm. That is, if $\mathbf{x}_0$ is a limit point of a set S with respect to one norm, then it is a limit point of S with respect to every norm, and the same goes for the other definitions referred to above. It follows, in particular, that these basic limit concepts are in no way dependent upon a euclidean inner product.

An example of a norm on $\mathscr{R}^n$ different from the euclidean norm is the so-called **box norm** defined, for any $\mathbf{x} = (x_1, \ldots, x_n)$, by

$$\| \mathbf{x} \| = \max \{ | x_1 |, \ldots, | x_n | \}.$$

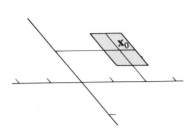

Figure 1

If $\mathbf{x}_0 = (2, 1)$, the set of all $\mathbf{x}$ in $\mathscr{R}^2$ such that $|| \mathbf{x} - \mathbf{x}_0 || < 0.5$ is the parallelogram shown in Figure 1. We have purposely drawn nonperpendicular coordinate axes with different scale to emphasize the fact that this norm is not euclidean.

For any two norms $\| \ \|_1$ and $\| \ \|_2$ on a vector space $\mathscr{V}$, we define $\| \ \|_1$ to be **equivalent** to $\| \ \|_2$ if there exist positive real numbers k and K such that, for any $\mathbf{x}$ in $\mathscr{V}$.

$$k \| \mathbf{x} \|_1 \leq \| \mathbf{x} \|_2 \leq K \| \mathbf{x} \|_1. \tag{1}$$

It is easy to check that this is a true equivalence relation, that is, it satisfies the three requirements

Reflexivity: Every norm is equivalent to itself.

Symmetry: $\| \ \|_1$ is equivalent to $\| \ \|_2$ if and only if $\| \ \|_2$ is equivalent to $\| \ \|_1$.

Transitivity: If $\| \ \|_1$ is equivalent to $\| \ \|_2$ and if $\| \ \|_2$ is equivalent to $\| \ \|_3$, then $\| \ \|_1$ is equivalent to $\| \ \|_3$.

More important is the fact that equivalent norms result in the same definitions of limit point, limit, interior point, and differentiability. Continuity, open set, boundary, and closed set, which are defined in terms of the preceding concepts, are therefore also independent of a choice between equivalent norms.

To verify the above contention, let $\| \ \|_1$, and $\| \ \|_2$ be equivalent norms, and suppose that $\mathbf{x}_0$ is a limit point of S with respect to $\| \ \|_1$. Then, for any $\epsilon_1 > 0$, there exists a point $\mathbf{x}$ in S such that $0 < \| \mathbf{x} - \mathbf{x}_0 \|_1 < \epsilon_1$. Thus, if $\epsilon_2 > 0$ is given arbitrarily, we may set $\epsilon_1 = \epsilon_2/K$ and obtain, by inequality (1),

$$0 < \| \mathbf{x} - \mathbf{x}_0 \|_2 \leq K \| \mathbf{x} - \mathbf{x}_0 \|_1 < K\epsilon_1 = \epsilon_2.$$

Hence, $\mathbf{x}_0$ is a limit point of S with respect to $\| \ \|_2$. Suppose, next, that with respect to $\| \ \|_1$ we have

$$\lim_{\mathbf{x} \to \mathbf{x}_0} f(\mathbf{x}) = \mathbf{y}_0.$$

Then, as we have just proved, $\mathbf{x}_0$ is a limit point of the domain of f with respect to both norms. For any $\epsilon_1 > 0$, there exists $\delta_1 > 0$ such that if $\mathbf{x}$ is in the domain of f and $0 < \| \mathbf{x} - \mathbf{x}_0 \|_1 < \delta_1$, then $\| f(\mathbf{x}) - \mathbf{y}_0 \|_1 < \epsilon_1$. Let

$\epsilon_2 > 0$ be given arbitrarily, set $\epsilon_1 = \epsilon_2/K$, and then choose $\delta_2 = \delta_1 k$. If $0 < \|\mathbf{x} - \mathbf{x}_0\|_2 < \delta_2$, it follows by inequality (1) that

$$0 < \|\mathbf{x} - \mathbf{x}_0\|_1 \le \frac{1}{k}\|\mathbf{x} - \mathbf{x}_0\|_2 < \frac{\delta_2}{k} = \delta_1.$$

Hence,

$$\|f(\mathbf{x}) - \mathbf{y}_0\|_2 \le K\|f(\mathbf{x}) - \mathbf{y}_0\|_1 < K\epsilon_1 = \epsilon_2,$$

and we conclude that $\lim f(\mathbf{x}) = \mathbf{y}_0$ with respect to $\|\ \ \|_2$. The arguments for the definitions of interior point and differentiability are similar, and we omit the details.

With respect to a given norm on a vector space $\mathscr{V}$, the ϵ-**ball with center** $\mathbf{x}_0$ is the set of all $\mathbf{x}$ in $\mathscr{V}$ such that $\|\mathbf{x} - \mathbf{x}_0\| < \epsilon$. In general, an ϵ-ball doesn't look very ball-like. For example, with respect to the box norm on $\mathscr{R}^2$, every ϵ-ball is a parallelogram (see Figure 1). It follows directly from the inequalities (1) that two norms are equivalent if and only if any ϵ-ball about $\mathbf{x}_0$ with respect to one norm is contained in some δ-ball about $\mathbf{x}_0$ with respect to the other norm, and vice versa (see Figure 2). We now turn to the principal theorem:

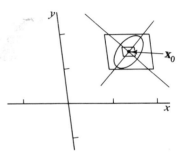

Figure 2

2.4 Theorem. Any two norms on a finite-dimensional vector space $\mathscr{V}$ are equivalent.

Proof. Let $\|\ \ \|$ be an arbitrary norm on $\mathscr{V}$. Choose a basis $\{\mathbf{x}_1, \ldots, \mathbf{x}_n\}$ for $\mathscr{V}$, and define a Euclidean norm on $\mathscr{V}$ by setting

$$|\mathbf{x}| = \sqrt{x_1^2 + \ldots + x_n^2},$$

for any $\mathbf{x} = x_1\mathbf{x}_1 + \ldots + x_n\mathbf{x}_n$. We shall show that $\|\ \ \|$ is equivalent to $|\ \ |$, that is, there exist positive real numbers k and K such that $k|\mathbf{x}| \le \|\mathbf{x}\| \le K|\mathbf{x}|$, for all $\mathbf{x}$ in $\mathscr{V}$. By the transitivity property of the equivalence relation between norms, it then follows that any two norms on $\mathscr{V}$ are equivalent.

For any $\mathbf{x} = x_1\mathbf{x}_1 + \ldots + x_n\mathbf{x}_n$, we have

$$\|\mathbf{x}\| \le \sum_{i=1}^{n} |x_i| \|\mathbf{x}_i\| \le \left(\sum_{i=1}^{n} \|\mathbf{x}_i\|\right) \max_{i} \{|x_i|\}$$

$$\le \left(\sum_{i=1}^{n} \|\mathbf{x}_i\|\right)\sqrt{\sum_{i=1}^{n} x_i^2} = K|\mathbf{x}|,$$

where $K = \sum_{i=1}^{n} \|\mathbf{x}_i\| > 0$. We now prove that k exists. We contend that as a function of $\mathbf{x}$ the real-valued function $\|\ \ \|$ is continuous with respect to the Euclidean norm $|\ \ |$. For if $\epsilon > 0$ is given, we pick $\delta = \epsilon/K$. Then, if $|\mathbf{x} - \mathbf{x}_0| < \delta$,

$$|\, \|\mathbf{x}\| - \|\mathbf{x}_0\| \,| \leq \|\mathbf{x} - \mathbf{x}_0\| \leq K|\mathbf{x} - \mathbf{x}_0| < \epsilon.$$

Let k be the minimum value of the function $\|\ \ \|$ restricted to the Euclidean unit sphere $|\mathbf{x}| = 1$. Then, for any $\mathbf{x} \neq 0$, it follows that $\|\mathbf{x}/|\mathbf{x}|\,\| \geq k$, and hence that

$$\|\mathbf{x}\| \geq k|\mathbf{x}|, \qquad \text{for any } \mathbf{x} \text{ in } \mathscr{V}.$$

This completes the proof of the equivalence of norms.

3. ARC LENGTH AND INTEGRATION

To appreciate fully the significance of the connection between arc length and the formula $\int_a^b |f'(t)|\, dt$ that is used to compute it, it is necessary to know that the formula doesn't always work. The reason is that there is a continuous curve C in $\mathscr{R}^2$ which has length 2, but such that if the integral formula is applied to it the result is 1. The construction of such an example is fairly complicated, and showing that the relevant integral has value 1 is itself nontrivial. For the curve C we can take the graph of the so-called Cantor function. (See R. P. Boas, *A Primer of Real Functions*, John Wiley and Sons, 1960, p. 131, or B. R. Gelbaum and J. M. H. Olmstead, *Counterexamples in Analysis*, Holden-Day, Inc., 1964, p. 97.) Once the Cantor function is understood, it is fairly easy to show that its graph has length 2, as defined by the least upper bound of the lengths of inscribed polygons.

For a piecewise smooth curve γ, given by a piecewise continuously differentiable function $\mathscr{R} \xrightarrow{g} \mathscr{R}^n$ for $a \leq t \leq b$, we have the following theorem, stated in Chapter 2. (The graph of the Cantor function is not, of course, a piecewise smooth curve.)

Theorem. Let γ be a piecewise smooth curve as described above. Then $l(\gamma)$, the length of γ, is finite, and

$$l(\gamma) = \int_a^b |g'(t)|\, dt.$$

Proof. We show first that $l(\gamma) \leq \int_a^b |g'(t)|\, dt$, noting that since $|g'|$ is continuous on each of finitely many closed intervals, $|g'|$ is bounded, and the integral will be finite. The inequality will be proved if we can show that

$$(1) \qquad \sum_{k=1}^{K} |g(t_k) - g(t_{k-1})| \leq \int_a^b |g'(t)|\, dt,$$

when $a = t_0 < t_1 < \ldots < t_K = b$ is an *arbitrary* partition P of $[a, b]$. But, by the triangle inequality for the norm, we only increase the sum on the left if we add to the partition all end-points of the finitely many intervals on which g' is continuous. So we assume this has been done. Then for each interval $[t_{k-1}, t_k]$ we have

$$|g(t_k) - g(t_{k-1})| = \left| \int_{t_{k-1}}^{t_k} g'(t)\,dt \right|$$

$$\leq \int_{t_{k-1}}^{t_k} |g'(t)|\,dt.$$

The equality holds by Exercise 16 of Section 3, Chapter 2, and the inequality by Exercise 17 of the same section. Summing over $k = 1$, ..., K, gives (1).

To prove the reverse inequality, $\int_a^b |g'(t)|\,dt \leq l(\gamma)$, we shall show that for any $\eta > 0$, we can *find* a partition P of $[a, b]$ such that

(2) $$\int_a^b |g'(t)|\,dt - \eta \leq \sum_{k=1}^{K} |g(t_k) - g(t_{k-1})|.$$

This will show that no number smaller than the integral is an upper bound for the sums on the right. We take as an initial partition P_0, all the finitely many end-points of closed intervals on which g' is continuous. On each such interval, g' is uniformly continuous by Theorem 1.1 of this Appendix. This means that given $\epsilon > 0$, there is a $\delta > 0$ such that $|g'(t) - g'(u)| < \epsilon$, if $|t - u| < \delta$ and $t_{k-1} \leq t, u \leq t_k$. Since there are only finitely many intervals $[t_{k-1}, t_k]$, we can choose a single positive δ that will work for all of them. Now make a partition P fine enough that $\max (t_k - t_{k-1}) < \delta$, still including in P all the points of P_0. On each interval of the new partition we have $|g'(t)| \leq |g'(t_k)| + \epsilon$, by the uniform continuity of g'. Thus,

(3) $$\int_{t_{k-1}}^{t_k} |g'(t)|\,dt \leq [|g'(t_k)| + \epsilon](t_k - t_{k-1})$$

$$= |g'(t_k)|(t_k - t_{k-1}) + \epsilon(t_k - t_{k-1}).$$

But we also have the identity

$$|g'(t_k)|(t_k - t_{k-1}) = \left| \int_{t_{k-1}}^{t_k} (g'(t) + g'(t_k) - g'(t))\,dt \right|$$

$$\leq \left| \int_{t_{k-1}}^{t_k} g'(t)\,dt \right| + \left| \int_{t_{k-1}}^{t_k} (g'(t_k) - g'(t))\,dt \right|$$

$$\leq |g(t_k) - g(t_{k-1})| + \int_{t_{k-1}}^{t_k} |g'(t_k) - g'(t)|\,dt,$$

where in the last step we have again used the results of Exercises 16 and 17 of Section 3, Chapter 2. Again using the uniform continuity of g', together with the previous inequality, we get

$$|g'(t_k)|(t_k - t_{k-1}) \leq |g(t_k) - g(t_{k-1})| + \epsilon(t_k - t_{k-1}).$$

Applying this inequality to Equation (3) gives

$$\int_{t_{k-1}}^{t_k} |g'(t)|\,dt \leq |g(t_k) - g(t_{k-1})| + 2\epsilon(t_k - t_{k-1}).$$

Summing over k gives

$$\int_a^b |g'(t)|\, dt \leq \sum_{k=1}^{K} |g(t_k) - g(t_{k-1})| + 2\epsilon(b - a).$$

If ϵ is chosen so that $2\epsilon(b - a) < \eta$, then the desired inequality (2) will be satisfied for the partition P constructed above.

4. CONVERGENCE OF FOURIER SERIES

Theorem 5.3 of Chapter 3 asserts that the Fourier series of a piecewise smooth function f converges pointwise to the average of the right and left limits of f at each point. The assumption that f is piecewise smooth means that the interval $[-\pi, \pi]$ can be broken into finitely many subintervals, on each of which f and f' can be extended to be continuous. At the end-points of an interval $[x_k, x_{k+1}]$ we require f to be continuous if it is given the respective values $f(x_k +) = \lim_{u \to 0+} f(x_k + u)$ and $f(x_{k+1} -) = \lim_{u \to 0-} f(x_k + u)$. Similarly, we require f' to be continuous on the closed interval if it is given the values of the right and left derivatives respectively:

$$f^+(x_k) = \lim_{u \to 0+} \frac{f(x_k + u) - f(x_k +)}{u},$$

$$f^-(x_{k+1}) = \lim_{u \to 0-} \frac{f(x_{k+1} + u) - f(x_{k+1} -)}{u}.$$

We restate the convergence theorem as

4.1 Theorem. Let f be piecewise smooth on $[-\pi, \pi]$. Then the Fourier series of f converges at each point x of the interval to $(\frac{1}{2})[f(x -) + f(x +)]$. In particular, if f is continuous at x, then the series converges to $f(x)$.

Proof. We have to show that if a_k and b_k are the Fourier coefficients of f, then

$$\lim_{N \to \infty} s_N(x) = \lim_{N \to \infty} \left[\frac{a_0}{2} + \sum_{k=1}^{N} a_k \cos kx + b_k \sin kx \right]$$

$$= \tfrac{1}{2}[f(x-) + f(x+)], \quad \text{for all } x \text{ in } [-\pi, \pi].$$

Replacing a_k and b_k by their definitions, we get

$$s_N(x) = \frac{1}{2\pi} \int_{-\pi}^{\pi} f(t)\, dt$$

$$+ \frac{1}{\pi} \sum_{k=1}^{N} \left[\cos kx \int_{-\pi}^{\pi} f(t) \cos kt\, dt + \sin kx \int_{-\pi}^{\pi} f(t) \sin kt\, dt \right]$$

$$= \frac{1}{\pi} \int_{-\pi}^{\pi} f(t) \left[\frac{1}{2} + \sum_{k=1}^{N} \cos k(t - x) \right] dt.$$

But trigonometric identities (See Problem 6 of Chapter 3, Section 5.) show that

(1)
$$\frac{1}{2} + \sum_{k=1}^{N} \cos ku = \frac{\sin (N + 1/2)u}{2 \sin (1/2)u}.$$

Hence,

$$s_N(x) = \frac{1}{\pi} \int_{-\pi}^{\pi} f(t) \frac{\sin (N + 1/2)(t - x)}{2 \sin (1/2)(t - x)} dt.$$

We now extend f outside the interval $[-\pi, \pi]$ so that it has period 2π, and make the change of variable $t = x + u$. Then the new interval of integration is $[-\pi - x, \pi - x]$. But since the integrand has period 2π, the value of the integral remains unchanged if we shift back to the interval $[-\pi, \pi]$. Thus we have

(2)
$$s_N(x) = \frac{1}{\pi} \int_{-\pi}^{\pi} f(x + u) \frac{\sin (N + 1/2)u}{2 \sin (1/2)u} du.$$

We shall show that $\lim_{N \to \infty} s_N^+(x) = (1/2)f(x +)$, where

(3)
$$s_N^+(x) = \frac{1}{\pi} \int_{0}^{\pi} f(x + u) \frac{\sin (N + 1/2)u}{2 \sin (1/2)u} du.$$

A similar proof would show that $\lim_{N \to \infty} s_N^-(x) = (1/2)f(x -)$ where $s_N^-(x) = \frac{1}{\pi} \int_{-\pi}^{0} f(x + u) \frac{\sin (N + 1/2)u}{2 \sin (1/2)u} du$, and addition of the two equations will finish the proof.

To prove Equation (2), we observe from Equation (1) that

$$\frac{1}{\pi} \int_{0}^{\pi} \frac{\sin (N + 1/2)u}{2 \sin (1/2)u} du = \frac{1}{2}.$$

Multiplying both sides by $f(x +)$ and subtracting from Equation (3) gives

(4)
$$s_N^+(x) - \frac{1}{2}f(x +) = \frac{1}{\pi} \int_{0}^{\pi} \frac{\sin (N + 1/2)u}{2 \sin (1/2)u} [f(x + u) - f(x +)] du.$$

The proof will be complete if we show that this last integral tends to zero as N tends to infinity. But this is an immediate consequence of the following:

4.2 Riemann's lemma. If g is continuous on the closed interval $[a, b]$, then

$$\lim_{\lambda \to \infty} \int_{a}^{b} g(u) \sin \lambda u \, du = 0.$$

Proof of 4.2. Let

(5)
$$G(\lambda) = \int_{a}^{b} g(u) \sin \lambda u \, du,$$

and let $\epsilon > 0$ be given. We must show that there is a number λ_0 such that whenever $\lambda > \lambda_0$, then $|G(\lambda)| < \epsilon$. Replacing u by $u + \pi/\lambda$ in Equation (5) gives

(6)
$$2G(\lambda) = -\int_{a-\pi/\lambda}^{a} g(u + \pi/\lambda) \sin \lambda u \, du + \int_{b-\pi/\lambda}^{b} g(u) \sin \lambda u \, du$$
$$+ \int_{a}^{b-\pi/\lambda} [g(u) - g(u + \pi/\lambda)] \sin \lambda u \, du.$$

We assume λ is large enough so that $\pi/\lambda \leq (b - a)$. Then, letting M be the maximum of the continuous function $|g|$ on $[a, b]$, and using the fact that $|\sin \lambda u| \leq 1$, we have

(7)
$$2|G(\lambda)| \leq \frac{2M\pi}{\lambda} + \int_{a}^{b-\pi/\lambda} |g(u) - g(u + \pi/\lambda)| \, du.$$

But since g is continuous on the closed, bounded interval $[a, b]$, it is even uniformly continuous there by Theorem 1.1 of this Appendix. Hence, we can find a λ_0 such that $|g(u) - g(u + \pi/\lambda)| < \epsilon/(b - a)$, for all $\lambda > \lambda_0$ and all u in $[a, b]$. If necessary, we choose λ_0 still larger so that $2M\pi/\lambda < \epsilon$ when $\lambda > \lambda_0$. Then, from Equation (7), we get

$$2|G(\lambda)| < \epsilon + (b - a)\epsilon/(b - a) = 2\epsilon,$$

and so $|G(\lambda)| < \epsilon$ for $\lambda > \lambda_0$, as we wanted to show.

To finish the proof of Theorem 4.1, we continue to hold x fixed, and apply Riemann's lemma to the function

$$g(u) = [f(x + u) - f(x +)]/2 \sin (u/2), \qquad 0 \leq u \leq \pi.$$

We have assumed that on each of finitely many intervals, f' is continuous. Hence, on each of these intervals g is continuous. The reason is that, for $u \neq 0$, the function g is differentiable on each interval, and so is continuous. And near $u = 0$ we consider

$$g(u) = \frac{f(x + u) - f(x +)}{u} \frac{u/2}{\sin (u/2)}.$$

But because $\lim_{u \to 0+} (u/2)/\sin (u/2) = 1$, we have $\lim_{u \to 0+} g(u) = f^+(x)$. Defining $g(0) = f^+(x)$ will make g continuous on the right at $u = 0$, so g is continuous on each of the finitely many subintervals. Application of Riemann's lemma to Equation (4) on each of the subintervals yields

$$\lim_{N \to \infty} s_N^+(x) - \tfrac{1}{2}f(x +) = 0,$$

thus completing the proof of Theorem 4.1.

5. PROOF OF THE INVERSE FUNCTION THEOREM

The deepest mathematics in Chapter 2 is contained in the inverse and implicit function theorems, Theorems 13.1 and 13.2 respectively. The former, which we have not yet proved, served as the basis of our proof of the latter.

The purpose of this section is to fill the gap in the argument. We begin with the following lemma.

5.1 Lemma. A linear transformation $\mathscr{R}^n \xrightarrow{L} \mathscr{R}^n$ is one-one if and only if there exists a positive real number m such that, for any $\mathbf{x}$ in $\mathscr{R}^n$,

$$|L(\mathbf{x})| \geq m|\mathbf{x}|.$$

Proof. If L is not one-one, there exists a nonzero vector $\mathbf{x}_0$ such that $L(\mathbf{x}_0) = 0$. Then, for any positive real number m,

$$0 = |L(\mathbf{x}_0)| < m|\mathbf{x}_0|.$$

Conversely, suppose L is one-one. Then the inverse function is a linear transformation $\mathscr{R}^n \xrightarrow{L^{-1}} \mathscr{R}^n$. By Theorem 2.3 of Chapter 2, there exists a positive real number k such that

$$|L^{-1}(\mathbf{y})| \leq k|\mathbf{y}| \qquad \text{for all } \mathbf{y} \text{ in } \mathscr{R}^n.$$

Setting $m = 1/k$, we therefore obtain, for any $\mathbf{x}$ in $\mathscr{R}^n$,

$$m|\mathbf{x}| = m|L^{-1}L(\mathbf{x})| \leq mk|L(\mathbf{x})| = |L(\mathbf{x})|.$$

This completes the proof.

A function $\mathscr{R}^n \xrightarrow{f} \mathscr{R}^m$ is continuously differentiable at $\mathbf{x}_0$ if the function that assigns to each $\mathbf{x}$ the differential $d_\mathbf{x} f$ is continuous at $\mathbf{x}_0$. Since continuity has been defined with respect to a norm, it is desirable when working with the notion of continuous differentiability to choose a norm on the space of differentials, that is, on the vector space $\mathscr{L}$ of linear transformations $\mathscr{R}^n \xrightarrow{L} \mathscr{R}^m$. It was proved in Section 2 that one norm is as good as another. A convenient norm for $\mathscr{L}$ is defined as follows: For every linear transformation $\mathscr{R}^n \xrightarrow{L} \mathscr{R}^m$, Theorem 2.3 of Chapter 2 assures the existence of a positive real number k with the property that

(1) $\qquad\qquad |L(\mathbf{x})| \leq k|\mathbf{x}|, \qquad \text{for all } \mathbf{x} \text{ in } \mathscr{R}^n.$

We define $\|L\|$ to be the greatest lower bound of all such numbers k. The reader should supply the simple proofs that

(a) The function $L \longrightarrow \|L\|$ is a norm on $\mathscr{L}$, that is, it satisfies Properties 2.1, 2.2, and 2.3, and
(b) For any $\mathscr{R}^n \xrightarrow{L} \mathscr{R}^m$,

(2) $\qquad\qquad |L(\mathbf{x})| \leq \|L\| |\mathbf{x}|, \qquad \text{for all } \mathbf{x} \text{ in } \mathscr{R}^n.$

Notice that the proof that the function $L \longrightarrow \|L\|$ is a norm makes no use of any distinguishing features of the euclidean norms on $\mathscr{R}^n$ and $\mathscr{R}^m$. An equivalent norm on $\mathscr{L}$ can be defined in the same way with respect to any two norms on $\mathscr{R}^n$ and $\mathscr{R}^m$.

5.2 Lemma. Let $\mathscr{R}^n \xrightarrow{f} \mathscr{R}^n$ be a differentiable function that is continuously differentiable at $\mathbf{x}_0$ and such that $d_{\mathbf{x}_0} f$ is one-one. Then there exist positive real numbers δ and M such that if $|\mathbf{x} - \mathbf{x}_0| < \delta$, then

$$|d_\mathbf{x} f(\mathbf{y})| \geq M|\mathbf{y}|, \qquad \text{for any } \mathbf{y} \text{ in } \mathscr{R}^n.$$

Proof. By Lemma 5.1, there exists $m > 0$ such that

$$|d_{\mathbf{x}_0} f(\mathbf{y})| \geq m|\mathbf{y}|, \qquad \text{for any } \mathbf{y} \text{ in } \mathscr{R}^n.$$

Since f is continuously differentiable at $\mathbf{x}_0$, there exists $\delta > 0$ such that if $|\mathbf{x} - \mathbf{x}_0| < \delta$, then $\|d_{\mathbf{x}} f - d_{\mathbf{x}_0} f\| < m/2$. Hence, by Inequality (2), for any $\mathbf{y}$ in $\mathscr{R}^n$, we have

$$|(d_{\mathbf{x}} f - d_{\mathbf{x}_0} f)(\mathbf{y})| \leq \|d_{\mathbf{x}} f - d_{\mathbf{x}_0} f\| \, |\mathbf{y}| \leq \frac{m}{2}|\mathbf{y}|.$$

It follows by the triangle inequality that

$$|d_{\mathbf{x}} f(\mathbf{y})| \geq |d_{\mathbf{x}_0} f(\mathbf{y})| - |(d_{\mathbf{x}} f - d_{\mathbf{x}_0} f)(\mathbf{y})| \geq \frac{m}{2}|\mathbf{y}|.$$

The proof is completed by setting $M = m/2$.

It is a consequence of 5.1 and 5.2 that if a differentiable function $\mathscr{R}^n \xrightarrow{f} \mathscr{R}^n$ is continuously differentiable at $\mathbf{x}_0$, and if $d_{\mathbf{x}_0} f$ is one-one, then $d_{\mathbf{x}} f$ is one-one in a neighborhood of $\mathbf{x}_0$. The following is the key lemma in the proof of the inverse function theorem.

5.3 Lemma. Let $\mathscr{R}^n \xrightarrow{f} \mathscr{R}^n$ be a differentiable function that is continuously differentiable at $\mathbf{x}_0$ and such that $d_{\mathbf{x}_0} f$ is one-one. Then there exist positive real numbers δ and M such that $|f(\mathbf{x}') - f(\mathbf{x})| \geq M|\mathbf{x}' - \mathbf{x}|$ whenever $|\mathbf{x} - \mathbf{x}_0| < \delta$ and $|\mathbf{x}' - \mathbf{x}_0| < \delta$.

Proof. By Lemma 5.1, there exists $m > 0$ such that

$$(3) \qquad\qquad |d_{\mathbf{x}_0} f(\mathbf{y})| \geq m|\mathbf{y}| \qquad \text{for all } \mathbf{y} \text{ in } \mathscr{R}^n.$$

Set $M = m/2\sqrt{n}$. Since f is continuously differentiable at $\mathbf{x}_0$, there exists $\delta > 0$ such that if $|\mathbf{x} - \mathbf{x}_0| < \delta$, then $\|d_{\mathbf{x}} f - d_{\mathbf{x}_0} f\| < M$. Let $\mathbf{x}$ and $\mathbf{x}'$ be any two vectors satisfying $|\mathbf{x} - \mathbf{x}_0| < \delta$ and $|\mathbf{x}' - \mathbf{x}_0| < \delta$. We set $\mathbf{z} = \mathbf{x}' - \mathbf{x}$. Then, for all t in the interval $0 \leq t \leq 1$,

$$\begin{aligned}
|\mathbf{x} + t\mathbf{z} - \mathbf{x}_0| &= |t\mathbf{x}' + (1 - t)\mathbf{x} - \mathbf{x}_0| \\
&= |t(\mathbf{x}' - \mathbf{x}_0) + (1 - t)(\mathbf{x} - \mathbf{x}_0)| \\
&\leq t|\mathbf{x}' - \mathbf{x}_0| + (1 - t)|\mathbf{x} - \mathbf{x}_0| < \delta,
\end{aligned}$$

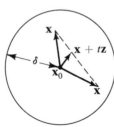

Figure 3

that is, the δ-ball about $\mathbf{x}_0$ is convex (see Figure 3). We conclude that $\|d_{\mathbf{x}+t\mathbf{z}} f - d_{\mathbf{x}_0} f\| < M$, and thence, by Inequality (2), that

$$(4) \qquad |(d_{\mathbf{x}+t\mathbf{z}} f - d_{\mathbf{x}_0} f)(\mathbf{y})| \leq M|\mathbf{y}|,$$

$$\begin{cases} \text{for any } \mathbf{y} \text{ in } \mathscr{R}^n, \\ 0 \leq t \leq 1. \end{cases}$$

For each $k = 1, \ldots, n$, let $\mathscr{R}^n \xrightarrow{\pi_k} \mathscr{R}$ be the projection on the kth coordinate axis, that is, $\pi_k(x_1, \ldots, x_n) = x_k$. We define a set of real-valued functions $g_1, \ldots, g_n$ of a real variable by

$$g_k(t) = \pi_k f(\mathbf{x} + t\mathbf{z}), \qquad \begin{cases} k = 1, \ldots, n, \\ 0 \le t \le 1. \end{cases}$$

Since every linear transformation, and in particular π_k, is its own differential, it follows from the chain rule that

$$g'_k(t) = \pi_k(d_{\mathbf{x}+t\mathbf{z}}f)(\mathbf{z}).$$

By the mean-value theorem, there exists t_k satisfying $0 < t_k < 1$ such that $g_k(1) - g_k(0) = g'_k(t_k)$. Hence,

$$\pi_k f(\mathbf{x}') - \pi_k f(\mathbf{x}) = \pi_k(d_{\mathbf{x}+t_k\mathbf{z}}f)(\mathbf{z}).$$

Using the triangle inequality, we therefore obtain

$$|f(\mathbf{x}') - f(\mathbf{x})| \ge |\pi_k f(\mathbf{x}') - \pi_k f(\mathbf{x})|$$
$$\ge |\pi_k(d_{\mathbf{x}_0}f)(\mathbf{z})| - |\pi_k(d_{\mathbf{x}+t_k\mathbf{z}}f - d_{\mathbf{x}_0}f)(\mathbf{z})|.$$

Now, for every $k = 1, \ldots, n$,

$$|\pi_k(d_{\mathbf{x}+t_k\mathbf{z}}f - d_{\mathbf{x}_0}f)(\mathbf{z})| \le |(d_{\mathbf{x}+t_k\mathbf{z}}f - d_{\mathbf{x}_0}f)(\mathbf{z})|.$$

Since the length of any vector in $\mathscr{R}^n$ is less than or equal to $\sqrt{n}$ times the maximum of the absolute values of its coordinates, we have that, for at least one $k = 1, \ldots, n$,

$$|\pi_k(d_{\mathbf{x}_0}f)(\mathbf{z})| \ge \frac{1}{\sqrt{n}}|d_{\mathbf{x}_0}f(\mathbf{z})|.$$

Hence,

$$|f(\mathbf{x}') - f(\mathbf{x})| \ge \frac{1}{\sqrt{n}}|d_{\mathbf{x}_0}f(\mathbf{z})| - |(d_{\mathbf{x}+t_k\mathbf{z}}f - d_{\mathbf{x}_0}f)(\mathbf{z})|.$$

Finally, therefore, by Inequalities (3) and (4), we obtain

$$|f(\mathbf{x}') - f(\mathbf{x})| \ge 2M|\mathbf{z}| - M|\mathbf{z}| = M|\mathbf{x}' - \mathbf{x}|,$$

and the proof is complete.

We are now ready to prove the inverse function theorem. The statement of this theorem that appears below is somewhat stronger than the one in the text.

5.4 Inverse function theorem. Let $\mathscr{R}^n \xrightarrow{f} \mathscr{R}$ be a continuously differentiable function such that $d_{\mathbf{x}_0}f$ is one-one. Then there is a neighborhood N of $\mathbf{x}_0$ such that f restricted to N has a continuously differentiable inverse f^{-1}. The image set $f(N)$ is open. For any point $\mathbf{x}$ in N,

$$d_{\mathbf{y}}f^{-1} = (d_{\mathbf{x}}f)^{-1}, \qquad \text{where} \quad \mathbf{y} = f(\mathbf{x}).$$

Proof. By Lemmas 5.2 and 5.3, there exist positive real numbers δ and M such that, where N is the set of all $\mathbf{x}$ such that $|\mathbf{x} - \mathbf{x}_0| < \delta$, we have

(5) $\quad |d_{\mathbf{x}}f(\mathbf{y})| \geq M|\mathbf{y}|$, $\qquad$ for any $\mathbf{x}$ in N, and $\mathbf{y}$ in $\mathscr{R}^n$.

(6) $\quad |f(\mathbf{x}') - f(\mathbf{x})| \geq M|\mathbf{x} - \mathbf{x}'|$, $\qquad$ for any $\mathbf{x}$ and $\mathbf{x}'$ in N.

It follows from relation (6) that if $\mathbf{x} \neq \mathbf{x}'$, then $f(\mathbf{x}) \neq f(\mathbf{x}')$. Thus f restricted to N is one-one and consequently has an inverse f^{-1}. It remains to prove:

I. *The image set $f(N)$ is open.* Let $\mathbf{y}_1$ be an arbitrary point in $f(N)$. We must show that every $\mathbf{y}$ in $\mathscr{R}^n$ sufficiently close to $\mathbf{y}_1$ also lies in $f(N)$. Let $\mathbf{x}_1$ be the pre-image in N of $\mathbf{y}_1$, that is, $f(\mathbf{x}_1) = \mathbf{y}_1$. Since N is open, there exists $\delta_1 > 0$ such that the set B of all $\mathbf{x}$ such that $|\mathbf{x} - \mathbf{x}_1| \leq \delta_1$ is contained in N (see Figure 4). Notice that B contains its boundary.

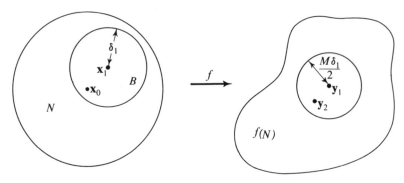

Figure 4

We contend that the number $M\delta_1/2$ is an adequate measure of what is sufficiently close to $\mathbf{y}_1$. Hence let $\mathbf{y}_2$ be an arbitrary vector such that $|\mathbf{y}_2 - \mathbf{y}_1| < M\delta_1/2$. The proof of part I is completed by showing that there exists a vector $\mathbf{x}_2$ in N (actually in B) such that $f(\mathbf{x}_2) = \mathbf{y}_2$. Let $\mathbf{x}_2$ be a vector in B such that the distance between $\mathbf{y}_2$ and $f(\mathbf{x}_2)$ is a minimum. Minimizing distance is the same as minimizing the square of distance. Hence, $\mathbf{x}_2$ is a minimum point for the function g defined by

$$g(\mathbf{x}) = |f(\mathbf{x}) - \mathbf{y}_2|^2 = (f(\mathbf{x}) - \mathbf{y}_2) \cdot (f(\mathbf{x}) - \mathbf{y}_2), \qquad \text{for any } \mathbf{x} \text{ in } B.$$

We claim that $\mathbf{x}_2$ lies in the interior of B. For suppose otherwise; that is, suppose that $|\mathbf{x}_2 - \mathbf{x}_1| = \delta_1$. Then, by relation (6),

$$|f(\mathbf{x}_2) - \mathbf{y}_1| = |f(\mathbf{x}_2) - f(\mathbf{x}_1)| \geq M|\mathbf{x}_2 - \mathbf{x}_1| = M\delta_1.$$

Hence, by the triangle inequality,

$$|f(\mathbf{x}_2) - \mathbf{y}_2| \geq |f(\mathbf{x}_2) - \mathbf{y}_1| - |\mathbf{y}_1 - \mathbf{y}_2| > \frac{M\delta_1}{2} > |\mathbf{y}_1 - \mathbf{y}_2|$$
$$= |f(\mathbf{x}_1) - \mathbf{y}_2|,$$

and this contradicts the minimality of $|f(\mathbf{x}_2) - \mathbf{y}_2|$. We conclude (see Theorem 1.1 of Chapter 3) that $d_{\mathbf{x}_2}g = 0$. It follows by the chain rule and the expression for the differential of the square of the euclidean norm that, for any $\mathbf{z}$ in $\mathcal{R}^n$,

$$(7) \qquad 0 = (d_{\mathbf{x}_2}g)(\mathbf{z}) = 2(f(\mathbf{x}_2) - \mathbf{y}_2) \cdot (d_{\mathbf{x}_2}f)(\mathbf{z}).$$

We know, by relation (5) and Lemma 5.1, that $d_{\mathbf{x}_2}f$ is one-one. Its range is therefore equal to $\mathcal{R}^n$, and there therefore exists a vector $\mathbf{z}$ such that $d_{\mathbf{x}_2}f(\mathbf{z}) = f(\mathbf{x}_2) - \mathbf{y}_2$. Thus, by Equation (7),

$$0 = 2(f(\mathbf{x}_2) - \mathbf{y}_2) \cdot (f(\mathbf{x}_2) - \mathbf{y}_2),$$

and we obtain finally $f(\mathbf{x}_2) - \mathbf{y}_2 = 0$. This completes the proof that $f(N)$ is open.

II. *For any $\mathbf{x}$ in N, the inverse of $d_{\mathbf{x}}f$ satisfies the condition for being the differential of f^{-1} at $\mathbf{y} = f(\mathbf{x})$.* This amounts to proving

$$\lim_{f(\mathbf{x}') \to f(\mathbf{x})} \frac{\mathbf{x}' - \mathbf{x} - (d_{\mathbf{x}}f)^{-1}(f(\mathbf{x}') - f(\mathbf{x}))}{|f(\mathbf{x}') - f(\mathbf{x})|} = 0.$$

Regarding $\mathbf{x}$ as a fixed vector in N, we set

$$\mathbf{s} = \frac{\mathbf{x}' - \mathbf{x} - (d_{\mathbf{x}}f)^{-1}(f(\mathbf{x}') - f(\mathbf{x}))}{|f(\mathbf{x}') - f(\mathbf{x})|},$$

$$\mathbf{r} = \frac{f(\mathbf{x}') - f(\mathbf{x}) - (d_{\mathbf{x}}f)(\mathbf{x}' - \mathbf{x})}{|\mathbf{x}' - \mathbf{x}|},$$

for $\mathbf{x}'$ in N and $\mathbf{x}' \neq \mathbf{x}$. Then,

$$\mathbf{s} = -\frac{|\mathbf{x}' - \mathbf{x}|}{|f(\mathbf{x}') - f(\mathbf{x})|} (d_{\mathbf{x}}f)^{-1}(\mathbf{r}).$$

From relation (5) we have $|f(\mathbf{x}') - f(\mathbf{x})| \geq M|\mathbf{x}' - \mathbf{x}|$. Hence, if $\lim_{\mathbf{x}' \to \mathbf{x}} \mathbf{s} = 0$, it follows that $\lim_{f(\mathbf{x}') \to f(\mathbf{x})} \mathbf{s} = 0$. Furthermore,

$$\frac{|\mathbf{x}' - \mathbf{x}|}{|f(\mathbf{x}') - f(\mathbf{x})|}$$

is bounded. Finally, since every linear transformation is continuous,

$$\lim_{\mathbf{x}' \to \mathbf{x}} (d_{\mathbf{x}}f)^{-1}(\mathbf{r}) = (d_{\mathbf{x}}f)^{-1}[\lim_{\mathbf{x}' \to \mathbf{x}} \mathbf{r}] = (d_{\mathbf{x}}f)^{-1}(0) = 0.$$

We conclude that $\lim_{\mathbf{x}' \to \mathbf{x}} \mathbf{s} = 0$, and the proof of part II is complete. We now know f^{-1} is differentiable; it only remains to prove that

III. *f^{-1} is continuously differentiable.* We must prove that, for any $\mathbf{x}_1$ in N, if $\mathbf{y}_1 = f(\mathbf{x}_1)$, then

$$\lim_{\mathbf{y} \to \mathbf{y}_1} d_{\mathbf{y}}f^{-1} = d_{\mathbf{y}_1}f^{-1}.$$

Since we have established that $d_{\mathbf{y}}f^{-1} = (d_{\mathbf{x}}f)^{-1}$, it suffices to prove that

$$\lim_{\mathbf{x} \to \mathbf{x}_1} (d_{\mathbf{x}}f)^{-1} = (d_{\mathbf{x}_1}f)^{-1}.$$

For convenience, we abbreviate $d_{\mathbf{x}}f = L_{\mathbf{x}}$. By setting $\mathbf{y} = L_{\mathbf{x}}^{-1}(\mathbf{z})$ in inequality (5), we obtain

(8) $\qquad |L_{\mathbf{x}}^{-1}(\mathbf{z})| \le \dfrac{1}{M}|\mathbf{z}|$, $\qquad$ for any $\mathbf{x}$ in N, and $\mathbf{z}$ in $\mathscr{R}^{n}$.

Choose $\epsilon > 0$ arbitrarily, and, using the continuous differentiability of f at $\mathbf{x}_{1}$, choose $\delta_{1} > 0$ such that the set N_{1} consisting of all $\mathbf{x}$ with $|\mathbf{x} - \mathbf{x}_{1}| < \delta_{1}$ is contained in N and such that if $\mathbf{x}$ is in N_{1}, then $\|L_{\mathbf{x}} - L_{\mathbf{x}_{1}}\| < \epsilon M^{2}$. Then, by relations (2) and (8), we have, for any $\mathbf{x}$ in N_{1} and $\mathbf{z}$ in $\mathscr{R}^{n}$,

$$|(L_{\mathbf{x}}^{-1} - L_{\mathbf{x}_{1}}^{-1})\mathbf{z}| = |L_{\mathbf{x}}^{-1}(L_{\mathbf{x}} - L_{\mathbf{x}_{1}})L_{\mathbf{x}_{1}}^{-1}(\mathbf{z})|$$

$$\le \frac{1}{M}|(L_{\mathbf{x}} - L_{\mathbf{x}_{1}})L_{\mathbf{x}_{1}}^{-1}(\mathbf{z})|$$

$$\le \epsilon M|L_{\mathbf{x}_{1}}^{-1}(\mathbf{z})| \le \epsilon|\mathbf{z}|.$$

It follows that $\|L_{\mathbf{x}}^{-1} - L_{\mathbf{x}_{1}}^{-1}\| \le \epsilon$, and the proof is complete.

It is worth remarking that the hypothesis that f be continuously differentiable at points other than $\mathbf{x}_{0}$ is used in the above proof only to show that the differentiable inverse function f^{-1} is continuously differentiable on all of $f(N)$. If we alter the conditions of Theorem 5.4 to read that f is a differentiable function with continuous differentiability at $\mathbf{x}_{0}$, then the only change in the conclusions of the theorem is that f^{-1} is a differentiable function and continuously differentiable at the one point $\mathbf{y}_{0} = f(\mathbf{x}_{0})$.

6. EXISTENCE OF THE RIEMANN INTEGRAL

We shall prove the existence theorem for multiple integrals that is given in Theorem 2.1, Section 2, of Chapter 4. The statement of the theorem is as follows.

Theorem. Let f be defined and bounded on a bounded set B in $\mathscr{R}^{n}$, and let the boundary of B be contained in finitely many smooth sets. If f is continuous on B except perhaps on finitely many pieces of smooth set S, then f is integrable over B. The integral $\int_{B} f \, dV$ is independent of the values of f on any smooth set.

By a **smooth set** in $\mathscr{R}^{n}$ is meant the image of a closed bounded set under a continuously differentiable function $\mathscr{R}^{m} \xrightarrow{\phi} \mathscr{R}^{n}$, $m < n$.

We turn first to the problem of showing why smooth sets are negligible when they lie in the domain of integration of a function. The box norm, denoted by double vertical bars $\|\ \ \|$, is used frequently in this section because of the convenience of having rectangular "spheres" in defining the integral. The proofs may, of course, be adapted to any norm.

6.1 Theorem. Let $\mathscr{R}^m \xrightarrow{g} \mathscr{R}^n$ be continuously differentiable. (We do not assume $m < n$.) Then, for every closed bounded subset K in the domain of g, there is a constant M such that, for all $\mathbf{x}$ and $\mathbf{y}$ in K,

$$\|g(\mathbf{y}) - g(\mathbf{x})\| \le M\|\mathbf{y} - \mathbf{x}\|.$$

Proof. Denote by $K \times K$ the subset of $\mathscr{R}^{2m}$ consisting of all $2m$-tuples $(\mathbf{x}, \mathbf{y})$ such that $\mathbf{x}$ and $\mathbf{y}$ are each in K. It is easy to see that $K \times K$ is closed and bounded in $\mathscr{R}^{2m}$. Consider the function

$$F(\mathbf{x}, \mathbf{y}) = \begin{cases} \dfrac{\|g(\mathbf{y}) - g(\mathbf{x}) - (d_\mathbf{x}g)(\mathbf{y} - \mathbf{x})\|}{\|\mathbf{y} - \mathbf{x}\|}, & \text{if } \mathbf{x} \ne \mathbf{y}. \\ 0, & \text{if } \mathbf{x} = \mathbf{y}. \end{cases}$$

We shall show that F is continuous. At points $(\mathbf{x}, \mathbf{y})$ for which $\mathbf{x} \ne \mathbf{y}$, F is continuous because both numerator and denominator are continuous and the denominator is not zero. On the other hand, if both $\mathbf{x}$ and $\mathbf{y}$ tend to some point $\mathbf{z}$ in the domain of g, then $(\mathbf{x}, \mathbf{y})$ tends to $(\mathbf{z}, \mathbf{z})$, and we have to show that F tends to zero. We can apply the mean-value theorem, Theorem 8.2 of Chapter 2, to the coordinate functions g_k of g, $k = 1, \ldots, n$. We have, for each k,

$$g_k(\mathbf{y}) - g_k(\mathbf{x}) = (d_{\mathbf{x}_k}g_k)(\mathbf{y} - \mathbf{x}),$$

for $\mathbf{x}$ and $\mathbf{y}$ in a sufficiently small neighborhood of $\mathbf{z}$ and for some $\mathbf{x}_k$ on the segment joining $\mathbf{x}$ and $\mathbf{y}$. Then

$$\|g(\mathbf{y}) - g(\mathbf{x}) - d_\mathbf{x}g(\mathbf{y} - \mathbf{x})\| = \max_{1 \le k \le n} |(d_{\mathbf{x}_k}g_k)(\mathbf{y} - \mathbf{x}) - (d_\mathbf{x}g_k)(\mathbf{y} - \mathbf{x})|$$

$$= \max_{1 \le k \le n} \left| \sum_{j=1}^m \left(\frac{\partial g_k}{\partial x_j}(\mathbf{x}_k) - \frac{\partial g_k}{\partial x_j}(\mathbf{x}) \right)(y_j - x_j) \right|$$

$$\le \max_{1 \le k \le n} \left| \sum_{j=1}^m \left(\frac{\partial g_k}{\partial x_j}(\mathbf{x}_k) - \frac{\partial g_k}{\partial x_j}(\mathbf{x}) \right) \right| \|\mathbf{y} - \mathbf{x}\|.$$

Since the partial derivatives are continuous, and each $\mathbf{x}_k$ tends to $\mathbf{z}$ as $\mathbf{x}$ and $\mathbf{y}$ do, it follows that

$$\lim_{(\mathbf{x}, \mathbf{y}) \to (\mathbf{z}, \mathbf{z})} F(\mathbf{x}, \mathbf{y}) = 0.$$

We conclude that F is continuous.

Since F is continuous on the closed bounded set $K \times K$, it attains its maximum value M', and so $F(\mathbf{x}, \mathbf{y}) \le M'$, for $\mathbf{x}$ and $\mathbf{y}$ in K. Hence,

$$\|g(\mathbf{y}) - g(\mathbf{x}) - d_\mathbf{x}g(\mathbf{y} - \mathbf{x})\| \le M'\|\mathbf{y} - \mathbf{x}\|,$$

and the inequality $\|A\| - \|B\| \le \|A - B\|$ shows that

(1) $$\|g(\mathbf{y}) - g(\mathbf{x})\| \le M'\|\mathbf{y} - \mathbf{x}\| + \|d_\mathbf{x}g(\mathbf{y} - \mathbf{x})\|,$$

for all $\mathbf{x}$ and $\mathbf{y}$ in K. But we have

$$\| d_{\mathbf{x}} g(\mathbf{y} - \mathbf{x}) \| = \max_{1 \le k \le n} \left| \sum_{j=1}^{m} \frac{\partial g_k}{\partial x_j}(\mathbf{x})(y_j - x_j) \right|$$

$$\le \max_{1 \le k \le n} \left| \sum_{j=1}^{m} \frac{\partial g_k}{\partial x_j}(\mathbf{x}) \right| \| \mathbf{y} - \mathbf{x} \|.$$

The continuity of the partial derivatives on K implies the existence of a constant M'' such that

$$\| d_{\mathbf{x}} g(\mathbf{y} - \mathbf{x}) \| \le M'' \| \mathbf{y} - \mathbf{x} \|.$$

This inequality together with (1) implies that

$$\| g(\mathbf{y}) - g(\mathbf{x}) \| \le (M' + M'') \| \mathbf{y} - \mathbf{x} \|, \qquad \mathbf{x}, \mathbf{y} \text{ in } K,$$

which was to be shown.

6.2 **Theorem.** If S is a smooth set in $\mathscr{R}^n$, then S can be covered by finitely many coordinate rectangles of arbitrarily small total content. The covering can be done in such a way that no point of S lies on the boundary of the union of the set of covering rectangles.

Proof. The case in which S is just a point is trivially true, so we assume $m \ge 1$. The smooth subset S is the image under a continuously differentiable function $\mathscr{R}^m \xrightarrow{g} \mathscr{R}^n$, $m < n$, of a closed bounded set K in $\mathscr{R}^m$. We enclose K in a cube of side length s, and subdivide the cube into smaller cubes of side length s/N, where N is an integer bigger than 1. There are N^m of these little cubes. On each of the little cubes that contain any points of K we have by Theorem 4.1

$$\| g(\mathbf{x}) - g(\mathbf{y}) \| \le M \| \mathbf{x} - \mathbf{y} \| \le M \frac{s}{N},$$

where M is a constant depending only on K and g. This means that the image under g of the part of K in each little cube is contained in a cube of side length $M(s/N)$. Then the surface S is contained in N^m cubes each of volume $(Ms/N)^n$. The total volume of the cubes containing S is at most $N^m (Ms/N)^n = (Ms)^n / N^{n-m}$. Since $n > m$, the total volume can be made arbitrarily small by making N large. By enlarging the side length of each covering rectangle to $(Ms + 1)/N$, the last condition of the theorem can be met.

As a corollary, we get the fact that *a smooth set has zero content.*

Now we can prove the existence theorem for integrals stated at the beginning of the section. Suppose that f and B are as described in the hypotheses. We must produce a number which we shall prove is the Riemann integral of f over B. Let f_B be the function f extended to be zero outside B.

For an arbitrary grid G covering B, let R_k be the kth bounded rectangle of G, and let f_k be the *infimum* of f_B on R_k. Define

$$\underline{S}(G) = \sum_{k=1}^{N} \underline{f_k} V(R_k).$$

Similarly, define

$$\bar{S}(G) = \sum_{k=1}^{N} \bar{f_k} V(R_k),$$

where $\bar{f_k}$ is the *supremum* of f_B on R_k. Then clearly

$$(2) \qquad \underline{S}(G) \le \sum_{k=1}^{N} (f_B(\mathbf{x}_k)) V(R_k) \le \bar{S}(G),$$

if the Riemann sum is an arbitrary one formed from the grid G. Furthermore, if G' is a grid consisting of a subdivision of the rectangles of a grid G, we have

$$\underline{S}(G) \le \underline{S}(G') \le \bar{S}(G') \le \bar{S}(G).$$

In particular, if G and G'' are two grids, and G' contains all the rectangles of both of them, then

$$(3) \qquad \underline{S}(G) \le \underline{S}(G') \le \bar{S}(G') \le \bar{S}(G'').$$

We define

$$I_B f = \text{supremum of } \underline{S}(G),$$

where the *supremum* is taken over all grids G covering B. We have from relation (3) that

$$\underline{S}(G) \le I_B f \le \bar{S}(G),$$

or

$$-\bar{S}(G) \le -I_B f \le -\underline{S}(G).$$

This inequality added to (2) gives

$$\left| \sum_{k=1}^{N} (f_B(\mathbf{x}_k)) V(R_k) - I_B f \right| \le \bar{S}(G) - \underline{S}(G),$$

in which the Riemann sum has been formed from the grid G.

Now all we have to do is show that $\bar{S}(G) - \underline{S}(G)$ can be made arbitrarily small if the mesh of G is made small enough. Then according to the definition of the integral we will have shown that the integral of f over B exists and is $I_B f$. Let ϵ be a positive number. By Theorem 6.2, we can cover the boundary of B, the smooth surfaces containing the discontinuity points of f, and any other smooth surface on which we would like to disregard the values of f, with finitely many open rectangles $R'_1, \ldots, R'_l$, of total content less than ϵ. On the part of B not covered by these rectangles, f is continuous, so by Theorem 1.1 there is a $\delta > 0$ such that $\bar{f_k} - \underline{f_k} < \epsilon$ over any rectangle R_k belonging to a grid with mesh less than δ. By making the mesh still smaller, say less than δ', we can arrive at a mesh size such that the rectangles $R'_1, \ldots,$ R'_l, are always contained in finitely many rectangles $R''_1, \ldots, R''_m$ of any grid with mesh less than δ' and such that the total content of the latter rectangles is less than 2ϵ. Suppose that the remaining rectangles of such a grid G are $R_1, \ldots, R_n$, that $|f| < M$ on B, and that B is contained in a rectangle of volume C. Then

$$\bar{S}(G) - \underline{S}(G) = \sum_{k=1}^{m} (\bar{f}''_k - \underline{f}''_k)V(R''_k) + \sum_{k=1}^{n} (\bar{f}_k - \underline{f}_k)V(R_k)$$

$$< (2M)(2\epsilon) + \epsilon C = \epsilon(4M + C).$$

Thus we have made

$$\left| \sum_{k=1}^{N} f_B(\mathbf{x}_k)V(R_k) - I_B f \right| < \epsilon(4M + C),$$

for any grid of small enough mesh. Since ϵ can be made arbitrarily small, the proof is complete.

7. THE CHANGE-OF-VARIABLE FORMULA FOR INTEGRALS

This section contains a proof of the change-of-variable theorem (Theorem 3.1) of Chapter 4.

Theorem. Let $\mathscr{U}^n \xrightarrow{T} \mathscr{R}^n$ be a continuously differentiable transformation. Let R be a set in $\mathscr{U}^n$ having a boundary consisting of finitely many smooth sets. Suppose that R and its boundary are contained in the interior of the domain of T and that

(a) T is one-one on R.
(b) J, the Jacobian determinant of T, is different from zero on R, except perhaps on finitely many smooth sets.

Then, if the function f is bounded and continuous on $T(R)$ (the image of R under T),

$$\int_{T(R)} f \, dV = \int_R (f \circ T)|J| \, dV.$$

If f should be discontinuous on a smooth set S contained in R, then the formula can be applied to R with S deleted. The subsequent inclusion of S and $T(S)$ in the domains of integration will affect neither integral.

Proof.* We first consider the special case in which f is the constant function 1, and T is linear. Then, by Theorem 9.12 of Chapter 1, T can

---

*The proof we give is contained in one by J. Schwartz, "The Formula for Change of Variable in a Multiple Integral," *American Math. Monthly*, vol. 61, no. 2 (February, 1954). See also D. E. Varberg, "On Differentiable Transformations in R^n," *American Math. Monthly*, vol. 73, no. 1, part II, (April, 1966).

be written as the product of elementary linear transformations of two types: numerical multiplication of a coordinate,

(1) $\qquad M(x_1, \ldots, x_k, \ldots, x_n) = (x_1, \ldots, ax_k, \ldots, x_n),$

and addition of a multiple of one coordinate to another,

(2) $\qquad A(x_1, \ldots, x_k, \ldots, x_n) = (x_1, \ldots, x_k + rx_j, \ldots, x_n).$

By looking at the matrices of these transformations, it is easy to see that det $M = a$ and det $A = 1$. Once the special case of the theorem has been verified for each of these two types, it follows for arbitrary nonsingular linear transformations by successive application of the product rule for determinants. Let R_k be the projection of R on the subspace perpendicular to the kth coordinate axis. For each point $(x_1, \ldots, x_{k-1}, x_{k+1}, \ldots, x_n)$ in R_k, let I_k be the set of all x_k such that $(x_1, \ldots, x_n)$ is in R. For the linear transformation (1), we have by iterated integration

$$\int_R |J|\, dV = \int_{R_k} dV_{n-1} \int_{I_k} |a|\, dx_k.$$

If we denote by $|a|\, I_k$ the set of all numbers of the form $|a|\, x_k$, where x_k is in I_k, we obtain by 1-dimensional change of variable

$$\int_{R_k} dV_{n-1} \int_{I_k} |a|\, dx_k = \int_{R_k} dV_{n-1} \int_{|a|\, I_k} du_k$$

$$= \int_{M(R)} dV.$$

For the linear transformation (2), we denote by $I_k + rx_j$ the set of all numbers $x_k + rx_j$, where x_k is in I_k. Then iterated integration and 1-dimensional change of variable yield

$$\int_R |J|\, dV = \int_R dV = \int_{R_k} dV_{n-1} \int_{I_k} dx_k$$

$$= \int_{R_k} dV_{n-1} \int_{I_k + rx_j} dx_k = \int_{A(R)} dV.$$

This completes the proof of the theorem for linear transformations T and constant functions f.

In proving the general theorem, we shall use the following norm for the matrix (l_{ij}) of a linear transformation L. Let

$$\|L\| = \max_{1 \le i \le n} \sum_{j=1}^{n} |l_{ij}|.$$

If we also use the box norm $\|\mathbf{x}\|$ for vectors, then $\|L(\mathbf{x})\| \le \|L\|\, \|\mathbf{x}\|$. Suppose now that C is a cube of side length $2s$ contained in R and with center $\mathbf{p}$. We have by the mean-value theorem

$$T_k(\mathbf{x}) - T_k(\mathbf{p}) = T_k'(\mathbf{y}_k)(\mathbf{x} - \mathbf{p}), \qquad \mathbf{x} \text{ in } C, k = 1, \ldots, n,$$

where the T_k are the coordinate functions of T, and $\mathbf{y}_k$ is some point on the segment joining $\mathbf{x}$ to $\mathbf{p}$. Then

$$\| T(\mathbf{x}) - T(\mathbf{p}) \| \leq \max_{\mathbf{y} \text{ in } C} \| d_y T \| \, \| \mathbf{x} - \mathbf{p} \|,$$

which implies that TC is contained in the cube defined by

$$\| \mathbf{z} - T(\mathbf{p}) \| \leq s \{ \max_{\mathbf{y} \text{ in } C} \| d_y T \| \}.$$

Because of this, we have

(3) $$V(T(C)) \leq \{ \max_{\mathbf{y} \text{ in } C} \| d_y T \| \}^n V(C).$$

Notice that if L is an arbitrary one-one linear transformation, and S is a set bounded by finitely many smooth sets, then $V(L(S)) = |\det L| V(S)$. This follows from the special case of the change-of-variable theorem that we have just proved for linear transformations. Now we take $S = T(C)$ and $L = (d_x T)^{-1}$. Then, applying (3) with T replaced by $(d_x T)^{-1} \circ T$, we get

$$| \det (d_x T)^{-1} | V(T(C)) = V((d_x T)^{-1} \circ T(C))$$
$$\leq \{ \max_{\mathbf{y} \text{ in } C} \| (d_x T)^{-1} \circ d_y T \| \}^n V(C),$$

or

(4) $$V(T(C)) \leq | \det (d_x T) | \{ \max_{\mathbf{y} \text{ in } C} \| (d_x T)^{-1} \circ d_y T \| \}^n V(C).$$

Let the cube C be subdivided into a finite set $C_1, \ldots, C_N$ of nonoverlapping cubes with centers $\mathbf{x}_1, \ldots, \mathbf{x}_N$, and suppose that δ is the maximum side length of all of them. Apply (4) to each C_k, taking $\mathbf{x} = \mathbf{x}_k$ in each case. Addition gives

$$V(T(C)) \leq \sum_{k=1}^{N} | \det (d_{x_k} T) | \{ \max_{\mathbf{y} \text{ in } C_k} \| (d_{x_k} T)^{-1} \circ d_y T \| \}^n V(C_k).$$

Since T is continuously differentiable, $d_y T$ is a continuous function of $\mathbf{y}$, and $(d_{x_k} T)^{-1} \circ d_y T$ approaches the identity as $\mathbf{y}$ tends to $\mathbf{x}_k$. Then there is a function $h(\delta)$, tending to zero with δ such that

$$\{ \max_{\mathbf{y} \text{ in } C_k} \| (d_{x_k} T)^{-1} \circ d_y T \| \}^n \leq 1 + h(\delta).$$

This gives

$$V(T(C)) \leq [1 + h(\delta)] \sum_{k=1}^{N} | \det (d_{x_k} T) | V(C_k).$$

As δ approaches zero, the sum on the right approaches $\int_C |J| \, dV$, because $\det (d_x T) = J(\mathbf{x})$. Then the last inequality becomes

(5) $$\int_{T(C)} dV \leq \int_C |J| \, dV.$$

Having proved this last inequality, we use it to prove the formula for more general sets than cubes. We shall assume $f \geq 0$. The general case follows by considering the positive and negative parts of f separately and adding the resulting formula for each part. Let G be a cubical grid covering R and having mesh δ. Let $C_1, \ldots, C_N$ be the cubes of G that are contained in R. If we let R_N be the part of R that is not contained in any of the cubes C_k, then $R = C_1 \cup \ldots \cup C_N \cup R_N$. Whenever $\mathbf{y}_k$ is a point of C_k and $\mathbf{x}_k = T(\mathbf{y}_k)$, we shall write f_k for $(f \circ T)\mathbf{y}_k$ and $f(\mathbf{x}_k)$. Then, because of (5), we have

$$\sum_{k=1}^{N} f_k \int_{T(C_k)} dV \leq \sum_{k=1}^{N} f_k \int_{C_k} |J| \, dV.$$

From this it follows that

$$D = \int_{T(R)} f \, dV - \int_{R} (f \circ T) |J| \, dV$$

$$\leq \int_{T(R)} f \, dV - \sum_{k=1}^{N} f_k \int_{T(C_k)} dV + \sum_{k=1}^{N} f_k \int_{C_k} |J| \, dV - \int_{R} (f \circ T) |J| \, dV.$$

Since $T(R) = T(C_1) \cup \ldots \cup T(C_N) \cup T(R_N)$, we have

$$D \leq \int_{T(R_N)} f \, dV + \sum_{k=1}^{N} \int_{T(C_k)} (f - f_k) \, dV$$

$$+ \sum_{k=1}^{N} \int_{C_k} (f_k - f \circ T) |J| \, dV - \int_{R_N} (f \circ T) |J| \, dV.$$

Because T is continuously differentiable, it follows from Theorem 6.1 of this appendix that there is a constant B for which

(6) $\quad \| T(\mathbf{x}) - T(\mathbf{y}) \| \leq B \| \mathbf{x} - \mathbf{y} \|, \qquad$ for all $\mathbf{x}$ and $\mathbf{y}$ in R.

Now let ϵ be a positive number. Since f is uniformly continuous on $T(R)$ (apply Theorem 1.1 of this appendix to $T(R)$ together with its boundary), we can choose δ, the mesh of G, small enough so that

$$|(f \circ T)\mathbf{y} - f_k| \leq \epsilon, \qquad \text{for } \mathbf{y} \text{ in } C_k, \, k = 1, \ldots, N.$$

By using (6), and, if necessary, taking δ still smaller, we can get

$$|f(\mathbf{x}) - f_k| \leq \epsilon, \qquad \text{for } \mathbf{x} \text{ in } T(C_k), \, k = 1, \ldots, N.$$

Then

$$D \leq \int_{T(R_N)} f \, dV - \int_{R_N} (f \circ T) |J| \, dV + \epsilon \{V(T(R)) + V(R)\}.$$

Since R is assumed to have a volume, there is a mesh such that $V(R_N) \leq \epsilon$. Again using (6), and, if necessary, decreasing the mesh again, we can get $V(T(R_N)) \leq B^n \epsilon$. Then

$$D \leq \epsilon \{MB^n + M + V(T(R)) + V(R)\},$$

where M is a number such that $f \leq M$ on $T(R)$ and $(f \circ T) |J| \leq M$ on R. Since ϵ is arbitrary, we must have $D \leq 0$, that is,

$$\int_{T(R)} f \, dV \leq \int_{R} (f \circ T) |J| \, dV.$$

If we apply this last inequality to the situation in which T is replaced by T^{-1}, we get

$$\int_R (f \circ T)\,|J|\,dV \le \int_{T(R)} (f \circ T \circ T^{-1})\,|J \circ T^{-1}|\,|J^{-1}|\,dV,$$

where J^{-1} is the Jacobian determinant of the transformation T^{-1}. But $(J \circ T^{-1})(J^{-1}) = 1$, so

$$\int_{T(R)} f\,dV \le \int_R (f \circ T)\,|J|\,dV \le \int_{TR} f\,dV,$$

and the desired equality has been proved.

If J is zero on some piece of smooth surface S in R, then the above proof breaks down, because T^{-1} may fail to be continuously differentiable. However, by Theorem 6.2 of this appendix, S can be enclosed in the interior of a union U of finitely many rectangles of arbitrarily small content v, and the image surface $T(S)$ will be contained in an image region $T(U)$ having content at most $B^n v$, where B is the constant of relation (6). Then, applying the change of variable formula to the region R with U deleted, we get

$$\left| \int_{T(R)} f\,dV - \int_R (f \circ T)\,|J|\,dV \right| \le \left| \int_{T(U)} f\,dV \right| + \left| \int_U (f \circ T)\,|J|\,dV \right|$$
$$\le MB^n v + Mv,$$

where $|f|$ and $|f \circ T|\,|J|$ are both less than M. Letting v tend to zero, we get the final equality.

INDEX